Materials and Techniques for

REINHOLD PUBLISHING CORPORATION
New York, N. Y.
CHAPMAN & HALL, LTD., *London*

ELECTRON TUBES

A COMPLETELY REVISED EDITION OF
"Materials Technology for Electron Tubes"

by WALTER H. KOHL

Senior Engineering Specialist, Special Tube Operations
Sylvania Electric Products Inc.
A Subsidiary of General Telephone & Electronics Corporation

Lecturer, Department of Electrical Engineering, Stanford University
and Consultant, Stanford Research Institute

GENERAL TELEPHONE & ELECTRONICS TECHNICAL SERIES

TO
JEAN

INTRODUCTION

This is the first volume in a new technical series to be written by scientists and engineers of General Telephone & Electronics, covering various aspects of the science and technology involved in the over-all organization's many fields of operation—including communications, electronics, lighting, chemistry, metallurgy, and photography.

Our scientists and engineers have a two-fold objective in participating in this series: first, to make available new knowledge and to report new applications of existing knowledge; secondly, to organize and present this information in such a manner as to make each volume both a ready reference and a definitive exposition of the subject.

The obligations of technical personnel are many, but none is more important than the widespread dissemination, for the ultimate general good, of new concepts that they have been able to develop and to apply successfully in services and products. For this reason, we of General Telephone & Electronics are honored that our scientists and engineers have been selected, as individuals of high professional attainment, to prepare this new series.

DONALD C. POWER

New York, N. Y.
January, 1960

Chairman of the Board
General Telephone & Electronics Corporation

PREFACE

This book, as suggested on the title page, is a completely revised version of the former "Materials Technology For Electron Tubes" which was published in 1951. A slightly modified title was chosen for the present book to set it apart from the old one and to describe its content in simpler terms. The present book, like the old one, is intended as a source of information for the tube engineer, the experimenter in the laboratory, and the technician, all of whom need to know how the basic materials behave under given conditions, and what techniques are available for assembling these materials into useful structures.

The list of contents indicates the scope of this book and will suggest to the casual reviewer that the subject matter is likely to be of interest not only to those concerned with electron tubes but, in a broader sense, to the electron device engineer and to workers in quite different areas where glass, ceramics, and metals are used under ordinary conditions or in rarified atmospheres.

The wide acceptance of the original version of this book has been most gratifying, and I hope that the changes which have been made in the new text will likewise find approval. After an author has lived with his book for a few years, he becomes aware of its shortcomings and feels an obligation to do better the next time.

Before embarking on this venture, a questionnaire was circulated among some hundred competent users of the former book, asking which were the most useful chapters, which chapters should be left out, and what new subjects to cover. From the many replies received, a clear pattern evolved which greatly helped in casting the new frame. In addition, all chapters of the new book were submitted for review to experts in the respective fields, so that errors could be corrected and gaps be filled in.

The organization of the text has been greatly improved by presenting the material in a more consistent manner. Subjects formerly covered in separate chapters and now left out, because they are better studied by consulting available texts, are those on atomic structure, the phase rule, and high-vacuum technique, but reference is made to these topics throughout the book.

The former four chapters on glass were condensed into one. To save space, the interaction of glass and radiation was left out, but some reference to this topic is made in the *Introductory Review*. For the same reason, soft soldering is not discussed in the new book. New chapters have been added on iron and steel, the precious metals, and getters. Information on cathode materials and the treatment of cathodes has been gathered in a chapter on this subject. Everything in the old book was rewritten; there is hardly a paragraph which was taken over unchanged. A good many of the illustrations were retained, however, but many new ones were added.

"Materials and Techniques" is not a textbook from which to learn first concepts, but it is a very useful reference book to be used in conjunction with other texts; as such, it has been used in several colleges. A graduate course on "Tube Techniques" has been given by the author for the past six years at Stanford University. A laboratory course was formerly given in conjunction with the lectures but recently discontinued. Such laboratory courses are now being given at junior colleges and trade schools, at least in the San Francisco Bay Area. A student enrolling in the lecture course should be familiar with the fundamentals of physics and chemistry and have had some instruction in metallurgy. In this sense, the present book is an advanced text. Tube technicians who have reached this level will be able to benefit from the book.

Acknowledgments

In addition to the author's affiliation with Sylvania he holds a lectureship at Stanford University. He was also engaged at Stanford Research Institute as a consultant on several Government-sponsored surveys which afforded opportunities to gather up-to-date information, inspect facilities, and make personal contacts which were most useful in advancing the content of the book. The help received from all these quarters during the writing is gratefully acknowledged.

Special thanks are due my many friends in industry, both in this country and abroad, who were kind enough to review the various chapters, as they became available, to offer their criticism, their contributions, and, indeed, their encouragement. This cooperation was extremely helpful.

I am especially grateful to Mrs. J. O. Randisi of Los Altos who transcribed and typed the bulk of the manuscript and took care of all the correspondence in a most expeditious manner. Several other ladies were involved in this task in the earlier stages for short periods of time. Mrs. Sive Barbro Sandberg of the Stanford Electronics Laboratories made nearly all the many line drawings which were added to the new book and corrected some of the old ones. Her craftsmanship should be reflected in the reproductions. I am indebted to the management of the laboratory for making this arrangement possible under favorable terms.

Mr. Raymond Andersen, technical art director of Stanford Research Institute, kindly undertook the lay-out and supervision of printing of Table 12.1 on Brazing Filler Metals For Electron Tubes to make it serve the double purpose of separate distribution and reproduction in the book. Other tables and illustrations separately available from the author are marked accordingly by a footnote.

Many publishers kindly granted permission to reproduce text exerpts, illustrations, and tables from their publications, as acknowledged in the text. A list of these publishers is given on the following page.

My friends of the Reinhold Book Division, especially G. G. Hawley and F. P. Peters, showed infinite patience when one deadline after another was not met and graciously accepted the many last-minute additions and changes.

The one who of necessity bore the brunt of my prolonged preoccupation with this task is my wife to whom I dedicate this book with deep thanks for her sympathetic understanding and continuous encouragement. She also helped in proofreading the final manuscript and in preparing the index, which is one of the most important features.

Los Altos, California
January, 1960   WALTER H. KOHL

LIST OF PUBLISHERS AND INSTITUTIONS

The following Publishers, Institutions, and Industrial Establishments have permitted reproduction or quotation of material contained in their respective publications and reports, as indicated in the acknowledgments and references:

Academic Press, Inc.
New York, N. Y.

Allegheny Ludlum Steel Corporation
Pittsburgh, Pa.

The American Ceramic Society
Columbus, Ohio

The American Chemical Society
Washington, D. C.

The American Institute of Electrical Engineers
New York, N. Y.

The American Institute of Mining, Metallurgical, and Petroleum Engineers
New York, N. Y.

The American Institute of Physics
New York, N. Y.

American Metal Climax, Inc.
New York, N. Y.

The American Society For Metals
Novelty, Ohio

The American Society For Testing Materials
Philadelphia, Pa.

The American Welding Society
New York, N. Y.

Bendix Aviation Corporation
Red Bank Division
Eatontown, N. J.

Briggs Associates, Inc.
Norristown, Pa.

The British Ceramic Society
Stoke-on-Trent, England

The British Institution of Radio Engineers
London, England

The British Thomson-Houston Co., Ltd.
Research Laboratories
Rugby, Warwickshire, England

Chapman & Hall Ltd.
London, England

The Clarendon Press
Oxford, England

C-Stellerator Associates
Princeton, N. J.

Collins Radio Company
Cedar Rapids, Ia.

Corning Glass Works
Corning, N. Y.

Driver Harris Company
Harrison, N. J.

Edgerton, Germeshausen & Grier, Inc.
Boston, Mass.

Edwards High Vacuum Ltd.
Crawley, Sussex, England

Eitel-McCullough, Inc.
San Carlos, Calif.

The Electrochemical Society
New York, N. Y.

Encyclopaedia Britannica, Inc.
Chicago, Ill.

Engelhard Industries, Inc.
East Newark, N. J.

Fansteel Metallurgical Corporation
North Chicago, Ill.

Foote Mineral Company
Philadelphia, Pa.

The Gage Publishing Company
New York, N. Y.

General Electric Company
Schenectady, N. Y.

General Electric Company
Power Tube Department
Schenectady, N. Y.

General Electric Company
Receiving Tube Department
Electronic Components Division
Owensboro, Ky.

General Electric Company, Ltd.
Research Laboratories
Wembley, England

Handy & Harman
New York, N. Y.

Imperial Chemical Industries, Ltd.
London, England

The Institute of Metals
London, England

The Institute of Physics
London, England

The Institute of Radio Engineers
New York, N. Y.

The Institution of Electrical Engineers
London, England

International Graphite & Electrode Corp.
St. Marys, Pa.

The International Nickel Company, Inc.
New York, N. Y.

Johnson, Matthey & Co., Ltd.
London, England

The Kennedy Press Ltd.
Manchester, England

Kaiser Aircraft & Electronics Laboratory
Palo Alto, Calif.

Kimble Glass Company
A Subsidiary, Owens-Illinois
Toledo, Ohio

Lancashire Dynamo Nevelin, Ltd.
Oxted, Surrey, England

Rudolf A. Lang Verlag
Berlin-Charlottenburg, Germany

Machlett Laboratories, Inc.
Springdale, Conn.

Macmillan and Co., Ltd.
London, England

McGraw-Hill Book Company
New York, N. Y.

Metal-Verlag GMBH
Berlin, Germany

Mica Fabricators Association
New York, N. Y.

Mycalex Corporation of America
Clifton, N. J.

National Research Corporation
Cambridge, Mass.

New York University Press
New York, N. Y.

Pergamon Press, Inc.
New York, N. Y.

Philips Gloeilampenfabrieken
Eindhoven, Netherlands

Philips Laboratories
Irvington-on-Hudson, N. Y.

Quinn-Brown Publishing Corporation
Stamford, Conn.

RCA Laboratories
Radio Corporation of America
Princeton, N. J.

Reinhold Publishing Corporation
New York, N. Y.

Dr. Riederer Verlag GMBH
Stuttgart, Germany

Rutgers University, The State University of
  New York
College of Engineering
New Brunswick, N. J.

Services Electronics Research Laboratories
Baldock, England

Société Française Des Ingénieurs Techni-
ciens Du Vide, Paris, France

The Society of Glass Technology
Sheffield, England

Speer Carbon Company
Saint Marys, Pa.

Julius Springer-Verlag
Berlin, Germany

Stanford University
Stanford, Calif.

Superior Tube Company
Norristown, Pa.

Sylvania Research Laboratories
Bayside, N. Y.

Sylvania Tube Operations
Sylvania Electric Products Inc.
Emporium, Pa.

Synthetic Mica Company
Division of Mycalex Corporation of America
Caldwell, N. J.

Telefunken A. G.
Ulm, Germany

Ultek Corporation
Palo Alto, California

U. S. Air Force
Air Force Cambridge Research Center
Air Research and Development Command

Wright Air Development Center
Wright-Patterson Air Force Base, Ohio

United States Atomic Energy Commission

U. S. Department of the Navy
Bureau of Ships
Bureau of Aeronautics
Office of Naval Research

National Bureau of Standards
Washington, D. C.

U. S. Steel Corporation
Pittsburgh, Pa.

University of Buffalo
Buffalo, N. Y.

University of California
Department of Engineering
Los Angeles, Calif.

Vacuum Metals Corporation
Division of Crucible Steel Co. of America
Syracuse, N. Y.

Varian Associates
Palo Alto, Calif.

Verband Deutscher Electrotechniker
Frankfurt a. M., Germany

Verlag Johann Ambrosius Barth
Leipzig, Germany

Westinghouse Electric Corporation
Pittsburgh, Pa.

Wilbur B. Driver Company
Research Department
Newark, N. J.

John Wiley & Sons, Inc.
New York, N. Y.

LIST OF REVIEWERS

The following Companies and Institutions, through the members of their staff, have, in greatly varying degrees, assisted by reviewing sections of the manuscript. Manufacturers of brazing alloys who helped in the preparation of Table 12.1 are separately listed at the end of that table.

American Metal Climax, Inc.
New York, N. Y.

Battelle Memorial Institute
Columbus, Ohio

Bell Telephone Laboratories Inc.
Murray Hill, N. J.

Bendix Aviation Corporation
Red Bank Division
Eatontown, N. J.

Briggs Associates, Inc.
Norristown, Pa.

The British Thomson-Houston Co., Ltd.
Research Laboratory
Rugby, Warwickshire, England

Chase Brass & Copper Co.
Research and Development Dept.
Waterbury, Conn.

Corning Glass Works
Research & Development Division
Corning, N. Y.

Engelhard Industries, Inc.
Hanovia Liquid Gold Division
East Newark, N. J.

Fansteel Metallurgical Corporation
Research Division
North Chicago, Ill.

Ford Radio & Mica Corporation
Brooklyn, N. Y.

Frenchtown Porcelain Company
Trenton, N. J.

General Electric Company
Research Laboratory
Schenectady, N. Y.

General Electric Company
Lamp Wire and Phosphors Department
Cleveland, Ohio

General Electric Company
Aircraft Gas Turbine Development Dept.
Cincinnati, Ohio

General Electric Company
Microwave Laboratory at Stanford
Palo Alto, Calif.

The General Electric Company, Ltd.
Research Laboratories
Wembley, England

Hughes Aircraft Company
Microwave Tube Development Department
Los Angeles, Calif.

The International Nickel Company, Inc.
Development and Research Division
New York, N. Y.

Johnson, Matthey & Company, Inc.
New York, N. Y.

Kemet Company
Division of Union Carbide Corporation
Cleveland, Ohio

Lancashire Dynamo Nevelin Ltd.
Oxted, England

Litton Engineering Laboratories
Grass Valley, Calif.

Machlett Laboratories, Inc.
Engineering Division
Springdale, Conn.

Minneapolis-Honeywell Regulator Co.
Research Center
Hopkins, Minn.

Department of the Navy
Material Laboratory
New York Naval Ship Yard
Brooklyn, N. Y.

National Carbon Company
Research Laboratories
Division of Union Carbide Corporation
Cleveland, Ohio

Philips Laboratories
Division of North American Philips Co.
Irvington-on-Hudson, N. Y.

Revere Copper and Brass Incorporated
Research Department
Rome, N. Y.

Sperry Electronic Tube Division
Sperry Rand Corporation
Gainesville, Fla.

Stackpole Carbon Company
Research and Engineering Division
St. Marys, Pa.

Superior Tube Company
Norristown, Pa.

Chemical and Metallurgical Division
Sylvania Electric Products Inc.
Towanda, Pa.

Sylvania Electric Products Inc.
Bayside Laboratories
Bayside, N. Y.

Tung-Sol Electric, Inc.
Newark, N. J.

Ultek Corporation
Palo Alto, Calif.

Western Electric Company Incorporated
Allentown Works
Allentown, Pa.

Western Gold and Platinum Company
Belmont, Calif.

Westinghouse Electric Corporation
Electronic Tube Division
Elmira, N. Y.

CONTENTS

INTRODUCTORY REVIEW[1]

The selection of materials for the construction of electron tubes depends in a large measure on the type of tube to be made and on the environment to which it will be exposed in service. When speaking of "tubes" in the generally accepted sense of the word, one thinks of receiving tubes, transmitting tubes, picture tubes, camera tubes (the devices used to pick up the image), photo tubes, counter tubes, switch tubes, voltage regulators, cathode ray tubes, klystrons, magnetrons, and traveling-wave tubes, to name a few. All these devices consist of sealed envelopes in which a degree of vacuum is maintained where free electrons, emitted from a cathode, perform certain useful functions on their way to the anode while being subjected to the influence of electric and magnetic fields, as the case may be.

In a well-evacuated tube, a large number of gas molecules is still present, (3×10^9/cc at 10^{-7} mm Hg) but they do not seriously interfere with the movement of electrons at this level of population. At higher pressures, a sufficient number of gas ions are produced by electron collisions with the gas molecules to seriously affect the satisfactory operation of a "high-vacuum" tube. The presence of a controlled amount of gas, on the other hand, permits new effects to take place which are utilized in "gas-filled" tubes, such as voltage regulators and thyratrons. The "filler gas" must be exceptionally pure. In order to avoid contamination by foreign gases, gas-filled tubes are first prepared as high-vacuum tubes, and the desired gas is then added before seal-off from the pump.

Some devices which utilize effects produced by electrons or ions in evacuated envelopes are so large that they cannot properly be classified with tubes, although the materials problems encountered in their construction are basically the same as those met in smaller vacuum devices; the emphasis may shift, however, from one aspect to another. Particle accelerators, such as cyclotrons, betatrons, linear accelerators, and Van de Graaf machines fall into this category, and so do electron microscopes; these machines are usually pumped continuously during operation.

Vacuum capacitors look like tubes; but in this case the evacuated envelope is provided to insure the absence of gas which, when ionized by spurious radiation, might cause breakdown in the presence of high electric fields. The condenser functions best in the complete absence of ions and electrons and is thus not a tube; nevertheless, being a high-vacuum device, it presents problems in its manufacture which are solved by applying tube technology. Encapsulated devices, such as crystal diodes, transistors, film resistors, and others, also often have the appearance of tubes. Here, the evacuated or gas-filled envelope simply serves the purpose of

1

eliminating the harmful effect of atmospheric moisture. Semiconductor devices are not tubes and do not fall within the scope of this book, but many processes used in their manufacture are an outgrowth of tube techniques.

Every electron tube consists of an internal electrode structure and a housing, or envelope. It may, in addition, have external gear, such as resonators, radiators, cooling jackets, bases and caps. The material requirements are basically different for internal and external components, and they will be separately reviewed in the following pages.

Internal Components

When a tube has been carefully exhausted and sealed off the pump, it is necessary for the successful operation of the tube that a high vacuum be preserved within the envelope during the life of the tube. The envelope itself and the material components which make up the "mount" must be made from materials which have a low vapor pressure not only at the operating temperature but also at elevated temperatures to which the tube is exposed during processing on the pump and possibly during unforeseen overloads during service. The materials used for joining the components, such as brazing filler metals, must fulfill the same condition, i.e., they must not give off any vapors or gases which would spoil a vacuum of the order of 10^{-7} mm Hg (Torr*).

In order to be able to take full advantage of the basically favorable vacuum characteristics of suitably chosen materials, they must be in a rigorously clean condition. Even during initial forming and machining operations the end-use in a vacuum must be kept in mind. Sulfur-free lubricants must be used for machining, drawing, stamping, and grid winding. While surface films of oil are readily removed in the subsequent degreasing and cleaning operations, some microscopic pockets in the metal might be rolled over in machining and trap oil which might not be released until much later when the part is in the tube. The presence of sulfur would then easily poison an oxide-coated cathode if such is used as the source of electrons. After chemical cleaning, vacuum tube components are generally fired in a hydrogen furnace at near 1000°C to reduce remaining oxides and outgas the bulk of the metal by replacing occluded gases with hydrogen which then easily escapes on the pump. Firing in vacuum is frequently done for power tube components and other critical tubes of smaller-volume produc-

---

* The term Tor, or Torr, is used instead of "mm Hg" by international agreement of several Committes on Standards for the definition of terms used in vacuum technology, i.e. The American Vacuum Society, and corresponding agencies in other countries. "Tor" honors the name of Torricelli who discovered atmospheric pressure in 1643.

tion where this more costly procedure is economically justified. Careful parts processing and pre-outgassing in a separate envelope is well worthwhile and pays off in terms of faster pump cycles and longer tube life. Similar cleaning and outgassing operations apply to ceramics, mica, and glass.

A further important consideration for the selection of materials for internal vacuum tube components is their mechanical strength at elevated temperature and their compatibility with each other. When materials are in contact at high temperature, they may enter into chemical reaction with each other, or form alloy phases which are brittle and have lower strength values even at room temperature. Oxide ceramics may be reduced in contact with graphite and thus set free high-vapor-pressure components.

A variety of physical characteristics, apart from mechanical strength, must be carefully considered before a component material is chosen. These desired properties naturally depend on the function to be performed by the part. High electrical conductivity of conductors is generally desired but often is not too critical. Thermal conductivity of grid siderods and laterals should be as high as possible in order to reduce operating temperature so that primary electron emission from these parts in the presence of low-work-function films deposited by the cathode is not encountered. Cathode tails and cathode support members, on the other hand, should have as low a thermal conductivity as possible in order to reduce the drain of heat from the cathode. "Nilvar"* is frequently chosen as the material for such parts.

In order to obtain high power dissipation from anodes, their surfaces should have a high thermal emissivity; this is a specific property of any material but varies with the condition of the surface, depending on its smoothness or roughness, degree of cleanliness, or the presence of oxides. Black surfaces radiate better than shiny surfaces. This makes graphite a suitable anode material although it is more difficult to outgas than metals. Nickel, which is ordinarily bright, can be carbonized for increased radiating power, and the same technique can be applied to iron. Black chrome-vanadate can be obtained on many metal surfaces by electroplating.[2] Tantalum, on the other hand, cannot be blackened by any of these techniques, and the recourse is to roughen its surface by grit-blasting, or to increase its surface by the addition of fins.

The magnetic properties of the material are important in many cases, especially when the component is part of an electron gun structure, or when it is mounted in the proximity of the path of an electron beam. In general, nonmagnetic materials must be used in such cases. Brillouin-flow type guns, on the other hand, will require a magnetic shield in front of

* Registered Trademark, Driver-Harris Co.

the cathode in klystrons and traveling-wave tubes (TWT) where a solenoid is used to focus the beam along its path to the collector, and the cathode itself is not intended to be immersed in the magnetic field. Deflector plates in cathode ray and picture tubes must be nonmagnetic in order to prevent interference with the electrostatic deflection characteristic by uncontrolled magnetic deflection.

The Tube Envelope

The tube envelope is essentially a vacuum container; it must be vacuum-tight. The pressure differential between the external atmosphere and the vacuum inside also raises particular mechanical problems in regard to strength which are magnified by elevated processing temperatures.

The familiar glass envelope is a case in point. Some machine-blown receiving tube bulbs may be barely $\frac{1}{32}$ inch thick. The bulbs are generally made of soda-lime glass (Corning 0080) while the stems are made of a lead glass (Corning 0120) which has higher electrical surface and volume resistivity. The lead wires which are sealed into the stem, or header, are rather closely spaced, and good insulation between them is essential. Glass electrolysis at high operating temperatures would not only reduce insulation but also release gas at the electrodes; a glass of high resistivity is thus required. The bulb, on the other hand, should preferably have a degree of surface conductivity in order to leak off wall charges that might arise from stray electrons impinging on the glass and which could cause puncture of the envelope if the charges were allowed to build up.

These so-called soft glasses have a much lower softening point in comparison to hard glasses, and the temperature to which such envelopes may be heated during the bake-out cycle on the pump is thus limited. The lower softening point makes for easier handling by sealing-in machines so that production economy and basic cost are in favor of soft glasses; for this reason, they are also used for TV picture tubes. Power tubes, on the other hand, are generally made of hard glass, especially Corning 7720 which is also known as "Nonex." In such cases, tungsten is the commonly used material for lead-in wires and rods. Lead-in wires for the common soft glasses are made from a copper-clad iron-nickel alloy wire known as "Dumet."

Tube envelopes often take on a cylindrical shape where metallic and nonmetallic sections of equal diameter are joined at alternate levels by means of glass-to-metal seals or ceramic-to-metal seals depending on the material used for the insulating section. Glass-to-metal seals are much more common than ceramic-to-metal seals, although the latter have come to be used more extensively, if not exclusively, for UHF tubes such as klystrons, magnetrons, and also for x-ray tubes in some cases.

Ceramic envelopes are preferable to glass envelopes on several counts; they are much stronger, mechanically, and permit baking of the tube structure at much higher temperatures; high-alumina ceramics, which are the preferred body for tube envelopes, also have a much greater resistance to thermal shock in comparison to glass and their dielectric losses at high frequencies are considerably lower in value than is the case for glass.

External Components

Materials for external vacuum tube components require little comment in this general review. High-voltage breakdown, corrosion resistance, contact resistance and other characteristics will have to be considered before a material is chosen for a particular application. Ceramic-insulated bases may be necessary instead of plastic bases if high voltage gradients are encountered; special low-temperature solders must be selected for operation at great altitudes, or in sub-zero climates, where ordinary solders for the attachment of radiators and other components might lose their mechanical strength. Careful attention to such details is very important because a tube is no stronger than its weakest link; this might be a corroded contact pin of the base connection even though everything inside the tube is in perfect condition. Gold-plated pins and socket contacts are thus used in critical applications.

Tube Reliability

It is of great importance to the user of electron tubes that he have some data on their life expectancy, so that they can be replaced in commercial or military equipment when the specified life span is about to expire. Unfortunately, this objective is not easily realized. Similar to the problems encountered in forecasting the life expectancy of human beings, it is impossible to foretell how long any one tube will live, but a reasonable forecast can be made about the average life expectancy of a group of tubes made under carefully controlled conditions. This approach calls for the statistical analysis of the manufacturing processes (quality control), and that of the failure rate encountered in service.

The importance of this effort was recognized after the end of World War II, both by the military services and by commercial users, such as the airlines, where sudden failure of tubes in the electronic equipment of an airplane can have disastrous results. When a tube fails suddenly, long before its statistically expected life has expired, one speaks of a catastrophic failure. Such a failure usually has mechanical causes, such as a broken filament, a broken weld, or a cracked glass envelope. These catastrophic failures generally occur early in life and can be greatly reduced by more careful selection of materials and a more rigorous control over the manufacturing techniques used in the factory.

Long-term failures of tubes are caused by gradual deterioration of electrical characteristics that may be due to several reasons. The emission from the oxide-coated cathode may fail on account of the poisoning effects of gases released within the tube to such an extent that the getter becomes saturated and a proper vacuum can no longer be maintained. The components of the tube may not have been properly outgassed during the manufacturing stage, or the ambient temperature may be excessively high, so that gases are released by the glass envelope; or electrolysis may set in within the glass between electrical leads, causing gases to be released, as mentioned above.

In order to minimize both these types of failures, a premium-brand type of tube for critical applications is made by most tube manufacturers; these tubes are known as "reliable tubes," or "trustworthy valves," in the British Isles. Such premium tubes are made under carefully controlled conditions, a much more extensive inspection of all components is employed, and design features are added that minimize adverse effects from exposure to shock, vibration, and moderately high temperatures, say up to 250°C, by using a harder glass for the envelope. These changes involve techniques which are more expensive than conventional procedures for regular mass production, and it stands to reason that premium tubes are thus more expensive.

The rapid technological advances of our modern age have brought about conditions where tubes must operate in increasingly critical environments.[3, 4] Jet aircraft and missiles not only travel at very high speeds but also undergo great rates of acceleration during which tubes suffer mechanical shocks. Very low temperatures are encountered at high altitudes, and very high temperatures when the aircraft, or missile, reenters the earth's atmosphere. In addition to acceleration and shock, high levels of vibration may be encountered, and the use of atomic energy for propulsion may expose the tube to high levels of radiation by neutrons and gamma-rays which may cause damage to the materials used in the construction of the tube. These and other applications require quite a different level of reliability which cannot be met by tubes made in a conventional manner; the more stringent requirements for tube operation may thus be described as follows:

The tube must operate in a specified circuit within the limits of its published characteristics and tolerances for a specified minimum of time and suffer no harmful effects from temperature, acceleration, shock, vibration, or bombardment by neutrons and gamma-rays within the limits specified for these factors.

It becomes apparent from these remarks that one cannot justly speak of an over-all tube reliability for all kinds of applications. The tube must be tailored to its use, or, to put it differently, a tube quite satisfactory for one application may fail prematurely when used in the wrong circuit or in an unsuitable environment. In a critical analysis of the reliability of components used in the construction of computers, ordinary vacuum tubes were found to be the most unreliable item of all.[5] By careful selection of the tubes and rigorous control of all circuit variables as well as of environmental conditions, it was nevertheless possible to achieve system lifetimes of over 100,000 hours and predict over 90 per cent of the failures to be expected. Tubes made especially for transatlantic cable service are expected to have a life of over 20 years.[6] These examples refer to static environments at ordinary temperatures in the absence of vibration and shock, or nuclear radiation. Glass envelopes are satisfactory under these conditions.

For more severe environments, ceramic-envelope tubes have been developed which can be operated for several thousand hours at temperatures of the order of 500°C without suffering harm from severe vibration, acceleration, shock, or bombardment by neutrons and gamma rays. It turns out that ceramic tubes are farther advanced than other circuit components, such as resistors, capacitors, inductances and the like, which are at present limited to operation at much lower temperatures. These results on ceramic tubes are so far based on pilot plant runs, but should soon be extended to regular production.

Heat Transfer in Electron Tubes*

"The transfer of heat within an electron tube is a complicated process. A high-temperature emitting surface is necessary to maintain electronic emission. Heater temperatures range from 1000 to 1300°C. Cathodes operate in the neighborhood of 750°C. To reduce heater power to a minimum, tube structures are designed so that the thermal resistance from the heater and cathode to the envelope and external leads is as great as possible. However, tubes must also have short leads from the internal elements to provide low inductances and low resistances into their external circuits. These leads conduct heat from the cathode or filament, and a compromise between these two incompatible requirements results.

"Most of the heat dissipated in an electron tube appears at the plate. Not only is the plate heated by its normally dissipated energy, but much of the heat originating at the filament, cathode, control grid, and screen grid is transmitted into the plate by radiation. The remainder of the heat

---

* Reproduced from an article by J. P. Welsh[8] with the kind permission of The Gage Publishing Company.

produced by tube elements other than the plate is radiated into the tube envelope and/or conducted into the tube pins along the tube element leads

"Plate temperatures in electron tubes, other than transmitting types,. range from 350°C to as high as 600°C. Most of the energy dissipated by a plate is transmitted internally by radiation and is transmitted through, or absorbed, by the glass envelope dependent upon the configurations and relative temperatures. Owing to its transmission characteristics, electron tube glass usually begins to be a poor transmitter of infrared radiation at 2 to 5 microns; thus, radiation-wise, it is semi-absorbing. (See Figure 1).

"Figure 2 presents the relationship between the transmittance of glass and the energy distribution at several plate temperatures. Note that the energy in areas A and B is transmitted directly through the glass when a plate is at 500°C. Conversely, only the energy in area B is transmitted through the glass when a plate is at 300°C. Consequently, less energy is transmitted through the glass and more energy is absorbed by the glass when the plate is at a lower temperature; this, of course, results in a higher bulb temperature.

"Because the operating spread of plate temperatures falls within the infrared absorption or transmission range of electron tube glasses, it is sometimes possible for a bulb to be at a normal temperature when the internal elements are overheating and, conversely, it is also possible for the glass to be hotter than normal while the internal elements are at normal operating temperatures. It has been found that the plate temperature is the best index of the true thermal condition of a tube. Thus, a well-cooled tube may, under certain conditions, exhibit a higher glass temperature

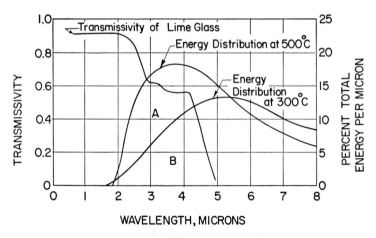

Figure 1

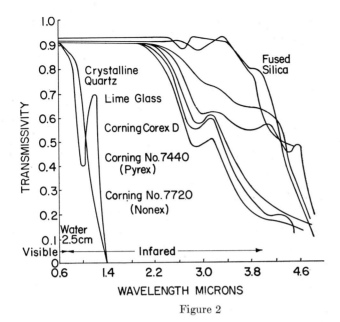

Figure 2

than a poorly-cooled tube. The glass temperatures should be as low as possible, but not at the expense of higher internal element temperatures.

"In general, plate and bulb temperatures of a glass-envelope electron tube at a constant power dissipation will increase or decrease in unison, but in varying degrees, dependent upon the temperatures, emissivities, and transmittances of the surfaces which the radiating plate 'sees.' As the cooling is improved, the plate temperature will tend to level off, while the bulb temperature continues to drop. However, the plate temperature plateau is seldom reached with tube shields, and then only when the unit heat dissipation and concentration are low. The plateau condition can be achieved, however, with adequate forced-air and liquid cooling.

"The primary effect of excessive temperature on tube life is a slow deterioration of characteristics. The life is drastically reduced through decreased emission, evaporation of getter and emitting materials, increased interelectrode leakage, gas leakage, glass failure, insulation failures, and grid loading. These temperature-sensitive effects accelerate rapidly with increasing temperature and can only be alleviated through the proper electrical and thermal operation of tubes.

"It can be concluded that electron tubes must be cooled by removing the heat from the envelopes. Only a small portion of the heat can normally be removed through the pins or leads at the base. The cooling of a tube is the most important mechanical consideration in its mount and socket.

"In general, the hot-spot envelope temperature of receiving-type tubes should be less than 175°C. Several organizations currently recommend maximum envelope temperatures in the neighborhood of 100°C for optimum life and reliability. It is definitely known that hot-spot bulb temperatures ranging from 200 to 250°C will reduce tube life and cause accelerated deterioration of transconductance. The above values are considered to be only "bench marks" because glass temperature does not necessarily indicate the degree of overheating which may exist in a given instance. Further, electron-tube ratings are compromises. It is recommended that the plate temperature be monitored in applications wherein the envelope temperature exceeds 175°C, or is in excess of the manufacturer's rating. The reduction of element temperatures can improve tube reliability more than any other single factor.

"When tubes must be operated at high environmental temperatures or under conditions that will result in abnormal plate and envelope temperatures, derating is usually in order. Exact derating values remain to be determined. Since plate temperature, however, is an index of the thermal condition of a tube, it is recommended that tubes be derated on the basis of plate temperature."[8]

REFERENCES

1. An original version of this review was written several years ago and recently published: W. H. Kohl, "Materials Problems of the Electron-Tube Industry," Engineering Materials Handbook, Charles L. Mantell, editor; McGraw-Hill Book Company, Inc., New York, 1958, pp. 42-11 to 42-18. A German translation of this handbook article was published in Vakuum-Technik, Vol. 4 (Febr. 1956), pp. 139–142. The present 'Introductory Review' is a recent version and extension of the earlier material.

2. M. F. Quaely, "Black chromium-base electroplating," Proc. 40th Annual Convention. American Electroplaters Society, June 15–18, 1953, pp. 48–52.

3. W. H. Kohl, "Electron tubes for critical environments," 1957 IRE National Convention Record, Pt. III, pp. 141–149.

4. W. H. Kohl and P. J. Rice, "Electron tubes for critical environments," Final Report, Stanford Research Institute for Wright Air Development Center (Contract AF 33(616)-3460, July 1957; WADC Tech. Rep. 57-434, Office of Technical Services, PB 131852 (price $3.50); ASTIA Report No. AD151158.

5. N. H. Taylor, "Designing for reliability," Proc. IRE, **45** (June 1957), pp. 811–822.

6. J. O. McNally, G. H. Metson, E. A. Veezie, and M. F. Holmes, "Electron tubes for the transatlantic cable system," Bell Syst. Tech. Jour., **36** (Jan. 1957), pp. 163–188.

7. E. G. Rowe, "On some aspects of tube reliability," "Advances in Electronics and Electron Physics," Vol. **10,** pp. 186–238 (1958).

8. J. P. Welsh, "Techniques of cooling electronic equipment," Pt. 2, *Elec. Mfg.*, **62,** 87–95 (Dec., 1958).

CHAPTER 1

GLASS

Introduction

The usefulness of glass as a structural material for electron tubes has been established over a period of several decades, i.e., ever since the manufacturing techniques of the lamp industry were taken over by the rapidly growing tube industry in the 20's. While the transparency of glass to visible radiation in the presence of a substantial amount of heat makes this material the ideal choice for the incandescent lamp, there exists no such compelling reason to use glass for a radio tube. Indeed, many such tubes are now being made of metal, but all the miniature and sub-miniature tubes are still glass tubes, and so are many power tubes. The replacement of glass by ceramics has been mentioned in the Introductory Review as an ever-growing trend, especially for microwave tubes, ruggedized tubes, and tubes to be operated at high temperatures; what consideration is it then that determines the selection of glass, metal, or ceramic, as the preferred envelope material in a given design problem? In a large measure, the cost of the material itself, and that of its fabrication, will be the decisive factor as long as any one of these possible choices would fulfill the operational requirements.

Let us now consider the basic advantages and disadvantages of glass as a tube envelope material.

Advantages of glass:

1. Transparency to radiation
2. Low vapor pressure
3. Chemical inertness
4. Impermeability to gases
5. Workability to various shapes
6. Reasonable strength
7. Possibility of sealing to metals
8. Availability in many stock sizes
9. Good insulation properties
10. Reasonable cost

Disadvantages of glass:

1. Fragility on impact
2. Poor mechanical strength in presence of strains
3. Poor thermal shock resistance
4. Relatively high dielectric loss factor
5. Deterioration in presence of actinic radiation

Many of these properties require more detailed discussion because it is impossible to make an all-inclusive statement that would be true for the many types of glass that exist.* The following pages will give this amplification on the entries made in the tabulation of advantages and disadvantages. First, it will be necessary to discuss the nature of glass, because many of its properties will then be better understood.

The Nature of Glass

While glass is a solid in the sense that it has the rigidity which is generally associated with solid bodies, it lacks the continuous crystalline structure which is characteristic of metals. The short-range, ordered domains, within which a crystalline structure exists in glass, are of sub-microscopic dimensions, and in this respect glass is very similar to a liquid. When molten glass is cooled, a tendency toward crystallization exists over a fairly narrow range of temperature. The rapid increase of viscosity prevents the formation of large crystal domains, so that on solidification the liquid state is "frozen in." Glass is thus thermodynamically unstable and tends to crystallize when it is held at the proper temperature for a sufficiently long time.

This phenomenon of crystallization is called *devitrification* and presents an ever-present threat to the glass worker. The range of temperature within which devitrification is likely to take place is specific for different glass compositions and will be determined by the values of viscosity and crystallization velocity. For crystallization to take place, the viscosity must be low enough (about 10^4 poises) † to permit aggregation of whatever short-range crystal domains exist. In practice, this devitrification range is passed quickly when a glass melt is cooled, or, for that matter, when glass ware is heated in the blow torch by the glass worker.

It is one of the characteristics of glass that it does not possess a sharply defined melting point where liquid and solid phases exist in equilibrium. Glass loses its solid-like character gradually, on heating, by virtue of a continuous decrease in the value of the viscosity.

* Widespread use of Corning glasses makes it desirable to clarify the code numbers by which they are specified, and to clear up some misconceptions which prevail in regard to the Corning trademark "Pyrex." This name is applied to some 150 different glass compositions and does thus not convey the composition of a glass, although many authors use the name "Pyrex" with the implication that it refers to chemically resistant glass 7740; this practice is not justified. The only clear-cut designation of Corning glasses is the four-number code which has been in use for some time. The old "laboratory code" has been discontinued years ago, and only the four-number code will be used in this book, even when references are quoted which use the old designations in the original text. For the comfort of "old glass workers," and to avoid confusion, both codes are reproduced in the Appendix, Table A1. Table A2 gives the code numbers for Kimble glasses which are of course also widely used.

† The unit of viscosity is one "poise" which has the dimension $ML^{-1}T^{-1}$. In the c-g-s system of units it is thus measured in dynes/sec/cm². Glycerol has a viscosity of 120 poises at 0°C, golden syrup 350 poises at 250°C, pitch 10^8 poises at 25°C, water 0.015 poises at 20°C, and air 0.183×10^{-8} poises at 18°C.

Another characteristic of glass is the existence of a "transformation range" where several properties undergo a discontinuous change of their temperature coefficients when the rate of heating or cooling is too rapid to permit the establishment of equilibrium. This range of temperature (400 to 600°C) is associated with a range of viscosities from 10^{12} to 10^{15} poises, generally indicated by a marked increase of the thermal expansion coefficient of the glass during normal rates of heating. Other glass properties also change discontinuously in the "transformation range," i.e., density, refractive index, heat capacity, electrical resistivity, etc. These property changes are markedly affected by the thermal history of the glass; quite different curves will result on first heating and cooling runs, for purposes of measurement, depending on whether the glass has undergone a prior heat treatment, or cooling, under different conditions.

The optical industry takes advantage of this phenomenon at times to adjust, say, the refractive index of a glass melt by modifying the rate of cooling in order to correct small errors in batch composition, if such have occurred. Figure 1.1 illustrates the influence of the cooling rate from the transformation range on the expansivity of a glass.

The different behavior of glass on heating and cooling, when its thermal history is different, is illustrated in Figure 1.2 a, b. Tool, Lloyd, and Mer-

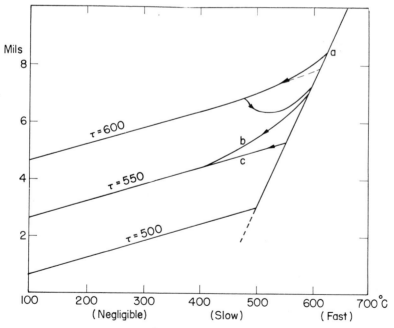

Figure 1.1. Idealized linear expansion plot in the transformation range. After Condon.[8] (*Courtesy American Institute of Physics.*)

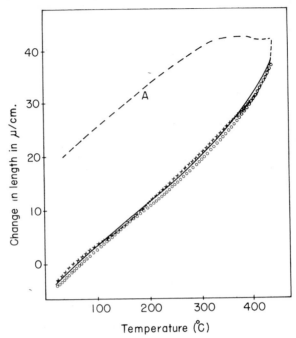

Figure 1.2(a). Influence of thermal history of glass on expansion rate. After Tool, Lloyd, and Merritt.[1] (*Courtesy American Ceramic Society.*)

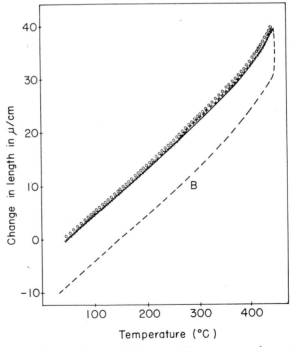

Figure 1.2(b). Influence of thermal history of glass on expansion rate. After Tool, Lloyd, and Merritt.[1] (*Courtesy American Ceramic Society.*)

ritt,[1] "working with a medium flint glass,* treated samples of the glass at a number of temperatures between 360°C and 620°C, the times of treatment varying from a few minutes at the highest temperature to several weeks at the lowest temperature. The sample treated at 620° was quenched in water, the remainder air-chilled. The expansion properties of the samples were then determined, using a heating rate of 3°C per minute from room temperature to 443°C, the samples being held at this temperature for a time sufficiently long to attain a constant length, that is, a length which would not change with further holding at the same temperature; finally the sample was cooled at approximately 3°C per minute to room temperature. A selection from the results is shown in Figure 1.2. Curve A shows the results obtained on the sample previously treated at 620°C for 15 minutes and quenched in water. In this case, at temperatures above about 250°, a contraction was superimposed upon the normal expansivity, the rate of this contraction increasing with increase in temperature so that at temperatures above about 350° the glass had an apparently negative expansion coefficient; at the holding temperature of 443° the contraction continued for some time until the glass sample approached equilibrium at this temperature. Curve B shows the results obtained with a sample previously treated at 360°C for 47 days and cooled in air. In this case, holding for 1 hour at 443°C, after the normal expansivity measurements, produced a marked increase in length at constant temperature. The cooling curves obtained, following each of the expansivity curves A and B, are also shown, and are clearly very nearly the same. Had complete equilibrium been obtained at 443°C in both cases, no doubt the cooling curves would have been identical."[2]

"Tool[3] has recently attempted an interpretation of results of the above type on the basis of his conception of 'fictive' temperature. The idea of fictive temperature is introduced in order to give mathematical expression to the fact that the physico-chemical state or condition of a glass at a given temperature in the critical region changes with *time* at constant temperature until equilibrium is reached. When this physico-chemical equilibrium is attained, the fictive temperature is equal to the actual temperature. Before equilibrium is reached, however, the physico-chemical state of the glass corresponds to the equilibrium state at some different (higher or lower) temperature; that is, if the glass were heated very quickly

---

* The term "flint glass" is used in two ways: (1) to denote any clear glass, and (2) to denote an optical glass with a high refractive index and great dispersive power. Most optical flint glasses contain lead oxide. "Crown glass," on the other hand, has a low refractive index and small dispersive power. Soda-lime-silica glass is a typical crown glass; by adding the appropriate oxide, one may obtain borosilicate crowns, barium crowns, and even a borate crown.

to this different temperature it would be found to be in equilibrium at this temperature, called by Tool the 'fictive' temperature."[2]

These concepts are very important in the interpretation of the behavior of glass and its "fluid" character. For more detailed study, see references 4–9.

From x-ray analysis, first applied by Wyckoff and Morey[10] then by Randall, Rooksby, and Cooper,[11] and later by Warren,[12] Loring, and Biscoe[13, 14] and theoretical deductions by Zachariasen,[15] the concept gradually evolved that "glassy silica is a random network in which each silicon is tetrahedrally surrounded by four oxygens, each oxygen bonded by two silicons, the two bonds to an oxygen being roughly diametrically opposite. The orientation of one tetrahedral group with respect to a neighboring group about the connecting Si-O-Si bond can be practically random. This is the simplest picture of silica glass free from all specialized assumptions, which will completely explain the x-ray diffraction pattern. There is a definite scheme of structure involved. Each atom has a definite number of nearest neighbors at a definite distance, but no unit of structure repeats itself identically at regular intervals in three dimensions; and hence the material is not crystalline. This is essentially the picture of an oxide glass at which Zachariasen arrived from consideration of the chemical composition."[5]

Figure 1.3 schematically illustrates in two dimensions the irregular structure of a glass as distinguished from the regularly repeating structure of a crystal. Figure 1.4 similarly illustrates the structure of a soda-silica glass, after Warren and Biscoe.[14]

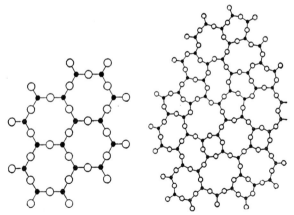

Figure 1.3. Schematic representation in two dimensions of the difference between the structure of a crystal (left) and a glass (right). After Zachariasen.[15] (*Courtesy American Chemical Society.*)

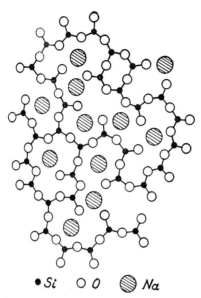

Si   O O   Na

Figure 1.4. Schematic representation in two dimensions of the structure of soda-silica glass. After Warren and Biscoe.[14] (*Courtesy American Ceramic Society.*)

"As the soda content is increased and the proportion of oxygen atoms to silicon atoms increases, more and more sodium atoms find places in the irregular openings in the three-dimensional silicon-oxygen network. The atoms of that network oscillate about average positions as the result of temperature motion, and, under the influence of an electric field, the sodium ions readily migrate from one hole to another, and the electrical conductivity is due to this stepwise migration.

"The lowering of the softening point of silica glass on addition of soda (See p. 20) is the result of breaks in the silicon-oxygen framework resulting from an increasing number of oxygens being bonded to only one silicon; as more and more of these bonds are broken, the structure becomes less rigidly braced in three dimensions. 'Since there is no scheme of repetition in the glass, no two points are exactly identical. There are points with widely varying degrees of weakness, at which flow or breakage can occur at a continuous variety of temperatures. Hence it is readily understood why glass gradually softens, rather than having a definite melting point like a crystal.' "[5]

The so-called random-network hypothesis attributed to Zachariasen and Warren has not been uniformly successful in explaining the physical properties of glass, and several investigators have recently proposed different refinements.[16] Of particular interest, in this regard, is the model proposed by Tilton[16a] who is able to explain many of the heretofore baffling properties of glass by assuming a network of pentagonal rings of tetrahedra with 12-sided regular cavities. A cluster of such dodecahedral cavities is called a "vitron."

The Composition of Glass

Glass is made by melting controlled amounts of carefully mixed raw materials (the batch), which results in a concentrated solution of oxides; the main glass constituents are: SiO_2, B_2O_3, Al_2O_3, CaO, PbO, K_2O, Na_2O, and others to be mentioned shortly. While the structure of these various oxides in their crystalline form has been explored, very little can be said about the state of aggregation that prevails when they are in molten form and are able to interact with each other and become a liquid.

Glassformers are oxides which, by themselves, form glassy networks; these include primarily: SiO_2, B_2O_3, P_2O_5, GeO_2, and As_2O_3. The following oxides will also form glasses when melted with the right amount of a suitable modifying oxide: TeO_2, V_2O_5, Al_2O_3, MoO_3, WO_3, and TiO_2. The first three oxides form quite stable binary glasses, but the last three form only very unstable glasses; thus TeO_2 and V_2O_5 form fairly stable glasses when melted with BaO or PbO, and Al_2O_3 forms a stable glass with CaO.*

"Other types of oxides, notably those of the alkalies and alkaline earths, take no part in the glassy network. When Na_2O is added, every oxygen becomes part of the tetrahedral coordination of four oxygens around each silicon. This necessitates that some of the bridging atoms uniting SiO_4-tetrahedra be broken, as shown in Figure 1.4. Atoms of this type are known as network modifiers."

Intermediates occupy a position somewhere between purely network formers and purely network modifiers; they are represented by BeO, ZnO, CdO, PbO, and other oxides.

Impurities present in glass may originate in the original batch components and from chemical or physical interaction with the tank walls at elevated temperatures; some impurities often present in glass are Fe_2O_3, Mn_2O_3, SO_3, F, and others. Numerous addition agents are used to produce colored glasses.[19] For the intricacies of glass manufacture the reader is referred to the literature.[20]

The relative distribution of network formers, modifiers and intermediates, in terms of weight percentage, in a given glass batch has a marked effect on the properties of the resulting glass. Table 1.1 classifies a number of

---

* Personal communication from The British Thomson-Houston Co., Ltd. Rugby, England. Other workers, notably Mrs. A. Winter, claim to have made other simple oxide glasses, i.e. PbO, SnO, and In_2O_3, which could not be obtained in the extensive research carried out at B.T.H.

TABLE 1.1 CLASSIFICATION OF SEALING GLASSES ACCORDING TO CONTENT OF GLASS-FORMING OXIDES[21]

Group number	Group I 100% glass-forming oxides	Group II Between 80 and 100% glass-forming oxides						Group III Between 60 and 80% glass-forming oxides		Group IV Between 40 and 60% glass-forming oxides			Special lamp glass
Glass type	Fused silica	"Borosilicate" glasses						"Soda" glasses		"Lead" glasses, iron sealing glasses			Special lamp glass
Glass number		R.48	R.49	R.50	C.38	C.9	C.11	C.19	C.22	C.12	C.31	C.76	C.14
Silica SiO_2	100	83.5	78.5	74.5	68.5	75.3	72.2	72.5	67.5	56	52	48.2	58.5
Boric oxide B_2O_3		12.5	17.5	17.5	30	16.9	15.0		0.7				3
Alumina Al_2O_3		4	4	4		2.0	3.0	1.3	3.9	1.3	1		22.5
Lead oxide PbO										30	30		
Oxides of the divalent metals MgO, CaO, BaO				4			3.0	9.5	6.7		2.5	30	15.2
Calcium fluoride CaF_2					1.5							5	
Oxides of alkali metals						5.8	6.5	16.3	20.7	12.5	14.5	16.8	0.8
Average thermal expansion coefficient between 50 and 400°C ($\times 10^7$)	5.5	13	18	23	30	36.5	45.5	95	105	91	100	115	37

British sealing glasses according to their content of glass forming oxides, after Dale and Stanworth.[21]

Fused silica, a tightly bonded glass network, stands by itself; it has the lowest expansion coefficient, the greatest heat shock resistance, high transparency to ultraviolet light, the lowest dielectric constant and loss factor, but (unfortunately but naturally) the highest softening point. Fused silica would be the ideal material for a tube envelope if it were not so difficult to work on conventional sealing machines, and if there were a metal which matched its low expansion coefficient. Special power tubes have been made of fused silica, and "quartz"* lamps are being made in ever-increasing numbers for street, highway, and industrial lighting.

The melting point of cristobalite, the most stable form of crystalline silica, is 1723°C—a temperature quite beyond the working range of commercial furnaces. Furthermore, molten silica has such a high viscosity that it would be difficult to remove bubbles from the melt where they are formed from volatile components. The addition of 25 per cent soda (Na_2O) lowers the melting point of silica by nearly 1000°C, and also lowers the viscosity of this melt, thus overcoming the handicaps to practical workability mentioned above. Unfortunately, such a binary glass is soluble in water, and other constituents must be added to overcome this difficulty; the soda content is thus usually limited to 15 per cent. Lime (CaO) is generally chosen as the second additive, and thus results the well-known soda-lime-silica glass which had its origin with the Egyptians, and has been used with little modification since that time to the present.

The effect of various glass components on viscosity has been studied by Gehlhoff and Thomas[22], who summarized their results as follows:

1. Alkalies decrease viscosity more than any other oxide, especially at high temperatures, and Na_2O more than K_2O.

2. Na_2O-K_2O glasses have a minimum viscosity in certain proportions, which is particularly noticeable at lower temperatures.

3. MgO and ZnO increase viscosity, especially at lower temperatures.

4. CaO raises viscosity more than any other oxide at low temperatures, but at higher temperatures it first decreases, then increases viscosity.

5. NaO and PbO decrease viscosity at all temperatures.

---

* "Quartz" is the name of a natural mineral which undergoes several transformations under the influence of heat and turns into tridymite at 870°C, cristobalite at 1470°C, and vitreous silica at 1723°C, the melting point of SiO_2 . Having been once molten, fused silica exists as a glass at all temperatures below 1723°C and is thus an unstable, undercooled liquid. "Fused Silica" is thus the proper term for all fabricated ware which has been worked at high temperature; the name "quartz" nevertheless persists in common use for lamps, tubing, and the like.

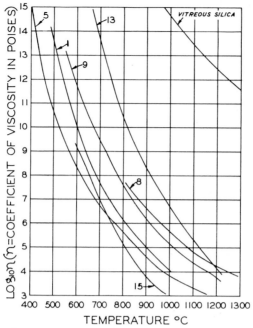

Figure 1.5(a). Viscosity-temperature curves for some glasses listed in Table 1.1; After Douglas.[24] (*Courtesy Institute of Physics, London.*)

6. Addition of B_2O_3 up to 15 per cent increases viscosity, but further addition diminishes it, the effect being much greater at low temperatures.

7. Al_2O_3 increases, and Fe_2O_3 decreases viscosity.

Figure 1.5(a) shows the change of viscosity as a function of temperature for a number of glasses listed in Table 1.1, and Figure 1.5(b) gives similar curves for various Corning glasses. The curves are generally hyperbolic in form and can be described within limited temperature ranges by an empirical expression suggested by Fulcher:[23]

$$\log_{10} \eta = -A + \frac{B}{T - T_0} \qquad (1.1)$$

where

η = viscosity at any temperature T

A, B = constants

T_0 = a reference temperature

This formula is of the general type

$$\eta = A' e^{b/T} = A' e^{B'/RT} \qquad (1.2)$$

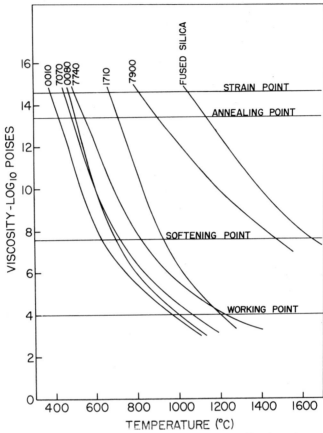

Figure 1.5(b). Viscosity-temperature curves for some Corning glasses. (*Courtesy Corning Glass Works, Bulletin B-83, 1957.*)

where

  B' = activation energy

  R = gas constant

  T = absolute temperature

and plots of $\log \eta$ vs $1/T$ give straight lines whose slopes are a measure of the activation energy.

Referring again to Table 1.1, it is evident that one arrives at the following main glass types which are useful for tube applications:

  (a) Aluminoborosilicate glasses

  (b) Borosilicate glasses

  (c) Soda-lime silicate glasses ("crown")

  (d) Lead-alkali silicate glasses ("flint")

The first two groups are generally referred to as "hard glasses" and the last two as "soft glasses." Soft glasses are easily worked by mass-production machinery; for this reason, receiving tubes and TV tubes are made of soft glass. Power tubes, microwave tubes, and other special-purpose tubes which are low-production items, relatively speaking, ultilize hard glasses in order to permit outgassing on the pump at higher temperatures. Table 1.2* gives the chemical composition of a number of glasses used for high-vacuum devices under the main groupings of glass types and their applications.[24, 25] Addition of PbO, up to 50 per cent of the glass batch, greatly improves the workability of the resulting glass. Because of the scarcity and high cost of lead oxide in recent years, there has been a tendency to substitute barium oxide for part of the lead oxide in these glasses.[25]

Gas Diffusion Through Glass

The impermeability of glass to gases of various kinds is generally taken for granted, and is thus listed at the beginning of the chapter as one of the principal advantages of glass for tube envelopes. More careful investigation discloses, however, that gases do find their way through glass envelopes and thus increase the pressure within. It naturally takes a considerable period of time before such an increase of pressure becomes noticeable, and the effect is much more pronounced for some gases than for others. Similarly, certain types of glass are more subject to gas permeation than others, and the structure of the glass has a decided bearing on this effect. Obviously, the denser the structure of the solid, the less likely it will be that gas atoms or molecules will penetrate it, and, by the same reasoning, the smaller the gas atom, ion, or molecule, the easier it will be for it to enter. The atomic diameters from the gas kinetic theory, which relies mainly on viscosity measurements, are given in Table 1.3 for a temperature of 700°C.

Gas atoms which are too large to pass through the crystalline network might well penetrate the glass network of fused silica. On the other hand, when the open meshes of fused silica are occupied in part by network modifiers such as sodium (Figure 1.4), it becomes again more difficult for gas atoms to enter. These concepts have in general been confirmed by experiments conducted by Norton,[27] who investigated the permeation of helium through nine different types of glass, for which the compositions are given in Table 1.4, where the glasses are arranged in the order of decreasing rate of helium permeation; fused silica was investigated by Rayleigh, whose data are included in the table by Norton; it shows the highest rate, and lead borate the lowest.

---

* Some additional entries were made in this table by the present author to include data kindly supplied by The British Thomson-Houston Co., Ltd.

TABLE 1.2. Approximate Chemical Compositions of Some Glasses used in High-Vacuum Devices[24, 25]

No.	Designation	Constituent Oxides (Weight Per cent)									Uses
		SiO_2	Na_2O	K_2O	CaO	MgO	B_2O_3	Al_2O_3	PbO	BaO	
1	Fused silica	99.5	—	—	—	—	—	—	—	—	Quartz Lamps
2	96% silica glass	96.3	0.2	0.2	—	—	2.9	0.4	—	—	
3	Soda-lime	70.12	16.82	0.35	5.40	3.60	0.78	2.58	—	SO_3: 0.20	*Soft glasses* — Envelopes for radio tubes, lamps, and fluorescent signs
4		73.6	16.	0.6	5.2	3.6	—	1.	—	—	
5		70.5	16.7	0.8	6.7	3.4	—	1.8	—	—	
6		69.	17.5	1.9	5.8	1.6	—	4.	—	—	
7		69.3	16.8	0.6	5.6	3.4	1.2	3.1	—	—	
8		71.5	14.	1.5	5.7	3.	—	2.2	—	1.7	
9		72.5	16.3		6.5	3.	—	1.3	—	—	
10	Lead silicate	56.0	5.2	7.5	0.5	0.3	—	1.0	30.0	—	*Soft glasses* — Stems for radio tubes and lamps
11		63.	7.6	6.	0.3	0.2	0.2	0.6	21.	—	
12		56.	4.5	8.	—	—	—	1.3	30.	—	
13		35.	—	7.2	—	—	—	—	58.	—	
14	Borosilicate	65.5	4.3	3.1	1.0	—	16.0	5.5	ZnO: 1.9; F_2: 0.2	2.5	*Hard glasses* — Power tubes, micro-wave tubes, diffusion pumps, chemical apparatus
15		75.5	4.0	2.0	—	—	16.3	2.2	—	—	
16		71.	5.3	2.4	0.3	—	13.7	7.4	—	—	
17		80.5	3.8	0.4	—	—	12.9	2.2	—	—	
18		70.0	4.5	0.5	0.1	0.2	28.0	1.1	—	Li_2O: 1.2	
19		73.	—	1.0	—	—	16.5	—	6.	—	
20		67.3	4.6	4.1	—	0.2	24.6	1.7	—	—	
21		65.5	4.1	—	—	—	24.1	2.2	—	—	
22		75.3	4.0	1.8	—	—	16.9	2.0	—	—	
23		72.2	3.5	3.0	3.0	—	15.0	3.0	—	—	

No.									
	Aluminosilicate								*Extra-hard glasses* High-temperature tubes and mercury discharge lamps
24	54.25	—	13.25	—	7.5	22.0	—	—	
25	54.5	1.1	13.5	—	7.4	21.1	—	3.5	
26	58.7	—	5.9	8.4	3.	22.4	—	—	
27	57.	1.0	5.5	12.	4.	20.5	—	3.1	
28	55.8	—	13.0	—	5.1	23.0	P_2O_5: 3.8	3.1	
29	54.5	—	11.3	0.5	—	23.5		6.3	
	Aluminoborosilicate								*Special glass* for sodium vapor lamps
30	22.6	6.5	10.	0.2	37.	23.7	—	—	
31	8.0	14.0	6.0	—	48.0	24.0	Fe_2O_3: <0.01	—	

No.	Corning Glass Works	Notes	No.	British Thomson-Houston Co.,* Ltd.	Notes	No.	Osram-G. E. C. Glass Works*	Notes
2	7900, 7910, 7911		8	C94		3	X8	5
4	0080	4	9	C19	4	10	L1	4,6
11	0010	4	12	C12	4	14	SBN124	3
13	8870		21	C40	3	15	W1	1
17	7740	1	22	C 9	1	24	H26X	2
18	7070	1	23	C11	2	31	NA.10	2
19	7720	3	28	C37	2			
20	7050	2	29	C46	2			
27	1710, 1720							

* According to data furnished by the manufacturer to the present author.

Detail of Notes: 1. Tungsten-sealing; 2. Molybdenum-sealing; 3. Kovar-sealing; 4. Dumet-sealing; 5. 28 Chrome-Iron-sealing; 6. 50/50 Nickel-Iron-sealing. (See Table 13.3 for further details.)

TABLE 1.3. ATOMIC OR MOLECULAR DIAMETERS (IN AU) FOR SEVERAL GASES, AND THE PERMEATION RATE AT 700°C (IN cm^3 (NTP) PER SEC, PER cm^2 AREA, PER MM THICKNESS, PER CM Hg GAS PRESSURE DIFFERENCE) FOR HELIUM[*]

Gas	Permeation Rate (700°C)	A.U.[†]
Helium	2.1×10^{-8}	1.95
Hydrogen	2.1×10^{-9}	2.5
Deuterium	1.7×10^{-9}	2.55
Neon	4.2×10^{-10}	2.4
Argon	under 10^{-15}	3.15
Oxygen	under 10^{-15}	3.2
Nitrogen	under 10^{-15}	3.4

[*] After F. J. Norton[26]
[†] From Landolt-Börnstein Tabellen, Vol. 1, 1950, p. 325.

TABLE 1.4. GLASS COMPOSITIONS STUDIED BY NORTON[27]

	Glass No.								
	1 Fused SiO_2 (G)	2 Vycor brand (C)	3 No. 7740 (C)	4 No. 650 (L)	5 Phosphate (H)	6 No. 0080 (C)	7 No. 1720 (C)	8 X-ray (P)	9 Pb borate (G)
SiO_2	100	96	81	}90	0	72	62	31	0
B_2O_3		3	13		5		5		22
P_2O_5					77				
Al_2O_3		1	2	3	11	1	18		
CaO } MgO							10	15	
BaO								8	
PbO								61	78
ZnO					7				
Na_2O } K_2O			4	7		17			
Sum of percentage of glass-formers SiO_2 + B_2O_3 + P_2O_5	100	99	94	90	82	72	67	31	22

At the bottom of Table 1.4 the total percentage content of glass formers (SiO_2 + B_2O_3 + P_2O_5) is given for any one glass composition, and it is apparent that the permeation rate increases rapidly with the increasing content of glass formers. Figure 1.6 gives a graphical representation of this trend.

The permeation of helium through crystalline quartz is ten million times less than it is through silica glass. Hydrogen, deuterium, and neon, which have a larger atomic size than helium, will permeate at a slower rate, and

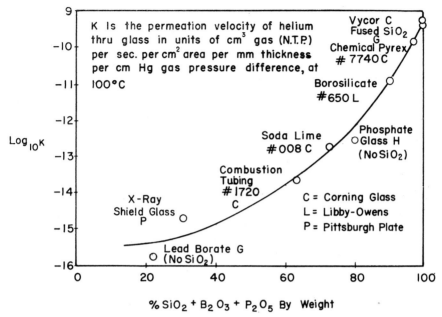

% SiO$_2$ + B$_2$O$_3$ + P$_2$O$_5$ By Weight

Figure 1.6. Permeation velocity K of helium diffusing through various glasses at 100°C. The permeation velocity K is in units of cm³ gas (N.T.P.)/sec/cm² area/mm thickness/cm Hg (gas pressure difference). (A) Lead borate glass (no SiO$_2$); (B) X-ray shield glass; (C) combustion tubing No. 1720; (D) soda-lime glass No. 0080; (E) phosphate glass (no SiO$_2$); (F) borosilicate glass No. 650; (G) chemical Pyrex brand glass No. 7740; (H) fused silica; (I) Vycor brand glass. After Norton.[26] (*Courtesy American Ceramic Society.*)

for argon, oxygen, and nitrogen the permeation rate at the same temperature becomes less by a factor of 100,000 or more; hence glass may be considered impermeable to these latter gases for practical purposes. Atomic size is not the only factor which affects the permeation rate. The neon atom, which is smaller than the hydrogen molecule, diffuses more slowly through glass by a factor of five. Norton states that this difference is probably due to surface and solubility effects. Weyl[28] has emphasized the importance of chemical interactions in trying to explain mechanical effects encountered with glass; diffusion is one of these. Weyl thus explains the slower diffusion of hydrogen through glass, in comparison to that of helium, by the greater chemical affinity of H$_2$ for the oxygen ions in the glass network, thus requiring a greater activation energy for the diffusion process.

"A distinction is drawn between the terms permeation and diffusion, especially the permeation constant and diffusion constant. Permeation is the overall steady-state flow process from the gas phase on one side of the membrane or wall to the gas phase on the other side. Strictly speaking, the term diffusion in a solid applies to the internal process by which an atom is handed on, or changed from one lattice position to another. In the case of gases going through solids, diffusion as a separate process is difficult to measure. The overall process of permeation is much easier to study.

"Permeation involves several steps as follows: (1) impact of the gas atoms or molecules on the surface; (2) absorption; (3) possible dissociation upon absorption; (4) solution of the gas in the wall material at the incoming surface to some equilibrium solubility value; (5) movement of the gas atoms from the saturated surface layer through the interior as atoms or ions, under a concentration gradient, to the outgoing surface; this constitutes diffusion proper. The concentration gradient is the driving force for diffusion and the process is given quantitative formulation in Fick's law;* (6) transfer of the dissolved gas to the outgoing surface layer with possible recombination; (7) desorption of this gas and release on the low-pressure side of the membrane."[27]

Item (3) leads to an important distinction between various diffusion processes. When hydrogen diffuses through iron, it is absorbed at the surface as a molecule but is then dissociated into atoms; i.e., it diffuses through the iron in the form of atoms, or protons, and recombines on the other side into molecules. In this case, the rate of hydrogen permeation depends on the square root of the pressure difference on the two sides of the solid wall. For glass and polymers, the rate of permeation varies directly as the pressure, indicating that no surface dissociation takes place. Hydrogen thus permeates glass as a molecule.

For the case of nondissociation and the rare gases, the total amount q, of material permeating a membrane at constant temperature is given by

$$q = \frac{KAt \times (p_1 - p_2)}{d} \tag{1.3}$$

where
  K = permeation velocity constant
  A = area of membrane exposed
  t = time
  p_1 = gas pressure on high side
  p_2 = gas pressure on low side
  d = thickness of membrane

*
$$\frac{\partial n}{\partial t} = D \frac{\partial^2 n}{\partial x^2}$$

where
  n = number of atoms/cc
  D = diffusion constant

The equation relating the permeation constant K to temperature is

$$K = A\,e^{-Q/RT} \tag{1.4}$$

where

   A = a constant

   Q = activation energy in calories per gram atom

   R = the gas constant in calories per mole

   T = absolute temperature (°K)

From this equation it is evident that, if Q does not vary appreciably with temperature, log K plotted vs $1/T$ will yield a straight line, the slope of which is proportional to the activation energy Q.

Plots of this kind are given in Figure 1.7 for the various glasses investigated by Norton. The activation energies obtained from the slope of these lines are given in Table 1.5. If two values of the permeation velocity K

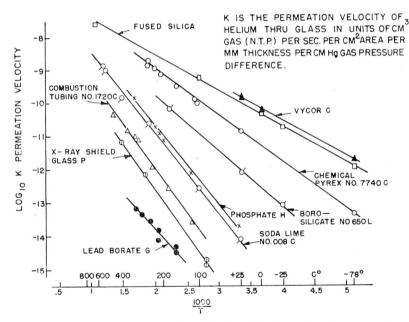

Figure 1.7. Permeation velocity K of helium diffusing through various glasses. The permeation velocity, $\log_{10}$ K, is plotted against the reciprocal of the absolute temperature, 1000/T. The permeation velocity K is in units of cm³ gas (N.T.P.)/ sec/cm² area/mm thickness/cm Hg (gas pressure difference). Curve (A) lead borate glass; (B) X-ray shield glass; (C) combustion tubing No. 1720; (D) soda-lime glass No. 0080; (E) phosphate glass; (F) borosilicate glass No. 650; (G) chemical Pyrex brand glass No. 7740; (H) fused silica; and (I) Vycor brand glass. After Norton.[26] (*Courtesy American Ceramic Society.*)

TABLE 1.5. ACTIVATION ENERGY OF THE VARIOUS GLASSES STUDIED BY NORTON[27]

Glass	Activation energy (cal/gm atom)
Vycor brand (C)	4,900
Fused silica (G)	4,900
Chemical Pyrex brand No. 7740 (C)	6,400
Borosilicate No. 650 (L)	7,600
Phosphate (H)	11,000
Soda-lime No. 0080 (C)	11,000
Combustion tubing No. 1720 (C)	12,000
X-ray shield (P)	12,500
Lead borate (G)	9,300

at two temperatures are known, the following equation will determine Q:

$$\log_{10} \frac{K_2}{K_1} = \frac{Q}{4.57} \left(\frac{1}{T_1} - \frac{1}{T_2} \right) \tag{1.5}$$

where $4.57 = 2.3 \times R$; R is the universal gas constant in calories per mole.

It must finally be noted that the permeation constant of the gas is proportional to the diffusion constant D of the gas, according to the following relation:

$$K = \frac{D \times S \times (p_2 - p_1)}{d} \tag{1.6}$$

where S = solubility.

As a convenience to the reader interested in further details on gas diffusion and permeation, additional references (Ref. 29–43a) are given in the bibliography at the end of the chapter.

The Mechanical Strength of Glass

Glass is a brittle material which ruptures suddenly without yield or deformation; it always fails in tension. Tempered glass with compressive strain in its surface is thus stronger than annealed glass. The strength of glass depends to a very large extent on the residual stresses resulting from previous thermal treatment, the physical size and shape of the article tested, the surrounding atmosphere, and, above all, the condition of its surface. Maximum strength is obtained when a virgin surface exists on the specimen under test. Freshly drawn glass fibers (10^{-4} in. dia.) have shown a strength of 10^7 psi[44] and thus exhibit the intrinsic strength of glass that has been calculated by Orowan[45] by assuming that a force of $0.2 \ E$ is required to overcome the attractive forces in an interatomic plane (E is Young's modulus). Orowan thus arrived at a value of about 1000 kg/mm² (1.4×10^6 psi).

These high strength values decrease rapidly for larger fibers, and "for

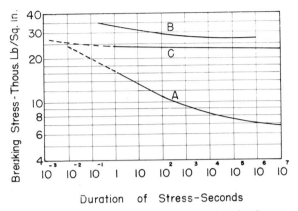

Figure 1.8. Stress-time characteristics of glass broken in flexure tests at room temperature. Composite curves; A-Annealed glass, tested in air; B-Tempered glass, tested in air; C-Annealed glass, tested in vacuum. After Shand.[25, 106] (*Courtesy Corning Glass Works.*)

freshly drawn soda-lime glass, 0.25 in. in dia., they drop to 73,000 psi. If such rods are etched with hydrofluoric acid, the strength increases to 250,000 psi; if fine sand is then dropped onto the rod from a height of 3 in., the strength decreases to 40,000 psi; more severe sandblasting will reduce the strength to anywhere between 2,000 and 20,000 psi. The generally used design figure for the strength of glass is 1000 psi."*

It is obvious then that no general statement can be made on the strength of glass but that the special circumstances of any particular application will have a determining effect. There is also evidence that the strength increases above and below room temperature,[46] and it is known that the strength decreases with duration of load application. Figure 1.8 illustrates this effect and also brings out the influence of the surrounding atmosphere. For loads of indefinite duration, in air, the breaking stresses are of the order of 40 to 45 per cent of the 5-second breaking stresses of annealed glasses.[25]

It was first suggested by Griffith[47] that all glass bodies are riddled with a large number of small cracks, many of them of submicroscopic size, which act as stress multipliers. The stress at the tip of the crack is greater than the applied stress by a factor depending on the dimension and location of the crack; this factor may reach a value of 100.† It is now believed that these microscopic flaws are confined to the surface and are produced in manufacture and in subsequent handling. The absorption of moisture

* These data were presented by E. U. Condon during a lecture at Stanford University on 11/10/55; see also Reference 8.

† A condensed review of and a bibliography to the many investigations of the strength of glass is given by Lynch and Tooley.[48]

from the atmosphere diminishes the surface energy and thus reduces the strength.*

Distinct from this short-term effect of water on glass strength, and opposite in its consequence, is the prolonged immersion of glass fibers in water for periods of 24 hours or more. Stockdale, Tooley, Yuig, and Moorthy[50, 51] have shown that the tensile strength of glass increases by as much as 30 per cent after such treatment and that the increase is dependent on the temperature of the water and the composition of the glass. Lead glass reaches a maximum strength increase at 60°C, soda-lime glass also near 60°C, and borosilicate glass above 90°C.

As pointed out above, the strength of glass may be increased by as much as a factor of 10, by treating the surface with dilute hydrofluoric acid for a short time, provided that care is taken not to touch the surface after this treatment. For most purposes, the removal of a surface layer from 0.002 to 0.003 in. thick will be adequate to produce the desired strengthening effect. This effect has been known since 1894,[52] and the rinsing of tube envelopes in dilute hydrofluoric acid is a common practice in the tube industry today. The strength of the acid used varies anywhere from 1 to 25 per cent. The purpose of the treatment is not so much to strengthen the glass as to leach off a surface layer of alkali hydrates which form on exposure of the glass surface to the atmosphere; this layer is the source of a prolonged gas release on the pump (p. 67).

Another method used to increase the strength of glass by surface treatment consists in heating the glass near to its annealing temperature in an atmosphere containing sulfur dioxide and oxygen. The treatment produces a reaction at the glass surface resulting in the formation of sodium sulfate, which may be washed away easily with water, leaving a clean and stronger surface. There is no doubt that this treatment diminishes the alkali content, and that this surface composition difference will place a very thin surface layer in high compression once the glass has cooled again to room temperature after the heat treatment. This surface compression will tend to prevent opening up of the surface flaw under applied tensile stress and may, therefore, at least partly account for the effectiveness of the treatment.[2]

Richardson[53] discusses the importance of having a controlled amount of sulfur dioxide in the gas used on glass-working machinery, particularly for the forming of flares and for stem-sealing. When the incandescent lamp industry of Cleveland, Ohio, was notified, in 1929, that they would have to change their equipment to adapt it for the use of natural gas because

---

* When setting out to break a piece of glass tubing or rod, an experienced glass worker will scratch the glass with a glass cutter and then, before applying tension to the scratch, briefly exhale on it or wet it with saliva.

the supply of manufactured gas would be discontinued, it was soon found that the flaring of glass tube ends was not successful after the changeover because the flares were wrinkled and the tools wore out quickly, indicating the absence of a lubricating ingredient in the gas. The manufactured gas contained 20 grains of sulfur per 100 cubic feet of gas and the natural gas had only 1 grain per 100 cubic feet. It is a common practice in the incandescent lamp and radio tube industry today to add controlled amounts of sulfur dioxide to natural gas used for glass forming. The content of free sulfur in manufactured gas is generally kept below 15 grains per 100 cubic feet of gas, or 0.025 per cent by volume.

Sulfur is, of course, a notorious poisoning agent for oxide-coated cathodes, and great care must be taken not to have sulfur or sulfur dioxide present in sealing fires.[54] The action of water and of sulfur dioxide on glass surfaces has been discussed in detail by Douglas and Isard.[55]

The Annealing of Glass

Before dealing with this subject in some detail, it may be well to introduce some "Standard Definitions of Terms Relating to Glass and Glass Products," which are taken from the ASTM* Standard C 162–52 (revised 1956) which was prepared jointly by the American Ceramic Society and the American Society for Testing Materials (Committee C-14 on Glass and Glass Products). Of the many terms defined in this Standard only a few are presented here which have a bearing on annealing and glass working:

Annealing Range: The range of glass temperature in which stresses in glass articles can be relieved at a commercially desirable rate. For purposes of comparing glasses, the annealing range is assumed to correspond to the temperatures between the annealing point (A.P.) and the strain point (St. P.).

Strain Point (St. P.): The temperature at which the internal stress is substantially relieved in 4 hrs. The strain point corresponds generally to the lower end of the annealing range. The strain point corresponds to a viscosity of $10^{14.50}$ poises when measured by the Tentative Method of Test for Annealing Point and Strain Point of Glass (ASTM Designation: C 336). This test prescribes a linear extrapolation of the data obtained in the annealing point determination to an apparent viscosity of $10^{14.50}$ poises.†

Annealing Point (A. P.): The temperature at which the internal stress is substantially relieved in 15 min. The annealing point corresponds

* American Society For Testing Materials, 1916 Race Street, Philadelphia 3, Pennsylvania.

† Glass is a solid body below the temperature for which the viscosity equals 10^{15} poises.[56] It is interesting to note that this value approximately represents the viscosity of aluminum at room temperature.[57]

generally to the upper end of the annealing range. The annealing point corresponds to a viscosity of $10^{13.00}$ poises when measured by the Tentative Method of Test for Annealing Point and Strain Point of Glass (ASTM Designation: C 336). This test prescribes a rate of cooling of approximately 4°C per min. with a fiber approximately 0.0065 cm in diameter.

Deformation Point: The temperature observed during the measurement of expansivity by the interferometer method at which viscous flow exactly counteracts thermal expansion. The deformation point generally corresponds to a viscosity in the range from 10^{11} to 10^{12} poises.

Softening Point (S. P.): The temperature at which a uniform fiber, 0.55 to 0.75 mm in diameter and 23.5 cm in length, elongates under its own weight at a rate of 1 mm per min. when the upper 10 cm of its length is heated in the manner prescribed in the Tentative Method of Test for Softening Point of Glass (ASTM Designation: C 338) at a rate of approximately 5°C per min. For glass of density near 2.5, this temperature corresponds to a viscosity of $10^{7.6}$ poises.

Working Range: The range of surface temperature in which glass is formed into ware in a specific process. The "upper end" refers to the temperature at which the glass is ready for working (generally corresponding to a viscosity of 10^3 to 10^4 poises), while the "lower end" refers to the temperature at which it is sufficiently viscous to hold its formed shape (generally corresponding to a viscosity greater than 10^6 poises). For comparative purposes, when no specific process is considered, the working range of glass is assumed to correspond to a viscosity range from 10^4 to $10^{7.6}$ poises.

Melting Temperature: The range of furnace temperatures within which melting takes place at a commercially desirable rate, and at which the resulting glass generally has a viscosity of $10^{1.5}$ to $10^{2.5}$ poises. For purposes of comparing glasses, it is assumed that the glass at melting temperature has a viscosity of 10^2 poises.

The various temperatures and temperature ranges corresponding to the terms described above are indicated for different glass types in Figure 1.5b and Table A3.

The purpose of annealing is the equalization of stresses which have arisen in the glass body during cooling from a high temperature where, owing to the low viscosity of the glass, no strains can be maintained. When a glass body is cooled from the molten state, say when entering the mold, or when being drawn from the tank, the surface will cool more rapidly than the interior, so that the contraction of the surface will exert a force on the interior. This interplay of forces sets up a hydrostatic pressure exerted by the interior of the surface layer, which must flow to relieve the pressure. As long as such flow is possible, no stresses will result. On further cooling, the interior body will become rigid, but will remain hotter than the surface throughout the cooling cycle and maintain its stress-free condition as long as the temperature gradient is constant.

The temperature distribution through the cross-section of a glass slab which is being cooled at a constant rate is parabolic, as shown in Figure 1.9.* Assuming uniform cooling of the slab from both sides, the temperature of the slab at the midplane, parallel to the surfaces, is higher by an amount ΔT in comparison to the temperature at the surfaces. It can be shown that the apex of the parabola lies above the mean temperature by an amount $T/3$, and that the parabola intersects this mean-temperature reference line at a distance of $0.298a$ from the midplane if a is the total thickness of the slab. The temperature difference T is expressed by the relation

$$T = \frac{a^2 \times R}{8K} \tag{1.7}$$

where

a = the total thickness of the slab in cm
R = the cooling rate in degrees centigrade per sec
K = thermal diffusivity which equals $k/c_p\xi$ (c.g.s. units)† where
$\qquad k$ = thermal conductivity
$\qquad \xi$ = density
$\qquad c_p$ = specific heat

When the temperature throughout the slab is finally constant at room temperature, the vanishing of the temperature gradient will introduce a *permanent strain*. The sequence of events discussed, so far, is illustrated in Figure 1.10 a-c, where temperature distribution and stress distribution through the slab is shown, one above the other, for three stages of the cooling cycle. Figure 1.10(a) applies to events above and within the annealing range of temperatures, and Figure 1.10(b) to conditions below the annealing range where the glass is completely set, for all practical purposes; a temperature gradient exists between the center of the slab and its surfaces but there are no strains present. In Figure 1.10(c) the slab has assumed uniform temperature throughout, and a parabolic stress distribution appears as a consequence of the removal of the temperature gradient. The center of the

---

* For a more sophisticated mathematical treatment of this problem see Ref. 57a.

† Thermal diffusivity has the dimension $L^2 \times T^{-1}$; it is commonly expressed in cm² per second. Values for K at room temperature, when expressed in these units, are the following:

silica glass	0.009
soda-lime glass	0.005
borosilicate glass	0.007
high-lead glass	0.0026

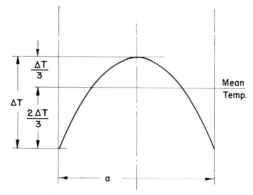

Figure 1.9. Temperature distribution through a section of glass being cooled at a constant rate. After Shand.[25] (*By permission from "Glass Engineering Handbook" by E. B. Shand; Copyright 1958 (2nd ed.), McGraw-Hill Book Company, Inc.*)

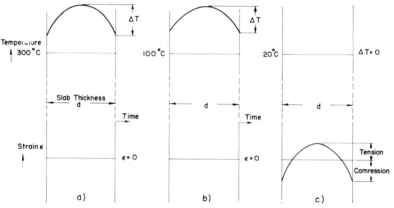

Figure 1.10. Stress distribution in glass slab on cooling. (a) Onset of cooling in annealing range; (b) Continued cooling below annealing range; (c) Equalization of temperature gradient within the glass slab at room temperature.

slab will tend to continue to contract when the surfaces cease to do so at room temperature. The center is thus put into tension and the surface into compression by reaction forces.

It is obvious that the magnitude of the permanent strain remaining after cooling from the annealing range will depend on the magnitude of the temperature gradient established in the annealing range, and therefore on the rate of cooling. As there naturally is a limit to the compression strain at the surface that a glass can safely withstand, the details of the annealing cycle are of extreme practical importance.

It is of interest to note that the permanent strain remaining in the glass slab after cooling from the annealing range at a uniform rate is equal and opposite in sign to the strain removed in the viscous state when the temperature gradient was originally established.

Ordinarily, when a glass slab is cooled after it has attained uniform temperature below the annealing range, where equilization of stresses cannot take place in a limited time, the interior is put into compression by the contraction of the surfaces, so that the latter are left in tension as long as the temperature gradient exists. On removal of the gradient, the stresses will disappear; hence they are *temporary strains*. The reverse pattern develops on heating a glass surface from room temperature to well below the annealing range. The interior is then put into tension by the expanding surfaces, and surface compression will result. Figure 1.11 illustrates the development of temporary strains below the annealing range.

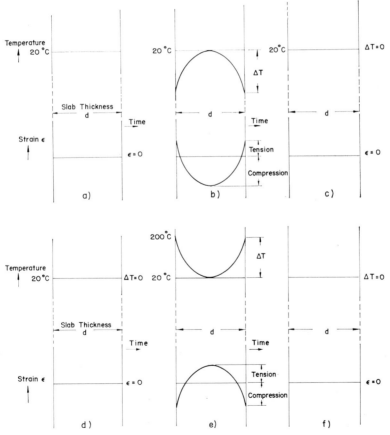

Figure 1.11. Development of temporary strains on heating and cooling of a glass slab below the annealing range (a–c: cooling of surface; d–f: heating of surface).

It was stated above that the strength of glass is much greater under compression than under tension. From the experiment just described it follows that rapid heating of a glass article is much less likely to cause breakage than is rapid cooling. When a glass article is to be tested for its thermal endurance, it is common practice to heat it by immersion in boiling water and then chill it by immersion into icewater, or even liquid nitrogen. If a joint between two different types of glass, or one between glass and metal, successfully survives several such heat shocks in succession, some assurance is gained about the realiability of the joint.

Redston[58] has reported on tests performed on electron tubes with the aim of establishing a correlation between tube failure on heat shock tests and that occurring during life; he comes to the conclusion that "the chill-shock test has been found to reproduce more nearly the types of base failures which are obtained in service and hence its results are considered more functionally significant than those of the B test." (The B test specifies heating of the tube to 100°C while a metal cone is forced between the pins of the base.)

As the permanent compression strain at room temperature is equal and opposite in sign to the amount of strain released by viscous flow in the annealing range when the temperature gradient was first established, i.e., when cooling began, the annealing schedule can be so chosen that not all of this original strain is equalized by viscous flow, and some permanent surface tension is retained at room temperature which counteracts the permanent surface compression strain.

The magnitude of the hypothetical stress introduced at any point in a glass slab by the establishment of a temperature gradient will be proportional to the difference between the temperature at this point and the average temperature across the section (Figure 1.9). For a point in the midplane of the section, the strain is given by

$$\sigma = \frac{E\alpha' \Delta T}{3(1 - \gamma)} \tag{1.8}$$

By combining this expression with Eq. 1.7, one obtains

$$\sigma_t = \frac{E\alpha' a^2 R}{24K(1 - \gamma)} \tag{1.9}$$

where

σ = stress corresponding to temperature difference from average value (psi)

σ_t = tensile stress at midplane after temperature equalization (psi)

E = Young's modulus

T = temperature difference between midplane and surface

α' = coefficient of expansion in the annealing range (°C)
α = coefficient of expansion below the strain point (°C)
γ = Poisson's ratio
a = thickness of section (inches)
R = cooling rate (°C/sec)
K = thermal diffusivity (inch²/sec)

The rate of expansion in the annealing range is usually two to three times that measured at lower temperatures. By assuming $\alpha' = 2\alpha$ and substituting this value in Eq. 1.9, one obtains

$$\sigma_t = \frac{E\alpha a^2 R}{12K(1-\gamma)} \qquad (1.10)$$

This then is the amount of tension prevailing at the midplane after equalization of temperature. The amount of permanent compression at the surface will be twice this amount (Figure 1.9), or

$$\sigma_c = \frac{E\alpha a^2 R}{6K(1-\gamma)} \qquad (1.11)$$

By introducing the following common values:

$$E = 10^7 \text{ psi}$$

$$K = 0.00077 \text{ in}^2/\text{sec}$$

$$\gamma = 0.22$$

one obtains

$$\sigma_t = 1.38 \times 10^9 a^2 R \qquad (1.12)$$

or

$$R = \frac{\sigma_t}{1.38(\alpha \times 10^9)a^2} \qquad (1.13)$$

These expressions apply to the condition where the glass section is cooled from both surfaces. In the case of a hollow vessel, or a tube, where cooling is confined to the outer surface, the effective thickness will be doubled, and will become $2a$.

On the basis of these expressions, annealing schedules can be worked out for glass sections of different thicknesses and different coefficients of expansion. Table 1.6 gives an idealized schedule for commercial ware worked out by Corning Glass Works;[59] annealing data for various Corning glasses are given in Table 1.7. These particular schedules are computed for values of residual stress which are considerably lower than those which

TABLE 1.6. SCHEDULES (IDEAL) FOR COMMERCIAL ANNEALING—ORDINARY WARE*

Annealing periods
A—Heating to 5°C above annealing point.
B—Hold temperature for time t.
C—Initial cooling to α°C below strain point.
D—Cooling—next 50°C.
E—Final cooling.

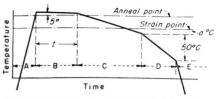

Expansion coeff. of glass per °C	Thickness of glass		Cooling on one side					Cooling on two sides				
			A	B	C	D	E	A	B	C	D	E
	in.	mm	Heating rate, °C/min	Time t, min	Temp, °C	Cooling rate, °C/min	Cooling rate, °C/min	Cooling rate, °C/min	Heating rate, °C/min	Time t, min	Temp, °C	Cooling rate, °C/min	Cooling rate, °C/min	Cooling rate, °C/min
33 × 10⁻⁷	⅛	3.2	130	5	5	12	24	130	400	5	5	39	78	400
	¼	6.3	30	15	10	3	6	30	130	15	10	12	24	130
	½	12.7	8	30	20	0.8	1.6	8	30	30	20	3	6	30
50 × 10⁻⁷	⅛	3.2	85	5	5	8	16	85	260	5	5	26	52	260
	¼	6.3	21	15	10	2	4	21	85	15	10	8	16	85
	½	12.7	5	30	20	0.5	1.0	5	21	30	20	2	4	21
90 × 10⁻⁷	⅛	3.2	50	5	5	4	8	50	140	5	5	14	28	140
	¼	6.3	11	15	10	1	2	11	50	15	10	4	8	50
	½	12.7	3	30	20	0.3	0.6	3	11	30	20	1	2	11

Glasses are annealed by raising their temperature to the annealing point and then cooling them gradually to a temperature somewhat below the strain point. The rate of cooling within this range establishes the magnitude of the residual stresses in the glass after it reaches room temperature. Below the strain point the cooling rate is limited only by the transient stresses developed. Table 1.6 provides annealing schedules for glassware of different section thicknesses and rates of expansion. These schedules are computed on a conservative basis and may be shortened considerably in specific cases. As indicated in Table 1.6, cooling rates must be reduced when only one surface of the glass is exposed to the lehr gases.

* Courtesy Corning Glass Works, Corning, N. Y.

are generally acceptable for ordinary commercial annealing. Consequently, the cooling rate may be increased materially for the annealing of simple geometrical shapes where it is not important to reduce the residual stresses to low values.[25]

These general principles on annealing seem to be quite straight-forward and may raise the question in the reader's mind why so much mystery is often attached to the establishment of successful annealing schedules for given ware with given equipment. There are indeed many complicating factors entering into this art which cannot be treated here in detail; they

TABLE 1.7. ANNEALING DATA FOR CORNING GLASSES
OF VARIOUS THICKNESSES*

Glass thickness		Annealing time		Annealing temperature (°C)							
in.	mm	min	sec	0010	0080	0120	7040	7050	7070	7720	7740
1.00	25.40	240	0	395	470	395	450	460	455	485	520
0.50	12.70	60	0	413	489	413	467	478	473	503	542
.25	6.35	15	0	431	505	431	484	495	490	520	563
.125	3.18	3	45	449	523	449	501	513	508	538	585
.062	1.59	0	56	467	540	467	518	530	525	555	606
.031	0.79	0	14	485	558	485	535	548	543	573	628
.015	0.39	0	3.5	503	575	503	552	565	560	590	649
2 × temp. interval to halve viscosity				18	17.5	18	17	17.5	17.5	17.5	21.5
Strain point				395	470	395	450	460	455	485	520
Annealing point				430	510	433		500	495	525	565
Softening point				626	696	630		703		755	820

* Courtesy Corning Glass Works, Corning, N. Y.

are of two categories: one group comprises the specific features of the ware (its shape, thickness, and initial stress distribution) and the properties of the annealing furnace (its size, temperature distribution within the chamber and heat control); the other group is concerned with the physical mechanism of annealing within the glass. From both categories arise factors which cannot be taken into account by an idealized theory. The contribution from the first group is fairly obvious. Large differences in thickness of the ware, in any one piece, or variations from piece to piece, necessitate an approximation of the value a to be entered into the equations given above. If the furnace or lehr is not long enough, or of sufficient volume, temperature gradients may exist in the ware while it is supposed to be soaking at a uniform temperature, and additional permanent strains may thus be introduced on cooling. Lillie has evaluated these factors.[59]

Fundamental investigations on the theory of annealing were undertaken in 1917 at the Carnegie Institute of Washington by Adams and Williamson and coworkers[60-62] when sudden demands for large quantities of optical glass for the Armed Forces found the United States with little experience in its manufacture.

"Adams and Williamson carefully worked out the permissible temperature gradients within a block of cooling glass of any size and type (provided the necessary physical properties of the glass were known) to give any desired (usually low) final degree of stress in the block at uniform room temperature. Adams and Williamson, however, were less successful in their understanding of the mechanism by which the stress is released in a block

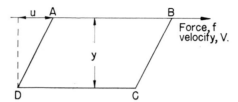

Figure 1.12. Analysis of a shear stress acting on a glass body. After Stanworth.[2] (*Courtesy Oxford at the Clarendon Press.*)

of stressed glass held at a constant temperature in the annealing range. As we shall see, they had to devise a completely empirical equation for the relation between stress and time at constant temperature.

"The simplest conception of the release of stress is that originally due to Maxwell, and may be derived as follows: Consider (Figure 1.12) a body of viscosity η and rigidity modulus G, subjected to a shear stress f. Then the velocity of displacement v is equal to the sum $v_1 - v_2$, where v_1 is the velocity of the elastic displacement and v_2 that of the viscous displacement.

"Now,

$$v_1 = \frac{du}{dt} \quad \text{and} \quad \frac{\partial u}{\partial y} = f/G, \tag{1.14}$$

from which,

$$\frac{\partial v_1}{\partial y} = \frac{1}{G}\frac{df}{dt}; \tag{1.15}$$

also,

$$\frac{\partial v_2}{\partial y} = \frac{f}{\eta}. \tag{1.16}$$

From the last two equations one obtains

$$\frac{dv}{dy} = \frac{f}{\eta} + \frac{1}{G}\frac{df}{dt} \tag{1.17}$$

In considering the release of stress in glass, during the annealing process, we may consider that $dv/dy = 0$ and so

$$\frac{f}{\eta} + \frac{1}{G}\frac{df}{dt} = 0 \tag{1.18}$$

from which, if $G\tau = \eta$, we may write

$$f = f_0\, e^{-t/\tau} \tag{1.19}$$

"Now, we have seen that for stabilized glasses in the annealing range,

$\eta = A e^{B/RT}$, so, assuming a constant value of G with change in temperature (which is approximately true in that G varies much less rapidly than η), we have

$$\tau = \tau_0 \, e^{B'/T} \tag{1.20}$$

"The relaxation time τ should vary exponentially with the inverse of absolute temperature, with a rate of change with temperature approximately the same as that found for viscosity. This was expressed in an approximate way by Twyman,[63] who suggested that the relaxation time was halved for each increase in temperature of c.8°.

"According to Eq. (1.19) above, the stress in glass held at a constant temperature in the annealing range should decrease exponentially with time. Adams and Williamson, however, found that the results of their measurements could not be described in this way, but that a better straight line was obtained by plotting the reciprocal of stress against time, their equation being

$$\frac{1}{f} - \frac{1}{f_0} = At \tag{1.21}$$

"Adams and Williamson did not claim that their equation was anything other than empirical, and stated that it was intended to apply only in the restricted temperature range of greatest technical importance in the annealing of glass. By way of illustration we may indicate (Figure 1.13) the results obtained by Lillie[64] for stress release in a soda-lime-silicate glass at 453°C. It was Lillie's work, however, which first indicated the major reason for the failure of the stress-time data to fulfil the above simple exponential law. For Lillie showed that, in ordinary chilled glass, the viscosity is

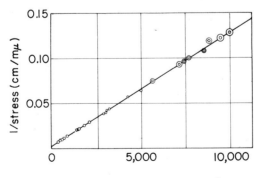

Figure 1.13. The reciprocal of birefringence plotted against time. After Stanworth.[2] (*Courtesy Oxford at the Clarendon Press.*)

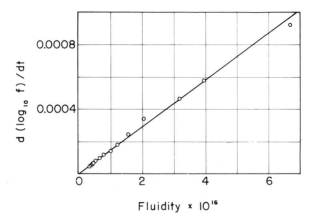

Figure 1.14. The relationship between $-d(\log_{10}f)/dt$ and fluidity at 453°C. After Stanworth.[2] (*Courtesy Oxford at the Clarendon Press.*)

changing with time during the annealing process, which necessarily means (the rigidity modulus remaining relatively constant) that the relaxation time is also changing during the annealing process. Lillie made careful checks of the change of viscosity with time in samples prepared so as to have as nearly as practically possible the same previous thermal history as the samples used for the determination of the release of stress with time. This enabled him to determine the stress as a function of time and viscosity; he found that a plot of $-[d(\log f)]/dt$ against the reciprocal of viscosity gave a straight line, showing the results obtained at the same temperature and for the same glass as in Figure 1.14. It was shown that

$$-\frac{d\,(\log f)}{dt} = \frac{M}{\eta} \tag{1.22}$$

where M equals 5.5×10^{10} dynes/cm², approximately.

"Lillie mentioned that the constant M had a value about one-quarter of that of the rigidity modulus at room temperature, but did not attempt to explain this fact. Taking the simple Maxwell Eq. (1.1) above, we may write, however,

$$\frac{d\,(\log f)}{dt} = -\frac{1}{\tau} = -\frac{G}{\eta} \tag{1.23}$$

which is identical with Lillie's equation if $G = M$, that is, if M is the rigidity modulus at the temperature of stress release. It is known that the rigidity modulus decreases with increase in temperature in the annealing range, so that, qualitatively, the agreement is satisfactory.

"It is clear then, that the Adams and Williamson stress-release equation is one which embodies a change of viscosity with time. This fact was also clearly recognized by Tool,[65] who made use of his concept of a "fictive" temperature in order to derive a new equation describing the rate of stress release at a constant temperature, in a glass whose viscosity is changing with time."[2]

Redston and Stanworth[66] suggested that M is very nearly equal to G in the annealing range of the glass. On this basis, one arrives at the following relation by integration of Eq. (1.23).

$$t = \frac{\eta}{G} \ln \frac{(f_0)}{(f)} \tag{1.24}$$

For a stress release factor $f_0/f = 1000$, the following expression results for the time for which the glass must be held at the annealing temperature T:

$$t = \frac{\eta}{5.5 \times 10^{10}} \times \frac{2.3 \times 3}{60} \text{ minutes}$$

Assuming that η is invariant with time and equal to 10^{13} poises at T, the annealing time becomes 21 minutes.

"The values used for T were based on measurements of the viscosity of samples held for 30 minutes at the temperature of observation. For shorter times than this, the viscosity of the chilled glass will be somewhat lower, so that the stress release will be faster for these shorter times. This means that the method of calculation gives a margin of safety, that is, somewhat longer times than are actually required. More precise calculation would have to take into account the marked differences between glasses of various types in the rate at which viscosity changes with time.[67] Such calculations would needlessly complicate the present schedules. Again, for simplicity, we assume that the glass viscosity decreases by half for every 10°C rise in temperature, a value sufficiently correct for most glasses. The time of holding will also become halved, as shown in Figure 1.15."[66]

After stresses have been released at the annealing temperature T to a sufficient extent, the ware must be cooled to room temperature at such a rate as to strike a compromise between economical factors and the introduction of permanent strains. Adams and Williamson derived the following expression for the cooling rate h:

$$h = \frac{s}{ca^2} \quad \text{°C/min} \tag{1.25}$$

where s is the strain introduced during cooling, measured as birefringence in $m\mu/cm$, a the half-thickness of the sample in cm, and c a constant depending on the shape and composition of the glass. For a slab or disk of soda-lime-silica glass, $c \sim 13$; for "Pyrex" glass, $c \sim 3$.

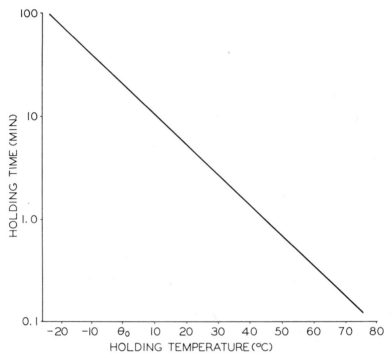

Figure 1.15. Relation between time and temperature of holding for 1000-fold stress reduction in glass. θ_0 is the temperature at which the glass viscosity is 10^{13} poises. After Redston and Stanworth.[66] (*Courtesy The Society of Glass Technology.*)

Redston and Stanworth made the simplifying assumption that "the cooling rate is independent of holding time and temperature. Actually, for a given stress introduction, the glass may be cooled more quickly with decrease in the holding temperature, particularly as the temperature drops markedly below T. This fact again provides a margin of safety in the annealing schedule adopted. The full expression of c is given by

$$c = \frac{\alpha E \beta}{6K(1 - \sigma)} \tag{1.26}$$

where α is the linear thermal expansion coefficient (per °C), E is Young's modulus in kg/cm², β is the stress-optical coefficient in mμ/cm per kg/cm², σ is Poisson's ratio, and K is the thermal diffusivity in cm²/min. Using typical values for $(1 - \sigma)/E$ and for K, and assuming that these are practically the same for all glasses, the cooling rates which leave a final strain of 2.5 mμ/cm at the center are plotted in Figure 1.16 for slabs of various thicknesses." Taking the thermal expansion coefficient of the glass as a parameter, a family of parallel lines is obtained from which it is apparent

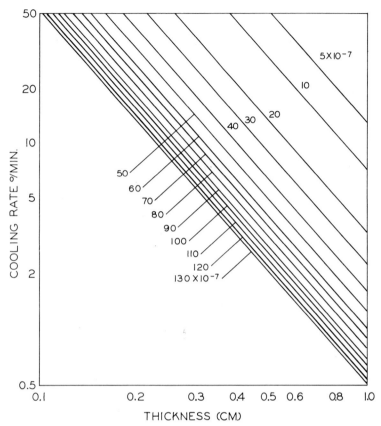

Figure 1.16. Effect of thickness and linear expansion coefficient on cooling rate necessary to produce 2.5 mμ/cm retardation at the center of a glass slab. After Redston and Stanworth.[66] (*Courtesy The Society of Glass Technology.*)

that a low-expansion glass of a given thickness can be cooled at a much faster rate than a high-expansion glass of the same thickness.

It is apparent from Figure 1.15 that a wide choice of annealing schedules is available. In Figure 1.17 six possible schedules are shown, all of which would anneal the sample to about the same extent. It is evident that schedule 4 requires the least amount of time and is thus the most economical, provided that the loss incurred from breakage is the same as in the others. "To ensure that the total time of the schedule is a minimum, the holding temperature must be that at which the slope of the holding temperature against holding time curve equals the cooling rate required. Now the holding time (t) at any temperature (θ) is given by

$$t = t_0 \times 2^{(\theta_0 - \theta)/10} \tag{1.27}$$

where t_0 is the stress-release time at $\theta_0°$C.

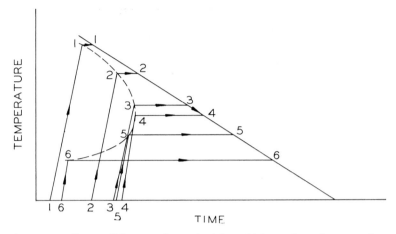

Figure 1.17. Six possible annealing schedules which produce the same degree of annealing. Schedule No. 4 occupies the least time. After Redston and Stanworth.[66] (*Courtesy The Society of Glass Technology.*)

"Hence

$$\frac{d(\theta_0 - \theta)}{dt} = \frac{10}{t_0 \times 2^{(\theta_0 - \theta)/10} \ln 2} \qquad (1.28)$$

must equal the cooling rate. It has already been shown that $t_0 = 21$ minutes; thus, for minimum annealing time, the holding temperature θ is given by the expression:

$$\text{Calculated cooling rate} = \frac{10}{21 \times 2^{(\theta_0 - \theta)/10} \ln 2}$$

"The following table shows some calculated values which are plotted in Figure 1.18."

Cooling rate °C/Minute	$(\theta_0 - \theta)$ optimum holding temperature above the 10^{13} poise temperature
10	-39
3	-21
1	-5.5
0.1	$+28$

According to Redston and Stanworth, a practical annealing schedule can be set up from the graphs in Figures 1.15 to 1.18 provided the following data are given:

Thermal expansion coefficient (α)

Annealing Point (T_A) (for $\eta = 10^{13}$)

Strain Point (T_S)

Thickness of the glass article (d)

First, the cooling rate (h) is obtained from Figure 1.16 then the optimum holding temperature (T_{opt}) from Figure 1.18 and finally the holding time (t) from Figure 1.15. Following these steps for Corning 7720 "Nonex" glass and assuming a thickness of 0.3 cm the following data are obtained:

$$\alpha = 36 \times 10^{-7} \qquad T_s = 484°C$$

$$T_A = 518°C \qquad d = 0.3 \text{ cm}$$

From the graphs it follows that:

$$h = 20°C/\text{min}$$

$$T_{opt} = T - 49° = 567°C$$

$$t_0 = 0.7 \text{ min}$$

Schedule A would thus be:

(1) heat to 567°C (at 400°C/min)

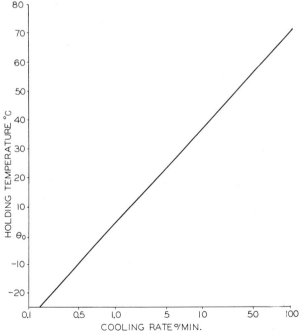

Figure 1.18. Dependence of optimum holding temperature for glass annealing on cooling rate. After Redston and Stanworth.[66] (*Courtesy The Society of Glass Technology.*)

(2) hold at 567°C for 42 sec
(3) cool to 484°C at 20°C/min
(4) cool to room temperature (100°C/min)

The data given in Table 1.7 would suggest the following (Schedule B):

(1) heat to 523°C at 400°C/min
(2) hold at 523°C for 5 min
(3) cool to 479°C at 39°C/min
(4) cool to 429°C at 78°C/min
(5) cool to 25°C at 400°C/min

Depending somewhat on the cooling rate adopted in Schedule A, both schedules take about 10 minutes. In practice, compromises are necessary, depending on available facilities and temperature control gear. A uniform rate of cooling from the holding temperature all the way to near room temperature is generally advantageous. On the other hand, too short holding times may be difficult to control, and nothing is gained by aiming at optimum holding time when it turns out to be less than a minute. The analysis of the remaining strain will in the end determine the feasibility of any chosen schedule.

Strain Analysis

It was first observed by D. Brewster in 1813[68] that strained glass displays the properties of a birefringent crystal and that the birefringence is proportional to the intensity of the stress. When viewed in polarized light between crossed nicols or sheets of "Polaroid," patterns of different light intensity or different colors become visible from which the directions and amounts of strain may be deduced.

Ordinary light, when it enters a birefringent crystal, or strained glass, behaves as if it were split into two components which are respectively called the "ordinary ray" and the "extra-ordinary ray." These two rays have their electrical vibrations at right angles to each other and travel through the specimen at different velocities. The orientation in space of the planes of vibration depends on the orientation of the optical axis of the crystal, which is defined as the direction in which light is transmitted without birefringence (i.e., the ordinary and extra-ordinary rays coincide along the optical axis and travel with the same velocity). In the case of calcite ($CaCO_3$), the optical axis coincides with the axis of trigonal symmetry. In certain other crystals, the ordinary and extra-ordinary rays can coincide and travel with equal velocities in two mutually perpendicular directions in the crystal. Crystals of the first type, like calcite, are called "uniaxial"; crystals of the second type, for which mica is an example, are called "bi-axial."

When light is incident on a crystal at an angle to the optical axis, the direction of vibration at any point in the ordinary-wave front is perpendicular to the plane containing the extra-ordinary ray and the optical axis. The relative intensities of the two beams depend on the direction of vibration in the incident beam with respect to the optical axis. If this direction of vibration in the incident beam is inclined 45° to the optical axis, the intensities of the ordinary and extra-ordinary ray may be greater or smaller than that for the ordinary ray (n_ω) and, therefore, its velocity less or more ($v = c/n$) than that of the ordinary ray in different crystals. If the ordinary ray travels faster than the extra-ordinary ray, one speaks of a positive crystal; in the reverse case, of negative crystals. Quartz, according to this definition, is a positive uniaxial crystal and calcite a negative uniaxial crystal. Glass in tension behaves as a positive uniaxial crystal, and in compression as a negative uniaxial crystal.

Unfortunate terminology was established for polarized light before the directions of vibration in a polarized beam were determined. The plane of polarization is the plane normal to the plane in which the electrical vibrations of a plane-polarized light beam take place. A light beam is said to be "polarized" in the plane of incidence when the vibrations of the electric vector take place at right angles to the plane of incidence. As the electric and magnetic vectors are mutually perpendicular to each other, and intensity is associated with the electric vector, one may say that the plane of polarization, as defined above, is understood to be the plane containing the magnetic vector. Whenever possible, the use of these terms will be avoided; but they are firmly established in the literature.

The optical path difference δ, in mμ, can be measured by the observation of the relative phase retardation in a polariscope equipped with a Babinet compensator, or a quartz wedge, and is given by the following relation:

$$\frac{\delta}{l} = \Delta n = F \times B \qquad (1.29)*$$

where:

Δn = the difference of the refractive indices for the ordinary and extraordinary ray, $n_\epsilon - n_\omega$

l = thickness of the glass specimen through which the light travels.

$F = P/A$ = stress

B = stress-optical coefficient

Since refractive indices are pure numbers, the dimension of B is that of reciprocal stress; a convenient unit for B is the brewster, defined as 10^{-13} cm^2/dyne; the stress-optical coefficients of most glasses are then expressed by numbers between 1 and 10. In these units, a retardation of 1 Ang-

* In equation 1.26, the symbol β was used for B by Redston and Stanworth.

TABLE 1.8. STRESS-OPTICAL COEFFICIENTS OF GLASSES[25]

	Brewsters
Silica	3.47
96% Silica	3.65
Soda-lime	2.45–2.65
Lead alkali silicate	
Medium lead content	2.55–2.75
60% PbO	2.05
73% PbO	0.24
80% PbO	−1.05
Borosilicate, low expansion	3.9
Borosilicate, low electrical loss	4.8
Aluminosilicate	2.65

strom per millimeter of light path is produced by a stress of 1 bar (10^6 dynes/cm²) in a material possessing a stress-optical coefficient of 1 brewster. A convenient form of Eq. 1.29 is the following:

$$\text{Stress (kg/cm}^2) = \frac{\text{retardation (m}\mu)}{0.981 \times B \text{ (brewsters)} \times l \text{ (cm)}}$$

Table 1.8 gives values of B in brewsters for a variety of glass types after Shand.

Several experimental procedures are available for the observation and measurement of birefringence in glass[70-76]; the choice of any of these will depend on the accuracy required. Common methods used in the electronics industry permit the measurement of δ to ±5 mμ. Refined methods will allow the measurement of ±0.05 mμ.[76] For optical glass, an optical path difference per cm equal to 5 mμ is considered satisfactory. For electronic glassware, a strain equal to $\frac{1}{20}$ of the breaking strength is acceptable for annealing. Taking the safe loading at 1 kg/mm², or 100 kg/cm², gives $\delta = 300$ mμ as an upper limit (1 kg/cm² = 3×10^{-7} cm). Therefore, the range of accuracy required for routine strain determinations is not excessive.

V. C. De Maria[77] has described a low-cost, portable polariscope that is built from a standard two-cell flashlight and remarks: "Since portable polariscopes have been assigned to our glass shop employees, rejects due to detrimental stresses in the glass have been almost eliminated. Flaws are discovered early in processing, and corrective annealing measures can be taken. The polariscope has now taken its place with micrometers and calipers as a much used measuring tool in the glass industry." This trend is to be encouraged, to be sure, but the user of the common polariscope should also be aware of the limitations of this tool, especially when odd-shaped articles, or glass-to-metal seals, are to be judged by it.[78-80]

Photoelasticity is a rather involved subject and requires tensors for its proper treatment.[81-85a] The relative retardation observed in the polariscope is proportional to the resultant stress, but it gives no indication of the magnitudes or signs of the principal stresses. A small resultant compressive stress could arise equally from two large tension stresses, two compressive stresses, or one compressive and one tension stress. To determine the absolute values of the principal stresses, additional measurements are required which might give the sum of the principal stresses, or, by means of integration of points along a stress-free boundary, permit the calculation of principal stresses from the conditions of elastic equilibrium. These methods have been described in great detail by Partridge.[69]

A polarimeter which permits observations at temperatures up to 800°C is available from E. Leitz, Wetzlar, Germany. This instrument is specially designed to cover the needs of the tube industry. Engel[85b] reports on its use in determining hysteresis effects observed on taking stress-temperature curves for glass-to-metal seals.

Electrolysis in Glass

Stresses in glass may arise not only by virtue of improper annealing but also on account of a local change in chemical composition brought about by electrolysis. This defect may have serious practical consequences and deserves the particular attention of the tube designer. Electrolysis will occur at elevated temperature when a voltage gradient is impressed on the glass which permits the migration of alkali ions, particularly sodium ions. The general mechanism of glass electrolysis in the presence of glass-embedded current leads has been known for a considerable time and was studied by Becquerel[86] and Thomson[87] as early as 1854 and 1875, and, more recently, by Gallup[88] and Peysson,[89] who came to the following conclusions:

(1) Positive sodium ions migrate toward the electrode which is at the most negative potential (i.e., the "effective cathode").

(2) At the "effective cathode" metallic sodium is released and accumulated, whereas the glass layers near the "effective anode" will be depleted in sodium, resulting in a poorly conducting, silica-rich glass.

(3) Oxygen is released at the "effective anode" and hydrogen at the "effective cathode." It is known that all commercial glasses contain minor amounts of CO_2, SO_3, and H_2O, which, like the anions CO_3^{--}, SO_4^{--}, and OH^-, participate in the glass structure. These gases can be reduced electrolytically to CO, SO_2, and H_2—reactions which are more likely to occur than the reduction of Na^+, or Ca^{++}. Passing a current through a soda-lime glass, therefore, reduces its gas content.[90] Molybdenum or tungsten seals may become overoxidized by virtue of the water content of the glass, and porous and leaky seals thus result under the influence of electrolysis.

These primary effects may lead to the following discernible changes in appearance:

(1) The vicinity of the "effective cathode" will develop a dark discoloration because of the reduction of lead oxide to lead by the released sodium. In the absence of lead oxide, the colloidal dispersion of sodium in itself will give a brown or blue appearance. "Dumet" (see Chapter 13) leads are likely to become light-colored because of the reduction of cuprous oxide.

(2) The Dumet lead representing the "effective anode" will, by the same token, take on a darker color because of the formation of higher copper oxide.

(3) Gas bubbles will appear at the electrodes and be released into the tube, spoiling the vacuum. Spectrometric analysis of the gas content, using 8160 glass stems, disclosed the presence of the following gases in order of decreasing amounts: H_2, H_2O, O_2, CO, CO_2 and N_2.

(4) The change in composition of the glass near the electrodes sets up considerable strains leading to fracture.

It is important to realize that the anode lead of a rectifier tube will act as the effective cathode during the inverse voltage half-cycle, and that the magnitude of the inverse voltage frequently exceeds the operating forward anode voltage by a large factor. Electrolysis effects can also be present when symmetrical a-c voltages are applied, since surface effects at the leads often cause a preferred conduction in one direction. Gallup[88] also describes an effect which shows that electrolysis of stems can occur between a current lead and the surface of the glass stem when the latter is exposed to bombardment by stray electrons, thus leading to the creation of a virtual cathode. This condition was found responsible for the appearance of longitudinal cracks along the filament leads of a rectifier tube. Electrolysis may also occur between the turns of a helix in a traveling-wave tube if the glass barrel is in contact with the helix, and ring patterns and cracks will result.*

Volume Conductivity

Glasses are electrolytic conductors at all temperatures, and the resistivity may range from 10^{19} ohm·cm at room temperature to 1 ohm·cm at 1200°C, depending on the glass composition. This fact was established by the classic work of E. Warburg (1884), who showed that Faraday's law of electrolytic conduction is satisfied. A distinction must be made between surface and volume conductivity, and precautions should be taken during measurements unless the presence of one overshadows the other. Figure 1.19 shows curves for volume resistivity as a function of temperature for Corning Glasses 7740, 0010, and 0080. When resistivity is plotted on a logarithmic scale vs the reciprocal of temperature, straight lines result, as shown in Figure

* Private communication from Sperry-Rand Corporation.

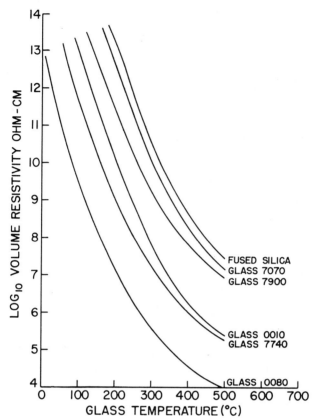

Figure 1.19. Volume resistivity as a function of temperature for Corning glasses 0010, 0080, 7070, 7900 and fused silica. (*By permission from "Glass Engineering Handbook" by E. B. Shand; Copyright 1958 (2nd ed.) McGraw Hill Book Company, Inc.*)

1.20 where data for some additional glasses are given. It is apparent that the ohmic resistance in d-c fields drops rapidly with increasing temperature. Lead glass 0120 has a higher electrical resistivity, by a considerable margin, than either 7740 "Pyrex" or soda-lime glass 0080. It is, therefore, common practice to make conventional stems for receiving tubes from 0010 or 0120 glass, while bulbs are made from soda-lime glass 0080, or its equivalent.* Electrolysis between lead wires at elevated temperatures is thus minimized. On the other hand, the use of a more conductive glass for the envelope prevents the accumulation of charges deposited by stray electrons,

* This established practice does not imply, as Stanworth[2] points out, that lime glasses of even higher resistivity than lead glasses cannot be made. On a factory scale, however, lead glasses are produced more easily, without difficulties arising from devitrification and unfavorable viscosity-temperature relationships.

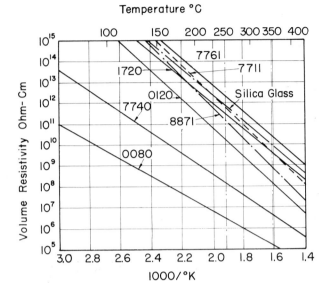

Figure 1.20. Volume resistivity versus temperature of commercial glasses, direct-current values. After Shand.[25, 106] (*Courtesy Corning Glass Works.*)

an effect which can lead to puncture of the envelope if the charges are not leaked off.

The addition of soda increases the volume conductivity more than that of any other oxide while the addition of lime decreases it. The fact that sodium ions are the carriers of conduction in all glasses is readily demonstrated by the formation of sodium films on the inside glass wall of an evacuated bulb, when an electron emitter serves as cathode on the inside and a sodium nitrate bath as anode on the outside of the bulb. The amounts of sodium deposited agree with Faraday's law. The effect of increasing soda content on the volume resistivity of glass is illustrated in Figure 1.21, according to studies by Sedden, Tippett, and Turner.[91] The introduction of certain other modifying ions into the glass structure tends to reduce the mobility of the sodium ion. Gehlhoff and Thomas[92] and Stevels[93] investigated these effects in detail. Figure 1.22 shows plots of the temperature at which a reference conductivity of 10^{-8} ohm$^{-1} \cdot$cm^{-1} is reached by a glass of original composition 18 Na_2O–82 SiO_2 when an increasing weight percentage of the SiO_2 content is replaced by the oxide marked on the curves. Soda, potash and alumina thus increase the conductivity progressively, while lime, magnesia and boron oxide decrease it by varying amounts. BaO, PbO, ZnO, Fe_2O_3 have little effect. A combination of soda and potash in proper proportions can reduce the alkali mobility below that extant for either constituent by itself.

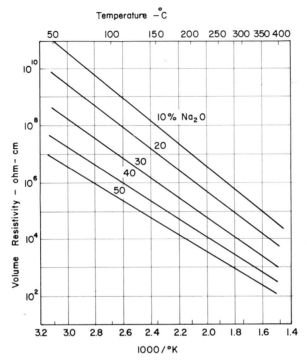

Figure 1.21. Effect on volume resistivity of increasing the amount of Na_2O in a soda-silica glass. After Sedden, Tippett and Turner.[91] (*Courtesy The Society of Glass Technology.*)

The dependence of conductivity on temperature has been expressed by two experimental equations:

$$\ln x = A + BT \tag{1.30}$$

$$\ln x = C - D/T \tag{1.31}$$

where x is the specific conductivity, T is the absolute temperature, and A, B, C, and D are constants. Equation 1.31 is known as Rasch and Hinrichsen's Law;[94] it has also been derived from theoretical considerations of the binding forces acting on the Na ions in the glass network. Glasses seem to fall into two groups which satisfy either one or the other of the two equations given above.

Kirby[95] gives a review of the phenomena involved in the electrical conduction in glass.

The measurement of the volume resistivity of glass is obscured by the presence of "anomalous charging currents" or "dielectric absorption."[96-98] When a voltage is first applied, the charging current in glass is much larger

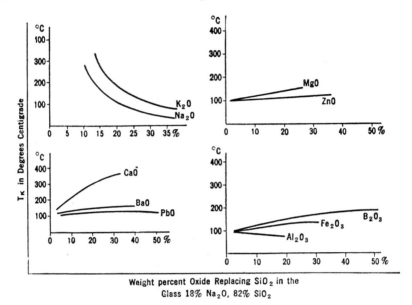

Weight percent Oxide Replacing SiO$_2$ in the
Glass 18% Na$_2$O, 82% SiO$_2$

Figure 1.22. The temperature at which the specific conductivity becomes 10^{-8} mho/cm plotted against the percentage by weight of the indicated oxide replacing SiO$_2$ in the glass 18 Na$_2$O, 82 SiO. After Gehlhoff and Thomas.[92]

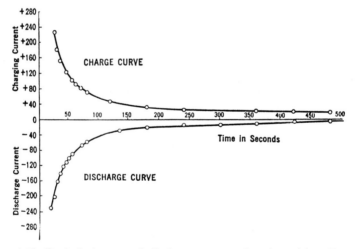

Figure 1.23. Typical charge and discharge curves of a glass. After Guyer.[99, 105] (*Courtesy American Ceramic Society.*)

than the normal conduction current and only after several hours does it decrease to assume a constant value. Similarly, after removal of the applied voltage, a discharge current is observed which is the reverse of the charging current.

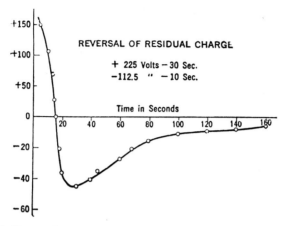

Figure 1.24. Reversal of residual charge in a borosilicate glass. The charging cycle is given in the figure; readings were taken after disconnecting the charging battery. After Guyer.[99, 105] (*Courtesy American Ceramic Society.*)

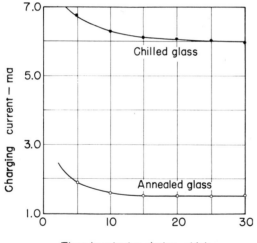

Figure 1.25. Effect of chilling and subsequent annealing on the charging current in an opal borosilicate glass. After Guyer.[99, 105] (*Courtesy American Ceramic Society.*)

On repetitive application of charging or discharging cycles, the principle of superposition, stated by Hopkinson applies, according to which "the variation in charging current resulting from several successive variations in the applied voltage is the summation of the individual variations in charging current which would have taken place if each voltage variation had been separately impressed upon the uncharged condenser."[5] Guyer[99] has described measurements of these effects on various glasses; Figures 1.23–1.25 show his results. The differences between charge and discharge currents will be constant at different time intervals for completely reversible charging currents and also represent the true conduction current through the glass. Absorption currents in annealed glass are smaller than those in unannealed glass (Figure 1.25). An interpretation of anomalous charge and discharge currents in glasses on the basis of their structure has been given by Weyl.[100]

Surface Conductivity

The surface conductivity of glass is due partly to films of water[101] and other contaminations, which are determined by the surrounding atmosphere and the relative humidity prevailing at the time, and partly to temperature and pressure. Different glasses are variously affected by these factors. Figure 1.26 gives representative plots of surface resistivity for fused silica, "Pyrex" 7740, and soda-lime glass 0080 at different relative humidities at 20°C. The improvement obtainable by surface treatment is also indicated by a dotted line. Such surface treatment may involve outgassing at elevated temperature, or the application of nonhygroscopic films, as outlined on p. 61. The effect of glass composition on the resulting surface resistivity is very pronounced, and, so far, has escaped satisfactory theoretical evaluation. Gehlhoff, Thomas[92] and Fulda[102] were among the first to explore this field systematically.

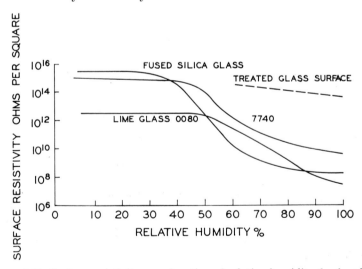

Figure 1.26. Surface resistivity as a function of relative humidity for fused silica glass, borosilicate electrical glass (Corning No. 7740) and lime glass (Corning No. 0080). After Guyer[99, 105] (*Courtesy The Institute of Radio Engineers.*)

According to investigations by Green and Blodgett,[103] surface conductivity can be imparted to glasses containing sufficiently high contents of lead, bismuth, or antimony oxides, or combinations of these, by reducing these oxides in hydrogen during heat treatment of several hours' duration. The thickness of the conductive film thus produced on the glass surface is of the order of 0.001 in., and the color of the treated surface is black. It is also reported that lead glass coatings were applied to borosilicate glass as a frit, which was then reduced in hydrogen. This search was extended by Katherine Blodgett,[104] and more recently by Funk[104a], who studied borate glasses in addition to lead glasses.

Surface conductivity of glass can be markedly reduced, particularly in atmospheres of high humidity, by the application of certain synthetic polymer films, such as silicones. Dow Corning 200, or Z-4141, are used for this purpose.[104b] DC-200 is available in a wide range of viscosities; a 2-percent solution by weight in methylene chloride, trichloroethylene, or perchloroethylene is prepared and the glass or ceramic article dipped into it and, on removal, air dried for one-half hour at room temperature. The film must then be cured by heating in air at 300°C for one-half hour, or at 275°C for one hour. DC-2-4141 requires no solvent; it is diluted with water and can be sprayed onto hot or cold glass; air drying, or a low-temperature bake, effect rapid curing.

Another method that is sometimes used for the surface treatment of glass, but which is not as free from objections as the previous two, is the application of chlorosilane solutions (e.g. dimethyldichlorosilane $(CH_3)_2$ $SiCl_2$) in an inert solvent. The glass can be dipped into this chlorosilane solution, or the chlorosilane can be vaporized onto the glass surface. Films of these materials, in thickness of the order of 100 molecular layers, react very rapidly with the absorbed water film on the glass. Hydrochloric acid gas is evolved, and a layer of dimethylsiloxane groups is left behind which presents a layer of methyl groups toward the outer free surface.[2] *

The surfaces of glasses can be made electrically conductive to any desired degree by applying thin films of semiconductors, or metals, to the surface. Conductive glass is commercially available in the U. S. A. under the trade names "Electrapane," "Nesa," and "E-C Glass" from Libbey-Owens-Ford Glass Company, the Pittsburgh Plate Glass Company, and Corning Glass Works, respectively. These glasses have a thin film of tin oxide with controlled additives applied to their surface by hydrolysis of stannic salt vapors at elevated temperature. The films are very resistant to

---

* A symposium on the use of silicones in the glass industry was held in April 1958 by the Society of Glass Technology and the papers were published in the Journal of the Society (Vol. 42) (August 1958)). The attention of the reader is also drawn to a review paper on the surface treatments of glass.[104c]

weathering and can be operated in air at several hundred degrees centigrade
without appreciably changing their resistance.

Dielectric Properties

Glass is a dielectric, which, like most of the common insulators, passes a
displacement current on application of intermittent or alternating electric
fields. In an ideal dielectric, the displacement current I is exactly 90 electrical degrees out of phase with the applied voltage and thus does not involve
a consumption of energy. Physical dielectrics never fulfill this condition,
and the amount of power, W, dissipated is given by the expression

$$W = E \times I \times \cos \theta \tag{1.32}$$

where E is the effective value of the alternating voltage $E = E_0 \sin wt$,
and I the resulting current which leads the voltage vector by the phase
angle θ. The complimentary angle $\delta = 90 - \theta$ is called the loss angle, and
$\tan \delta$ is the dissipation factor of the dielectric, or the dielectric dissipation
factor D. The *power factor*

$$PF = \frac{D}{\sqrt{1 - D^2}}$$
$$D = \frac{PF}{\sqrt{1 - (PF)^2}} \tag{1.33}$$

The *loss factor* (*LF*) is given by the product of the dissipation factor and
the dielectric constant K so that $LF = \tan \delta \times K$; it is proportional to
the energy loss per cycle per squared potential gradient F per unit volume,
as is apparent from the following equation:

$$\frac{W \text{ (watts)}}{(\text{cm}^3)} = 0.555 \times (LF) \times f(MC) \times F^2 \frac{(KV)}{(\text{cm})} \tag{1.34}$$

which gives the energy dissipated per unit volume when the field $F = E/d$
is applied across the dielectric of thickness d and cross-section A.

The dielectric strength of a dielectric is given by the voltage gradient, F,
at which breakdown occurs, and may be expressed by the *breakdown voltage* as long as all other experimental conditions are specified. The test
results obtained by different investigators often vary within wide margins
on account of the many variables which enter into the measuring procedures. The dielectric strength of glass, in particular, is so much higher
than that of other substances, including air and oils, that, in measuring
breakdown on glass samples, one is likely to measure the breakdown of the
surrounding medium, or the corona resistance of glass in the presence of
bombardment by ions from localized discharges in the weaker gaseous or
liquid medium.[105]

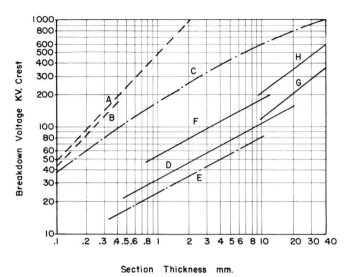

Section Thickness mm.

Figure 1.27. Breakdown voltage *vs.* thickness of glass for different comditions at room temperature, 60 cycle voltage raised continuously. (A) Intrinsic dielectric strength of borosilicate glass; (B) Intrinsic dielectric strength of soda-lime glass; (C) Highest test values available for borosilicate glass; (D) Borosilicate glass plate immersed in insulating oil; (E) Soda-lime glass plate immersed in insulating oil; (F) Borosilicate glass plate immersed in semi-conducting oil; (G) Borosilicate glass powder line insulator immersed in insulating oil; (H) Borosilicate glass powder line insulator immersed in semiconducting oil. After Shand.[25, 106] *(By permission from "Glass Engineering Handbook," by E. B. Shand; Copyright 1958 (2nd Ed.) McGraw Hill Book Company, Inc.)*

Figure 1.27 gives the peak breakdown voltage for various glasses, tested with continuously raised 60-cycle voltage in different surrounding medįa, plotted against specimen thickness.[106] It is apparent from these curves a nd measurements by other workers[107] that the so-called "intrinsic dielectric strength" in the absence of field concentrations caused by the electrodes (edge effects) can amount to several million volts per centimeter. At higher temperatures, the dielectric strength of glass diminishes rapidly, as is shown by Shand's measurements on Corning glasses in Figure 1.28. The different effects of d-c and a-c voltages on breakdown at elevated temperatures are illustrated for lime glass in Figure 1.29.[105] Moon and Norcross[108] measured breakdown on glass samples 0.008 in. thick at room temperature and at 300°C and found the values tabulated in Table 1.9 where the observed peak voltages for these specimens are extrapolated to KV/cm (d.c.). These data are indicative of the two types of breakdown distinguished in the theoretical treatment of the subject, i.e., "disruptive" or "electronic breakdown" vs "thermal breakdown." By changing the composition of glass, the dielectric constant and the dielectric dissipation factor can be

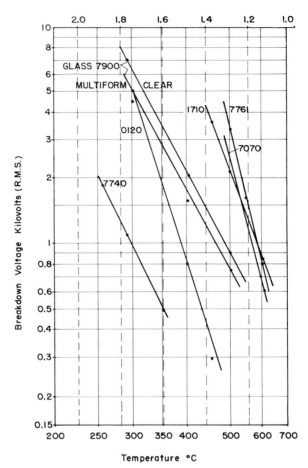

Figure 1.28. Dielectric breakdown of commercial glasses at higher temperatures. 1-minute breakdown for thickness of 2 mm at 60 cycles. After Shand.[25, 106] (*By permission from "Glass Engineering Handbook," by E. B. Shand; Copyright 1958 (2nd Ed.) McGraw Hill Book Company, Inc.*)

separately altered (Figure 1.30); the variation of K is differently affected by temperature and frequency of the applied voltage (Figure 1.31); loss factor and power factor undergo corresponding changes with temperature and frequency as shown in Figures 1.32 to 1.34.*

* The attention of the reader is directed to several papers by Vermeer[133-136] which have an important bearing on the subject discussed in the preceding paragraphs. It is shown that at low temperatures, or extremely short rates of rise (10^{-5} sec) of the applied voltage, the breakdown voltage of glass is indeed independent of specimen thickness, or electrode material, and reproducible within the limits given by ordinary experimental errors.

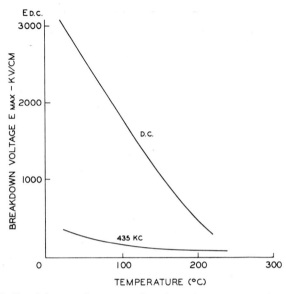

Figure 1.29. Breakdown voltage as a function of temperature for direct current and for 435 KC alternating current. After Guyer.[99, 106] (*Courtesy The Institute of Radio Engineers.*)

TABLE 1.9. ELECTRIC BREAKDOWN ON GLASS SAMPLES 8 MILS THICK
(Observed by Moon and Norcross[108])

Glass type	Dielectric strength kv/cm (peak)	
	at 20°C	at 300°C
Fused silica glass	5,000	560
Borosilicate glass	4,800	200
Lead glass	3,100	102
Lime glass	4,500	32

Outgassing of Glass

It is generally recognized that tube envelopes must be subjected to a baking cycle to remove adsorbed and occluded gases. Water vapor and carbon dioxide are the main constituents given off by glass on heating, but the noncondensible gases, such as hydrogen, nitrogen, oxygen, and carbon monoxide, are also present in varying amounts. An extensive series of investigations of the gases and vapors evolved from glass was carried out by Sherwood[109] and Shrader;[110] their work and that of other investigators has been summarized by Dushman.[111] The gas evolution on bake-out reaches a maximum at a temperature of a few hundred degrees centigrade; for lead glass, this occurs close to 200°C, for soda-lime glass at 150°C, and for hard glass, such as Nonex, at about 300°C. The gas evolution then

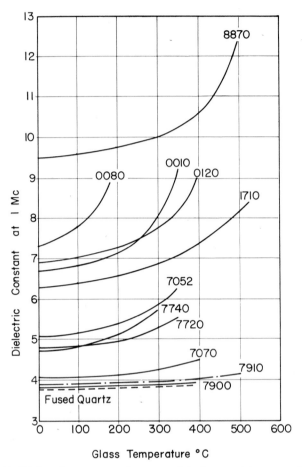

Figure 1.30. Dielectric constant of commercial glasses of 1 megacycle as a function of temperature. After Shand.[25, 106] (*By permission from "Glass Engineering Handbook", by E. B. Shand; Copyright 1958 (2nd Ed.) McGraw Hill Book Company, Inc.*)

drops off sharply at increasing temperatures and rises again steeply when the softening point of a glass is approached. The general conclusion from these observations is that adsorbed gases are effectively removed at the lower temperatures where the first peak in the gas evolution occurs, and that water vapor continues to diffuse to the surface from deeper layers when the temperature approaches the softening point of the glass. Langmuir[112] first concluded that water vapor would be most effectively removed from the glass wall by heating the envelope in steps, first to a high temperature, and then to a lower temperature.

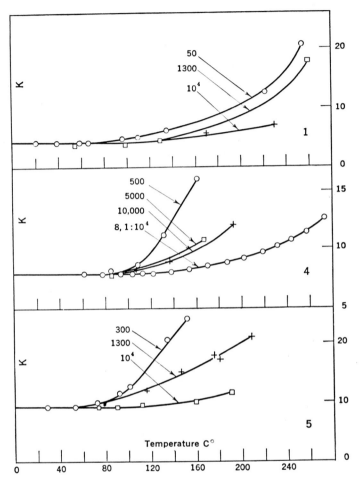

Figure 1.31. Dependence of dielectric constant, K, on temperature at various frequencies. After Strutt.[100a] (*Courtesy Julius Springer-Verlag, Berlin.*)

Todd[113] of the Corning Glass Works has recently carried out a series of investigations intended to put the outgassing treatment of glass on a more rational basis. He noted that water vapor constitutes by far the major component of the gas released during bakeout. The initial burst of gas at relatively low temperatures is due to a layer of hydrates on the surface facing the vacuum. This surface layer can be effectively removed by washing the glass envelope in a 1–percent solution of hydrofluoric acid; other reagents such as the widely used chromic acid cleaning solution, or hydro-

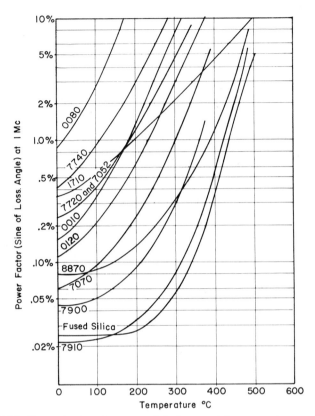

Figure 1.32. Power factor of commercial glasses at 1 megacycle as a function of temperature. After Shand.[25, 106] (*Courtesy Corning Glass Works.*)

chloric acid, sulfuric acid, ammonia, sodium hydroxide, all used in 2.5 molar solution, did not remove this critical surface layer of hydrates.*

The water which diffuses to the surface at higher temperatures increases in amounts proportional to the square root of the bakeout time, and linear plots obtained give the total volume of gas released against the square root of time. These linear plots will have an increasing slope, m, for increasing temperatures and the intersect with the ordinate will be partly determined by the gas released from the surface hydrate layer. The value

* Crawley[114] of the British Thomson-Houston Co. has described a glass cleaning solution which is much more effective than the conventional chromic acid solution; the composition is 5% HF, 33% HNO_3 , 2% Dreene (Teepol), 60% water. The solution is to be used cold and its composition can be varied over wide limits. The present author has used this solution to advantage in cleaning glass rods prior to the deposition of tin oxide films and noted a marked improvement in the luster of the films.

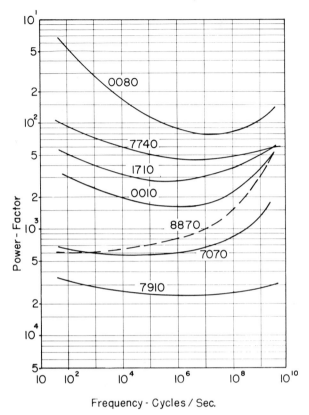

Figure 1.33. Power factor at room temperature versus frequency for commercial glasses. After Shand.[25, 106] (*Courtesy Corning Glass Works.*)

of the diffusion constant for water and the concentration gradients after bakeout can be calculated, so that it is possible to obtain the amount of water that will diffuse out with time at any temperature after some arbitrary bakeout. It has further been shown by Todd that the diffusion of water from glass is a reversible process. If the partial pressure of water in the surrounding space is greater than a given equilibrium value, water diffuses into the glass; if the partial pressure is less, water diffuses out. The rate at which the diffusion occurs depends on the partial pressure difference and also upon the temperature. By preheating a glass envelope in a dry atmosphere, absorbed water can be driven out at atmospheric pressure; a short vacuum bakeout will then effectively remove the water that has been absorbed on the surface during the short time that follows the air bakeout before the tube is connected to the pump.

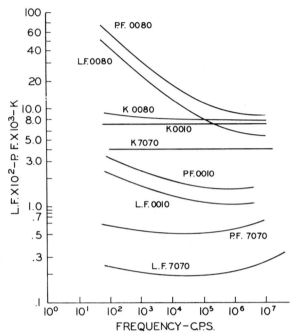

Figure 1.34. Variation of power factor (P.F.), loss factor (L.F.) and dielectric constant (K) with frequency for borosilicate glass (Corning No. 7070), lead glass (Corning No. 0010), and lime glass (Corning No. 0080). After Guyer.[99, 105] (*Courtesy The Institute of Radio Engineers.*)

Powdered Glass

The technique of forming various glass articles from powdered glass, or glass frit, is used not only on the production line but serves well in the laboratory when special glass shapes are required in small quantities. Glass headers with a suitable number of imbedded lead wires are frequently made in this manner. The molds may be made from graphite and heated by induction, or from suitably selected ceramic bodies and passed through a controlled-atmosphere furnace. A number of precautions must be observed if useful products are to result.

The inclusion of large air bubbles must be carefully avoided because electric fields tend to concentrate in them, causing ionization and breakdown; the uniform distribution of a large number of very small bubbles (several thousand per cubic millimeter), presents no such danger.

The coefficient of expansion of the material from which the mold is made should be smaller than that of the glass to permit easy removal of the glass product. A mold lubricant is frequently used, i.e., molybdenum disulfide, a suspension of colloidal graphite, or a coating of boron nitride. A mixture of a suspension of kaolin in water and graphite has also been suggested; it should have a suitable taper to facilitate removal of the molded glass article. Graphite molds have the disadvantage of oxidizing in ordinary atmosphere, and thus have a short life unless an oxygen-free atmosphere is provided. When metal leads are to be molded into the glass header at the same time, these leads are preferably prebeaded, or at least preoxidized.

When a feed-through atmosphere furnace is used for the production of molded headers on a continuous schedule, the composition of the atmosphere and its dewpoint must be carefully controlled. Natural gas may be mixed with air in a ratio of 1.0:8.5 to obtain exothermic gas by partial combustion; the approximate composition of this gas is 6 % CO_2 , 5 % CO, 3 % H_2 , the remainder being nitrogen.[115] The temperature of the furnace, or that to which the mold is raised, is of the order of 1000°C.

The glass powder, which is prepared by crushing glass cullet,* generally has a particle size equivalent to -20 or -30 mesh, i.e. such that it will not pass through a 20- or 30-mesh screen. It is very important to clean the powder carefully to avoid contaminations which would cause excessive bubbles and also hinder the sintering process. Washing in dilute hydrofluoric acid, followed by rinses in water and acetone, or alcohol, and hot-air drying, is one accepted procedure. The clean glass powder should not be stored more than one or two days before use.† Similar care should be applied to the cleaning of the metal leads, and they also should be used soon after cleaning.

When glass is ground into a very fine powder and a small amount of liquid binder added, it can be dry-pressed into various shapes and then sintered at a temperature slightly above the softening point of the glass. A vitreous body results which has roughly the same properties as the parent glass, except that it will be translucent rather than transparent because of the tiny voids which remain. Larger articles can also be produced by slip-casting, similar to the methods used in the forming of ceramic ware (Chapter 2).[116-118] Powdered-glass molded articles can be made to a much closer size tolerance (±5 mils) than is attainable for conventional glassware where $\pm\frac{1}{32}$ in. is a realistic tolerance.[119]

Glass powder disks, about one-half in. thick and 4 in. diameter are used for the lubrication of steel during extrusion. Thus a 5-in. diameter steel bar may be extruded through a tapered die and emerge with a major di-

---

* Glass cullet is a term used for broken, excess, or faulty glass, which is remelted in a subsequent furnace run.

† The preparation of glass powder samples for the measurement of resistance to chemical attack is described under method P-W in ASTM Standard Method of Test C 225-54, and serves to emphasize the need for great care in handling glass powder.

mension in cross-section of about 1 in. A bar about 20 meters long and weighing 100 kg is extruded in two or three seconds; during this operation, about 100 gm of glass is melted and forms a 20-microns-thick film on the extruded bar.[120]

Solder Glass

The method of joining two pieces of metal by a low-melting alloy, known as solder, has been known for many centuries, but the technique of joining two pieces of glass by a low-melting glass has been developed only during the past decade and, until recently, had found very limited commercial application. Glass solder, or frit, as it is called, can be applied not only to mating glass surfaces, where it produces a vacuum-tight seal, but also to joints between glass and metal and between mica and glass.

One of the first frit seals described by Donal[121] in 1942 used a low-melting glass suitable for the joining of mica to glass or metal at a temperature of 600°C. This technique was logically developed to the sealing of glass to glass by other workers, especially in Europe, and in recent years workers in the U. S. have applied themselves to the perfection of this technique.[122-132] Most of the solder glasses have a lead oxide content ranging from 70 to 85 per cent, boron oxide from 20 to 10 per cent and silicon oxide from 10 to 5 per cent, and their thermal expansion coefficient may range from 80 to $120 \times 10^{-7}/C$. Frequently, a small addition of zinc oxide and aluminum oxide is also used to modify the desired properties and to improve the chemical stability of the glasses. The expansion coefficient of the solder glass must necessarily be matched to the expansion coefficient of the parent glasses, but is generally chosen to lie somewhat below the expansion coefficient of the glass to be joined.[131]

One of the principal advantages of solder glasses is the fact that seals can be made at a substantially lower temperature, between 400° and 500°C, than is possible with conventional flame-sealing techniques where temperatures from 800° to 1000°C are required. Seals can thus be made in an oven, which obviates the use of flames and the danger of having objectionable gases enter the tube. The lower temperature also minimizes the danger of oxidation of the assembly. Miniature tubes and subminiature tubes, also hearing-aid tubes, which are particularly sensitive to these effects, are cases where solder glass sealing can be used to great advantage. The technique has also been applied to large tubes; Figure 1.35 shows a flat picture tube which has been sealed by this method. Mica windows for counter tubes are attached to the envelope in this manner, as mentioned previously.

After the constituents of the solder glass have been prepared in a platinum or silver crucible at a temperature of about 1000°C, the resulting solder glass is poured into water and ground into powder of about +100 mesh.

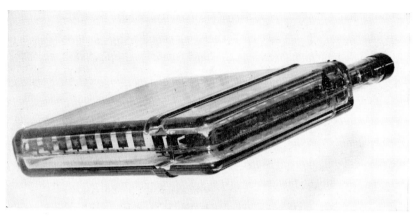

Figure 1.35. Flat picture tube. (*Courtesy Kaiser Aircraft & Electronics Laboratory.*)

The powder is usually mixed with a volatile liquid and either sprayed or flowed onto the part to be sealed. Binding agents such as nitrocellulose are sometimes used to give strength to the powdered glass layer, but this necessitates more careful firing to eliminate the organic matter. The powder may also be preformed into a special shape such as a washer, bead, bar, or disc, and lightly fired to give it strength. One of the best methods is to flow the liquid glass onto the sealing surface at the time the article is fabricated. In this way the article comes already provided with a layer of solder glass in the right place and requires only heating in an oven to complete the seal.[131] Generally, the powdered glass coating applied to the mating surfaces is quite thin (about 5 mils thick) so that the surfaces to be sealed must be originally prepared to a closer tolerance than is customary, or necessary, for parts joined by flame sealing. This requirement makes solder glass seals more costly.

Gallup and Dingwall[132] have investigated a number of solder glass compositions suitable for electron tube applications, and determined viscosity, thermal expansion, density, and index of refraction; Tables 1.10, 1.11, 1.12, and 1.13 are taken from their report.

"Glasses 2, 3, and 5 in Table 1.11 have been used as the cementing media in permanent marking inks for stamping type numbers on different kinds of electron tubes which used soft-glass envelopes having thermal expansion coefficients of approximately $90 \times 10^{-7}/C$. Because no difficulty was experienced with these three glasses, it appears that coefficient of thermal expansion is not a critical factor in the use of solder glasses in marking inks applied in thin layers over limited areas.

"Glasses 6 and 7 have been used in the sealing of lead-glass stems to

TABLE 1.10. SOLDER GLASS COMPOSITIONS (P.C. BY WEIGHT)*

No.	PbO Chem. analysis	PbO Calc. batch comp.	B_2O_3 Chem. analysis	B_2O_3 Calc. batch comp.	SiO_2 Chem. analysis	SiO_2 Calc. batch comp.
1	71.4	71.3	—	—	28.6	28.7
2	84.8	84.7	—	—	15.2	15.3
3	76.3	76.2	23.7	23.8	—	—
4	82.8	82.7	17.2	17.3	—	—
5	88.3	88.0	11.7	12.0	—	—
6	71.9	72.0	14.2	14.0	13.9	14.0
7	85.1	85.0	—	7.5	—	—

* After Gallup and Dingwall.[132]

TABLE 1.11. VISCOSITY DATA (POISES) FOR SOLDER GLASSES*

Mole Per Cent Composition	$10^{7.6}$† Softening point (°C)	$10^{13.4}$ Annealing point (°C)	$10^{14.6}$† Strain point (°C)	10^9 (°C)	10^{10} (°C)	10^{11} (°C)	10^{12} (°C)
40 PbO, 60 SiO$_2$	568	444.0	421.5	535.5	512.0	490.5	471.0
60 PbO, 40 SiO$_2$	429	357.5	344.5	410.0	397.0	384.5	373.0
50 PbO, 50 B$_2$O$_3$	435	376.5	365.5	419.0	408.5	398.0	389.0
60 PbO, 40 B$_2$O$_3$	383	327.0	317.0	368.0	357.5	348.0	339.5
69.5 PbO, 30.5 B$_2$O$_3$	330	281.5	272.5	317.0	308.0	300.0	292.0
42.7 PbO, 26.5 B$_2$O$_3$, 30.8 SiO$_2$	477	406.5	393.5	458.5	445.0	433.0	421.5
62.0 PbO, 17.6 B$_2$O$_3$, 20.4 SiO$_2$	371	311.0	300.0	355.0	344.5	333.5	324.0

* After Gallup and Dingwall.[132]
† Extrapolated from measured values.

TABLE 1.12. COMPARISON OF SOLDER GLASS AND STANDARD
GLASSES AT THREE VISCOSITY LEVELS*

Glass	Softening point (°C)	Annealing point (°C)	Strain point (°C)
Solder Glass	477	406.5	393.5
Corning 0080 Lime	696	510	478
Corning 0120 Lead	630	433	400

* After Gallup and Dingwall.[132]

TABLE 1.13. COEFFICIENT OF THERMAL EXPANSION FOR
HIGH-LEAD GLASSES*

Composition Mole (%)	Composition Weight (%)	Coefficient of thermal expansion 30° to 300°C
(1) 40 PbO 60 SiO$_2$	71.3 PbO, 28.7 SiO$_2$	74×10^{-7} in./in./°C
(2) 60 PbO 40 SiO$_2$	84.7 PbO, 15.3 SiO$_2$	108×10^{-7}
(3) 50 PbO 50 B$_2$O$_3$	76.2 PbO, 23.8 B$_2$O$_3$	93×10^{-7}
(4) 60 PbO 40 B$_2$O$_3$	82.7 PbO, 17.3 B$_2$O$_3$	108×10^{-7}
(5) 69.5 PbO 30.5 B$_2$O$_3$	88 PbO, 12 B$_2$O$_3$	124×10^{-7} (only to 280°C)
(6) 42.7 PbO 26.5 B$_2$O$_3$ 30.8 SiO$_2$	72 PbO, 14 B$_2$O$_3$ 14 SiO$_2$	85×10^{-7}
(7) 62 PbO 17.6 B$_2$O$_3$ 20.4 SiO$_2$	85 PbO, 7.5 B$_2$O$_3$, 7.5 SiO$_2$	117×10^{-7}

* After Gallup and Dingwall.[132]

steel shells. Glass 6 proved most generally satisfactory for this work because of its intermediate working range (500 to 600°C). Glass 7 provides a better thermal-expansion match for steel and, therefore, axial tension stresses are lower when it is used.

"Glass 6 has also been useful in sealing mica to soft glass and to chrome-iron-alloy metal cups. In the seals, thermal-expansion match was found important because of the large external seal circumference. Glasses closely similar to glass 6 have been used in the sealing of lime-glass diaphragms to chrome-iron rings. For these seals close expansion matches are necessary.

"In brief, thermal expansions proved important in all seals except those in which very thin films of solder glass covered small areas such as occur with marking inks, and those in which the solder-glass seal was kept under high compression by an external steel shell.

"None of the solder glasses investigated had either the mechanical strength or the chemical stability of standard soft glasses. When the solder-glass seals are made properly, however, both their strength and weathering resistance have proved adequate to maintain electron devices in a vacuum-tight state for many years."[132]

One of the disadvantages of the more conventional solder glasses described above is their thermoplastic nature. The softening point of these frits lies below the bake-out temperature of glasses used for color TV picture tubes and would thus permit shifting of the face plate if the tubes were baked at the 450°C-level. For these reasons, thermosetting solder glasses were developed at RCA with the cooperation of engineers at Corning Glass Works and Kimble Glass Company.[137] These glasses change their structure on the application of heat during the sealing process and subsequently have a higher softening point, of the order of 500°C, so that bake-out temperatures above 400°C can be used during exhaust. High dielectric strength, resistance to weathering in humid atmospheres, and proper expansion match to the glasses used for face plate and funnel have been achieved in this development described by Becker et al.[137] The Pyroceram cements described at the end of the next chapter (p. 120) offer another approach to this problem.

At the other extreme of the temperature scale, very low-melting glasses have recently been developed by workers at the Bell Telephone Laboratories[138] for the protection of solid-state devices, such as crystal diodes and transistors, against the harmful effects of atmospheric moisture. These glasses* consist of binary or ternary mixtures of thallium, arsenic, and sulfur which are fluid in the range of 200 to 400°C; they are available in powder form or as preforms pressed from powder but can also be produced by vacuum deposition as thin film on the order of 1 mil thick. For dip coat-

* Available from Baker and Adamson, 40 Rector St., New York 6, N. Y

ing, the powder is molten in specially prepared fused-silica containers to preserve their purity, and the device to be coated is immersed in the molten glass for 10 to 20 seconds and then withdrawn and allowed to cool to room temperature. The operation is carried out in an inert atmosphere, such as nitrogen, under a fume hood to remove any toxic vapors evolved during heating. Satisfactory electric performance of coated semiconductor devices has been demonstrated in exposure to 100% relative humidity for several months.

REFERENCES

1. A. Q. Tool, D. B. Lloyd and G. E. Merritt, "Dimensional changes caused in glass by heating cycles," *J. Am. Ceram. Soc.*, **13**, 632–654 (Sept. 1930).
2. J. E. Stanworth, "Physical Properties of Glass," 159–161. The Clarendon Press, Oxford, 1950. The description of the experiments is quoted with the permission of Clarendon Press.
3. A. Q. Tool, "Relation between inelastic deformability and thermal expansion of glass in its annealing range," *J. Am. Ceram. Soc.* **29**, 240–253 (Sept. 1946).
4. A. Q. Tool and C. G. Eichlin, "Variations caused in heating curves of glass by heat treatment," *J. Am. Ceram. Soc.*, **14**, 276–308 (Apr. 1931).
5. G. W. Morey, "The Properties of Glass," 2nd ed., Reinhold Publishing Corp., New York, 1954.
6. G. O. Jones, "Viscosity and related properties in glass," Repts. *Progr. Phys.*, **12**, 133–162 (1948/49). The Physical Society, London.
7. G. O. Jones, "Glass," John Wiley & Sons, Inc., New York, 1956.
8. E. U. Condon, "Physics of the glassy state," Four lectures delivered at the 15th Annual Colloquium of College Physicists at the State University of Iowa, June 19 and 20, 1953. *Am. J. Physics*, **22**, 43–53, 132–142, 224–232, 310–317 (Feb., Mar., Apr., May 1954).
8a. H. Salmang, "Die Glasfabrikation-Physikalische und Chemische Grundlagen," Springer-Verlag, Berlin, 1957. (Reviewed in *J. Am. Ceram. Soc.*, Aug. 1958).
9. H. N. Ritland, "Limitations of the fictive temperature concept," *J. Am. Ceram. Soc.*, **39**, 403–406 (Dec. 1956).
10. R. W. G. Wyckoff and G. W. Morey, "X-ray diffraction measurements on some soda-lime-silica glasses," *J. Soc. Glass Technol.*, **9**, 265–267 (1925).
11. J. T. Randall, H. P. Rooksby and B. S. Cooper, "The diffraction of x-rays by vitreous solids and its bearing on their constitution," *Nature*, **125**, 458 (Mar. 1930) (Supplement 3151).
12. B. E. Warren, "X-ray determination of the structure of liquids and glass," *J. Appl. Phys.*, **8**, 645–654 (Oct. 1937).
13. B. E. Warren and A. D. Loring, "X-ray diffraction study of the structure of soda-silica glass," *J. Am. Ceram. Soc.*, **18**, 269–276 (Sept. 1935).
14. B. E. Warren and J. Biscoe, "Fourier analysis of x-ray patterns of soda-silica glass," *J. Am. Ceram. Soc.*, **21**, 259–265 (1938).
15. W. H. Zachariasen, "The atomic arrangement in glass," *J. Am. Chem. Soc.*, **54**, 3841–3851 (Oct. 1932).
16. O. L. Anderson, "Effect of pressure on glass structure," *J. Appl. Phys.*, **27**, 943–947 (Aug. 1956).

16a. L. W. Tilton, "Noncrystal ionic model for silica glass," *J. Research Natl. Bur. Standards*, **59**, 139–154 (Aug. 1957) (RP2782).

16b. L. W. Tilton, "Roll of vitrons in alkali silicate binary glasses," *J. Research Natl. Bur. Standards*, **60**, 351–364 (Apr. 1958) (RP2854).

17. P. L. Baynton, H. Rawson and J. E. Stanworth, "New types of glasses," *Nature*, **178**, 910–911 (Oct. 27, 1956).

18. P. L. Baynton, H. Rawson and J. E. Stanworth, "Research on new glasses based on the oxides of tellurium, vanadium, molybdenum, and tungsten." The Proceedings of the Fourth International Congress on Glass, Paris, 1956. Also: "Semiconducting properties of some vanadate glasses," *J. Electrochem. Soc.*, **104**, 237–239 (Apr. 1951).

19. W. A. Weyl, "Coloured Glasses," The Society of Glass Technology, Sheffield, England, 1951.

20. F. V. Tooley, "Handbook of Glass Manufacture," Ogden Publishing Co., New York, 1953.

21. A. E. Dale and J. E. Stanworth, "Sealing Glasses," *J. Soc. Glass Technol.*, **29**, 77–91 (1948).

22. G. Gehlhoff and M. Thomas, "The physical properties of glasses and their dependence on composition" (in German), *Z. Tech. Phys.*, **7**, 260–278 (June 1926).

23. G. S. Fulcher, "Analysis of recent measurements of the viscosity of glasses," *J. Am. Ceram. Soc.*, **8**, 339–355 (June 1925).

24. R. W. Douglas, "The use of glass in high-vacuum apparatus," *J. Sci. Instr.*, **22**, 81–87 (May 1945). Some additional entries were made in this table by the present author to include data kindly supplied by the British Thomson-Houston Co., Ltd.

25. E. B. Shand, "Glass Engineering Handbook," 2nd ed., McGraw Hill Book Co., Inc., New York, 1958.

26. F. J. Norton, "Permeation of gases through solids," *J. Appl. Phys.*, **28**, 34–39 (Jan. 1957).

27. F. J. Norton, "Helium diffusion through glass," *J. Am. Ceram. Soc.*, **36**, 90–96 (Mar. 1953).

28. W. A. Weyl "Chemical aspects of some mechanical properties of glass," *Research*, **2**, 50–61 (1948).

29. R. M. Barrer, "Diffusion in and through solids," Cambridge University Press, Cambridge, 1951.

30. P. L. Smith and N. W. Taylor, "Diffusion of helium through several glasses," *J. Am. Ceram. Soc.*, **23**, 139–146 (May 1940).

31. T. F. Newkirk and F. V. Tooley, "Study of effect of cation concentration and size of helium permeability of alkali-silica glasses," *J. Am. Ceram. Soc.*, **32**, 272–278 (Sept. 1949).

32. Lord Rayleigh, "Attempt to detect passage of helium through a crystal lattice at high temperatures," *Proc. Roy. Soc. London*, **A 163**, 376–380 (1937).

33. W. H. Keesom, "Helium," Elsevier Book Company, Inc., New York, 1942.

34. Saul Dushman, "Scientific Foundations of Vacuum Technique," John Wiley & Sons, Inc., New York, 1949.

35. J. D. Fast, "Gas permeability of metals," *Philips Tech. Rev.*, **6**, 365–71, 635–40 (1941); **7**, 74–82 (1942).

36. N. W. Taylor and William Rast, "Diffusion of helium and hydrogen through pyrex brand chemically resistant glass," *J. Chem. Phys.*, **6**, 612–619 (Oct. 1938).

37. W. D. Urry, "Further studies in rare gases; permeability of various glasses to helium," *J. Am. Chem. Soc.*, **54,** 3887–3901 (Oct. 1932).

38. W. D. Urry, "Diffusion of hydrogen and helium through silica glass and other glasses," *J. Am. Chem. Soc.*, **44,** 2160–67 (1922).

39. C. C. Van Voorhis, "Diffusion of helium through several widely differing glasses," *Phys. Rev.*, **A23, 557** (May 1924).

40. L. S. T'Sai and T. R. Hogness, "Diffusion of gases through fused quartz," *J. Phys. Chem.*, **36,** 2595–2600 (Oct. 1932).

41. G. A. Williams and J. B. Ferguson, "Solubility of helium and hydrogen in heated silica glass and the relation of this to the permeability," *J. Am. Chem. Soc.*, **45,** 635–39 (1924).

42. W. A. Rogers, R. S. Buritz and D. Alpert, "Diffusion coefficient, solubility and permeability for helium in glass," *J. Appl. Phys.*, **25,** 868–75 (July 1954).

43. M. B. Reynolds, "Diffusion of argon in a potassium-lime-silica glass," *J. Am. Ceram. Soc.*, **40,** 395–398 (Nov. 1957).

43a. K. B. McAfee, Jr., "Stress-enhanced diffusion in glass," *J. Chem. Phys.*, **28,** 218–229 (Feb. 1958).

44. S. Schurkow, "On the influence of absorbed surface layers on the strength of fine silica fibers" (in German), *Physik. Z. Sowjetunion*, **1,** 123–131 (Jan. 1932).

45. E. Orowan, "Notch brittleness and the strength of metals," *Trans. Inst. Engrs. Shipbuilders in Scot.*, **89,** 165–215 (Dec. 1945).

46. R. H. Kropschort and R. P. Mikesell, "Strength and fatigue of glass at very low temperatures," *J. Appl. Phys.*, **98,** 610–614 (May 1957).

47. A. A. Griffith, "The phenomena of rupture and flow in solids," *Trans. Roy. Soc. London*, **A 221,** 163–198 (Oct. 1920).

48. E. D. Lynch and F. V. Tooley, "Effect of stress and temperature during forming on strength of glass," *J. Am. Ceram. Soc.*, **40,** 107–112 (Apr. 1957).

49. E. Orowan, "The increased strength of thin fibres, the Joffée effect, and related phenomena in the light of Griffith's theory of fracture" (in German), *Z. Phys.*, **86,** 195–213 (Oct. 1933).

50. G. F. Stockdale, F. V. Tooley and C. W. Yuig, "Changes in tensile strength of glass caused by water immersion treatment," *J. Am. Ceram. Soc.*, **34,** 116–121 (Apr. 1951).

51. V. K. Moorthy, F. V. Tooley and G. F. Stockdale, "Influence of water immersion treatment on tensile strength of glass: Effect of temperature," *J. Am. Ceram. Soc.*, **39,** 395–398 (Nov. 1956).

52. C. Brodmann, *Nachr. kgl. Ges. Wiss. Göttingen*, p. 44 (1894).

53. H. K. Richardson, "Sulphur in gas for glass working," *Glass Ind.*, **35,** 319, 346 (June 1954).

54. J. Morrison, "Some effects of gases on thermionic oxide-coated cathodes," Report on 15th Annual Conference Physical Electronics pp. 21–27 (March 1955).

55. R. W. Douglas and J. O. Isard, "The action of water and of sulphur dioxide on glass surfaces," *J. Soc. Glass Technol.*, **33,** No. 154, 289–349 (Oct 1949).

56. A. Winter, "Glass formation," *J. Am. Ceram. Soc.*, **40,** 54–58 (Feb. 1957).

57. T'ing-Sui Kê, "Experimental evidence of viscous behavior of grain boundaries in metals," *Phys. Rev.*, **71,** 533–546 (Apr. 15, 1947).

57a. R. Gardon, "Calculation of temperature distributions in glass plates undergoing heat treatment," *J. Am. Ceram. Soc.*, **41,** 200–209 (June 1958).

58. G. D. Redston, "The control of thermionic valve envelope quality by thermal shock testing," *Elec. Eng.*, **28,** 470–475 (Nov. 1956).

59. Lillie, H. R., "Basic principles of glass annealing," *Glass Ind.*, **31**, 355–358, 382 (July 1950).

60. L. H. Adams and E. D. Williamson, "The annealing of glass," *J. Franklin Inst.*, **190**, 597–631, 835–870 (1920).

61. L. H. Adams, "The annealing of glass as a physical problem," *J. Franklin Inst.*, **216**, 39–71 (July 1933).

62. F. W. Preston, "A re-examination of the Adams and Williamson law of annealing," *J. Soc. Glass Technol.*, **36**, 287–296 (Oct. 1952).

63. F. Twyman, *J. Soc. Glass Technol.*, **1**, 61–74 (1917).

64. H. R. Lillie, "Stress release in glass, a phenomenon involving viscosity as a variable with time," *J. Am. Ceram. Soc.*, **19**, 45–54 (Feb. 1936).

65. A. Q. Tool, "Relaxation of stresses in annealing glass," *J. Research Natl. Bur. Standards*, **34**, 199–211 (Feb. 1945).

66. G. D. Redston and J. E. Stanworth, "The theoretical development of simplified annealing schedules," *J. Soc. Glass Technol.*, **32**, 32–39 (Feb. 1948).

67. A. E. Dale and J. E. Stanworth, "On the viscosity of some glasses in the annealing range," *J. Soc. Glass Technol.*, **29**, 414–427 (Dec. 1945).

68. Sir David Brewster, "Results of some recent experiments on the properties impressed upon light by the action of glass raised to different temperatures and cooled under different circumstances," *Phil. Trans. Royal Soc. London*, 436–439 (1814); *ibid.*, Numerous other papers by the same author, (1814–1816).

69. J. H. Partridge, "Glass-to-Metal Seals," Society of Glass Technology, Sheffield, England, 1949.

70. L. H. Adams and E. D. Williamson, "The relation between birefringence and stress in various types of glass," *J. Washington Acad. Sci.*, **9**, 609–625 (1919).

71. A. A. Padmos and J. de Vries, "Stresses in glass and their measurement," *Philips Tech. Rev.*, **9**, 277–284 (1947–1948).

72. C. D. Spencer and S. Jones, "Design and construction of polariscopes for use in glass factories," *J. Am. Ceram. Soc.*, **14**, 512–517 (July 1931).

73. J. Fortey, "A projection type of strain-viewer," *J. Soc. Glass Technol.*, **29**, 124–127 (1945).

74. R. W. Goranson and L. H. Adams, "A method for the precise measurement of optical path-difference, especially in stressed glass," *J. Franklin Inst.*, **216**, 475–504 (1933).

75. W. T. Read, "Optical measurements of residual stresses in glass bulbs," *Bell Labs. Record*, **28**, 62–65 (Feb. 1950); *J. Appl. Phys.*, **21**, 250–257 (Mar. 1950).

76. A. A. Padmos and J. de Vries, "Stresses in glass and their measurement," *Philips Tech. Rev.*, **9**, 277–284 (1947/4918).

77. V. C. DeMaria, "A low-cost portable polariscope," *Sylvania Technologist*, **8**, 64 (Apr. 1955).

78. F. W. Preston, "The use of polariscopes in the glass industry," *J. Am. Ceram. Soc.*, **13**, 595–623 (Sept. 1930).

79. W. T. Read, "An optical method for measuring the stress in glass bulbs," *J. Appl. Phys.*, **21**, 250–257 (Mar. 1950).

80. A. A. Padmos, "The estimation of the thermal expansion coefficient of a glass by the measurement of stresses produced by fusion to a standard glass," *Glass Ind.*, **33**, 199 (Apr. 1952).

81. E. G. Coker and L. H. G. Filon, "A Treatise on Photoelasticity," Cambridge University Press, 1931.

82. C. Mylonas and M. Greek, "The optical system of polariscopes as used in photoelasticity," *J. Sci. Instr.*, **25**, 77–81 (Mar. 1948).

83. A. W. Hull and E. E. Burger, "Glass-to-metal seals," *Physics*, **5**, 384–405 (Dec. 1934).

84. H. Poritsky, "Analysis of thermal stresses in sealed cylinders and the effect of viscous flow during annealing," *Physics*, **5**, 406–411 (1934).

84a. P. M. Sutton, "Stress measurements in circular cylinders," *J. Am. Ceram. Soc.*, **41**, 103–109 (Mar. 1958).

85. F. W. Martin, "Stresses in glass-to-metal seals; I. The cylindrical seal," *J. Am. Ceram. Soc.*, **33**, 224–229 (July 1950).

85a. T. D. Riney, "Photoelastic determination of residual stress in the dome of electron tube envelopes," *Proc. Soc. Exp. Stress Anal.*, **15**, No. 1, 161–170 (1957).

85b. F. Engel, "On the hysteresis of polarimeter curves" (in German), *Glastech. Ber.*, **31**, 133–137 (Apr. 1958).

86. A. C. Becquerel, "Note on production of thermal electricity" (in French), *Compt. Rend.*, **38**, 905 (1854).

87. W. Thomson, "Electrolytic conduction in solids; first example, hot glass," *Proc. Roy. Soc.*, **23**, 468–472 (June 1875).

88. J. Gallup, "Electrolysis phenomena in soft-glass stems of rectifier tubes," *J. Am. Ceram. Soc.*, **29**, 277–281 (Oct. 1946).

89. J. Peysson, "Electrolysis phenomena in glass" (in French), *Ann. radioél. compagn. franc. assoc. T.F.S.*, **3**, 107–114 (Apr. 1948).

90. G. E. Rindone, E. C. Marbee and W. A. Weyl, "Oxidation and reduction of glasses by means of electrolysis," *J. Am. Ceram. Soc.*, **30**, 314–319 (Oct. 1947).

91. E. Sedden, E. J. Tippett and W. E. S. Turner, "The electrical conductivity of solium metasilicate-silica glasses," *J. Soc. Glass Technol.*, **16**, 450T–477T (1932).

92. G. Gehlhoff and M. Thomas, "The physical properties of glasses as a function of their composition" (in German), *Z. Tech. Physik.*, **6**, 544–554 (Oct. 1925).

93. J. M. Stevels, "Progress in the Theory of the Physical Properties of Glass," Elsevier Publishing Co., Inc., New York, 1948.

94. E. Rasch and F. W. Hinrichsen, "On a relation between electrical conductivity and temperature" (in German), *Z. Elektrochemie*, **14**, 41–46 (Jan. 1908).

95. P. L. Kirby, "Electrical conduction in glass," *Brit. J. Appl. Phys.*, **1**, 193–202 (Aug. 1950).

96. J. B. Whitehead, "Lectures on Dielectric Theory and Insulation," New York, McGraw-Hill Book Co., Inc., 1927.

97. E. J. Murphy and S. O. Morgan, "The dielectric properties of insulating materials," Pt. 1, *Bell System Tech. J.*, **16**, 493–512 (1937); *ibid.*, Pt. 2, **17**, 640–669.

98. J. T. Littleton and G. W. Morey, "The Electrical Properties of Glass," New York, John Wiley & Sons, Inc., 1933.

99. E. M. Guyer, "The electrical behavior of glass at room temperature," *J. Am. Ceram. Soc.*, **16**, 607–618 (Dec. 1933).

100. W. A. Weyl, "The dielectric properties of glass and their structural interpretation," *J. Soc. Glass Technol.*, **33**, 220–238 (1949).

100a. M. J. O. Strutt, "Dielectric properties of various glasses as a function of frequency and temperature" (in German), *Arch. Elektrotech.*, **25**, 715–722 (Oct. 1931).

101. H. Veith, "Simple method for the determination of the water film adhering to glass" (in German), *Z. Physik. Chemie.*, **193**, 378–385 (1944).

102. F. Fulda, *Sprechsaal*, **60**, 769, 789, 810, 831 (1927).

103. R. L. Green and K. B. Blodgett, "Electrically conducting glasses," *J. Am. Ceram. Soc.*, **31**, 89–100 (Mar. 1948).

104. K. B. Blodgett, "Surface conductivity of lead silicate glass after hydrogen treatment," *J. Am. Ceram. Soc.*, **34**, 14–27 (Jan. 1951).

104a. H. H. Funk, "On the surface conductivity of glasses after treatment in hot hydrogen" (in German), *Glastech. Ber.*, **31**, 269–272 (July 1958).

104b. Dow Corning Silicone Notes 3-207 (Oct. 1956), and 8-409a (Oct. 1957); Dow Corning Corporation, Midland, Michigan.

104c. K. L. Loewenstein, "A survey of the surface treatments of glass," *J. Soc. Glass Technol.*, **42**, 70N–84N (Oct. 1958).

105. E. M. Guyer, "Electrical glass," *Proc. I.R.E.*, **32**, 743–450 (Dec. 1944).

106. E. B. Shand, "The dielectric strength of glass—an engineering view point," *Trans. A.I.E.E.*, **60**, 814–818 (Aug. 1941).

107. S. Whitehead, "Dielectric Breakdown of Solids," The Clarendon Press, Oxford, 1951.

108. P. H. Moon and A. S. Norcross, "Three regions of dielectric breakdown," *Elec. Eng.*, **49**, 755–762 (Apr. 1930).

108a. D. W. Rinehart and J. J. Bonino, "Dielectric losses of some simple ternary silicate glasses," *J. Am. Ceram. Soc.*, **42**, 107–112 (Mar. 1959)

109. R. G. Sherwood, "Effects of heat on chemical glassware," *J. Am. Chem. Soc.* **40**, 1645–1653 (Nov. 1918); "Gases and vapors from glass," *Phys. Rev.*, **12**, 448–458 (Dec. 1918).

110. J. E. Shrader, "Residual gases and vapors in highly exhausted glass bulbs," *Phys. Rev.*, **13**, 434–437 (June 1919).

111. S. Dushman, "Scientific Foundations of Vacuum Technique," John Wiley & Sons, Inc., New York, 1949.

112. I. Langmuir, "Tungsten lamps of high efficiency—I: Blackening of tungsten lamps and methods of preventing it," *Trans. Am. Inst. Elec. Engrs.*, **32**, 1913–1933 (Oct. 1913); II. Nitrogen-filled lamps, *ibid.*, 1935–1954.

113. B. J. Todd, "Outgassing of glass," *J. Appl. Phys.*, **26**, 1238–1243 (Oct. 1955); "Equilibrium between glass and water vapor at bake-out temperatures," *ibid.*, **27**, 1109–1120 (Oct. 1956).

114. R. H. A. Crawley, "A universal reagent for cleaning glassware and silica," *Chem. Ind.*, **45**, 1205–1206 (1953).

115. A. G. Hotchkiss and H. M. Webber, "Protective Atmospheres," John Wiley & Sons, Inc., New York, 1953.

116. E. G. Dorgelo, "Sintered glass," *Philips Tech. Rev.*, **8**, 2–7 (Jan. 1946); see also *Glass Ind.*, **27**, 347–348, 364, 368–370 (July 1946).

117. R. W. Degrasse, "Molding tube stems from powdered glass," Stanford University Electronics Laboratories, unpublished report on work in the Tube Techniques Laboratory, (1954).

118. W. H. McKnight, "Pressed and sintered glass powder shapes," Materials & Methods, **40**, 94–96 (Oct. 1954).

119. J. A. Jolly, "Advantages of ceramics in electron tubes," National Electronics Conference, Chicago, Oct. 9, 1957.

120. I. Peyches and J. Sejournet, "Glass as a lubricant in metallurgical operations" (in French), *Verres et réfractaires*, **8**, 131–135 (Mar. 1954).

121. J. S. Donal, Jr., "Sealing mica to glass or metal to form a vacuum-tight joint," *Rev. Sci. Instr.*, **13**, 266–267 (June 1942).

122. G. Alma and F. Prakke, "New series of small radio valves," *Philips Tech. Rev.*, **8**, 289–295 (Aug. 1946).
123. A. E. Dale and J. E. Stanworth, "A note on very soft glasses and some of their electrical applications," *J. Soc. Glass Technol.*, **32**, No. 146, 147T–153T (June 1948).
124. A. E. Dale and J. E. Stanworth, "The development of some very soft glasses," *J. Soc. Glass Technol.*, **33**, No. 152, 167–175 (June 1949).
125. W. Espe, "On some new glass solders for vacuum techniques" (in German), *Feinwerktech.*, **55**, 303–306 (1951).
126. Yukata Ikeda, "Sealing methods of vacuum tubes with low-melting glass," (in Japanese), *J. Ceram. Soc. Japan*, **59**, No. 66, 580–584 (1951).
127. H. Kalsing, "Solder glasses" (in German), *Sprechsaal.*, **86**, No. 15, 363–365 (1953).
128. A. Danzin, "Solder glasses of low expansion" (in French), Silicates ind. **8**, 321–324 (Aug. 1953); **18**, 371–378 (Sept. 1953).
129. H. Kalsing, "Solder glasses" (in German), *Sprechsaal.*, **86**, No. 9, 212–216 (1953); No. 14, 339–341; No. 16, 389–392.
130. A. P. Haase and C. E. Horton, "Sealing techniques for miniature tubes," *Ceram. Age*, **66**, 16–18 (Nov. 1955).
131. R. H. Dalton, "Solder glass sealing," *J. Am. Ceram. Soc.*, **39**, 109–112 (Mar. 1956).
132. J. Gallup and A. G. F. Dingwall, "Properties of low-temperature solder glasses," *Ceram. Bull.*, **36**, 47–51 (Feb. 1957).
133. J. Vermeer, "The impulse breakdown strength of Pyrex glass," *Physica*, **20**, 313–326 (1954).
134. J. Vermeer, "The electric strength of glasses with different sodium contents," *ibid.*, **22**, 1247–1253 (1956).
135. J. Vermeer, "The electrical conduction of glasses at high field strengths," *ibid.*, **22**, 1257–1268 (1956).
136. J. Vermeer, "On the relation between ionic conductivity and breakdown strength of glass," *ibid.*, **22**, 1269–1278 (1956).
137. B. N. Becker, C. H. Mattson and R. H. Zachariason, "Development of round glass bulbs for RCA-21CYP22 color picture tubes," paper presented at the 1957 Conference on Electronic Devices, Washington, D. C.
138. S. S. Flaschen, A. D. Pearson and W. R. Northover, "Low-melting inorganic glasses with high melt fluidities below 400°C," *J. Am. Ceram. Soc.*, **42**, 450 (Sept. 1959).

CHAPTER 2

CERAMICS

Introduction

The widespread use of various types of ceramics, not only in tube manufacture but also for auxiliary equipment clearly establishes the need for the tube engineer to have a working knowledge of this field. It would be still better to have a trained ceramist at his side on whose experience he could draw in developing his own designs. Obviously, the trained ceramist will know everything that can possibly be said in this chapter; but the tube engineer, especially a newcomer to the field, may derive some benefit from a general introduction to the subject of ceramics, whereupon he can turn to more specialized texts. For a general introduction, he should read the section on ceramics by Thurnauer, contained in the book entitled "Dielectric Materials and Applications,"[1] and then turn to a review article by Robinson and Bloor[2] and one by Navias[3] on the more special applications of ceramics to electron tubes, and consult references 4–5 where extensive bibliographies are given. A book on "High-Temperature Technology" edited by I. E. Campbell[6] of Battelle Memorial Institute, and sponsored by the Electrochemical Society, is an indispensable source of information on materials which are to operate at high temperature, on methods of their fabrication and techniques for the measurement of their properties.* A survey prepared by Stanford Research Institute for the U. S. Air Force[8] deals with the problems encountered in constructing all kinds of electron tubes which are to operate in a thermal environment of 500°C and should be of some interest to the reader.† A more recent report, also prepared by SRI for the U. S. Air Force, deals with the "Mechanical and Physical Properties of Refractory Nonmetallic Crystalline Materials and Intermetallic Compounds."[9] Another valuable compilation of data has been prepared by Bradshaw and Matthews[10] of the Lockheed Aircraft Corporation.

This chapter describes the physical properties of the various types of

---

* A series of papers on thermal conductivity of ceramic materials was published in a separate section of the Journal of the American Ceramic Society, Vol. 37, No. 2, Pt. 2 (Feb. 1954); see also Ref. (7).

† The author was connected with this project as a consultant at the time when the first part of this revised edition was being prepared. Material originally written for this book has found its way into the SRI Report, and, vice versa, reviews prepared for the SRI report have in some cases been incorporated into this book.

ceramics which are of interest in the construction of electron tubes; the important subject of ceramic-to-metal seals is treated at some length in Chapter 14.

The word "ceramic" is derived from the Greek word "Keramos," meaning a "potter," "potter's clay," or "pottery," and is related to the older Sanskrit root "to burn."[1] In its present-day usage, the word "ceramic" refers to inorganic materials which are given permanent shape and hardness by high-temperature firing. Materials such as abrasives, cements, enamels, glass, clay products, refractories, terra cotta, and whiteware are covered by this definition. "Refractory metals" are not ceramics but are often produced by methods akin to those used in the field of ceramics. The term "powder metallurgy" covers these procedures when a metallic body is the end product. "Cerametals," "cermets," or "ceramals" are metal ceramics consisting of mixtures of metal powders and metal-oxide powders processed into solids by the methods of powder metallurgy.[11, 12] These materials are of great importance in the construction of turbine blades for jet engines and other high-temperature applications.

Raw Materials and Body Compositions

The constituents of the classic ceramic whiteware bodies are clay, feldspar, and flint, in varying proportions, depending on the desired characteristics of the end product. Clay is the plastic component which makes for the desired workability; feldspar and flint are nonplastic. Flint is rock quartz of high purity and provides the skeleton of the composite structure. Feldspar is an alkali-aluminum silicate which fuses on heating and dissolves part of the clay and flint, thus acting as a flux, while clay, or kaolin, may be regarded as the filler of the skeleton of flint. All three components are in interaction during the firing process, which leads to a reorientation of the crystal structure of the whole body. Table 2.1 gives the general composition of typical whiteware bodies.[13] The ceramist has his own nomenclature;[14] he uses many terms which are unfamiliar to the tube engineer. For example he talks in terms of "cones" rather than of degrees Fahrenheit or centigrade. Hence a student of electronics, or a physicist, will require some preparation before he can read these publications with full understanding.

Feldspar, clay, and flint are not terms which specifically define the properties of these materials; on the contrary, they differ widely in impurity content and admixtures depending on their place of origin. They are thus more or less suited for a given body preparation. It would lead too far afield to go into these details; a number of texts may be consulted on the detailed procedures employed in the manufacture of ceramics.[15-23]

Table 2.2 lists the names of a number of minerals and compounds which frequently occur in the discussion of ceramic bodies. Table 2.3 gives the

TABLE 2.1. GENERAL COMPOSITION OF SOME WHITEWARE BODIES*

	Chemical porcelain	Normal porcelains	Electrical porcelains	Vitreous china	Sanitary porcelain	Fine earthenware
	Cone 12–14 (2390– 2534F)	Cone 12–14 (2390– 2534F)	Cone 11–13 (2345– 2462F)	Cone 10–11 (2000– 2345F)	Cone 9–11 (2282– 2345F)	Cone 8–9 (2237– 2282F)
Feldspar or Nepheline Syenite	20–25	20–28	28–38	10–18	30–36	10–16
Whiting	0–1	0–1	0–3	0–1.5		
Dolomite				0–3.0		
Ball Clay	0–5		15–35	10–20	16–25	20–35
Kaolin, China Clay	50–58	40–50	20–35	20–30	20–30	20–35
Silica (200 Mesh "Flint")	10–15	22–35	15–25	30–38	20–30	32–36

* After J. H. Koenig.[13]

TABLE 2.2. MINERALS, REFRACTORY ROCKS, CLAYS AND EARTHS

Kaolinite, Kaolin, Clay	$Al_2O_3 \cdot 2SiO_2 \cdot 2H_2O$
Gibbsite, Diaspore, Hydrargillite	$Al_2O_3 \cdot 3H_2O$; $Al_2O_3 \cdot H_2O$; $Al_2O_3 \cdot 11H_2O$
Pyrophyllite	$Al_2O_3 \cdot 4SiO_2 \cdot H_2O$
Sillimanite, Andalusite, Kyanite, Bentonite	$Al_2O_3 \cdot 4SiO_2 \cdot 9H_2O$
Mullite	$3Al_2O_3 \cdot 2SiO_2$
Corundum, Sapphire	Al_2O_3
Flint (Cristobalite, tridymite, quartz)	SiO_2
Magnesite	$MgCO_3$
Magnesia	MgO
Steatite, Clinoenstatite	$MgO \cdot SiO_2$
Forsterite	$2MgO \cdot SiO_2$
Talc	$3MgO \cdot 4SiO_2 \cdot H_2O$
Cordierite	$2MgO \cdot 2Al_2O_3 \cdot 5SiO_2$
Feldspar	$Na_2O/K_2O \cdot Al_2O_3 \cdot 6SiO_2$
Zircon	$ZrO_2 \cdot SiO_2$
Zirconia	ZrO_2
Spodumene	$Li_2O \cdot Al_2O_3 \cdot 4SiO_2$
Wollastonite	$CaSiO_3$
Spinel (Mineral)	$MgO \cdot Al_2O_3$
Spinel-type	$R'O \cdot R_2O_3$
Magnetite	$FeO \cdot Fe_2O_3$

properties of pure, single refractory oxides and Table 2.4 gives those of some complex refractory oxides. The thermodynamic properties are presented in Table 2.5.* Typical physical properties of ceramic dielectrics are

* The author is indebted to John Wiley & Sons, Inc., New York, N. Y. for granting permission to reproduce Tables 2.3, 2.4, 2.5 as well as Figures 2.6 and 2.10 from "High-Temperature Technology" by I. E. Campbell (see ref. 6).

TABLE 2.3. PROPERTIES OF PURE SINGLE REFRACTORY OXIDES[6]

Material	Formula	Molecular weight	Melting point, °C	Boiling point, °C	Density g·cm⁻³	Hardness, Mohs' scale	Approximate price, $ per lb	Principal limitations	Percentage of metallic element in earth's crust	Other oxides
Aluminum oxide (corundum)	Al_2O_3	101.92	2015	2980	3.97	9	0.05	Hydration, toxicity	7	Al_8O_9 (2Al·3Al₂O₃)
Barium oxide (baria)	BaO	153.37	1917	2200	5.72	3.3	0.10	Price, toxicity	0.08	BaO_2
Beryllium oxide (beryllia, bromellite)	BeO	25.02	2550	4260	3.03	9	9.00	Hydration	0.47	BeO_2
Calcium oxide (calcia, lime)	CaO	56.08	2600	2850	3.32	4.5	0.01	Hydration	3.47	CaO_2
Cerium oxide (ceria)	CeO_2	172.13	>2600	>3000	7.13	6	0.82	Price, reduction	0.062	CeO_2, Ce_2O_3
Chromic oxide	Cr_2O_3	152.02	2265	—	5.21	—	2.00	Reduction	0.001	CrO, CrO_2, CrO_3
Cobalt oxide	CoO	74.94	1805	—	6.46	—	—	Price, reduction	10^{-9}	Co_3O_4, Co_2O_3
Gallium oxide	Ga_2O_3	187.44	1740	—	5.88*	—	25.00	Price, reduction	0.002	Ga_2O
Hafnium oxide (hafnia)	HfO_2	210.6	2777	—	9.68*	—	14.00	Price	—	—
Lanthanum oxide (lanthana)	La_2O_3	325.84	2305	4200	6.51	6	0.05	Price, hydration	—	—
Magnesium oxide (magnesia, periclase)	MgO	40.32	2800	2825	3.58	6	—	—	2.24	MgO_2
Manganese oxide (manganosite)	MnO	70.93	1780	4050†	5.40	5–6	0.07	Oxidation	0.10	Mn_3O_4, Mn_2O_3, MnO_2, MnO_3, Mn_2O_7
Nickel oxide (bunsenite)	NiO	74.69	1950	—	6.8	5.5	—	Reduction	0.02	NiO_4, Ni_2O_3, NiO_2
Niobium oxide	Nb_2O_5	233.82	1772	—	—	6.5	—	Price, oxidation	0.002	NbO (Nb_2O_2), NbO_2 (Nb_2O_4), Nb_2O_5
Silicon oxide (cristobalite)	SiO_2	60.06	1728	2950	2.32*	6–7	0.01	Hydration	25.80	SiO
Strontium oxide (strontia)	SrO	103.63	2415	3000	4.7	3.5	0.50	Price	0.02	SrO_2
Tantalum oxide	Ta_2O_5	441.76	1890	—	8.02	—	15.00	Price, radioactivity	0.001	TaO_2, (Ta_2O_4)
Thorium oxide (thoria, thorianite)	ThO_2	264.12	3300	4400	9.69	6.5	7.00	Price, radioactivity	0.002	Th_2O_7
Tin oxide (cassiterite)	SnO_2	150.70	>1900	1510‡	7.00	6–7	0.90	Price, reduction, volatility	10^{-5}	SnO
Titanium oxide (rutile)	TiO_2	79.90	1840	2227†	4.24†	5.5–6	0.18	Reduction	0.46	Ti_2O_3, TiO_5 (Ti_2O_5·TiO_2), TiO
Uranium oxide	UO_2	270.07	2280	4100	10.96	—	3.00	Price, oxidation, radioactivity	8×10^{-5}	U_3O_8, UO_3
Vanadium oxide	V_2O_5	149.90	1977	3000	4.87	—	12.50	Price, oxidation	0.033	V_2O_2 (VO), V_2O_4 (VO_2), V_2O_5
Yttrium oxide (yttria)	Y_2O_3	225.84	2410	4300	4.84	—	0.15	Volatility	—	—
Zinc oxide (zincite)	ZnO	81.38	1975	1950†	5.66*	4–4.5	—	Price	—	ZnO_2
Zirconium oxide (zirconia)	ZrO_2	123.22	2677	4300	5.56*	6.5	0.90	Price	0.017	ZrO_3

* Density depends on crystalline form.

SiO_2 (low quartz)	2.65 g·cm⁻³	
(low tridymite)	2.26	
(low cristobalite)	2.32	
(vitreous)	2.20	
TiO_2 (brookite)	4.17 g·cm⁻³	
(rutile)	4.24	
(anatase I)	3.84	
ZrO_2 (rhombic, cubic or trigonal)	6.27 g·cm⁻³	
(tetragonal)	6.10	
(monoclinic or rhombic)	5.56	
Ga_2O_3 (hexagonal)	5.88 g·cm⁻³	
(monoclinic)	6.44	
HfO_2 (monoclinic)	9.68 g·cm⁻³	
(tetragonal)	10.01	

TABLE 2.4. PROPERTIES OF SOME COMPLEX REFRACTORY OXIDES[6]

Material	Formula	Melting point, °C	Density g·cm⁻³
Aluminum silicate (mullite)	$3Al_2O_3 \cdot 2SiO_2$	1830*	3.16
Aluminum titanate	$Al_2O_3 \cdot TiO_2$	1855	—
Aluminum titanate	$Al_2O_3 \cdot 2TiO_2$	1895	—
Barium aluminate	$BaO \cdot Al_2O_3$	2000	3.99
Barium aluminate	$BaO \cdot 6Al_2O_3$	1860	3.64
Barium silicate (orthosilicate)	$2BaO \cdot SiO_2$	>1755	5.2
Barium zirconate	$BaO \cdot ZrO_2$	2700	6.26
Beryllium aluminate (chrysoberyl)	$BeO \cdot Al_2O_3$	1870	3.76
Beryllium silicate (metasilicate)	$BeO \cdot SiO_2$	>1755	2.35
Beryllium silicate (phenacite)	$2BeO \cdot SiO_2$	>1750*	2.99
Beryllium titanate	$3BeO \cdot TiO_2$	1800	—
Beryllium zirconate	$3BeO \cdot 2ZrO_2$	2535	—
Calcium chromate	$CaO \cdot CrO_3$	2160	3.22
Calcium chromite	$CaO \cdot Cr_2O_3$	2170	4.8
Calcium phosphate (orthophosphate)	$3CaO \cdot P_2O_5$	1730	3.14
Calcium silicate	$3CaO \cdot SiO_2$	1900*	2.91
Calcium silicate (orthosilicate)	$2CaO \cdot SiO_2$	2120	3.28
Calcium silicon phosphate	$5CaO \cdot SiO_2 \cdot P_2O_5$	1760	3.01
Calcium titanate (perovskite)	$CaO \cdot TiO_2$	1975	4.10
Calcium titanate	$2CaO \cdot TiO_2$	1800	—
Calcium titanate	$3CaO \cdot TiO_2$	2135	—
Calcium zirconate	$CaO \cdot ZrO_2$	2345	4.78
Cobalt aluminate (cobalt blue)	$CoO \cdot Al_2O_3$	1955	4.37
Magnesium aluminate (spinel)	$MgO \cdot Al_2O_3$	2135	3.58
Magnesium chromite	$MgO \cdot Cr_2O_3$	2000	4.39
Magnesium ferrite (magnesioferrite)	$MgO \cdot Fe_2O_3$	1760	4.48
Magnesium lanthanate	$MgO \cdot La_2O_3$	2030	—
Magnesium silicate (forsterite)	$2MgO \cdot SiO_2$	1885	3.22
Magnesium titanate	$2MgO \cdot TiO_2$	1835	3.52
Magnesium zirconate	$MgO \cdot ZrO_2$	2120	—
Magnesium zirconium silicate	$MgO \cdot ZrO_2 \cdot SiO_2$	1793	—
Nickel aluminate	$NiO \cdot Al_2O_3$	2015	4.45
Potassium aluminum silicate (kaliophilite)	$K_2O \cdot Al_2O_3 \cdot 2SiO_2$	1800	—
Strontium aluminate	$SrO \cdot Al_2O_3$	2010	—
Strontium phosphate (orthophosphate)	$3SrO \cdot P_2O_5$	1767	4.53
Strontium zirconate	$SrO \cdot ZrO_2$	>2700	5.48
Thorium zirconate	$ThO_2 \cdot ZrO_2$	>2800	—
Zinc aluminate (gahnite)	$ZnO \cdot Al_2O_3$	1950	4.58
Zinc zirconium silicate	$ZnO \cdot ZrO_2 \cdot SiO_2$	2078	—
Zirconium silicate (zircon)	$ZrO_2 \cdot SiO_2$	2420*	4.6

* Incongruent melting.

tabulated in Table 2.6 after Thurnauer,[1] and more recent values of thermal expansion coefficients at high temperatures are given in Table 2.7 after Whittemore and Ault.[24]

The materials listed in Table 2.6 are divided into two groups under the

TABLE 2.5. THERMODYNAMIC PROPERTIES OF REFRACTORY OXIDES[6]

Material	Formula	ΔH_{298}, kcal·mole⁻¹	ΔF_{298}, kcal·mole⁻¹	ΔS_{298}, cal·°C⁻¹·mole⁻¹	$C_{p\,298}$, cal·°C⁻¹·mole⁻¹	Temperature range, °K	Heat Capacity*			
							a	b	c	d
Aluminum oxide (α-corundum)	Al_2O_3	−399.09	−376.77	12.186	18.88	298–1800	27.43	3.06	8.47	11,155
Barium oxide	BaO	−133.4	−126.3	16.8	11.34	298–1000	9.79	5.21	—	—
Beryllium oxide	BeO	−146.0	−139.0	3.37	6.07	298–1200	8.45	4.00	3.17	3,760
Calcium oxide	CaO	−151.9	−144.4	9.5	10.23	298–1800	11.67	1.08	1.56	4,051
Cerium oxide	CeO_2	−233	−232	28.8†	15.1	273–373	15.1	—	—	—
Chromic oxide	Cr_2O_3	−269.7	−250.2	19.4	28.38	298–1800	28.53	2.20	3.74	9,759
Cobalt oxide	CoO	−57.2	−51.0	10.5						
Gallium oxide	Ga_2O_3	−258			20	298–923	11.77	25.2	—	—
Hafnium oxide	HfO_2	−271.5	−259	29.7†		298–1800	17.39	2.08	3.48	6,445
Lanthanum oxide	La_2O_3	−458	−435	39.9†	24.2	273–2273	22.6	5.44	—	—
Magnesium oxide	MgO	−143.84	−136.13	6.4	8.94	298–2100	10.18	1.74	1.48	3,609
Manganese oxide	MnO	−92.0	−86.8	14.4	10.27	298–1800	11.11	1.94	0.88	3,694
Nickel oxide	NiO	−58.4	−51.7	9.22	10.60	298–1400	8.80	6.00	—	—
Niobium oxide	Nb_2O_3									
Silicon oxide										
(α-cristobalite)	SiO_2	−205.0	−192.1	10.19	10.56	298–523	4.28	21.06	—	2,212
(β-cristobalite)	SiO_2	0.2‡				523–2000	14.40	2.04	—	4,696
(α-quartz)	SiO_2	−205.4	−192.4	10.00	10.62	298–848	11.22	8.20	2.70	4,615
(β-quartz)	SiO_2	0.29‡				848–2000	14.41	1.94	—	4,455
(α-tridymite)	SiO_2	−204.8	−191.9	10.36	10.66	298–390	3.27	24.80	—	2,077
(β-tridymite)	SiO_2	0.04‡				390–2000	13.64	2.64	—	4,395
(vitreous)	SiO_2	−202.5	−190.9	11.2	10.60	298–2000	13.38	3.68	3.45	5,310
Strontium oxide	SrO	−141.1	−133.8	13.0	10.76	298–2000	8.70	0.16	0.74	2,849
Tantalum oxide	Ta_2O_5	−499.9	−470.6	34.2	32.30					
Thorium oxide	ThO_2	−292	−296	19.6†	20.38	298–1800	15.84	2.88	1.60	5,388

Material	Formula									
Tin oxide	SnO₂	-138.8	-124.2	12.5	12.57	298-1500	17.66	2.40	5.16	7,103
Titanium oxide (rutile)	TiO₂	-218.0	-203.8	12.01	13.16	298-1800	17.97	0.28	4.35	6,829
Titanium oxide (anatase)	TiO₂	—	—	11.93	13.22	298-1300	17.83	0.50	4.23	6,757
Uranium oxide	UO₂	-270	-257	18.6	—	298-1500	19.20	1.62	3.96	7,125
Vanadium oxide	V₂O₃	-290	-271	23.58	24.83	298-1800	29.35	4.76	5.42	10,780
Yttrium oxide	Y₂O₃	-450	-429	—	23	273-373	23.2	—	—	—
Zinc oxide	ZnO	-83.17	-76.05	10.5	9.62	298-1600	11.71	1.22	2.18	4,277
Zirconium oxide	ZrO₂	-258.2	-244.4	12.03	—	298-1100	17.80	—	4.00	6,649
Aluminum silicate (mullite)	3Al₂O₃·SiO₂	—	—	—	—	298-600	59.65	67.0	—	20,763
Barium silicate (orthosilicate)	2BaO·SiO₂	-496.8	—	—	—	—	—	—	—	—
Beryllium aluminate (chrysoberyl)	BeO·Al₂O₃	—	—	—	25	—	—	—	—	—
Beryllium silicate (phenacite)	2BeO·SiO₂	—	—	15.4	22.84	—	—	—	—	—
Calcium chromate	CaO·CrO₃	-329.6	-305.3	32	—	—	—	—	—	—
Calcium phosphate (orthophosphate)	3CaO·P₂O₅	-986.2	-929.7	57.6	55.35	298-1373	48.24	39.68	5.00	17,824
Calcium phosphate	3CaO·P₂O₅	3.7‡	—	56.4	54.45	1373-1600	79.00	—	—	18,600
Calcium silicate	3CaO·SiO₂	-688.4	—	—	—	298-1800	49.85	8.62	10.15	18,651
Calcium silicate (orthosilicate)	2CaO·SiO₂	-538.0	—	—	—	298-948	27.16	19.60	—	8,969
	2CaO·SiO₂	0.35‡	—	22.4	23.34	948-1600	41.26	5.34	—	15,570
Calcium titanate (perovskite)	CaO·TiO₂	—	—	—	—	298-1530	30.47	1.36	6.69	11,389
	CaO·TiO₂	0.55‡	—	—	—	1530-1800	32.03	—	—	11,197
Ferrous chromite (chromite)	FeO·Cr₂O₃	-341.9	-317.7	34.9	31.9	298-1800	38.96	5.34	7.62	14,409
Magnesium chromite	MgO·Cr₂O₃	—	—	25.3	30.32	298-1800	40.02	3.56	9.58	15,304
Magnesium silicate (forsterite)	2MgO·SiO₂	-488.2	-459.8	22.7	28.21	—	—	—	—	—
Zirconium silicate (zircon)	ZrO·SiO₂	—	—	20.1	23.53	—	—	—	—	—

* $C_p = a + b \times 10^{-3}T - c \times 10^5 T^{-2}$. $H_T - H_{298} = aT + \frac{b}{2} \times 10^{-3}T^2 + c \times 10^5 T^{-1} - d$.

† Calculated from data by Rossini et al. and Brewer.

‡ Heat of transformation at transformation temperature.

TABLE 2.6 TYPICAL PHYSICAL PRO

	Vitrified products				
	1	2	3	4	5
Material→	High-voltage porcelain	Alumina porcelain	Steatite	Forsterite	Zircon porcelain
Typical applications → Properties ↓	Power line insulation	Sparkplug cores, thermocouple insulation, protection tubes	High-frequency insulation, electrical appliance insulation	High-frequency insulation, ceramic-to-metal seals	Sparkplug cores, high voltage-high temperature insulation
Specific gravity (g/cc)	2.3–2.5	3.1–3.9	2.5–2.7	2.7–2.9	3.5–3.8
Water absorption (%)	0.0	0.0	0.0	0.0	0.0
Coefficient of linear thermal expansion/°C (20–700)	5.0–6.8×10^{-6}	5.5–8.1×10^{-6}	8.6–10.5×10^{-6}	11×10^{-6}	3.5–5.5×10^{-6}
Safe operating temperature (°C)	1000	1350–1500	1000–1100	1000–1100	1000–1200
Thermal conductivity (cal/cm²/cm/sec/°C)	0.002–0.005	0.007–0.05	0.005–0.006	0.005–0.010	0.010–0.015
Tensile strength (psi)	3000–8000	8000–30,000	8000–10,000	8000–10,000	10,000–15,000
Compressive strength (psi)	25,000–50,000	80,000–250,000	65,000–130,000	60,000–100,000	80,000–150,000
Flexural strength (psi)	9000–15,000	20,000–45,000	16,000–24,000	18,000–20,000	20,000–35,000
Impact strength (ft-lb; ½-in. rod)	0.2–0.3	0.5–0.7	0.3–0.4	0.03–0.04	0.4–0.5
Modulus of elasticity (psi)	7–14×10^{6}	15–52×10^{6}	13–15×10^{6}	13–15×10^{6}	20–30×10^{6}
Thermal shock resistance	Moderately good	Excellent	Moderate	Poor	Good
Dielectric strength (v/mil; ¼-in. thick specimen)	250–400	250–400	200–350	200–300	250–350
Resistivity (ohm/cm³) at room temperature	10^{12}–10^{14}	10^{14}–10^{15}	10^{13}–10^{15}	10^{13}–10^{15}	10^{13}–10^{15}
Te-value (°C)	200–500	500–800	450–1000	above 1000	700–900
Power factor at 1 Mc	0.006–0.010	0.001–0.002	0.0008–0.0035	0.0003	0.0006–0.0020
Dielectric constant	6.0–7.0	8–9	5.5–7.5	6.2	8.0–9.0
L-Grade (JAN Spec. I-10)	L-2	L-2–L-5	L-3–L-5	L-6	L-4

headings "vitrified products" and "semivitreous and refractory products."
For electron tube application, dense vitrified bodies are required for
tube envelopes, whereas ceramic components used within the vacuum envelope may be less dense and have some degree of porosity for ease of
outgassing. Depending on the application of the ceramic part, a judicious
choice must be made between the physical characteristics that can be
attained with various bodies. The requirements are particularly severe
for high-frequency application where the dielectric loss factor (see p. 62)
is a measure of the usefulness of the ceramic body. The Armed Services
have set up specifications for low-loss, low-dielectric-constant materials

PERTIES OF CERAMIC DIELECTRICS[1]

	Semivitreous and refractory products				
6	7	8	9	10	11
Lithia porcelain	Titania, titanate ceramics	Low-voltage porcelain	Cordierite refractories	Alumina, aluminum silicate refractories	Massive fired talc, pyrophyllite
Temperature-stable inductances, heat resistant insulation	Ceramic capacitors, piezoelectric ceramics	Switch bases, Low-voltage wire holders, light receptacles	Resistor supports, burner tips, heat insulation, arc chambers	Vacuum spacers, high-temperature insulation	High-frequency insulation, vacuum tube spacers, ceramic models
2.34	3.5–5.5	2.2–2.4	1.6–2.1	2.2–2.4	2.3–2.8
0.0	0.0	0.5–2.0	5.0–15.0	10.0–20.0	1.0–3.0
1×10^{-6}	$7.0–10.0 \times 10^{-6}$	$5.0–6.5 \times 10^{-6}$	$2.5–3.0 \times 10^{-6}$	$5.0–7.0 \times 10^{-6}$	11.5×10^{-6}
1000	—	900	1250	1300–1700	1200
—	0.008–0.01	0.004–0.005	0.003–0.004	0.004–0.005	0.003–0.005
—	4000–10,000	1500–2500	1000–3500	700–3000	2500
60,000	40,000–120,000	25,000–50,000	20,000–45,000	15,000–60,000	20,000–30,000
8000	10,000–22,000	3500–6000	1500–7000	1500–6000	7000–9000
0.3	0.3–0.5	0.2–0.3	0.2–0.25	0.17–0.25	0.2–0.3
—	$10–15 \times 10^{6}$	$7–10 \times 10^{6}$	$2–5 \times 10^{6}$	$2–5 \times 10^{6}$	$4–5 \times 10^{6}$
Excellent	Poor	Moderate	Excellent	Excellent	Good
200–300	50–300	40–100	40–100	40–100	80–100
—	$10^{8}–10^{15}$	$10^{12}–10^{14}$	$10^{12}–10^{14}$	$10^{12}–10^{14}$	$10^{12}–10^{15}$
—	200–400	300–400	400–700	400–700	600–900
0.05	0.0002–0.050	0.010–0.020	0.004–0.010	0.0002–0.010	0.0008–0.010
5.6	15–10,000	6.0–7.0	4.5–5.5	4.5–6.5	5.0–6.0
L-3	—	—	—	—	—

which call for certain flexural strengths, dielectric strengths, porosity, thermal shock resistance,[25, 26] power factor, and dielectric constant. Grades L-1 to L-6 are established on the basis of the loss factor of the material, and the ceramics are further graded as "A," or "B," according to their ability to withstand thermal shock. The Joint Army Navy Specification JAN-I-10, on "Insulating Materials," Ceramic Radio, Class L, is reproduced in Table 2.8 and the L grades of the various ceramic bodies are listed in Table 2.6.

Conventional electrical porcelain is used for both low- and high-tension insulation. The quality of the final product and its degree of vitrification

TABLE 2.7. THERMAL EXPANSION OF VARIOUS CERAMIC MATERIALS TO 1500°C*

Specimen†	Coefficient of expansion $\times 10^6/°C$ from 25°C to				
	300	600	900	1200	1500°C
Al_2O_3 , 99%, coarse fused grain	6.7	7.6	8.1	9.0	10.2
Al_2O_3 , 99%, sintered high density	5.9	7.2	8.2	9.0	9.6
Al_2O_3 , 88%, clay-bonded fused grain	4.4	6.0	6.9	7.7	8.7
MgO, coarse fused grain	13.3	13.5	13.9	15.0	16.0
CaO, coarse fused grain	10.2	11.6	12.8	13.7	14.7
SiO_2 , fused	0.67	0.60	0.53		
TiO_2 , coarse fused grain	7.1	7.7	8.2	8.7	9.1 (to 1450°C)
ThO_2 , fine fused grain	7.1	8.5	9.0	10.3	10.4
ZrO_2 , 100% cubic, fused	7.6	9.2	10.0	10.8	11.6
ZrO_2 , coarse fused stabilized	6.9	8.4	8.9	9.5	9.4
ZrO_2 , coarse fused stabilized	5.9	7.4	6.9	5.6	7.4
$ZrO_2 \cdot SiO_2$, fine grain	3.7	4.2	4.7	5.6	5.8 (to 1300°C)
$Al_2O_3 \cdot TiO_2$, fine grain	0	0.2	1.7	3.4	4.4 (to 1450°C)
Lithium aluminum silicate, fine grain	−2.9	−1.1	−0.6	0	
$MgO \cdot Al_2O_3$, coarse fused grain	5.2	7.5	8.4	9.1	9.6
SiC, re-crystallized (heating element)	3.8	4.3	4.5	4.8	5.2
SiC, clay-bonded	3.6	4.7	4.9	5.1	5.6
SiC, bonded glazed brick	5.0	5.1	5.2	5.5	5.8
B_4C, hot-molded	5.2	5.3	5.8		
CaF_2 , sintered high density	22.3	24.8	26.1		
MgF_2 , fine grain	10.7	13.0	14.5		14.8 (to 1000°C)

* After Whittemore, Jr., and Ault.[24]
† High purity except where noted as bonded.

TABLE 2.8.[1] INSULATING MATERIALS, CERAMIC RADIO CLASS L (JAN-I-10)

Properties	Requirements

1. Porosity . . . . No penetration of liquid under 10,000 psi pressure
2. Flexural strength . . . . . . Not less than 3000 psi
3. Resistance to thermal
   change
   Grade . . . . A, 20 cycles; B, 5 cycles
   Requirements . . . . Boiling water to ice water
4. Dielectric strength . . . . Not less than 180 rms volts per mil
5. Loss factor . . . . (Power factor × dielectric constant)

Grade	L-1	L-2	L-3	L-4	L-5	L-6
Loss factor	<0.150	<0.070	<0.035	<0.016	<0.008	<0.004

Dielectric constant . Not over 12 after immersion in water for 48 hours

depend upon the fineness of grinding, the method of forming, and the firing temperature, which usually lies between 1300 and 1400°C. The fired product contains two main crystalline phases, namely mullite crystals and undissolved quartz crystals which are imbedded in a continuous glassy phase,

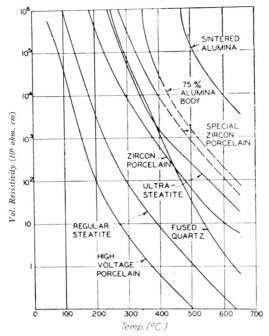

Figure 2.1. Relationship of volume resistivity to temperature for several ceramic insulating materials. After Russell and Mohr.[27] (*Courtesy American Ceramic Society.*)

originating from the feldspar, and ranging in some bodies of this kind as high as 40 per cent. By varying the proportions of the three main ingredients, clay, feldspar, and flint, it is possible to emphasize certain properties, such as heat-shock resistance, dielectric strength, or mechanical strength. In general, however, the loss factor of electrical porcelain is rather high, its heat-shock resistance only fair, and its electrical resistivity decreases rapidly with increase in temperature (Fig. 2.1).[27] The high loss factor of porcelains is due to the large glass content and the high polarizability of alkali ions. A decrease of the feldspar component generally lessens the dielectric strength of the porcelain and calls for higher firing temperature. New bodies were thus developed for high-frequency applications.

Low-loss steatite is widely used for electronic components; it is unsurpassed for economy in manufacture, especially in shapes which can be produced by either automatic dry-pressing or extrusion methods; it can be made to close tolerances and has good mechanical strength. These bodies were first introduced in Germany in the late 1920's under the trade names "Frequenta," "Steatit," "Calit," and "Calan." Steatites were introduced in the United States in 1930 and produced in very large quantity for military requirements during World War II.

A typical batch composition for steatite may consist of 60 per cent, or more, talc, 30 per cent, or less, clay to which alkali or alkaline-earth oxides are added as flux. To obtain plasticity and strength before firing, temporary organic binders, such as waxes, gums, dextrene, or polyvinyl alcohol, are added. After forming, the material is fired to a temperature between 1300 and 1400°C, depending on composition. Fired steatite bodies consist essentially of closely knit crystals of magnesium metasilicate ($MgSiO_3$) in the form of clinoenstatite or one of its polymorphous phases. The bond between the crystals consists of a glass high in alkali oxides.

Steatites are characterized by a very short firing range in which vitrification takes place. Staying below this range during firing will produce porosity because of "underfiring," and exceeding the prescribed firing range will lead to distortion or vesicular development because of "overfiring." The firing range for steatite may vary from 10 to 20°C for ultra-low-loss types to possibly 30 to 40°C for ordinary types. By comparison, many porcelains have firing ranges of from 50 to 90°C. Very accurate temperature control is thus necessary during the firing of steatite.[28]

Forsterite ceramics (Mg_2SiO_4) are produced from compositions containing talc to which magnesium oxide has been added to satisfy the stoichiometric composition. Suitable fluxes are again alkaline-earth oxides; on firing at about 1350°C, a ceramic body results which consists chiefly of forsterite crystals. The high melting point of pure forsterite (1910°C) is an advantage in making basic refractory products; these should not be confused with vitrified forsterite ceramics for high-frequency applications. The thermal expansion of forsterite ceramics is practically linear between room temperature and 1000°C, and the expansion coefficient rather high for a ceramic material (110×10^{-7}/C). Forsterite ceramics are thus quite sensitive to heat shock.

Zircon porcelains ($ZrO_2 \cdot SiO_2$) have been extensively used for spark plugs by virtue of their good mechanical strength and heat-shock resistance, properties which, incidentally, make this material well suited for furnace trays in high-temperature application. Zircon begins to dissociate, however, at temperatures above 1730°C. Its heat-shock resistance suffers at this temperature because of a rather large volume expansion which is largely due to the fact that one of the products of the dissociation, silica, has a much lower specific gravity than the original zircon. At very high temperatures, silica may be lost by vaporization, and the heat-shock resistance is then permanently impaired because of the erratic thermal expansion behavior of the excess zirconia. Despite this dissociation, new high-purity forms of zircon have been used continuously at temperatures above 1870°C.[6, 27, 29]

The composition of zircon porcelain is compared with that of high-tension porcelain and alumina porcelain in Table 2.9, and its physical charac-

TABLE 2.9. COMPOSITION OF VARIOUS PORCELAIN BODIES
(After Lindsay and Berberich)[30]

Constituent	Composition (%)		
	High tension porcelain	Zircon porcelain	Alumina porcelain
SiO_2	68.72	36.96	6.69
Al_2O_3	23.90	6.08	90.98
TiO_2	—	0.24	0.06
ZrO_2	—	49.72	—
Fe_2O_3	1.80	0.25	0.20
$Na_2O + K_2O$	5.46	0.13	0.21
CaO	0.25	6.48	1.08
MgO	0.12	0.14	0.66
Total	100.25	100.00	99.88
Total flux	5.83	6.75	1.95
Main crystalline constituent	Mullite ($3Al_2O_3 \cdot 2SiO_2$) Quartz (SiO_2)	Zircon ($ZrO_2 \cdot SiO_2$)	Alumina (α-Al_2O_3)

teristics can be gleaned from Table 2.6. It is apparent that zircon has a relatively high dielectric constant, which is offset, however, by its lower power factor at high frequencies.[27] Zircon bodies are generally rated as Grade L-4 dielectrics. Figures 2.1 to 2.5 present their pertinent charac-

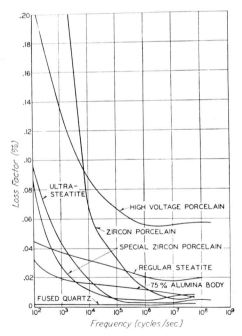

Figure 2.2. Relationship of loss factor to frequency for several ceramic insulating materials. After Russell and Mohr.[27] (*Courtesy American Ceramic Society.*)

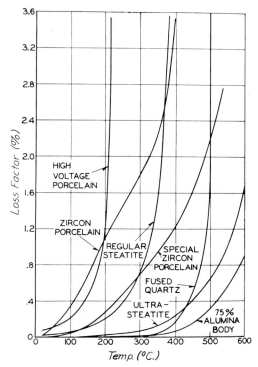

Figure 2.3. Relationship of loss factor to temperature for several ceramic insulating materials at 1 mc. After Russell and Mohr.[27] (*Courtesy American Ceramic Society.*)

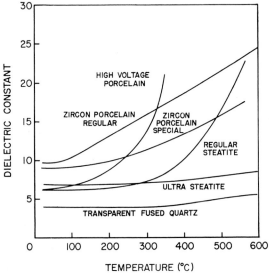

Figure 2.4. Dielectric constant of various ceramic bodies as a function of temperature. After Russell and Berberich.[28] (*Courtesy McGraw-Hill Publishing Company, Inc.*)

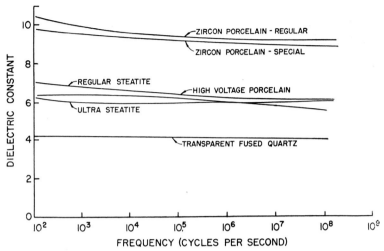

Figure 2.5. Dielectric constant of various ceramic bodies as a function of frequency. After Russell and Berberich.[28] (*Courtesy McGraw-Hill Publishing Company, Inc.*)

teristics after Russell, Mohr,[27] and Berberich.[28] Zircon bodies have found a limited application as envelope materials for electron tubes.

Alumina (Al_2O_3) is the most favored ceramic body for electron tube envelopes. While this material has a substantially higher thermal expansion coefficient than zircon and a lower thermal conductivity,[31] its mechanical strength and dielectric properties at elevated temperatures are far superior, so that high-grade alumina bodies fall into the classification grade L-5 and L-6. Figure 2.6 shows its electrical resistivity as a function of temperature for a number of ceramic bodies; it can be seen that, at room temperature, vitreous silica, beryllia and magnesia have a higher resistivity than alumina and, at 600°C, only thoria magnesia, and beryllia exceed it.

A wide variety of high-alumina bodies is available from commercial sources, and the number of suppliers who consistently furnish alumina bodies suitable for vacuum tube envelopes has steadily increased in recent years. The alumina content for such bodies may range from 85 per cent to close to 100 per cent; the increased purity makes for increased hot strength, higher electrical resistivity, and better dielectric properties (Table 2.10). Calcined and fused alumina are used as base materials for the fabrication of dense vitrified bodies, and extraordinary care must be exercised by the manufacturer to insure a high quality of the end product.

Pure alumina exists in several forms at low temperatures; of these the monohydrate diaspore ($Al_2O_3 \cdot H_2O$) and the trihydrate gibbsite ($Al_2O_3 \cdot 3H_2O$) are present in commercial bauxite. This raw material is rendered free of

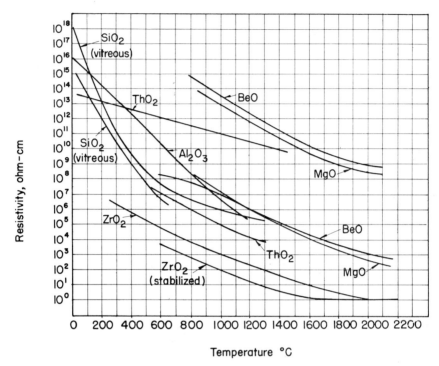

Figure 2.6. Electrical resistivity of refractory oxides. After Campbell.[6] (*Courtesy John Wiley & Sons, Inc., 1956.*)

impurities by the Bayer process and converted to the high-temperature-stable alpha-alumina by calcination at a temperature of at least 1100°C.[33] It is commercially available in the form of synthetic sapphire (see p. 100). Beta-alumina can be formed when the molten alumina is slowly cooled in the presence of certain impurities. Gamma-alumina can be prepared by heating $Al(OH)_3$ and is metastable, transforming to α-Al_2O_3 at about 1000°C.[31] *

Carruthers and Gill[34] have attempted to explain why alumina bodies, made of raw materials from identical sources and what appears to be under the same processing, often show so widely different physical characteristics.

"It may be seen from the results described that it is only when calcined to very high temperatures, probably considerably above those used industrially, that calcined aluminas from different sources are almost indistinguishable from one another. Even when calcined at 1720°C, alumina derived

---

* α-Al_2O_3 containing traces of chromium is red and called ruby, while that containing iron and titanium is blue and called blue sapphire.

TABLE 2.10. SOME PROPERTIES OF HIGH ALUMINA CERAMIC MATERIALS*

Material		Mechanical		Electrical		Thermal	
	% Al$_2$O$_3$	Compressive strength (lb/sq. in., 25°C)	Tensile strength (lb/sq. in., 25°C)	Dielectric constant (1 mc., 25°C)	Dissipation factor (1 mc., 25°C)	Coefficient of linear expansion (25°-700°C)	Softening temperature (°C)
Sapphire (single crystal)	100	30 × 10^4	6.5 × 10^4	10.3	0.00004	8.5 × 10^{-6}	2040
Alumina A	99+	42 × 10^4	3.4 × 10^4	10.0	0.0001	8.0 × 10^{-6}	>1600
Alumina B	97	28 × 10^4	2.7 × 10^4	9.5	0.0001	9.0 × 10^{-6}	>1600
Alumina C	96	30 × 10^4	2.6 × 10^4	9.0	0.0003	9.0 × 10^{-6}	>1600
Alumina D	94	19 × 10^4	1.5 × 10^4	9.2	0.0004	7.3 × 10^{-6}	>1600
Alumina E	85	20 × 10^4	1.8 × 10^4	8.2	0.0009	7.9 × 10^{-6}	1400

* After Rigterink.[32]

from the monohydrate differs from that made from the trihydrate in having a lower packing density. Examination under the microscope shows the grains to be aggregates of small crystallites and indicates that the grains of calcined monohydrate have larger void spaces within them than those of the calcined trihydrate. The lower the temperature of calcination the greater is the divergence of properties between the mono- and trihydrates. The calcined trihydrates have a proportionately higher surface area and a smaller amount of void space than the calcined monohydrates, and the crystallites of both materials are smaller and less well developed at lower temperatures."

Sintering and grain growth of alumina have been investigated by several workers.[35-38] Cahoon and Christensen[37] summarize their results as follows:

"The sintering (densification) and grain growth of alumina were studied to determine the effect of the variables raw material, particle size, grinding in acid media, molding pressure, various single additives in different amounts, and firing temperature. Fine grinding promoted sintering and the growth of large grains and caused the grains to be more elongated in habit. Sintering was facilitated by additions of iron oxide, manganese oxide, copper oxide, and titanium oxide, provided the amounts of these oxides and the temperature of firing were within certain bounds. The growth of large grains was facilitated by additions of iron oxide and manganese oxide. Nineteen other oxides had no effect or retarded sintering and large-grain growth. Both magnesium oxide and silica had a marked effect in inhibiting the growth of large grains. The alkali metal oxides, added singly, were especially deleterious to the production of strong alumina bodies. The maximum density and maximum strength of the fired body were attained approximately simultaneously with the onset of large-grain growth. The habit of the large grains was markedly altered by increasing amounts of each additive; the grains lost their characteristic crystalline shape and became nearly spheroidal particles. It is suggested that two grain-growth phenomena exist which are independent of each other. One is termed 'small-grain growth' and is associated with densification; the other is referred to as 'large-grain growth' and occurs in certain specimens, depending on the additions to the alumina, after the sintering (densification) is substantially complete."[37]

The effect of porosity on the physical properties of sintered alumina has been investigated by Coble and Kingery,[39] who also give numerous references to earlier work on the properties of sintered bodies in general.

Sapphire is a particularly pure form of aluminum oxide which is grown in the form of single crystals according to a method developed by A. Verneuil in the 1890's.* The purity of sapphire ranges from 99.98 to 99.99 per cent, and it is interesting to note that this form of alpha-alumina has been designated as a heat capacity standard over the range of temperatures from 10 to 1800°K.[31] Sapphire rod can be obtained either in the as-grown form with a tolerance of -5 mils on the diameter, or as centerless-ground rod with a diameter tolerance of ± 0.5 mil in lengths ranging up to 16 in. in the larger sizes, as disks in various thicknesses up to $5\frac{1}{2}$ in. dia., as domes and hemispheres, and as spheres as small as $\frac{1}{64}$ in. dia. up to 1 in. dia. with a size tolerance of ± 0.1 mil and a sphericity of .025 mil in the $\frac{3}{16}-\frac{5}{16}$ dia. range. The applications of sapphire in various shapes have been manifold in the tube industry, although its relatively high cost limits its application to special-purpose tubes.† Sapphire rods are being used quite extensively for supporting gun and helix structures in travelling-wave tubes where the great dimensional accuracy and fairly good dielectric properties of sapphire are appreciated. Such rods can be attached to the helix by various glazes, or by ceramic metallizing techniques. Flame-polished sapphire rods can be obtained in diameters up to 0.150 in. This treatment should reduce surface voltage breakdown difficulties which have been troublesome at times; the mechanical strength of flame-polished rods is increased by 30 per cent. Sapphire disks are being used for windows in klystrons and magnetrons. The great high-temperature stability of sapphire in contact with molybdenum and tungsten contributes to its usefulness in such applications.

Navias[41] reports that a sapphire rod can be heated in vacuum by a sur-

* Linde Company, a Division of Union Carbide Corporation, is the only producer of synthetic sapphire in the U. S. A.; various bulletins on the properties of sapphire and its applications can be obtained from this company.[40]

† Windows $\frac{1}{8}$ in. thick, 3-in. dia. cost $288, each, 1-in. dia. $17.50; centerless-ground rods, $\frac{1}{8}$ in. dia., cost $0.75 per inch length; sapphire balls $\frac{1}{8}$-in. dia. cost $1.20; all items quoted for minimum lots (1959).

rounding tungsten heater tube which is not in contact with the rod to a temperature of 1900°C for several hours without signs of reaction or disintegration. Kohl[42] has described a method for supporting long, narrow cathodes in the form of U-channels formed from cathode nickel on a 7-inch-long sapphire rod and maintained a grid-to-cathode spacing of 3 mils in this manner.* The same author has utilized a squirrel-cage structure of 12 sapphire rods to support the tungsten heater in a combination vacuum or hydrogen furnace which had a heat zone 10 in. long and 3 in. diameter. A conventional ceramic muffle always contains some impurities which will migrate into the heater if the latter is wound onto a muffle; the heater will have a much longer life if this contact area is reduced by a large factor. Such a structure also has a very much lower heat capacity so that it was possible to bring this furnace up to a temperature of 1800°C in 45 minutes.[43]

Sapphire is completely elastic at moderately low temperatures up to 900°C where creep sets in according to Wachtman.[44] Creep of more than 2 per cent is easily obtained in favorably oriented sapphire crystals at 1000°C.

Sapphire can be sealed to glass and matches Corning glass No. 7530. The coefficient of expansion of this glass is $71 \times 10^{-7}/°C$, its strain point is 525°C, and its annealing point is 557°C.[45-47]

Sapphire sections, 2 mm thick, transmit radiation over the wave length range from .17 to 6.0 microns with 40 per cent of the incident radiation being transmitted within these wave length limits. The infra-red transmission of sapphire is superior to that of fused silica windows in infra-red cells and optical elements in radiation detectors are thus made from sapphire.[48] The physical characteristics of sapphire are compiled in Table 2.11.

Wollastonite ($CaSiO_3$). "One of the most recently developed ceramics in the group of low-loss dielectrics is a material which is based on the mineral Wollastonite. The dielectric losses are sufficiently low to rate this material as L-6. Vitrification occurs at 1200 to 1250°C, considerably lower than for steatite, zircon, and similar bodies. The mechanical strength is good, and this material may find some uses in high-frequency applications."[1]

Beryllia (*BeO*), *Magnesia* (*MgO*), *Thoria* (*ThO₂*), *Titania* (*TiO₂*), and *Zirconia* (*ZrO₂*) are other pure-oxide ceramics with properties that make them interesting for special applications; they are not generally used for vacuum tube components, partly on account of their high cost, partly on account of the presence of crystalline inversions, or other disadvantages such as the health hazards involved in handling Beryllium compounds. The reader is referred to the literature describing these materials.[50-58]

* The U-channel was brazed onto square-cross-section tubing of A-nickel in such relationship that a rectangular-cross-section interspace permitted the insertion of the heater. The square cross-section tubing fitted closely around the sapphire rod. See U. S. Pat. 2,857,543 (Oct. 21, 1958).

TABLE 2.11. PHYSICAL PROPERTIES OF SAPPHIRE[40, 44, 49]

Specific gravity	3.98
Hardness, Mohs'	9
Knoop	1525–2000
Melting point	2040°C
Crystal structure	hexagonal
Water absorption (%)	0
Compressive strength	300,000 psi (at 25°C)
Elastic modulus in flexure for c-axis of	
30°	55×10^6 psi
45°	51×10^6
60°	50×10^6
75°	56×10^6
Maximum bending strength (Modulus of rupture) for c-axis orientation of	
30°	100,000 psi; 7000 Kg/cm²
45°	78,000 5500
60°	65,000 4600
75°	94,000 6600
Elastic modulus in torsion (Rigidity modulus)	21.5 to 27.5×10^6 psi
Specific heat at 25°C	0.18 cal gm⁻¹ deg⁻¹

Specific heat at 25°C	0.18 cal gm^{-1} deg^{-1}
Thermal conductivity*	
120°C	0.008 cal $sec^{-1}cm^{-1}°C^{-1}$
300°C	0.010 cal $sec^{-1}cm^{-1}°C^{-1}$
500°C	0.015 cal $sec^{-1}cm^{-1}°C^{-1}$

		Perpendicular to c-axis	Parallel to c-axis
Te Point		1,214°C	1,231°C
Dielectric constant ϵ'/ϵ_0	300 Mc	8.6	10.6
at 25°C	10 KMc	11.0	—
from 100 cy to 10 Mc		8.6 ± 0.2	10.55 ± 0.2
loss tangent	300 Mc	<0.0001	
	10 KMc	0.0002	—
Dielectric strength		480 KV/cm	
Electrical resistivity		$\log R = 0.3 + 7800/T°_K$ (ohm·cm)	
		at 500°C—10^{11} ohm·cm	
		1000°C—10^6 ohm·cm	
		1500°C—10^4 ohm·cm	

	Ultra-Violet (Sample 2mm. thick)	Infra-Red (Sample 1mm thick)
Optical transmission	66% at 2000 Angstrom	92% at 3 microns
	20% at 1500 Angstrom	50% at 6 microns
Chemical resistance	not attacked by common acids; resistant to attack by HF at 300°C, 10 p.c. and 50 p.c. H_2SO_4, 30 p.c. NaOH at 80°C.	

TABLE 2.11.—*Continued*

Mean Linear Thermal Expansion Coefficient from 20°C to Temperature Indicated[*]

Temperature °C	Parallel to c-Axis	Perpendicular to c-Axis
50	6.66×10^{-6}	5.0×10^{-6}
100	6.87	5.5
150	6.92	6.0
200	7.22	6.21
250	7.60	6.52
300	7.78	6.86
350	7.84	7.01
400	7.94	7.31
450	8.14	7.51
500	8.33	7.70
550	8.37	7.74
600	8.44	7.84
650	8.65	7.93
700	8.72	8.01
750	8.77	8.05
800	8.78	8.10
850	8.79	8.17
900	8.86	8.23
950	8.94	8.28
1,000	9.03	8.31

[*] After Austin.[49]

One interesting application of a mixture of titanium dioxide, zirconium oxide, and small percentages of magnesium and barium titanates and zirconates has been described by Rudy[59] who proposes to replace the commonly used mica sheet, on which the photo sensitive mosaic is deposited in a television camera tube of the iconoscope-type, by a sheet of ceramic of a thickness between 10 to 12 mils. The dielectric constant of this ceramic sheet is adjusted to a value near 28 by choosing the proper amount of titanium oxide. Since the ceramic target sheet has roughly five to six times the dielectric constant of mica, the ceramic need not be limited to the one to two mils required for the mica in order to provide the proper signal pulse when the scanning electron beam discharges the target surface. It is claimed that the use of a ceramic sheet in place of mica increases the photosenistivity of the target and provides a higher signal strength.

Boron nitride (BN), sometimes called white graphite because of its similar hexagonal structure and talc-like nature which gives it lubricating properties, has high insulation resistance and good dielectric properties at elevated temperatures of the order of 500°C and is much less brittle than other ceramic bodies; it can be easily machined to close tolerances. While its cost is relatively high, it offers interesting properties for vacuum tube construction and electric components.[60]

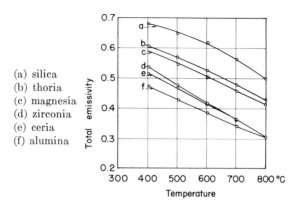

(a) silica
(b) thoria
(c) magnesia
(d) zirconia
(e) ceria
(f) alumina

Figure 2.7. Total emissivity of some pure oxides at various temperatures corrected for thickness. After Sully, Brandes, and Waterhouse.[61] (*Courtesy Institute of Physics, London.*)

Temperature Measurement. It is at times important to know the radiation emittance, generally called thermal emissivity, for a ceramic body; a distinction must be made between spectral emissivity e_λ and total emissivity e_t. Data given in the literature differ widely for these quantities because they are difficult to measure and depend on surface texture and grain size. The substantial corrections to be applied to temperature readings obtained with an optical pyrometer under other than black-body conditions make it necessary to know the spectral emissivity of the sighted body with reasonable accuracy.* The book by Campbell[6] contains valuable discussions on high-temperature measurements.† Specific data on emissivities of ceramics are given by Sully, Brandes, and Waterhouse,[61] by Pattison,[62] and by Michaud.[63] Figure 2.7 shows total emissivity values obtained by Sully *et al* for various pure oxide ceramics and Fig. 2.8 corresponding values for alumina according to Pattison and Heilmann.[64] In Figure 2.9, spectral and total emissivities for various alumina bodies are compared, after Michaud;[63] the chemical compositions and densities of these bodies are given in Table 2.12.

Metal-ceramic Interactions. "The stability of refractories in contact with different materials cannot be predicted with accuracy because the amount of reaction, or attack, which occurs depends upon physical factors as well as thermodynamic properties. It often is possible, therefore, to use materials in contact with each other at high temperatures which thermodynamically are not stable.

* The true temperature is always higher than the brightness temperature obtained from a pyrometer reading in this case. See Figure A2 for required corrections.
† See also Chapter 8 (p. 252) for data on high-temperature thermocouples.

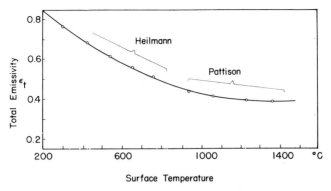

Surface Temperature

Figure 2.8. Total emissivity of alumina at elevated temperatures. After Pattison,[62] and Heilmann.[64] (*Courtesy British Ceramic Society.*)

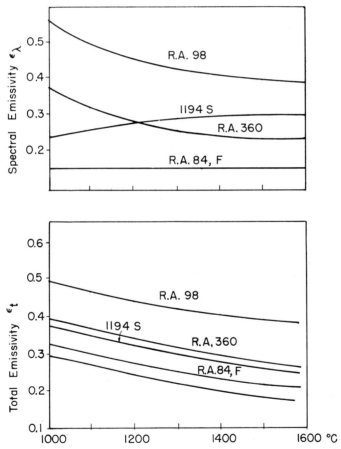

Figure 2.9. Spectral and total emissivities of alumina refractories. After Michaud.[63] (*Courtesy Silicates Industrieles, Brussels.*)

105

TABLE 2.12. CHEMICAL COMPOSITIONS OF REFRACTORIES
INVESTIGATED BY M. MICHAUD[63]

	SiO_2	Al_2O_3	Fe_2O_3	TiO_2	CaO	MgO	Alkalies	Ignition loss
R. A. 98	8.63	89.74	0.64	0.24				
R. A. 360	12.00	85.38	0.95	0.35				
R. A. 84	18.90	78.45	1.10	0.36	0.56	0.14	0.74	0.12
1194 S	2.7	96.7						
Body "F"		99.5						

TABLE 2.13. TEMPERATURES AT WHICH STABILITY NO LONGER EXISTS IN SURFACE-
TO-SURFACE CONTACT OF SOME REFRACTORY MATERIALS IN VACUUM.*

	C	W	Mo	ThO_2	ZrO_2	MgO	BeO
BeO	2300	2000	1900	2100	1900	1800	—
MgO	1800	2000	1600	2200	2000	—	1800
ZrO_2	1600	1600	2200	2200	—	2000	1900
ThO_2	2000	2200	1900	—	2200	2200	2100

* After Johnson.[67]

"For general stability with metals at very high temperatures some of the most refractory of the oxides may be listed in the following order of increasing reactivity: ThO_2, BeO, ZrO_2, Al_2O_3, and MgO. This order does not hold for all metals, by any means, and is completely changed for contact with some nonmetallic materials. Thoria, beryllia, and zirconia, however, not only have high chemical inertness but also have relatively low vapor pressures at high temperatures, and they may be used in many applications, particularly under vacuum, where other refractories fail.*

"Johnson[67] gives the tabulated data on the temperatures at which stability no longer exists in surface-to-surface contact of some refractory materials in vacuum (0.1–0.5 micron) (Table 2.13).

"Mallett,† found fused silica (vitreous SiO_2) to be superior to Al_2O_3 and comparable to BeO in contact with carbon in a high vacuum (10^{-6} mm Hg) at about 1500°C. He rates the refractory oxides in the following order of stability at 1700°C under these conditions: BeO, ThO_2, MgO, ZrO_2, and Al_2O_3. Fused silica cannot be used at 1700°C because it softens.

"Economos and Kingery[68] give the relative degrees of reaction between materials at 1800°C in an inert atmosphere as shown in Table 2.14.

"Although none of these refractories was satisfactory for containing

---

* Navias[65] concludes from experiments with different insulating materials for high-temperature hydrogen furnaces that zirconia insulation in contact with alumina may only be used for lower temperatures than 1800°C, or for short lengths of time at higher temperatures. Von Wartenberg and Reusch[66] found a broad eutectic band at about 1900°C in the system ZrO_2-Al_2O_3.

† M. W. Mallett, personal communication to P. D. Johnson.

TABLE 2.14. RELATIVE DEGREES OF REACTION BETWEEN MATERIALS
AT 1800°C IN AN INERT ATMOSPHERE*

	Mo	Ni	Nb	Ti	Zr	Be	Si
Al_2O_3	A	A	A	BC'	BC'	BD	BD
BeO	A	A	BCD	BC'	B	AB	BC
MgO	A	A	AB	BC'D	C'	BD	D
ThO_2	A	A	ABC	AB	AB	AB	BC
TiO_2	A	A	AC	C'	C'	C	—
ZrO_2	A	A	AB	BC'	AB	AB	D

A. Showed no physical alteration of the metal-ceramic interface.

B. Showed penetration along the grain boundaries and alteration of the oxide phase.

C. Showed some corrosion of the oxide.

C'. Showed considerable corrosion of the oxide.

D. Formed a new phase at the interface.

* After Economos and Kingery.[68]

molten titanium, Brace[69] rated ThO_2, BeO, and Al_2O_3 in decreasing order of stability in contact with molten titanium under vacuum but found all of them to be far more reactive with titanium than was expected from calculated oxygen dissociation pressures. (Fig. 2.10)

"At very high temperatures, the vapor pressures of some of the refractory oxides become appreciable and may limit their usefulness. Magnesia, for example, with a melting point of 2500°C cannot be used in vacuum at temperatures above 1600–1700°C because of volatilization.[67] Zinc oxide, with a melting point of 1975°C, volatilizes readily at temperatures above 1700°C and decomposes at atmospheric pressure at 1950°C;[70] tin oxide, with a melting point over 1900°C, sublimes at about 1510°C. Very few data on the vapor pressures of refractory oxides have been published, however.

"Mott[71] estimated the relative volatilities* of some refractories at high temperatures as shown in Table 2.15.

"Johnson[67] studied the behavior of refractory oxides in vacuum (0.35 micron) and obtained comparative data on volatilization as indicated by weight losses of the samples during firing (Table 2.16).

"Equations relating vapor pressure and temperature for some refractory oxides are given herewith."[6] (Table 2.17)

Kieffer and Benesovsky[77] have more recently reported on the stability of the furnace heating elements molybdenum, tungsten, and tantalum in the presence of graphite and various refractory oxides which are being used for the construction of furnaces. Table 2.18 gives their tabulation. These data assume physical contact of the respective materials. It has been demon-

* Determined by volatilizing these substances in an electric arc and observing the distances from the arc at which their vapors condensed.

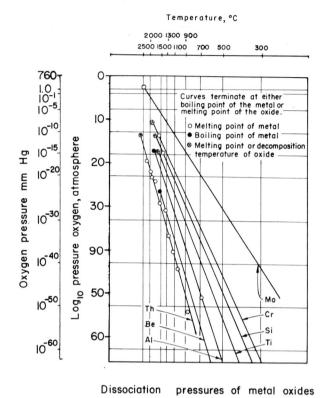

Dissociation   pressures of metal oxides

Figure 2.10. Dissociation pressures of metal oxides. After Campbell.[6] (*Courtesy John Wiley & Sons, Inc., 1956.*)

TABLE 2.15. RELATIVE VOLATILITIES OF SOME
REFRACTORIES AT HIGH TEMPERATURES.*

Material	Temperatures of vaporization, °C
BeO	2400
MgO	1900
CeO_2	1875
SiO_2	1800
Al_2O_3	1750
CaO	1700
SrO	1600

* After Mott.[71]

strated by the present author by tests performed at the Sylvania Mountain View Components Laboratory in 1958 that alumina will be reduced by tantalum when heated in vacuo at temperatures on the order of 1000°C while both materials are in contact with each other. A film of aluminum

TABLE 2.16. COMPARATIVE DATA ON THE VOLATIZATION OF
REFRACTORY OXIDES IN VACUUM.*

Material	Temperature of appreciable volatility, °C
ThO$_2$	2300
ZrO$_2$	2300
BeO	2100
MgO	1600

* After Johnson.[67]

TABLE 2.17. RELATIONS BETWEEN VAPOR PRESSURE AND TEMPERATURE
FOR SOME REFRACTORY OXIDES.*

Material	Ref.	log$_{10}$P$_{mm}$	Temperature range, °K
ThO$_2$	72	$-3.71 \times 10^4/T + 11.53$	(2050–2250)
BeO	73	$-3.22 \times 10^4/T + 10.93$	(2223–2423)
CaO	74	$-2.74 \times 10^4/T + 9.97$	(1600–1750)
SrO	74	$-3.07 \times 10^4/T + 13.12$	(1500–1650)
BaO	74	$-1.97 \times 10^4/T + 8.87$	(1200–1500)
Al$_2$O$_3$	75	$-2.732 \times 10^4/T + 8.415$	(2600–2900)
MgO	76	$-2.732 \times 10^4/T + 13.13$	(1800–2200)

* From "High Temperature Technology," I. E. Campbell,[6] Editor in Chief.
(*Courtesy John Wiley & Sons, Inc., N. Y.*)

TABLE 2.18. STABILITY OF HIGH-TEMPERATURE HEATING ELEMENT
MATERIALS TOWARDS OXIDES AND FURNACE PARTS*[77]

Material	Molybdenum	Tungsten	Tantalum
Graphite	Strong carbide formation beyond 1,200°C	Strong carbide formation beyond 1,400°C	Strong carbide formation beyond 1,000°C
Al$_2$O$_3$	Up to 1,900°C	Up to 1,900°C	Up to 1,900°C
BeO	Up to 1,900°C†	Up to 2,000°C†	Up to 1,600°C
MgO	Up to 1,800°C†	Up to 2,000°C† (Strong magnesia evaporation)	Up to 1,800°C
ZrO$_2$	Up to 1,900°C† (Strong molybdenum evaporation)	Up to 1,600°C†	Up to 1,600°C
ThO$_2$	Up to 1,900°C†	Up to 2,200°C†	Up to 1,900°C
Sillimanite	Up to about 1,700°C	Up to about 1,700°C	Up to about 1,600°C
Firebrick	Up to about 1,200°C	Up to about 1,200°C	Up to about 1,200°C
Magnesite brick	Up to about 1,600°C	Up to about 1,600°C	Up to about 1,500°C

* Courtesy Kennedy Press, Ltd.

† In vacuum of 10⁻⁴ Torr; under protective gas about 100–200°C lower temperatures.

is produced on the wall of a glass envelope in about one hour. Navias[41] has more recently shown that such a reaction takes place in the gaseous phase and sets in at 1600°C without tantalum and sapphire being in contact with each other. Tungsten does not show this reaction, as mentioned above.

Fabrication of Raw Materials and Processing Techniques*

The fabrication of the raw materials into finished ware comprises a number of steps which are critical in their influence on the quality of the end product. The raw materials are first reduced to a powder of suitable particle size distribution and freed of undesirable impurities. The critical amounts of constituent powders are then intimately mixed, either in the dry or wet state, and sufficient amounts of water, alcohol, organic or inorganic binder added to produce the desired plasticity.[79] A prolonged kneading process generally achieves this objective. In mechanized operations, this process is performed by a muller, which often removes occluded air at the same time to obtain a denser body.[80] In order to produce a desired object of a given shape, one has recourse to one of three principal techniques which are known as wet forming, slip casting, and dry pressing. These procedures will now be briefly described.

Wet forming implies shaping the clay by hand, or with simple tools, on the potter's wheel, pressing it into a plaster of Paris mold in its wet condition, at which time the cake usually contains about 25 per cent of water. This may be done by rotating the mold on a potter's wheel and pressing the clay against its surface by means of a contour-shaping tool (jiggering). The porous wall of the mold will then absorb some of the moisture of the body and cause it to set dry and to shrink away from the mold. After removal from the mold, the body is in the "green" state, and preliminary oven-drying will make it "leather hard" and permit trimming to dimension and removal of mold marks. Firing or "maturing" at the requisite temperature for the proper duration (bisque-fire), and controlled cooling, will transform the body into a hard permanent form, after which it may then be glazed and subjected to a second firing (glost-fire), if desired.

The *extrusion* of tubes, or cylinders, or rods, from dies is another wet-forming process. This may be done in auger machines or hydraulic presses.[81-85] During the firing or sintering of the body, substantial shrinkage in volume occurs, depending on the composition and to some extent on the shape of the body. Allowance must naturally be made for shrinkage when shaping the body before firing. Common tolerances are established for different body types. Finish grinding is necessary when closer tolerances are required.

Slip-casting, or casting, of ceramics requires a creamlike fluidity of the raw material. To obtain a uniform distribution of the components in the suspension medium and maintain its colloidal nature, deflocculants, such

---

* A special summer program at MIT was devoted to this subject in July 1956, and the presentations of some 20 experts were later published in book form after the following paragraphs had been written. Professor Kingery's "Ceramic Fabrication Processes"[78] is an indispensable text for anyone interested in this subject.

as silicates of soda and soda ash, are added. The proper preparation of slip is still an art which depends to a large extent on established formulas and on the know-how of the operator. The water content of the slip varies from 23 to 40 per cent depending on composition. The slip is poured into a mold of plaster of Paris, which takes up moisture from the slip and causes a solid shell to form. The slip in the center is then poured out (drain casting), and, after further drying, the mold is removed from the body, whereupon the subsequent treatment is essentially the same as for wet-forming. The thickness of the body is controlled by the time allowed for the slip to stand in the mold.[86, 87]

Dry-pressing refers to the pressing of a relatively dry granular mass, containing from 0.5 to 5 per cent water, in steel dies under considerable pressure. The processes of drying and firing are again similar to those used with wet forming.

Wet-pressing utilizes a paste-like consistency of the mixed raw materials to which more water (15 per cent) and some organic binder such as starch or flour paste has been added.

In dry- or wet-pressing by conventional presses, the pressure is applied to the work primarily in a vertical direction, only from top and bottom, so that greater densification takes place in the axial and lesser in the radial direction; shrinkage on firing is therefore more pronounced in the radial direction, leading to hour-glass shapes of an originally cylindrical body. A similar condition prevails with extrusion.

Isostatic pressing of dry powders refers to the compacting of powders in rubber molds. These molds are immersed in a liquid to which hydrostatic pressure is applied, so that a uniform compressive force acts on the mold from all sides and uniform densification of the body results in the green stage.[88, 89] Shrinkage on firing is correspondingly uniform and closer tolerances of the finished product can be achieved without the need for finish-grinding.[90]

Injection molding consists of combining the ceramic powder with a temporary plastic binder, molding the heated and soft mass, and burning out the binder before sintering.[91]

Firing. The ceramist refers to the temperature ranges in which the various ceramic bodies mature in terms of cone numbers. A cone is a trihedral pyramid made of a mixture of materials such as are used in the classical whiteware bodies described in Table 2.1; the cones thus behave similarly in a thermochemical sense and provide useful pyrometric guides for the proper firing of ceramics in terms of time and temperature. ASTM Specification C-24-46 covers the details of preparation, the technique for mounting the cones, and the definition of the pyrometric cone equivalent (P.C.E.), based on the work of Fairchild and Peters[92] and tentative revisions of the

1946 Standard in 1955. In the case of refractories, the pyrometric cone equivalent is the number of that standard pyrometric cone whose tip would touch the supporting plaque* simultaneously with the cone of the material being investigated when tested in accordance with the standard method of test for pyrometric cone equivalent of refractory materials of the American Society For Testing Materials. The characteristics of pyrometric cones are given in Table 2.19, but it is to be noted that the equivalent temperatures given are only approximate values which apply for the heating rate of 150°C per hour for cones 022-37, 100°C per hour for cone 38 and 600°C per hour for cones 39–42. The temperatures do not apply to the slower rates of heating common in commercial firing, and the use of refractory materials.†

The great importance of carefully controlling the firing temperature for various ceramic bodies has been emphasized on preceding pages. The correct choice of the maturing temperature and the time for which the body is held at this temperature determine to a large extent the microstructure of the resulting body, the absence of voids, and the density of the part. Janssen and Rigterink[94] have demonstrated that holding the fired density to very close tolerances ensures optimum performance of ceramics in microwave communication equipment and components. Centerless-ground steatite rods for the support of helices in travelling-wave tubes, to give an example, were required not to deviate by more than ±0.02 from the nominal value of their fired density in order to get uniform adherence of the glaze by which the helix turns are attached to the rods.

Fired ceramic bodies can be markedly affected in their physical properties by a post-firing treatment followed by exposure to an air blast at room temperature. Such a treatment is similar in principle to the tempering of glass which results in a great increase of its strength by virtue of the compression strain thus imparted to its surface. Hummel and Lowery[95] have demonstrated that the transverse strength of compacts of lead bisilicate and alumina can be almost doubled by the use of a quench technique similar to that employed by the glass industry. Rawson[96] has shown that the tangent of the loss angle, measured at a frequency of 30,000 Mc, can be materially reduced when a number of ceramic bodies, such as low-loss steatite, forsterite, and wollastonite, were subjected to an arbitrary heat treatment at 1000°C for 60 hours followed by rapid cooling. Smoke and Koenig[97] have more recently described the effects of "thermal condition-

---

* Freke[93] has described a method whereby the contact of the sagged tip with the base is indicated electrically, thus making for a more accurate determination of the softening point.

† Cones 022 to 11 are not listed in the ASTM Standard but still appear in the literature and are thus included for reference.

TABLE 2.19. PYROMETRIC CONE EQUIVALENTS (PCE)[92]

Cone no.	End point for heating rate 150°C/hr		Cone no.	End point for heating rate 150°C/hr	
	°C	°F		°C	°F
022	605	1121	13	1349	2460
021	615	1139	14	1398	2548
020	650	1202	15	1430	2606
019	660	1220	16	1491	2716
018	720	1328	17	1512	2754
017	770	1418	18	1522	2772
016	795	1463	19	1541	2806
015	805	1481	20	1564	2847
014	830	1526	23	1605	2921
013	860	1580	26	1621	2950
012	875	1607	27	1640	2984
011	905	1661	28	1646	2995
010	895	1643	29	1659	3018
09	930	1706	30	1665	3029
08	950	1742	31	1683	3061
07	990	1814	31½	1699	3090
06	1015	1859	32	1717	3123
05	1040	1904	32½	1724	3135
04	1060	1940	33	1743	3169
03	1115	2039	34	1763	3205
02	1125	2057	35	1785	3245
01	1145	2093	36	1804	3279
1	1160	2120	37	1820	3308
2	1165	2129			
3	1170	2138		100°C/hr	
4	1190	2174			
5	1205	2201	38	1835	3335
6	1230	2246			
7	1250	2282		600°C/hr	
8	1260	2300	39	1865	3389
9	1285	2345	40	1885	3425
10	1305	2381	41	1970	3578
11	1325	2417	42	2015	3659
12	1337	2439			

ing" on the transverse strength, impact strength, and modulus of elasticity for a number of hydraulically extruded specimens of steatite, mullite, and alumina in the form of one-half-inch-diameter rods six inches long. The specimens were heated at a rate of 260°C per hour to a temperature within 100 to 425°C of their maturing temperature, maintained at this temperature for one-half hour and then exposed to a blast of room temperature air. Table 2.20 is taken from their report and indicates the very substantial

TABLE 2.20. EFFECT OF THERMAL CONDITIONING ON MODULUS OF
RUPTURE AND IMPACT STRENGTH[97]

	Modulus of rupture					Impact strength				
Type of body	As received MOR (psi)	Thermal conditioned MOR (psi)	% increase	Quench temp.		As received (in.-lb/in.²)	Thermal conditioned (in.-lb/in.²)	% increase	Quench temp.	
				°F	°C				°F	°C
Steatite	17000	20600	21.0	1900	1038	22.5	23.1	2.6	1700	927
Mullite	18700	27700	48.5	2640	1449	21.4	32.1	50.0	2640	1449
Alumina original surface	35100	47800	36.2	2400	1315	29.3	38.2	30.4	2400	1315
Alumina centerless ground	21900	42500	94.1	2200	1205	26.6	39.8	47.7	2200	1205

TABLE 2.21. EFFECT OF THERMAL CONDITIONING ON HIGH-
ALUMINA BODIES VS. ALUMINA CONTENT[97]

	Al_2O_3	
	85%	95%
Modulus of rupture (psi)		
as received	30,800	31,900
thermal-conditioned	52,400	67,400
increase (%)	70	11
Impact strength (in.-lb/in.²)		
as received	30.0	38.0
thermal-conditioned	42.0	46.4
increase (%)	40	22

increase obtained for the modulus of rupture and the impact strength of a
number of ceramic bodies. It was also found that the impact resistance of
alumina rods was decreased by centerless grinding, and that thermal conditioning increased the values up to 48 per cent above the "as-received"
value. 95-per cent alumina rods showed a greater increase in modulus of
rupture and impact strength on thermal conditioning than did 85-percent
alumina rods as shown in Table 2.21.

Glazing. Glazing of ceramic ware may serve to seal the pores, to provide
impermeability to gases on less dense bodies, reduce water absorption and
thus increase volume resistivity (although the surface resistivity may be
decreased), or just add luster and color. Glazes are also used to increase
the mechanical strength of ceramics. For this purpose the thermal expansion
coefficient of the glaze is chosen to be less than that of the body to which it
is applied so that the glaze is in a state of compression. This compression
must not be excessive; otherwise "chipping" or "peeling" will occur. In

the opposite case, with the glaze having a higher expansion than the body, it will be in tension and tend to develop numerous cracks (crazing). Variations in glaze fit can affect the mechanical strength of porcelain by 300 to 400 per cent.[98, 99] Self-glazing bodies (cordierites) have also been developed. "For best results in thermal shock tests, the glaze should be in slight compression rather than in tension. Provided the glaze has the proper pyrochemical bonding, the very thin layer of glaze will exert enough bonding strength to the body to enable it to pass heat shock tests that the body could not pass without its help."[100]

The various steps involved in the production of electronic ceramics, particularly ferrites, have recently been critically reviewed by Economos[101] who says: "There is still considerable inertia in the industry which keeps it from discarding some of the older methods. Present difficulties show the necessity for employing newer and even novel techniques without regard to what is the generally accepted practice." Some of these newer techniques are then briefly described and should be of interest to the reader of this chapter.

Die Construction and Design Considerations

"To form the simplest article, the die consists of a stationary block, or die case, with a movable top and bottom punch. A solid article, round or square in cross-section, as the requirements may be, needs these three parts. If holes are required, stationary pins are added running up through the bottom punch and into the top punch. If several steps in thickness are required in an article, this necessitates moving parts within the bottom punch to distribute the pressure evenly to the various thicknesses. The cross-section of the die case and the punches are shaped to the design required by the customer, allowing for the shrinkage of the body in the firing operation. The finest die steels are used and the various die parts are machined and polished to a high degree of accuracy."[100, 102]

Figure 2.11, gives in diagrammatic form the basic die components which are generally incorporated in a commercial tabletting machine, or press. The abrasive nature of ceramics will lead to rapid wear of ordinary tool steel, hardened to a Rockwell "C" hardness of 58 to 60, so that only 100 to 200 parts can be pressed before the ceramics show objectionable fins and laminations on ejection from the die. Figure 2.12, illustrates the wear of poor quality dies, taking the form of an enlargement of the die cavity, so that the pressed part must be forced through a narrower channel on ejection. The use of "Carboloy" or tungsten carbide for the die and punches reduces the degree of wear to a considerable extent so that many thousands of parts can be pressed before any wear is noticeable.[90] Die and punch faces should be given a mirror finish and the clearance between them kept to a

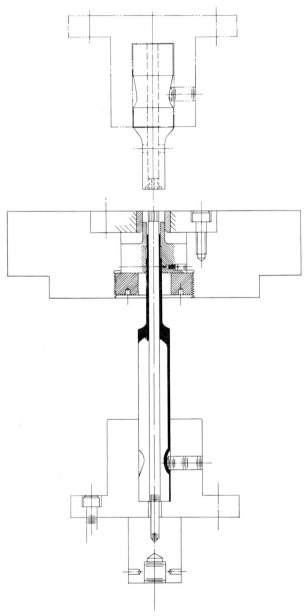

Figure 2.11. Ceramic die. After Reimann.[90] (*Courtesy Power Tube Department, General Electric Company.*)

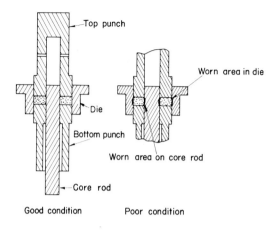

Top punch

Worn area in die

Die

Bottom punch

Worn area on core rod

Core rod

Good condition   Poor condition

Die, punch, core rod assembly.

Figure 2.12. Illustration of the wear of poor-quality ceramic dies. After Reimann.[90] (*Courtesy Power Tube Department, General Electric Company.*)

minimum, usually about 0.001 in. Excessively tight fit will prevent the escape of air from the die area and make satisfactory press operation impossible. The close fits required in the engaged position can naturally be relieved in the remainder of the assembly.

The available depth to which an available press can be filled limits the maximum length of the part that can be produced in such a press. Most commercial presses permit a range from $7/16$ in. to 4 in. for depth of fill. Since the compression ratio of most ceramic powders is 2.5:1, the maximum length of the unfired, pressed part is of the order of 1.5 in. Gleason[100] has compiled a few suggestions to the prospective purchaser of die-pressed parts which may aid in the intelligent design of ceramic parts and facilitate their economical manufacture.*

(1) "Give the ceramic supplier full information as to the size of parts that fit into or around the ceramic. Whenever possible, the supplier should be furnished with a sample assembly so that the economical design may be checked. Usually, the metal stamping dies are cheaper than the steatite-pressing dies and can be altered more easily.

(2) "Always allow as liberal toleral tolerances as possible. It may seem paradoxical that the ceramic manufacturer boasts of his ability to hold exacting tolerances and then asks for broad tolerances, but it reduces to this: The supplier can furnish ceramics to close tolerances; but when they are

* Reproduced with the permission of the editor of the *Journal of the British Institution of Radio Engineers.*

more restrictive than ordinary commercial tolerances, he must resort to costly individual gauging.

(3) "Bevelled edges are very helpful. As the die parts wear, the material crowds into the resulting crevice between punch and block and forms a fin or flash on the ceramic. Where a bevel is allowed, the supplier will profile his punch faces and the ceramic will be neater and the dies last longer.

(4) "Bosses, counterbores, or depressions should be kept as low or shallow as possible, and their walls should be tapered about three degrees.

(5) "The number of different levels should be kept at a minimum.

(6) "Wall thickness between the edge of the ceramic and holes or depressions should be as substantial as possible, else cracks will have a tendency to result.

(7) "Avoid very small pins, and all designs that necessitate dies of weak construction.

(8) "Holes can only be pressed-in when parallel to the axis of pressing. Other holes must be drilled into the article individually after pressing.

(9) "Pressed ceramics should not be too long in direction of pressing. They will have a tendency to have a center section smaller than the ends.

(10) "Thin sections, no matter where, should be avoided. They tend to crack, warp, or blister, thus making the ceramic hard to control.

(11) "Bosses should be used wherever flat, ground, parallel surfaces are required, thus keeping the ground area at a minimum.

(12) "Threads of tapped holes cannot be pressed in. Unless special binders are used, the pressed ceramic crumbles to some extent in the tapping operation, especially with fine pitches; so a thread as large and coarse as possible should be chosen. If the screw must enter the ceramic quite a distance, it would be advisable to counterbore a fraction of the hole so that any variation in firing shrinkage and its accompanying variation in pitch will still allow the screw to enter. Holes tapped into a ceramic perpendicular to the pressing axis will invariably fire out oval-shaped."

Precision Ceramics. A plea was made in the previous paragraph to design ceramic parts with as liberal tolerances as are possible within the limitations imposed by the use of the part. This request still holds for the regular run of commercial ceramics which can be made on a large scale to tolerances of about ± 0.005 in. for dimensions up to 0.5 in. and ± 1 per cent on larger dimensions. Unfortunately, these tolerances are far too wide for parts to be used in electron tubes in which critical spacings of the order of a fraction of a thousandth of an inch rely on the critical dimensions of the part. The producers of commercial ceramics will furnish parts for such tolerances by resorting to finish-grinding on diamond wheels.

Such finish-grinding operations can be performed fairly easily on flat surfaces or round corners, but they become next to impossible, or prohibitively costly, when complex shapes such as undercuts and ridges are to be controlled to close dimensions of the order of less than one thousandth of an inch. Several electron tube manufacturers have established their own ceramics division in recent years in order to produce ceramic products of greater uniformity in characteristics and they have also learned to produce fired parts to close tolerances without the need of finish grinding. By these carefully controlled techniques it has been possible to produce parts in the laboratory with minimum tolerances of ±0.0025 in. on dimensions up to 0.5 in. and ±0.5 per cent on larger dimensions. Some very small parts have been made to within 0.25 mil on the fired dimensions.

It is claimed by a number of workers in this field that objectionable strains are imparted to the ceramics by the process of finish grinding. Other laboratories have gone to great length in improving the grinding techniques, the machinery and fixtures employed, and the kind of abrasives used, thereby producing parts to close tolerances without any obvious harmful effects of the grinding operation.[103] High-alumina bodies, in particular, have enough inherent strength to be able to withstand a certain degree of weakening without harm, but steatites and zircon may well be seriously harmed by grinding.[104]

Similar precautions must be taken in cleaning ceramics. Air firing is adequate in many cases and avoids the danger of cleaning agents either attacking the skin in which strength resides (like in glass), or becoming absorbed in pores from which they may be difficult to remove. Cleaning with nitric acid has been found to be definitely harmful, and alkaline rinses are preferable. Etching ceramics by ion bombardment has been described by Bierlein, Newkirk, and Mastel[105] and may well be used for cleaning in critical applications.

"Pyroceram"* **(Glass Ceramics).** The high cost involved in preparing conventional ceramics to close tolerances may well be avoided by using a new material which was announced by the Corning Glass Works of Corning, New York in May, 1957. Under the leadership of Dr. S. D. Stookey, the originator of "Photoceram," a process was developed by which a specially prepared glass can be converted into a crystalline ceramic by heat treatment at about 1250°C. In order to bring about this transformation, suitable crystal seeds are incorporated into the glass and result in a very fine-grained structure where crystallites are less than 400 AU in size as compared with one to two microns for conventional ceramics. The glass is melted in platinum-lined containers and can be fabricated into desired shapes by the conventional processes of molding and casting. The conversion into the crystalline state after the glass has solidified entails a shrinkage in linear

* Trade mark, Corning Glass Works, Corning, N. Y.

dimensions of the order of one to two per cent while the corresponding shrinkage on firing of ceramic bodies is as much as 15 per cent and frequently not uniform in different directions. There is thus hope that intricate shapes made of Pyroceram can be produced on a large scale much more economically because finishing operations such as diamond grinding will not be necessary.

"While more than 400 types of Pyroceram have been experimentally melted, only four have been fully investigated and melted in pilot runs to date. Two of them, Pyroceram Code numbers 9607 and 9608, are handled and formed in their glassy state similar to borosilicate glass. They can be formed by conventional glass-forming methods, i.e., blowing, drawing, pressing, and rolling.

"The two other Pyroceram materials, Code numbers 9605 and 9606, are very fluid at high temperatures, and can most easily be formed by centrifugal casting. Experiments indicate that these latter two Pyroceram materials lend themselves to forming by investment casting techniques. Pilot runs indicate that all four of these new materials are adaptable to mass production techniques."[106]

Table 2.22 is a reproduction of a table issued by Corning Glass Works describing the properties of the four different types of "Pyroceram" and comparing these with the properties of various glasses, ceramics, and metals. It is apparent that the two types of "Pyroceram," numbers 9605 and 9606, are able to compete with conventional high-alumina bodies on the basis of their superior dielectric properties at high temperature and their exceedingly high resistance to thermal shock (Table 2.23). The other two types of Pyroceram, i.e., numbers 9607 and 9608 have electric characteristics about equivalent to those of lime glass and will find applications in areas where dielectric losses are not critical.

The thermal expansion coefficients of "Pyroceram" materials can be varied over a wide range, from slightly negative to 200×10^{-7} per °C. Bodies with expansion coefficients from 90 to 100 are under development to make them suitable for seals to stainless steels. It must be added, however, that so far the problem of metallizing "Pyroceram" has not been solved, but solderglass seals are possible and some seals with zirconium hydride as a bonding agent have been made at the Westinghouse Tube Plant at Elmira where the suitability of "Pyroceram" for magnetron output windows is under investigation and studies to use "Pyroceram" for small high-temperature receiving-tube envelopes are underway.

Ductile Ceramics

Ceramics are customarily considered to be materials which show brittle fracture when a tensile load exceeds the cohesive forces of neighboring

TABLE 2.22. COMPARISON OF PROPERTIES OF PYROCERAM, GLASS, AND CERAMIC*

	Pyroceram				Glass				Ceramic		
	9605	9606	9607	9608	Fused silica 7940	Vycor 7900	Pyrex 7740	Lime glass 0080	High-purity alumina (93%+)	Steatite MgO·SiO2	Forsterite 2MgO·SiO2
Specific gravity (25°C)	2.62	2.61	2.40	2.50	2.20	2.18	2.23	2.47	3.6	2.65 to 2.92	2.8
Water absorption (%)	0.00	0.00	0.00	0.00	0.00	0.00	0.00	0.00	0	0 to 0.03	0 to 0.01
Gas permeability	0	0	0	0	0	0	0	0	0	0	0
Thermal											
Softening temp. (°C)[1]	1350	1260		1250	1584	1500	820	696	1700	1349	1349
Specific heat (25°C)	0.185	0.185		0.190	0.176	0.178	0.186	0.200	0.181	—	—
Specific heat mean (25–400°C)	0.230	0.230		0.235	0.223	0.224	0.233	0.235	0.241	—	—
Thermal conductivity (cgs) 25°C mean temp.	0.0100	0.0087		0.0047	0.0028	—	0.0026	—	0.052 to 0.058	0.0062 to 0.0065	0.010
Linear coeff. of thermal expansion $\times 10^7$ (25–300°C)	14	57	−7	4 to 20[2]	5.5	8.	32.	92.	73 (20 to 500°C)	81.5 to 99. (20 to 500°C)	99. (20 to 500°C)
Mechanical											
Modulus of elasticity $\times 10^{-6}$ (psi)	19.8	17.3		12.5	10.5	9.6	9.5	10.2	40.	15.	19. [3]
Poisson's ratio	—	0.245		0.25	0.17	0.17	0.20	0.24	0.32	—	—
Modulus of rupture (abraded) $\times 10^{-3}$ (psi)	—	20.		16 to 23	—	5 to 9	6 to 10	—	40 to 50 [3]	20. [3]	—
Hardness: Knoop 100 gm	720.	698.		703.	—	532	481	—	1880	—	—
Hardness: Knoop 500 gm		619.		588.	—	477	442	—	1530	—	—
Electrical											
Dielectric constant—1 MC 25°C	(6.1)	5.58		6.78	3.78	3.8	4.6	7.2	8.81	5.9	6.3
300°C	(6.3)	5.60		—	—	3.9	5.9				
500°C	—	8.80									
10 KMC 25°C	(6.1)	5.45		6.54	3.78	3.8	4.5	6.71	9.03	5.8	5.8
300°C	(6.1)	5.51		6.65	3.78				8.79		
500°C	(6.1)	5.53		6.78	3.78						
Dissipation factor—1 MC 25°C	(0.0017)	0.0015		0.0030		0.0005	0.0046	0.009	0.00035	0.0013	0.0003
300°C	(0.014)	0.0154		—		0.0042	0.0130				
500°C	—	—									
10 KMC 25°C	(0.0002)	0.00033		0.0068		0.0009	0.0085	0.017	0.012	0.0014	0.0010
300°C	(0.0008)	0.00075		0.0115					0.0015		
500°C	(0.0025)	0.00152		0.040							
Loss factor—1 MC 25°C	(0.010)	0.008		0.02		0.0019	0.0212	0.065	0.0021	0.0077	0.0019
300°C	(0.078)	0.086		—		0.0164	0.0566		0.0031		
500°C	—	—									
10 KMC 25°C	(0.001)	0.002		0.045		0.0036	0.0282	0.114	0.108	0.0082	0.0058
300°C	(0.005)	0.004		0.077					0.0132		
500°C	(0.015)	0.008		0.27					0.019		
Volume resistivity Log 10 (ohm-cm) 250°C	10.1	10.	—	8.1	12.0	9.7	8.1	6.4	14.0 (100°C)	14. (20°C)	14. (20°C)
350°C	8.7	8.6	—	6.8	9.7	8.1	6.6	5.1	12.95 (300°C)		

Notes:
(1) Softening temperature; method of evaluation. a. Pyroceram: comparable to ASTM C 24-46. b. Glass: ASTM C 338-54T. c. Ceramics: ASTM C 24-46.
(2) Expansion coefficients depend on heat treatment.
(3) Unabraded values.

* Courtesy Corning Glass Works, Corning, New York: Bulletin on Pyroceram (May 1957) and PY-3 (1959).

TABLE 2.23. THERMAL STRESS RESISTANCE FACTOR R″ FOR VARIOUS
MATERIALS CALCULATED FROM PUBLISHED VALUES FOR K, α, T, AND E
(After Priest and Ruth Talcott[26])

Material	K C.G.S.	$\alpha \times 10^{-6}$	T p.s.i.	E p.s.i. $\times 10^{-6}$	R″ = KT/αE
Beryllium oxide	0.53	9.0	10,000	40.0	14.7
Fused silica	0.004	0.5	15,500	10.9	11.4
Pyroceram 9605	0.01	1.4	20,000*	20.0	7.0*
Sapphire (Linde)	0.065	6.7	35,000	50.0	6.8
Coors AI200	0.05	6.7	26,000	40.2	4.8
Zircon (Coors ZI 4)	0.009	3.36	11,500	19.4	1.6
Pyroceram 9606	0.007	5.7	20,000*	18.0	1.36*
Aluminosilicate glass (Corning 1723)	0.005*	4.6	10,000	6–13	1.1*
Steatite (Alsimag 228)	0.006	6.4	10,000	10*	0.94*
Forsterite (Alsimag 243)	0.008	9.1	10,000	10*	0.88*
Soda-lime-silica glass	0.004	9.0	10,000	9.5	0.47
Fireclay	0.0027	5.5	750	2.3	0.16

* Estimated values.

The thermal stress resistance factor

$$R'' = \frac{KT}{\alpha E}$$

is a simplified form of the formula

$$R' = \frac{KT(1 - \mu)}{\alpha E}$$

where:
  K = the thermal conductivity.
  T = the tensile strength.
  E = the modulus of elasticity.
  μ = Poisson's ratio.
  α = the coefficient of thermal expansion.

lattice planes; deformation, or plastic flow, is thus normally not observed prior to fracture. Another class of materials usually considered to be brittle are ionic solids, such as sodium chloride and potassium chloride and other cubic crystals. It has been shown, however, that such crystalline solids can exhibit ductility when freshly cleaved in air, or when cleaved while submerged in a suitable liquid, which excludes access of oxygen and nitrogen to the crystal surface. This earlier work by a number of investigators, notably Joffe and Stepanov, has been extended more recently by Gorum, Parker, and Pask[107] at the University of California at Berkeley to cover ceramic bodies, such as magnesium oxide, which, when freshly cleaved, show considerable ductility. This work is still in progress, and a full understanding of the factors which cause brittleness under ordinary conditions has not been gained as yet. The degree of purity of the material, apart from aforementioned environmental conditions, seems to be a determining factor.

REFERENCES

1. A. R. von Hippel, "Dielectric Materials and Applications," Chap. 4., The Technology Press of M.I.T. and John Wiley & Sons, Inc., New York, 1954.
2. W. G. Robinson and E. C. Bloor, "A survey of electrical ceramics," *Proc. Inst. Elec. Engrs.*, **100**, Pt. IIA, No. 3, 247–257, (Mar. 1953); Disc. pp. 266–275.
3. L. Navias, "Advances in ceramics related to electron tube development," *J. Am. Ceram. Soc.*, **37**, 329–350 (Aug. 1954).
4. F. G. Diver, "Materials used in radio and electronic engineering, a survey by the Technical Committee of the Institution, Pt. 3 'Ceramics'," *J. Brit. Inst. Radio Engrs.*, **15**, 506–517 (Oct. 1955).
5. L. Mitchell, "Ceramics," (a review of recent developments) *Ind. Eng. Chem.*, **48**, Pt. 2, 1702–1709 (Sept. 1956).
6. I. E. Campbell, Ed., "High-Temperature Technology," John Wiley & Sons, Inc., New York, 1956.
7. R. W. Powell, "Thermal conductivities of solid materials at high temperatures," *Research*, **7**, 492–501 (Dec. 1954).
8. W. H. Kohl and P. J. Rice, Jr., "Electron Tubes for Critical Environments," Final Report, prepared by Stanford Research Institute, Menlo Park, California, for Wright Air Development Center, Air Research and Development Center, Wright-Patterson Air Force Base, Ohio. WADC Tech. Report 57-434 (July 1957); Contract AF33(616)-3460. ASTIA No. AD 151158; PB 131852.
9. W. D. Smiley, Project Leader, "Mechanical Properties of Refractory, Non-metallic Crystalline Materials and Intermetallic Compounds," Final Report, Stanford Research Institute, Menlo Park, California, for Wright Air Development Center, Materials Laboratory, Wright-Patterson Air Force Base, Ohio; Contract No. AF33(616)-5907 (1958).
10. W. G. Bradshaw and C. O. Matthews, "Properties of Refractory Materials: Collected Data and References, Lockheed Aircraft Corporation, Missile Systems Division, Sunnyvale, California, Report LMSD-2466 (15 Jan. 1959).
11. C. G. Goetzel, "Treatise on Powder Metallurgy," Interscience Publishers, New York, 1952.
12. P. Schwartzkopf and R. Kieffer, "Refractory Hard Metals," Macmillan Co., New York, 1953.
13. J. H. Koenig, "Ceramics for engineering applications," *Materials & Methods*, Manual 62, **32**, 69–84 (Sept. 1950).
14. "Standard Definitions of Terms Relating to Ceramic Whiteware," ASTM Spec. C242-55.
15. F. H. Norton, "Ceramics," 3rd ed., McGraw-Hill Book Co., New York, 1949.
16. F. H. Norton, "Elements of Ceramics," Addison-Wesley Press, Cambridge, Mass. 1952.
17. A. T. Green and G. H. Stewart, "Ceramics—A Symposium," The British Ceramic Society, Stoke-on-Trent, 1953.
18. Hewitt Wilson, "Ceramics, Clay Technology," McGraw-Hill Book Co., New York, 1927.
19. Rexford Newcomb, Jr., "Ceramic Whitewares," Pitman Publishing Corp., New York, 1947.
20. E. Rosenthal, "Porcelain and Other Ceramic Insulating Materials," Chapman & Hall, London, 1944.
21. H. Salmang, "Die Keramik," Springer Verlag, Berlin, 1951.
22. A. B. Searle, "Refractory Materials" (Their Manufacture and Uses), 3rd ed., Charles Griffin & Company, Limited, London, 1950.

23. C. L. Mantell, Ed., "Engineering Materials Handbook." McGraw-Hill Book Co., New York, 1958.

24. O. J. Whittemore, Jr. and N. N. Ault, "Thermal expansion of various ceramic materials to 1500°C," *J. Am. Ceram. Soc.*, **30**, 443–444 (Dec. 1956).

25. E. J. Smoke, "Thermal shock and related properties of dense ceramics," *Ceramic Age*, **63**, 20–21, 38 (June 1954).

26. D. H. Priest and Ruth Talcott, "Thermal stresses in ceramic cylinders used in vacuum tubes," *Amer. Ceram. Soc. Bull.*, **38**, 99–105 (March 1959).

27. R. Russell, Jr. and W. G. Mohr, "Characteristics of zircon porcelain," *J. Am. Ceram. Soc.*, **30**, 32–35 (Jan. 1947).

28. R. Russell, Jr. and L. J. Berberich, "Low-loss ceramics," *Electronics*, **17**, 136–142, 338 (May 1944).

29. C. E. Curtis and E. A. Thomas, "Zircon and Zirconium Oxide Refractories," Titanium Alloy Manufacturing Co., 1948.

30. E. W. Lindsay and L. J. Berberich, "Electrical properties of ceramics as influenced by temperature," *Trans. AIEE*, **67**,[1] 734–741; (1948) Disc. 741–742.

31. G. T. Furukawa, T. H. B. Douglas, R. E. Coskey and D. C. Ginnings, "Thermal properties of aluminum oxide from 0° to 1200°K," *J. Research Natl. Bur. Standards*, **57**, 67–82 (Aug. 1956).

32. M. D. Rigterink, "Ceramic electrical insulating materials," *J. Am. Ceram. Soc.*, **41**, Pt. 2, 501–506 (Nov. 1958).

33. F. J. Hynes, "Alumina bodies for ceramic-to-metal seals," *Ceram. Ind.*, **67**, 87–91, 102 (Feb. 1956).

34. T. G. Carruthers and R. M. Gill, "The properties of calcined alumina," *Trans. Brit. Ceram. Soc.*, **54**, 59–81 (Jan. 1955).

35. W. J. Smothers and H. J. Reynolds, "Sintering and grain growth of alumina," *J. Am. Ceram. Soc.*, **37**, 588–595 (Dec. 1954).

36. D. R. Wilder and E. S. Fitzsimmons, "Further study of sintering phenomena," *J. Am. Ceram. Soc.*, **38**, 66–71 (Feb. 1955).

37. H. P. Cahoon and C. J. Christensen, "Sintering and grain growth of alpha-alumina," *J. Am. Ceram. Soc.*, **39**, 337–344 (Oct. 1956).

38. H. P. Cahoon and C. J. Christensen, "Effect of temperature and additives on the creep properties and recrystallization of aluminum oxide," Institute for the Study of Rate Processes, University of Utah, Salt Lake City, Utah. Tech. Rept. No. 42 (Jan. 15, 1955); Res. Contr. N7-onr-45101. ASTIA No. AD 54874

39. R. L. Coble and W. D. Kingery, "Effect of porosity on physical properties of sintered alumina," *J. Am. Ceram. Soc.*, **39**, 377–385 (Nov. 1956).

40. Linde Company, Bull. F-1176: Properties and Uses of Linde Sapphire.

41. L. Navias, "Comparison between Al_2O_3-Ta and Al_2O_3-W reactions above 1600°C in a vacuum," *Am. Ceram. Soc. Bull.*, **38**, 256–259 (May 1954).

42. W. H. Kohl, "A narrow, elongated cathode structure for all-metal tubes," presentation at the 2nd National Conference on Tube Techniques, New York, Oct. 13, 1953 (not published); see: Stanford University Electronics Research Laboratory Tech. Rept. No. 23 (Aug. 15, 1954), "Construction of a sealed-off, all-metal cyclotron resonance tube," by W. H. Kohl.

43. W. H. Kohl, "A combination vacuum and hydrogen furnace," *ibid* (not published).

44. J. B. Wachtman, Jr. and L. H. Maxwell, "Plastic deformation of ceramic-oxide single crystals," *J. Am. Ceram. Soc.*, **37**, 291–299 (July 1954).

45. E. Benz, "Sealing of Synthetic Sapphire to Glass," WADC Tech. Rept. 54-18 (Jan. 1954), Wright Air Development Center, Air Research and Development Command, United States Air Force, Wright-Patterson Air Force Base, Ohio.

46. H. Rawson, "A method for sealing sapphire to glass," *J. Sci. Instr.*, **28**, 208 (July 1951).

47. R. P. Chasmar, J. L. Craston, G. Isaacs and A. S. Young, "A method of sealing sapphire to glass and its application to infra-red photo cells," *J. Sci. Inst.*, **28**, 206–207 (July 1951).

48. R. W. Kebler, "Optical Properties of Synthetic Sapphire," Linde Air Products Company Tech. Bull. F-8727.

49. J. B. Austin, "The thermal expansion of some refractory oxides," *J. Am. Ceram. Soc.*, **14**, 795–810 (Nov. 1931).

50. D. A. Ditmars and D. C. Ginnings, "Thermal conductivity of BeO from 45 to 750°C," *J. Res. Natl. Bur. Standards*, **59**, 93–99 (Aug. 1957).

51. "Machined beryllium oxide," *Rev. Sci. Instr.*, **30**, 155 (Feb. 1959). (The Beryllium Corporation, Reading, Pa.)

52. G. Jaeger, "Special ceramic bodies for metallurgical applications" (in German), *Metall.*, **9**, 358–366 (1955).

53. C. E. Curtis and J. R. Johnson, "Properties of thorium oxide ceramics," *J. Am. Ceram. Soc.*, **40**, 63–68 (Feb. 1957).

54. C. A. Arenberg, H. H. Rice and H. Z. Schofield, "Thoria ceramics," *Am. Ceram. Soc. Bull.*, **36**, 302–306 (Aug. 1957).

55. W. Jackson, "The structure, electrical properties and potential applications of the barium-titanate class of ceramic materials," *Proc. Inst. Elec. Engrs.*, **97**, Pt. 3, 285–289 (Sept. 1950).

56. D. S. Campbell, "Barium titanate and its use as a memory store," *J. Brit. Inst. Radio Engrs.*, **17**, 385–395 (July 1957).

57. L. Davis, Jr. and L. G. Rubin, "Some dielectric properties of barium-strontium titanate ceramics at 3000 megacycles," *J. Appl. Phys.*, **24**, 1194–1197 (Sept. 1953).

58. O. J. Whittemore and D. W. Marshall, "Fused stabilized zirconia and refractories," *J. Am. Ceram. Soc.*, **35**, 85–89 (Apr. 1952).

59. W. G. Rudy, "Ceramic mosaic for camera pick-up tube," U. S. Patent 2,727,-170 (Dec. 13. 1955).

60. A. E. Javitz, "Integration of dielectric materials, processes, components," *Elec. Mfg.*, **60**, 90–99 (July 1957). (Contains property data on BN released by the Signals Research and Development Establishment, British Ministry of Supply, March 1957.)

61. A. H. Sully, E. A. Brandes and R. B. Waterhouse, "Some measurements of the total emissivity of metals and pure refractory oxides and the variation of emissivity with temperature," *Brit. J. Appl. Phys.*, **3**, 97–101 (Mar. 1952).

62. J. R. Pattison, "The total emissivity of some refractory materials above 900°C," *Trans. Brit. Ceram. Soc.*, **51**, 698–705 (Nov. 1955).

63. M. Michaud, "Facteurs d'émission d'oxydes métalliques et réfractaires à haute température," *Silicates Ind.*, **19**, No. 617, 243–250 (1954). (Reviewed in *Glass Ind.*, **36**, 193–197, 228 (Apr. 1955).

64. R. H. Heilmann, "Emissivities of refractory materials," *Mech. Eng.*, **58**, 291–292, (May 1936).

65. L. Navias, "Hydrogen-protected wire-wound resistance furnaces," Pt. 1, *Ceram. Bull.*, **36**, 262–267 (July 1957).
66. H. von Wartenberg and H. J. Reusch, "Melting diagrams of refractory oxides: IV Aluminum oxide," *Z. anorg. allgem. Chem.*, **207**, 1–20 (Jan. 1932).
67. P. D. Johnson, "Behavior of refractory oxides and metals, alone and in combination, in vacuo at high temperatures," *J. Am. Ceram. Soc.*, **33**, 168–171 (May 1950); see also: *Ber. Deutsche Keram. Ges.*, **31**, 81–84 (Mar. 1954); *Abstr. Vacuum*, **4**, 528 (Oct. 1954—publ. June 1957).
68. G. Economos and W. D. Kingery, "Metal-ceramic interactions: II. Metal-oxide interfacial reactions at elevated temperatures," *J. Am. Ceram. Soc.*, **36**, 403–409 (Dec. 1953).
69. P. H. Brace, "Reactions of molten titanium with certain refractory oxides," *J. Electrochem. Soc.*, **94**, 170–176 (Apr. 1948).
70. A. Silverman, "Data on chemicals for ceramic use," National Research Council, National Academy of Science, Washington, D. C., Bull. No. 118 (June 1949).
71. W. R. Mott, "Relative volatilities of refractory materials," *Trans. Am. Electrochem. Soc.*, **34**, 255–295 (1918).
72. E. Shapiro, "Vapor pressure of thorium oxide from 2050 to 2250°K," *J. Am. Chem. Soc.*, **74**[4], 5233–5235 (Oct. 20, 1952).
73. N. D. Erway and R. L. Siefert, "Vapor pressure of beryllium oxide," Argonne National Laboratory MDDC-1030, U. S. AEC (1946).
74. A. Claassen and C. F. Belenemaus, "Vapor pressure determination of BaO, SrO, and CaO, and their mixtures from measurements of the rate of evaporation" (in German) *Z. Physik*, **80** (5/6), 342–351 (1933).
75. K. K. Kelley, "The free energies of vaporization and vapor pressures of inorganic substances," U. S. Bur. Mines Bull. No. 383, (1935), 1–132 (see p. 15).
76. J. F. Wygant and W. D. Kingery, "Stability of ceramic materials," *Am. Ceram. Soc. Bull.*, **31**, 251–254 (July 1952).
77. R. Kieffer and F. Benesovsky, "Metallic heating element materials for high-temperature furnaces," *Metallurgia*, **58**, 119–124 (Sept. 1958).
78. W. D. Kingery, Ed., "Ceramic Fabrication Processes," The Technology Press of the Massachusetts Institute of Technology and John Wiley & Sons, Inc., New York; Chapman & Hall, Limited, London, 1958.
79. W. L. German, "Some applications of organic compounds in the ceramic industry," *Trans. Brit. Ceram. Soc.*, **54**, 399–412 (1955).
80. H. Z. Schofield, "Ball-milling of pure ceramic bodies," *J. Am. Ceram. Soc. Bull.*, **32**, 49–50 (Feb. 1953).
81. L. Navias, "Extrusion of refractory oxide insulators for vacuum tubes," *J. Am. Ceram. Soc.*, **15**, 234–251 (Apr. 1932).
82. J. H. Partridge and J. R. Lait, "The manufacture of refractory carbides from pure oxides of high melting point," *J. Soc. Glass Technol.*, **20**, 200–217 (1936).
83. R. A. Ijdens, "Ceramics and their manufacture," *Philips Tech. Rev.*, **10**, 205–213 (Jan. 1949).
84. J. F. W. Bishop, "The theory of extrusion," *Met. Rev.*, **2**, No. 8, 361–390 (1957).
85. E. K. L. Haffner and R. M. L. Elkan, "Extrusion presses and press installations," *Met. Rev.*, **2**, No. 7, 263–303 (1957).
86. W. E. Hauth, "Slip casting of aluminum oxide," *J. Am. Ceram. Soc.*, **32**, 894–899 (Dec. 1949).

87. D. S. Adcock and I. C. McDowall, "The mechanism of filler pressing and slip casting," *J. Am. Ceram. Soc.*, **40**, 355–362 (Oct. 1957).
88. F. H. Riddle, "Ceramic spark plug insulators," *J. Am. Ceram. Soc.*, **32**, 333–346 (Nov. 1949).
89. H. E. Wagner and C. G. Harman, "Hydrostatic pressing as a fabrication technique, *Am. Ceram. Soc. Bull.*, **30**, 341–344 (Oct. 1951).
90. A. G. Reimann, "Electron tube ceramic requirements and manufacturing considerations," Presented before American Ceramic Society, New York, April 25, 1956 (not published). Courtesy Power Tube Department, General Electric Company, Schenectady, N. Y.
91. K. Schwartzwalder, "Injection molding of ceramic materials," *Bull. Am. Ceram. Soc.*, **28**, 459–461 (Nov. 1949).
92. C. O. Fairchild and M. F. Peters, "Characteristics of pyrometric cones," *J. Am. Ceram. Soc.*, **9**, 701–743 (Nov. 1926).
93. A. M. Freke, "Two methods of detecting the softening points of pyrometric cones," *Trans. Brit. Ceram. Soc.*, **55**, 584–587 (Sept. 1956).
94. W. F. Janssen and M. D. Rigterink, "Microstructure of ceramics for communication equipment," *J. Am. Ceram. Soc.*, **37**, 152–156 (Mar. 1958).
95. F. A. Hummel and H. E. Lowrey, "Quenching vitreous body adds strength," *Ceram. Ind.*, **56**, 93–94 (June 1951).
96. H. Rawson, "Reduction in the loss factor of certain ceramics by heat treatment," *Nature (London)*, **173**, No. 4401, 447 (Mar. 6, 1954).
97. E. J. Smoke and J. H. Koenig, "Thermal properties of ceramics," Engineering Research Bull. No. 40 (Jan. 1958), College of Engineering, Rutgers, The State University, New Brunswick, New Jersey.
98. D. H. Rowland, "Porcelain for high-voltage insulators," *Elec. Eng.*, **55**, 618–626 (1936).
99. L. E. Thiess, "Influence of glaze composition on the mechanical strength of electrical porcelain," *J. Am. Ceram. Soc.*, **19**, 70–73 (Mar. 1936).
100. J. M. Gleason, "Steatite for high-frequency insulation," *J. Brit. Inst. Radio Engrs.*, **6**, 20–32 (Jan/Feb 1946).
101. G. Economos, "Current problems in the production of magnetic ceramics," *J. Electrochem. Soc.*, **106**, 465–467 (May 1959).
102. K. Torker, "Calculation of pressure distribution during the pressing of powders" (in German), Arch. Eisenhüttenw., **27**, 285 (1956).
103. W. F. Janssen, "Tailor-made precision ceramic parts," Materials & Methods, **44**, 107–109 (Sept. 1956).
104. R. F. Rea and J. W. Ripple, "Cutting and grinding ceramics," *Am. Ceram. Soc. Bull.*, **36**, 163–167 (May 1957).
105. T. K. Bierlein, H. W. Newkirk, Jr. and B. Mastel, "Etching of refractories and cermets by ion bombardment," *J. Am. Ceram. Soc.*, **41**, 196–200 (June 1959).
106. Corning Glass Works, Corning, N. Y. Bulletin on Pyroceram, May 1957; Progress Report No. 2 (Mar. 1958); No. 3 (1959).
107. A. E. Gorum, E. R. Parker and J. A. Pask, "Effect of surface conditions on room-temperature ductility of ionic crystals," *J. Am. Ceram. Soc.*, **41**, 161–164 (May 1958).

CHAPTER 3

MICA

Introduction

The universal use of mica spacers for the relative positioning of the elements of the internal tube structure, and their insulation from each other, has made mica nearly as indispensable for the mass production of receiving tubes as glass which is used for their envelopes. While ceramic spacers were used by some few manufacturers as long as 20 years ago, this practice could not survive for economic reasons because ceramic parts are of necessity more costly and, in days gone by, could not be produced in quantity to the accuracy required. Natural mica is thus being used for spacers in all mass-produced receiving-type tubes. ASTM Specifications* for grading and testing of mica and mica products are listed in Table 3.1.

Mineralogy. "Mica is found in all parts of the world, but commercially important deposits occur in India, Madagascar, the United States, Canada, South America, South Africa, and the U.S.S.R. The useful varieties are complex silicates:

Muscovite (white mica) . . . . $KAl_2(OH)_2(AlSi_3O_{10})$
Phlogopite (amber mica) . . . . $KMg_3(OH)_2(AlSi_3O_{11})$

"Part of the aluminum of muscovite has been replaced by magnesium in phlogopite. About 4% water of constitution occurs in the molecule, and other atoms, notably fluorine, are often included in the structure. These complex silicates may be considered as polymers based on $(Si_2O_5)^{2-}$ chains in which partial replacement of silicon by aluminum has occurred. The chains are cross-linked laterally by extensive sharing of oxygen, producing plane-polymerized layers, with weak bonding between layers through potassium ions. This structure permits cleavage of crystals into very thin laminae.

"Muscovite occurs in pegmatite veins (usually associated with feldspar) and is also common in metamorphic rocks such as gneiss and schist. Phlogopite is found in crystalline limestones, dolomites, and schists. Both micas form monoclinic prismatic crystals and possess excellent basal cleavage. In sheets at least 0.030 in. thick, micas show marked color; muscovite may be clear, green, yellow brown, or ruby, while phlogopite appears amber, brown, or ruby. Stains or spots in mica may be harmful if they are red or black; this indicates iron or manganese oxide, which impairs the dielectric proper-

* American Society For Testing Materials, 1916 Race St., Philadelphia 3, Pa. Reprints of these specifications can be obtained for a very nominal fee; users of mica should have copies on file. For general information on mica see references 1–7.

128

TABLE 3.1. ASTM SPECIFICATIONS FOR GRADING AND TESTING
OF MICA AND MICA PRODUCTS

D 351–57T	Natural muscovite mica, based on visual quality.
D 352–56T	Testing pasted mica, used in electrical insulation.
F 652–51	Measuring mica stampings, used in electronic devices and incandescent lamps.
D 748–54T	Natural block mica and mica films, suitable for use in fixed mica-dielectric capacitors.
D 1039–58	Glass-bonded mica, used as electrical insulation.
D 1082–54	Power factor and dielectric constant of natural mica.
D 149–55	Tentative methods of tests for dielectric breakdown voltage and dielectric strength of electrical insulating materials at commerical power frequencies.

ties. Yellow and green stains are clay or vegetable matter and affect only the clarity. Muscovite mica is somewhat harder than phlogopite, but the latter withstands exposure to higher temperature before losing the water of constitution. When this happens, both varieties turn silvery white and lose their physical strength. Both are chemically inert and unaffected by water, solvents, alkalies, and acids (except hydrofluoric and sulfuric). They are vulnerable to oil, however, which works its way into the laminae and separates them."[7]

Mining and Preparation. "Mica-bearing rock is blasted, and the crystals are removed by hand from the adhering material and then separated into two groups according to size. Pieces with a laminar area smaller than 1 sq. in. are set aside as scrap for grinding; the remainder are delaminated into pieces 0.007 to 0.040 in. thick and further separated. Punch and circle mica is that from which circles up to 2 in. in diameter can be punched. The balance is further trimmed of edge imperfections and graded by size and quality. It is then ready for sale as block or film mica, depending on thickness, or for separation into splittings ranging in thickness from 0.0006 to 0.0012 in.

"Splittings of various sizes are made by hand. Successive laminae are peeled off a block by inserting a pointed knife tip into the edge of the crystal. This process is established as a large-scale home industry in several sections of India, the major source of supply for the American electrical industry. While domestic muscovite mica is of suitable quality, the cost of splittings prepared in the United States would be much higher than that of the imported material. Mica-splitting machines have been developed over the past years, but none has come into successful commercial operation.

"The larger sizes of splittings are prepared in "book" form—each one being the same shape and size as the block from which it was split. A book may have 10 to 30 splittings. Small splittings are usually "loose," each one being of different size and shape."[7]

Fabrication. "Each mica pattern or part requires a special precision die to produce clean-edged parts, free from burrs, delaminations, and cracks. This die, even for the simplest design, must be made of special steel, and requires expert tool-making and precision equipment in its manufacture. A new die is required not only for each change in pattern, but also for each change in thickness. For instance, a die which has been designed to stamp out condenser films 3 mils thick cannot be used for films 1.2 mils thick; of course, the reverse is also true. Mica dies are so highly specialized in their design and construction that ordinary tool-making experience is insufficient to make a die capable of producing parts accurately and in satisfactory quantities.

"The physical characteristics of mica make it impractical to have tolerances less than 0.0005 in. The cost decreases as the tolerance increases. Since a mica die cannot be lubricated and mica must be punched dry, dust particles and mica flakes tend to distort the holes that have been punched, and, therefore, make inspection difficult for closer tolerances. Several punched parts must be checked in order to arrive at a satisfactory average reading.

"Holes in sheet metal may be pierced and other operations performed before the blanks are cut, but not so with mica, which comes in individual pieces. For this reason, compound dies must be used for fabricating the mica patterns. A compound die punches the outside shape and all the inside holes with one stroke of the press.

"Since the design of the die has direct bearing on the cost of the fabricated part, it is recommended that either a mica fabricator or a mica diemaker be consulted before designs are adopted. The limitations of the material necessitate that certain factors in design be considered by die engineers. Although, for the most part, problems of design vary with each pattern, there are certain rules that should apply to all designs.

"One rule is that the maximum thickness should not exceed 50 per cent of the diameter of the smallest hole. Holes cannot be placed too close to the outside edge because the material will break down through cracking and delamination. The distance, however, depends on the thickness of the mica and the size of the hole. The minimum wall, either between the hole and the edge of the blank, or between two holes, should be 80 to 100 mils for condenser films, and on other parts not less than 20 to 25 mils."[6]

Physical Properties. While mineralogists recognize eight distinct species of pure mica, only five of these are commercially important, of which the two mentioned above are being used in the electronic industry.[1] For spacers in electron tubes, muscovite has been used almost exclusively, and users have come to look upon India ruby mica as the most desirable grade, al-

TABLE 3.2. PROPERTIES OF NATURAL MICA[6]

Property	Muscovite	Phlogopite
Specific gravity	2.6–3.2	2.6–3.2
Hardness, Mohs scale	2.8–3.2	2.5–3.0
Modulus of elasticity, psi (10 mils thick)	25×10^6	25×10^6
Coefficient of thermal expansion per °C	3.6×10^{-5}	5.5×10^{-2}
Specific heat	0.207	0.207
Water of constitution, %	4.5	3
Dehydration temp, °C	625	1000
Refractive index	1.56–1.60	1.58–1.61
Optic axial angle, degrees	50–75	5–25
Permittivity	6.5–8.7	5–6
Volume resistivity, megohms per cu. cm.	2×10^7–1×10^{11}	*
Dielectric strength in air, volts per mil (1–3 mils thick)	3,000–6,000	3,000–4,200
Power factor	0.0001–0.0004	0.004–0.07

* Somewhat less than for muscovite.

though Brazilian muscovite is of equal quality and therefore coming into steadily increasing use.

Phlogopite, or amber mica, is mainly imported from Madagascar and Canada. Its chief uses are for domestic and industrial heating appliances.

The physical properties of muscovite and phlogopite are compared in Table 3.2.[6] Phlogopite stands out by its higher heat resistance but its dielectric properties are inferior to those of muscovite.

H. S. Endicott and G. E. Ledges of the General Electric Company Engineering Laboratories* recently discovered that certain naturally occurring micas could have their high-temperature electrical properties considerably improved by appropriate heat treatments. The majority of micas crumble when heated above 500 or 600°C, as combined water is released from within the lattice structure. Certain domestic micas (Canadian phlogopite) were not subject to such disintegration when heated for 4 hrs at 1000°C. The low-frequency resistivity of the material was increased by such heat treatment. At 500°C, the resistivity of the baked material was found to be four times that of the unbaked material. Capacitors have been produced which will operate successfully at temperatures as high as 800°C. This process should be of considerable interest for application in electron tubes.

Earlier investigators concluded that muscovite and phlogopite micas withstand heating between 400 and 600°C without appreciable change in their characteristics. Hidnert and Dickson[2] find that this statement is essen-

* General Electric Company Press Release No. 6, September 10, 1956. See also *Electronics*, Oct. 1956, p. 10. This work was performed on a subcontract under a prime Air Force Contract for the Electronic Components Laboratory of the Wright Air Development Center, Wright-Patterson Air Force Base, Ohio.

tially true for muscovite mica, but that appreciable changes in physical characteristics occurred when some samples of phlogopite were heated to 600°C. Powell and Griffiths[8] investigated the thermal conductivity of some muscovite and phlogopite micas up to 600°C. However, Canadian and Madagascan phlogopite micas indicated a pronounced decrease in thermal conductivity between 150 and 250°C, which was only partially reversible on cooling. Hidnert and Dickson[9] also investigated the effect of heat treatment on the power factor of mica and report as follows:

"The power factors of nearly all specimens of muscovite mica from Brazil and Guatemala were slightly greater at 100 kc than at 1,000 kc. The power factor of each specimen of phlogopite mica was considerably greater at 100 kc than at 1,000 kc. The power factors of the samples of phlogopite mica from Madagascar and Mozambique are considerably larger than the power factors of the samples of muscovite mica from Brazil and Guatemala. Heating the samples of phlogopite and muscovite micas to 600°C, with or without a load on each sample, caused considerable increases in the power factors of the phlogopite micas and only slight changes in the power factors of the muscovite micas. The power factors of the phlogopite mica from Madagascar which was heat-treated without a load, are less than the power factors of this mica heat-treated with a load. However, the power factors of the phlogopite mica from Mozambique heat-treated without a load are considerably greater than the power factors of this mica heat-treated with a load."

Roy[10] studied the effect of various heat-treating cycles on the weight loss of four species of mica which were pulverized and then decomposed by heat, water vapor under pressure, and electrodialysis. Figure 3.1 shows the weight loss of pulverized muscovite (80 per cent passing through a 200–mesh sieve) as a function of the heating time when exposed in a platinum crucible in air to the various temperatures indicated on the curves. It is apparent that dehydration at 450°C continues even after 100 hours and that only a heat treatment at 1050°C brings about total water loss in one hour. This observation must be correlated with the fact that the mica lattice breaks down between 940 and 980°C.[11] If the temperature is kept below 940°C, no phase change occurs, and the dehydration consists entirely of the expulsion of the hydroxyl ions. A baking treatment at about 900°C is thus indicated as most effective, but for tube applications it is general practice not to exceed 600°C.

The gas evolved by mica of unspecified origin was analyzed with the aid of the omegatron spectrometer at very low pressures and elevated temperatures by Wagener and Marth.[12] Table 3.3 gives their results.

Sudden heat shock is likely to affect the mica structure adversely, and the effect of heat treatment on the physical characteristics, such as thickness,

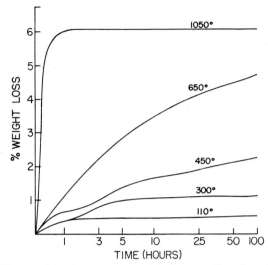

Figure 3.1. Change of total percentage weight loss as a function of time for muscovite held at various temperatures. After Roy.[10] (*Courtesy The American Ceramic Society.*)

thermal and electrical conductivity, transparency and color, must be borne in mind in critical applications such as windows for Geiger counters, target plates for storage tubes, and signal plates for television camera tubes. Fired micas should be stored in a dust-free, dry atmosphere and be used within not more than two days.

It is perhaps of some interest to quote here remarks made by Rudy[13] in a patent disclosure which had as its object the replacement of mica sheet used in iconoscopes by thin sheet of ceramic in order to avoid the inherent faults of mica.

"The target of such a tube has been made with a thin sheet of mica, upon one surface of which is formed a mosaic of photo-synthesized material. On the opposite surface of the mica sheet is applied a conductive coating of a suspension of carbon in a binder, or a commercial coating such as 'Aquadag.' The mica sheet used for the target electrode is one which is formed from a high-grade type of mica found principally in certain regions of Africa and India. This mica must conform to critical specifications in that it must not have any organic inclusions. It must have no gas bubbles

TABLE 3.3. PERCENTAGE COMPOSITION OF GAS EVOLVING FROM MICA[12]

Temperure, °C	Total p, Torr	H_2O	CH_4	CO	N	H_2
200	8.8×10^{-8}	3	0.5	67	26	3
300	3.2×10^{-6}	13	3	50	22	11
350	5.9×10^{-6}	10	2	34	14	39

between its surfaces.* The mica sheet must have no irregularities such as waves in the mica formed in any way. To be used for a target, the mica sheet must be carefully split so that the surfaces of the sheet present no jumps in laminations. Lastly, such a mica sheet must be one which, when subjected to a baking temperature in the order of 900°C, will not blister. The presence of any of the above effects tends to produce spurious signals in the output signal of the tube. These critical requirements entail expensive and careful processing to obtain proper targets . . . The mica target sheets used in iconoscope tubes, of the type described, normally have a thickness of between one to two mils, and a dielectric constant of about 5.5. These parameters provide the requisite capacity between the signal plate and the mosaic of the target for the electron beam of around 0.2 microampere to discharge each elemental area on each end of the beam across the target.''

The sorting of trimmed mica into various grades according to existing specifications used to be, and to a large extent still is, a highly specialized art which requires long years of training. Highly skilled operators can judge the thickness of mica within a tolerance of ± 1 mil by feel alone. In addition, many shades of color must be distinguished, and an account taken of the amount of stains present. The grading by color is complicated by the fact that mica from a single mine exhibits more or less variation in color from specimen to specimen, and from spot to spot within the same specimen.

In order to distinguish ruby mica from nonruby micas of the same qualities which tend to be brittle and have undesirably high power factors, Judd[15] has established a color standard for ruby mica on the basis of carefully controlled optical measurements.

At the beginning of World War II, the War Production Board inaugurated a mica conservation program with the object to search for new sources and stimulate the development of test methods that could be used at mine locations for rapidly classifying the electrical quality of mica for capacitor and electrical use so as to supplement the visual quality classification ASTM D351. This endeavor resulted in two portable, battery-operated instruments for (a) measuring the Q of mica at one megacycle and (b) locating conducting inclusions and mechanical faults that might adversely influence the dielectric strength of block mica or splittings. ASTM Specification D748 was issued as a result of these investigations conducted by Coutlee.[16] The results showed that mica previously judged unsuitable for use in highest-quality, as well as less-critical types of capacitors, by visual tests, can

---

* Mica contains interstitial cavities which are a prolific source of gas if distorted, or otherwise damaged by vibrational stresses, or shock.[14] (Footnote added by present author.)

be used on the basis of fast, reliable electrical tests which increased the supply of critical mica by 60 per cent.

Agreement on Q classification by the rapid methods of test was quite close when a wide variety of types of mica were submitted for test by this method to seven different laboratories. Muscovite mica from widely different sources gave uniform readings for the dielectric constant at one megacycle. India ruby mica maintained its top rating, but green-type mica which was on the basis of visual classification not acceptable for capacitor use in the past, now rated as a satisfactory material for critical applications. It is only natural, that the acceptance of these more scientific methods of grading by the industry, and particularly by the mica producers, will be slow, and that the human element of pride in a long-established skill for selecting mica grades and using them on that basis will be difficult to overcome. Considering the strategic importance of mica, however, it seems that we can ill afford outmoded inspection methods.

The Material Laboratory of the New York Naval Shipyard at Brooklyn, New York is now conducting an extensive investigation under the sponsorship of the Bureau of Ships with the object to establish quantitative tests for the physical properties of mica and mica-like materials suitable for electron tube spacers.[17] Special equipment has been constructed to determine such parameters as tensile strength, vibrational resistance, modulus of elasticity, hardness, dielectric properties, electrical resistivity, and thermal decomposition at elevated temperatures. There can be no doubt that this work will result in the establishment of greatly improved test procedures which will eliminate many of the uncertainties to which reference was made above.

Process Techniques. Efforts have been made in recent years to perform the operations of splitting of mica by automatic machinery but no real success has been achieved along these lines, as mentioned above.[18] Mica can be split into extremely thin and uniform layers which are still strong enough to withstand atmospheric pressure over a considerable area. Wu, Meaker, and Glassford[19] report that mica of a thickness corresponding to a weight of 5 mg/cm² has been found to withstand atmospheric pressure over an area of one and one-eighth inch diameter very well. For the laboratory worker who undertakes his own fabrication of mica, Strong[20] has described a method for obtaining thin mica splittings without tearing; after the edge has been pried open with a sharp dissecting needle, a drop of water is introduced which prevents tearing on parting the layers. Aharoni and Frei[21] have carried this method one step farther by performing the whole splitting operation under water and observing the mica sheet while it is illuminated with polarized light. Good layers equivalent to 0.8 mg/cm² were easily cleaved by using this method.

An "air-flow" classification system for separating mica parts of required thickness from those which do not meet thickness specification has been recently developed by Ford Radio & Mica Corporation.[22] Tube spacers in the thickness range from 0.006 to 0.015 in. are separated with a tolerance of 0.002 in. by regulated air streams which float the parts into bins for over-size, under-size, and normal lots. An additional electronic inspection for 0.002 in. thickness tolerance then follows.

To reduce surface leakage, an insulating coating is frequently sprayed onto mica and dried with hot air at about 80°C. The coating mixture consists of magnesium oxide in distilled water, zirconium oxide, or aluminum oxide, in methyl alcohol or polyvinyl alcohol, or mixtures of these constituents. Elaborate conveyor-belt furnaces have been built for spraying and drying on a mass-production basis, but barrel-coating seems to be generally preferred. The micas are tumbled in a barrel made from wire mesh and exposed to the spray material at the same time. A hot-air blast takes care of the drying during spraying, which is followed by a baking cycle.

Leakage resistance of natural mica spacers has been found to be frequency dependent by workers at the Arinc Research Corporation.[23] As predicted by theoretical investigations conducted earlier by James and Humphreys,[24] r-f leakage resistance above 10 KC drops sharply with increasing frequency. In the megacycle range of frequencies, the r-f leakage is smaller than the measured d-c leakage resistance by factors varying from 10^3 to 10^6.

In order to secure the tube mount firmly within the glass bulb and at the same time make allowance for the varying internal diameter of the bulb, it has been common practice to provide the top mica spacer with teeth at its periphery which can bend on insertion of the mount into the bulb if the latter is slightly undersize. This crushing of the mica teeth is naturally conducive to the formation of loose mica flakes which can lodge

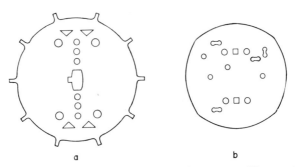

Figure 3.2. Old form (a) and new form (b) of mica spacers. The new form reduces the incidence of flaking and chipping. After Rodenhuis, Santing, and van Tol.[25] (*Courtesy Philips Gloeilampenfabrieken, Eindhoven, Netherlands.*)

between critical elements, become conductive by being coated with cathode material, cause shorts or noise, and poison the cathode if deposited on it. An improved contour of the mica spacer (Figure 3.2) circumvents this effect, especially if the glass envelope is accurately narrowed at the height of the spacer to an inner diameter about 0.1 to 0.2 mm smaller than the largest diameter of the spacer, as shown in Figure 3.3.[25] One might assume that the use of wire snubbers, which are inserted into the mica, would produce the same result except that the wires may wear loose in the holes and produce mica dust in the process of doing so. Raytheon Manufacturing Company[26] reports on an evaluation of "bulb pinching" intended to ensure good contact between spacer and bulb and concludes that this technique did not

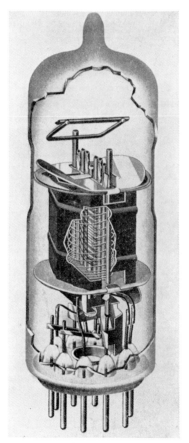

Figure 3.3. Type E80F pentode, fitted with mica spacers as in Figure 3.2. The upper spacer fits tightly in a constricted region of the envelope. After Rodenhuis, Santing, and van Tol.[25] (*Courtesy Philips Gloeilampenfabrieken, Eindhoven, Netherlands.*)

indicate advantages in terms of vibration noise or vibration life. The use of micas with ears is still common practice in U. S.; a premium is being paid, however, for bulbs that have a constant internal diameter. The case where the bulb has a sufficiently small diameter at the bottom to crush the mica ears on insertion of the mount and then a larger diameter at the final location of the mount in the upper region is particularly objectionable as it causes a loose fit.

Bulbs for critical subminiature tubes are given a specially flared rim by some manufacturers so that the mount can be easily inserted into the bulb without damage to the mica spacer points which, for critical tubes, are more numerous than on micas for regular tubes.[27] Figure 3.4a, b illustrates this measure. In order to further minimize the danger of vibration on exposure to mechanical shock, critical tubes are provided with two micas on each side of the mount, as shown in Figure 3.5a, so that the number of contact points is correspondingly enlarged. The clearance holes for support rods and cathodes are larger on the inner micas than they are on the outer micas so that leakage paths are interrupted and heat conduction loss of the cathode sleeve is minimized. Figure 3.5b gives a view of the inner mica backed up by the outer mica. Anti-leakage slots in both micas are also apparent. Figure 3.6 illustrates the use of an additional mica which serves as

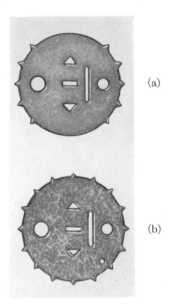

(a)

(b)

Figure 3.4(a, b) Mica spacers for critical tubes are provided with additional contact points, as shown at bottom, in comparison to regular spacers, shown at top. (*Courtesy General Electric Co. Receiving Tube Department.*[27])

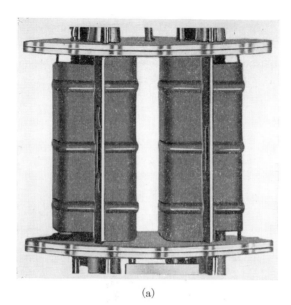

(a)

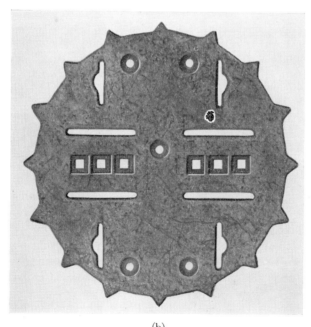

(b)

Figure 3.5(a, b) Illustration of the use of double spacers for reliable tubes. (*Courtesy General Electric Co. Receiving Tube Department.*[27])

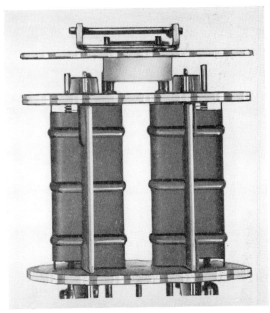

Figure 3.6. Tube mount with additional mica below getter to prevent conductive deposits on top mica of electrode structure. (*Courtesy General Electric Co. Receiving Tube Department.*[27])

a getter flash shield to prevent conductive deposits on the outer mica at the top of the mount.

A detailed review article on the applications of mica in electron tubes has recently been published by Espe.[28] The recent book by Knoll and Kazan[29] also contains a section on mica.

Synthetic Mica. The strategic importance of natural mica and its shortage of supply in times of emergency in countries where natural mica is not found have stimulated efforts to produce mica synthetically. The possibility of such a process was demonstrated in France by Moisson in 1865, and workers in Germany conducted active research on synthetic mica during the second World War with sufficiently promising results that a pilot plant was set up for production. Active research on the development of synthetic mica was taken up in the United States after World War II under sponsorship of private and government agencies. These efforts have been successful to a considerable extent. Phlogopite mica can be crystallized from a melt at atmospheric pressure by replacing the hydroxyl ion found in natural phlogopite mica with the fluorine ion. A few single crystals four by four inch in area and almost one-eighth inch thick have been grown. The details of the manufacturing procedures have been described in the

TABLE 3.4. PROPERTIES OF MICAS*

	Muscovite[1]	Phlogopite[2]	Fluor-phlogopite[3]
Chemical composition	$KAl_2 \cdot AlSi_3O_{10^-}$ (OH)$_2$	$KMg_3AlSi_3O_{10^-}$ (OH)$_2$	$KMg_3AlSi_3O_{10}F_2$
Maximum temperature of use, °C	600	850	870–1010
Purity	Fair–good	Poor–fair	Excellent
Transparency	Fair–good	Nil–poor	Excellent
Electrical properties:			
Power factor	0.0001–0.0004	0.004–0.07	0.0002
Dielectric constant	6.5–8.7	5–6	6.3
Dielectric strength, v/mil[5]	3,000–6,000	3,000–4,200	4,000 (approx)
Splittability	Good–excellent	Good	Fair–good**
Punchability	Good	Good[6]	Fair–good
Nuclear-radiation resistance	Excellent	Excellent	Excellent
Crystal or sheet sizes	2 × 3 in.–3 × 5 in. (common); 8 × 12 in. (rare)	2 × 3 in.–3 × 4 in. (common); 9 × 11 in. (rare)	1 × 1½ in. (common); 4 × 4 in. (very rare)
Forms available	Sheet; powder	Sheet; powder	Sheet; reconstituted sheet; 2 different ceramics; powder

* After Humphrey[35] by permission from "Engineering Materials Handbook," by C. L. Mantell, editor; Copyright 1958 McGraw Hill Book Co., Inc.

** See footnote.

[1] Potassium, or ruby, mica.

[2] Magnesium, or amber, mica.

[3] Fluorine, or diamond, mica.

[4] Pure synthetic mica.

[5] 1–3 mils in air.

[6] Less delamination than with other varieties.

literature.[30-34] Table 3.4 compares some of the more important properties of natural and synthetic mica.* Fluor-phlogopite has excellent dielectric properties which are equivalent to those of natural muscovite; its heat resistance is much greater, and its vapor pressure is exceedingly low. A report by Hanley[36] of the Naval Research Laboratory gives the following results from tests made on synthetic fluor-phlogopite mica:

1. "The material when pressed to 2.73 grams per cc was vacuum tight and maintained a constant pressure of 2.2×10^{-9} Torr after baking at 390°C (for 12 hrs.) and 5×10^{-7} Torr after air-baking at 800°C (for one hour).

* The splittability of synthetic mica is given as fair to good in Table 3.4. This seems to be an over-optimistic statement; it is generally very poor. The flakes adhere to each other firmly and resist separation; moreover they crack easily.

2. "The material was machinable to 10-mil disks with an ordinary high-speed cutoff tool and could be ground to 2.5 mils. However, attempts to punch holes in samples of 10 and 30 mils thickness were unsuccessful on the initial attempt. ("It was concluded that for production applications molding techniques would have to be used.")

3. "Synthetic fluor-phlogopite could be brazed at 820°C in vacuum with titanium-core solder to copper to form a vacuum-tight joint. Better wetting of the mica was obtained when titanium hydride was used in addition to the brazing material. ("The linear coefficient of expansion of the synthetic mica is 135×10^{-7} in the range of 0 to 800°C.")

4. "A dielectric constant of 5.72 was determined at 9375 Mc with a loss tangent less than 0.005." ("From measurements made also at 34,750 Mc, one can infer that the dielectric constant is essentially the same as that of natural mica.")

In a later report,[37] Hanley gives further data on the vacuum properties of synthetic mica which have been incorporated with the statements listed above but set apart in parentheses. When a 0.400-inch-dia. disk, 0.010-in. thick, was brazed onto a recessed shoulder of a metal cylinder and the assembly evacuated, the synthetic mica disk withstood atmospheric pressure, while a similar disk only 0.005-in. thick cracked. A rectangular sample (0.074 × 0.148 in.), such as might be used for a waveguide window at $\lambda = 5$ mm, withstood atmospheric pressure when 0.0025-in. thick.

"Some measurements were also made on the loss of weight of a sample of synthetic mica when heated in air. Figure 3.7 illustrates the effect of heating a powdered sample at 800°C in air. It is observed that the sample lost

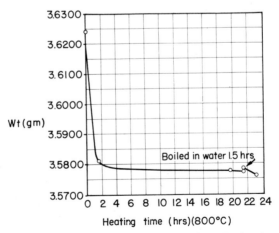

Figure 3.7. Effect of heating a powdered sample of synthetic mica at 800°C in air. After Hanley.[37] (*Courtesy American Ceramic Society.*)

about 11.7 mg/g during the first one and one-half hours and about 1 mg/g in the following 20 hours. Immersing the sample in boiling water for one and one-half hours had little effect. From these results it is concluded that air firing of the sample is desirable but that water absorption is small."[37]

The bulk of a melt of synthetic mica is in the form of small flakes and microscopic crystals which can be processed into one of the following three forms:

1. hot-pressed mica
2. ceramoplastics
3. reconstituted synthetic mica sheet.

Fluorine mica has the peculiar property of bonding to itself under heat and pressure (1). By mixing the mica powder with phosphoric acid, glass or ceramics, and molding the mass at about 600°C, one arrives at hard bodies which can be produced to tolerances in size close to 0.001 in., or be readily machined in the cold state (2). Reconstituted mica sheet, (3), synthetic or natural, is made by disintegrating scrap mica by hydraulic or mechanical force, heat, and/or chemical action and then recombining the small particles to form continuous, flexible sheets.[7] Additional data on these materials can be obtained from manufacturers* and in recent review articles.[38]

Glass-bonded natural mica is known under the trade names "Mycalex" 400, 410, 410X, and 385. Corresponding materials made by compounding synthetic mica with glass frit, or other inorganic materials, are marketed by the Mycalex Corporation of America under the trade name "Supramica Ceramoplastic," and several grades are available as Supramica 500, 555, 560, and 620 which are characterized by higher temperature stability. These materials can be machined to very close tolerances, or molded (555, 560). Supramica 620 is a machinable grade which is dimensionally stable up to 850°C. Table 3.5 gives its properties. In the preparation of this material, a glass frit is first formed into which synthetic mica flakes are completely dissolved at elevated temperature. The glass is then quenched and ground to a fine powder which is formed into disks, or sheets, and subsequently fired at temperatures as high as 1000°C. During the heating cycle, the synthetic mica precipitates from the glass as an extremely fine, interlocked crystal phase which greatly contributes to the improved properties. By improved processing techniques and slight composition changes, it has been possible to obtain a dissipating factor as low as 0.0006 and a loss tangent at 8,600 MC as low as 0.0003, values which compare favorably with those of high-purity aluminas and steatite.†

* Mycalex Corporation of America, Clifton, N. J.

† The author is indebted to Messrs. Backus and Hessinger[39] for providing him with an advance copy of their paper.

TABLE 3.5. PROPERTIES OF SUPRAMICA 620 CERAMOPLASTIC*

Electrical

Dissipation factor—1 megacycle................................. 0.0015
Dielectric constant—1 megacycle................................ 7.2
Loss factor—1 megacycle....................................... 0.011
Dielectric strength—volts/mil, $\frac{1}{8}$ in. thickness.................. 250.
Arc resistance—seconds....................................... 300.

Thermal

Maximum operating temperature............................. 1550°F (850°C)
Thermal expansion coef./°C. $\times 10^{-6}$, 0–300°C..................... 11.6
T_e value—temp/10^6 ohm. cm.................................. 550°C.
Thermal conductivity—cal/cm.² sec °C./cm at 100°C.............. 0.0012

Mechanical

Tensile strength—psi....................................... 5,000.
Compressive strength—psi.................................. 35,000.
Flexural strength—psi...................................... 10,000.
Modulus of elasticity $\times 10^6$—psi static loading.................... 12.5
Impact strength, Charpy—ft–lb................................ 0.5
Specific gravity.. 3.2
Rockwell M hardness... 110.

* Courtesy Mycalex Corporation of America

Ceramoplastics are easily outgassed and are being used for structural members in vacuum tubes.[34] Gould[40] has reported on the use of synthetic mica in the design of a keep-alive electrode for TR tubes and found it satisfactory at high peak-power levels for operation in excess of 1000 hours. Synthetic mica has been used successfully for high-temperature vacuum-tight windows which could be baked out at 700°C when a 0.015-in. thick, annealed copper gasket was used in compression to accomplish a seal to a stainless steel flange according to Sterzer.[41] The technique for making mica window seals described by Donal, Jr.[42, 43] made use of a glass frit (solder glass) which cannot be outgassed above 400°C. The same limitation, to a more marked degree, applies to mica seals to metal or glass made with the aid of silver chloride. Especially for demountable tubes, the copper gasket seal thus offers distinct advantages.

Reconstituted natural mica has been evaluated for use in electron tubes at the Receiving Tube Department of the General Electric Company at Owensboro, Ky. McNees[44] finds that all of the different samples tested evolve more gas than natural mica up to 600°C; at 800°C, however, natural mica spacers become very gassy, and reconstituted mica spacers show less gas evolution by comparison. Tubes Type 6201 were made with these spacers and life tested. Samples of reconstituted mica from different suppliers showed greatly varying performance; the best of these approached natural mica spacer tubes up to 320 hrs. life but, thereafter, deterioration of emission, transconductance, and plate current became apparent.

REFERENCES

1. I. W. Horton, "Mica," United States Department of the Interior, Bureau of Mines, Information Bull. (I.C.6822, revised Aug. 1941).
2. P. Hidnert and G. Dickson, "Some physical properties of mica," *J. Research Natl. Bur. Standards*, **35**, 309–353 (RP1675) (Oct. 1945).
3. A. B. Lewis, E. L. Hall and F. R. Caldwell, "Some electrical properties of foreign and domestic micas and the effect of elevated temperatures on micas," (RP 347); *J. Research Natl. Bur. Standards*, **7**, 403–418 (Aug. 1931).
4. R. R. Chowdhury, "Handbook of Mica," Chemical Publishing Co., Inc., Brooklyn, 1941.
5. Chand Mull Rajgarhia, "Mining, Processing and Uses of Indian Mica," McGraw-Hill Book Co., Inc., New York, 1951.
6. Mica Fabricators Association, New York, N. Y. "Handbook on Fabricated Mica," 13 pp. (1949); a bulletin *Mica Review* is published from time to time and available free of charge.
7. M. M. Fromm, "Natural Mica," Section 35, pp. 36–43 in "Engineering Materials Handbook," C. L. Mantell, Ed., McGraw-Hill Book Co., Inc., New York, 1958.
8. R. W. Powell and E. Griffiths, "The variation with temperature of the thermal conductivity and the x-ray structure of some micas," *Proc. Roy. Soc. London*, **A163**, 189 (1937).
9. E. L. Hall, "Equipment and method for measurement of power factor of mica," *Proc. IRE*, **32**, 393–396 (July 1944).
10. R. Roy, "Decomposition and resynthesis of the micas," *J. Am. Ceram. Soc.*, **32**, 202–209 (June 1949).
11. J. B. Holt, I. B. Cutler and M. E. Wadsworth, "Rate of thermal dehydration of muscovite," *J. Am. Ceram. Soc.*, **41**, 242–246 (July 1958).
12. J. S. Wagener and P. T. Marth, "Analysis of gases at very low pressures by using the omegatron spectrometer," *J. Appl. Phys.*, **28**, 1027–1030 (Sept. 1957).
13. W. G. Rudy, "Ceramic mosaic for camera pick-up tube," U. S. Patent 2,727,170 (Dec. 13, 1955).
14. D. O. Holland, I. E. Levy and H. J. Davies, "Loss of thermionic emission in oxide-coated cathode tubes due to mechanical shock," *Proc. IRE*, **40**, 587–590 (May 1952).
15. D. B. Judd, "Color standard for ruby mica," *J. Research Natl. Bur. Standards*, **35**, 245–256 (RP 1671) (Oct. 1945).
16. K. G. Coutlee, "Electrical quality classification of raw mica by a rapid, direct-reading test method," *Am. Soc. Testing Materials, Proc.*, **46**, 1486–1495 (1946).
17. New York Naval Shipyard, Brooklyn, N. Y., Material Laboratory, Project 5032-B-14.2. "Standardization of Objective Tests for Mica and Mica-Like Materials Suitable for Electron Tube Spacers."
18. Sylvania Electric Products Inc., Emporium, Pa., "Industrial preparedness measures for electron tubes in guided missile applications," (NObs-8023 Rept. #1) (Oct. 1, 1945 to Jan. 1, 1955) AD62045; see also: *Electronics*, **30**, 228–229 (July 1957).
19. C. S. Wu, C. L. Meaker and H. A. Glassford, "Thin-window counter with special mica-to-glass seal," *Rev. Sci. Instr.*, **18**, 693–695 (Oct. 1947).
20. J. Strong, "On splitting mica," *Rev. Sci. Instr.*, **6**, 243 (Aug. 1935).

21. A. Aharoni and E. H. Frei, "The cleaving of mica in water," *J. Sci. Instr.*, **34**, 513 (Dec. 1957).

22. "Air flow mica classifier developed by Ford Radio," *Electronic News* (July 15, 1957).

23. C. L. Noelcke, "Determination Mechanisms in Electron Tubes," Arinc Research Monograph No. 6 (Nov. 7, 1958); Arinc Research Corporation, Washington 6, D. C.

24. E. G. James and B. L. Humphreys, "Resistive films in valves," *Wireless Engr.*, **26**, 93–95 (Mar. 1949).

25. K. Rhodenhuis, H. Santing and H. J. M. Van Tol, "The life and reliability of valves," *Philips Tech. Rev.*, **18**, (1956/1957; Dec. 1956). See also U. S. Patent 2,837,681 (June 3, 1958).

26. Advisory Group on Electron Tubes, Status Report No. 32 (Apr. 16, 1956). Contract NObsr-63475.

27. "Five-Star High-Reliability Receiving Tubes," Bulletin ETD-1425 (10M) 10/57, Receiving Tube Dept. General Electric Company, Owenboro, Ky. (Oct. 1957).

28. W. Espe, "Mica, a material for high-vacuum applications" (in German), *Vakuum-Technik*, **8**, 15–19 (Pt. 1) (Feb. 1959); 29–38 (Pt. 2) (Mar. 1959); 67–75 (Pt. 3) (Apr. 1959).

29. M. Knoll and B. Kazan, "Materials and Processes of Electron Devices," Springer-Verlag, Berlin 1959.

30. A. Van Valkenburg and R. G. Pike, "Synthesis of mica," *J. Research Natl. Bur. Standards*, **48**, 360–369 (May 1952).

31. J. E. Comeforo, R. A. Hatch, R. A. Humphrey and W. Eitel, "Synthetic mica investigations: I. A hot-pressed machinable ceramic dielectric," *J. Am. Ceram. Soc.*, **36**, 286–394 (Sept. 1953).

32. J. E. Comeforo and R. A. Hatch, "Synthetic mica investigations: IV. Dielectric properties of hot-pressed synthetic mica and other ceramics at temperatures up to 400°C." *J. Am. Ceram. Soc.*, **37**, 317–322 (July 1954).

33. J. E. Comeforo, "Synthetic mica investigations: V. A low-shrinkage machinable ceramic of phosphate-bonded synthetic mica," *J. Am. Ceram. Soc.*, **37**, 427–432 (Sept. 1954).

34. R. A. Hatch, R. A. Humphrey, W. Eitel and J. E. Comeforo, "Synthetic mica investigations: IX. Review of progress from 1947 to 1955." Bureau of Mines, Report of Investigations 5337 (June 1957).

35. R. A. Humphrey, "Synthetic Mica," Section 35, pp. 43–45 in "Engineering Materials Handbook," C. L. Mantell, Ed., McGraw-Hill Book Co., Inc., New York, 1958.

36. T. E. Hanley, "Synthetic mica for vacuum tube use," The First National Conference on Tube Techniques, New York, Oct. 14, 1953; published in *ONR Research Rev.*, pp. 7–10 (Feb. 1954).

37. T. E. Hanley, "Vacuum properties of new synthetic mica," *Ceram. Age*, **66**, 40–41 (Oct. 1955). Presented at Second National Conference on Tube Techniques, New York, Oct. 26–28, 1954.

38. A. J. Monack, "Molded Inorganic and Organic Electrical Insulations." section 35, pp. 45–53 in "Engineering Materials Handbook," C. L. Mantell, Ed., Mc-Graw-Hill Book Co., Inc., New York, 1958.

39. A. S. Backus and P. S. Hessinger, "New Ceramoplastic insulating materials for 500°C electronic component application," Third National Convention on Military Electronics, Washington, D. C., June 29–July 1, 1959.

40. L. Gould, "Improved keep-alive design for TR tubes," *Proc. IRE*, **45**, 530–533 (Apr. 1957).
41. F. Sterzer, "Simple high-temperature vacuum-tight mica window," *Rev. Sci. Instr.*, **28**, 208–209 (Mar. 1957).
42. J. S. Donal, Jr., "Sealing mica to glass or metal to form a vacuum-tight joint," *Rev. Sci. Instr.*, **13**, 266–267 (June 1942).
43. J. Labeyrie, "Vacuum-tight sealing of glass and mica" (in French), *J. phys. radium*, **11**, 20 (Jan. 1950).
44. F. R. McNees, "Evaluation of Reconstituted Natural Mica for Use in Electron Tubes," Fourth Quarterly Progress Report (Apr. 1, 1958–June 30, 1958), Receiving Tube Department, General Electric Company, Owensboro, Ky. (Contr. No. DA36(039)-sc-75960. ASTIA No. 203605.

CHAPTER 4

CARBON AND GRAPHITE

Introduction

Carbon and graphite find many direct and indirect applications in the electrical industry; carbon brushes for commutators are a familiar item and so are carbon electrodes in electrolytic cells, or graphite electrodes in arc lamps. By far the largest tonnage of carbon and graphite is being used in the metallurgical and electrochemical industry in arc-melting furnaces. The largest carbon electrode made for submerged-arc furnaces was recently described as weighing seven tons and being more than five feet in diameter.[1] Carbon or graphite blocks, pipes, and beams are used as structural members; carbon blocks serve a useful purpose in block brazing. Diamond, another modification of carbon, is used for wire-drawing dies, as mentioned in preceding chapters, and as an abrasive for grinding ceramics. The abrasive properties of carbon and diamond stand in contrast to the lubricating quality of graphite which is used in a colloidal suspension to lubricate diamond dies.

These widely varying applications of carbon in its different modifications suggest a correspondingly wide range of physical properties which are brought about by different atomic arrangements. This story has been told by Kingswood[2] who gives a review of the role of carbon in the engineering and metallurgical industries. Other principle sources of information on carbon and graphite are listed in references 3–10.

The more specific applications of carbon and graphite in the electron tube industry have been described in an exhaustive review article in two parts by Espe[11] which is profusely illustrated and contains 85 references on the applications of carbon and graphite in high vacuum technique.

"*Carbon black* is a generic term for a group of intensely black, finely divided pigments made by thermal decomposition, or partial combustion, of the vaporizable portion of any carbonaceous material. Common soot produced by a smoky oil or coal fire is a form of carbon black similar to lamp black."[10] Depending on the method of manufacture and the raw material used, a great number of different carbon blacks with different properties are known. The present author well remembers investigating a variety of lamp blacks for the coating of tuning indicator targets to reduce the socalled "blocking effect" at low incident electron energies. The soot deposited onto the nickel target from an acetylene flame proved to be most effective, and the willemite powder was then sprayed on top of this soot

148

layer.[12, 13] Admixture of carbon to the willemite powder, or carbonization of a nitrocellulose spray carrier in a vacuum furnace, has also been practiced to impart a degree of conductivity to the luminescent coating.[14]

When carbon black is heated for a prolonged period to a temperature of 3000°C, *graphite* is formed which has a distinct crystalline structure;[10] its physical properties differ markedly from those of carbon black. Carbon which has been transformed into graphite at high temperature is known as *electrographite*. Just as in the case of carbon black, many varieties of electrographite are commercially available and differ in their properties depending on the raw materials used and the details of the graphitizing process. A very high degree of purity can be attained, and it is for this reason that graphite is used almost exclusively for electron tube components, or for surface coatings which are prepared from colloidal suspensions of graphite.

Physical and Chemical Properties

Figure 4.1 shows the phase diagram of carbon after Bundy and Hall,[15] and Table 4.1 gives the physical characteristics of carbon and electrographite.

Manufactured carbon products are predominantly of two types, both of which may be made from the same raw materials. When these materials

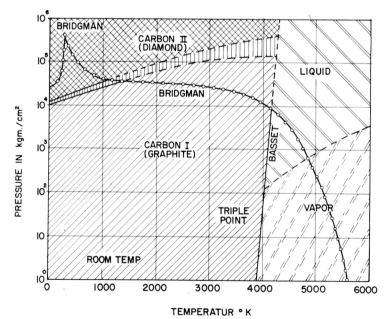

Figure 4.1. Phase diagram of carbon. After Bundy *et al.*[15] (*Courtesy Macmillan and Co., Ltd., London.*)

TABLE 4.1. PHYSICAL CHARACTERISTICS OF CARBON AND ELECTROGRAPHITE

Carbon	*Diamond*	*Graphite*
Atomic number: 6	Lattice type: A4* diamond	A9: hexagonal
Atomic weight: 12.010	Lattice constant:[16]† $a_0 = 3.56696 \pm 0.00005$A	$a_0 = 2.4612 \pm 0.0001$A $c_0 = 6.697$A
Atomic valence: 1, 2, 3, 4	No. atoms/unit cell: 8	4
Valance orbitals: $2\,s^2\,2\,p^2$	Closest approach of atoms:[1] 1.54A	1.415A (within layer) 3.35A (across layers)
Isotopes: (10), (11), 12, 13, (14)		
Thermal neutron cross-section:	$3.3 \pm 0.2 \dfrac{mbarn^{16}}{atom}$	AGOT:[2] $4.35 \dfrac{mbarn}{atom}$
	(1 barn = 10^{-24} cm²)	(Reactor graphite)
Density (g/cm³):[17, 18] 1.7–1.9	3.51	1.70 AGW: 1.65–1.68
Hardness (Mohs):[10]	10	0.5–2.0
Dielectric constant:[4] 2.4	16.5 (10KC)[5] 5.5 (100MC)	
Index of refraction:	2.40242–2.45922	1.93–2.07
Melting point (°C):[19] subl. 3,652–3,697	>3,500	subl. 3,652–3,697
Boiling point (°C):[19] 4,200	4,200	3700 (100 atm)
Sublimation temp. (°C): (4,350)		3700 (100 atm) 3400 (1 atm) Triple Point: 4000 (100 atm) (NCC Res. Lab.)
Heat of vaporization (Kcal/mole):		143[3]
Heat of sublimation (Kcal/mole):[21,29]		171.8 ± 0.24
Enthalpy ΔH_{298} (Kcal/mole):	−0.454 ± 0.03	0
Entropy S_{298} (cal/deg/mole):	0.583 ± 0.005	1.361 ± 0.005

Vapor pressure:[22, 21–24] Fig. 4.2

10^{-8}	10^{-7}	10^{-6}	10^{-5}	10^{-4}	10^{-3}	10^{-2}	10^{-1}	10^0	10^1	10^2	Torr
1950	2030	2140	2250	2380	2520	2700	2900	3140	3420	3800	°K

Rate of evaporation (gm/cm²/sec)[21] (Acheson graphite):

2400	2500	2600	2700	2800	2900	°K
4.4×10^{-8}	1.8×10^{-7}	7.2×10^{-7}	3.0×10^{-6}	1.2×10^{-5}	5.0×10^{-5}	Torr

Specific heat, C_p (cal/mole/°C)[3] (graphite):

25	127	327	527	727	927	1127	°C
2.066	2.851	4.03	4.75	4.15	5.42	5.67	

Thermal conductivity (cal/cm²/cm/°C/sec):

Varies widely (0.02 to 0.5 at 20°C)[25-28] depending on type of material, crystallite size, and direction of measurement; see Figure 4.3

* Symbols used by Ewald and Hermann for the classification of crystal structures in their "Strukturbericht."

†If more than one reference is given, the first one is the source of the quoted figures.

TABLE 4.1—(Continued)

Carbon	Diamond	Graphite

Coefficient of linear thermal expansion (cm/cm/°C); see Figure 4.4

  Varies widely (10 to 50 $\times$ 10^{-7} at 20°C) for polycrystalline material and differs markedly in two directions of crystallites.[18]

  Mean coefficient for polycrystalline material: 90 $\times$ 10^{-7} (0 $-$ 2500°C)

Thermal emissivity[29, 30]:

  Graphite: e_λ = (0.745 $\pm$ 0.012) + (1.88 $\pm$ 0.72) $\times$ 10^{-5} T_K for λ = 0.653 μ

  Carbon: e_λ = (0.789 $\pm$ 0.005) $-$ (1.40 $\pm$ 3.24) $\times$ 10^{-7} T_K

  Polished high-density graphite at 1480°K: e_λ = 0.780

  After repeated "sublimations" at 1480 and 2030°K, e_λ of originally polished, medium-density graphite rises from 0.75 to 0.905.

Thermal electron emission:[31-33, 19]

  Electron work function: 4.62 $\pm$ 0.02 e.v.

  Richardson constant A: 60 $\pm$ 2 a/cm^2/deg^2 (46[32], 30[33], 45–240[19])

  J = 0.5 to 2.2 ma/cm^2 at 2000°K[32]

Electrical resistivity (microhm. cm) (at 20°C):

  Varies widely (800 to 1300 for graphite; 3500 to 4600 for carbon) depending on type of material, heat treatment and direction of measurement; see Figures 4.5 and 4.6

Mechanical Properties:[36, 3-7, 35] (see Figures 4.7–4.10)

	Carbon	Graphite
Modulus of elasticity in tension (psi $\times$ 10^6)	1.6–2.3	0.8–1.4
Tensile strength (psi)	900–1100	440–2000
Compressive strength (psi)	6300–9000	1700–7500
Flexural strength (psi)	2500–3000	800–4000
Hardness (Scleroscope)	60–90	20–45

are heated to a temperature of the order of 1000°C, the resulting product is known as "industrial carbon" which is extremely hard and has low values of thermal and electrical conductivity. On heating to higher temperatures of the order of 2500°C, or more, "electrographite" results which is also known as "artificial graphite," or simply "graphite." Graphite is comparatively soft and can thus be easily machined. The conversion from carbon into graphite results in a 20-fold increase in thermal conductivity and a four-fold increase in electrical conductivity; graphite also has a lower tendency toward oxidation.[5] The combination of low thermal expansion rate on heating and high thermal conductivity results in an unusual resistance to heat shock; cracking or spalling of graphite is thus practically unknown.

It had been assumed at one time that carbon black was amorphous in distinction to graphite and diamond which show well-developed crystal lattices. Recent investigations have shown that carbon black also has a microcrystalline structure similar to that of graphite but probably much more irregular in nature.[2] According to Houska and Warren,[37] "a typical

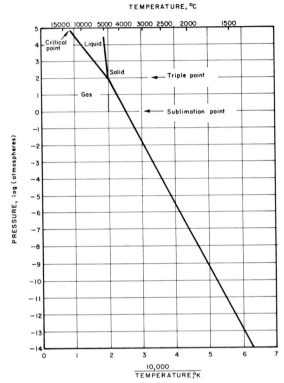

Figure 4.2. Vapor pressure of graphite. After Udy and Boulger.[3] (*Courtesy United States Atomic Energy Commission.*)

carbon black consists of parallel layer groups made up of individual graphite layers which are stacked roughly parallel to one another but random in orientation about the normal to the layer. The diameter of the layer is of the order 20–30A, and the thickness of the parallel layer groups, measured normal to the layers, is of the order 12–20A. On heat treating carbon blacks, the dimensions of the parallel layer groups increase, and the X-ray pattern sharpens. In the early stages, the layer diameter grows, and the number of layers in a parallel layer group increases, but the orientation of the layers about the layer normal remains random. When the layer diameter gets above a certain size ($L_a = 100A$), the layers begin to position themselves with respect to a neighboring layer in the graphite relation."

Diamond crystallizes in what is often called the "diamond-like lattice" in which each carbon atom is surrounded by four other carbon atoms which are located at the corners of a tetrahedron as shown in Figure 4.11. This structure is known as the diamond cubic lattice (A4) which is also characteristic for the structure of germanium. Graphite, on the other hand, forms

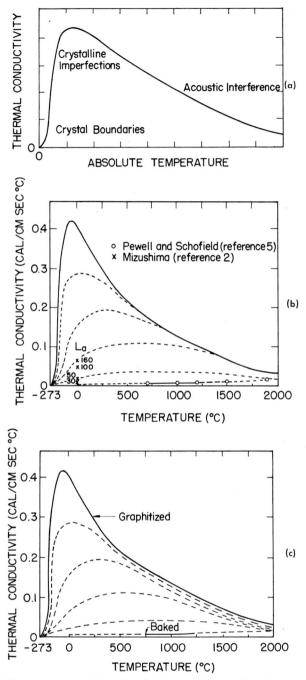

Figure 4.3. Thermal conductivity of carbon and graphite. After Castle.[26] (*Courtesy University of Buffalo.*)

(a) Schematic temperature dependence of the lattice heat conductivity. (b) Expected temperature dependence of the thermal conductivity of polycrystalline carbons as a function of crystallite size. Case of absence of intercrystalline resistances. (c) Same as b, but case of presence of intercrystalline resistances at high temperatures.

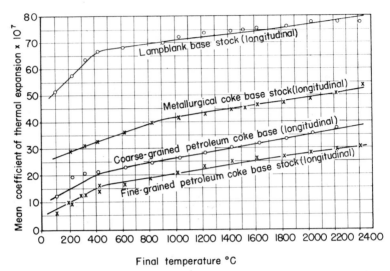

Figure 4.4. Mean coefficient of thermal expansion of National Carbon Company graphite grades. After Campbell.[6] (*Courtesy John Wiley & Sons, Inc.*)

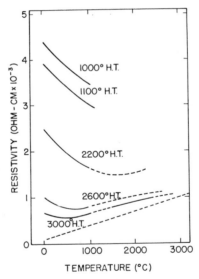

Fig. 4.5. Electrical resistivity *vs.* temperature for carbons of different heat treatment. After Mrozowski.[34] (*Courtesy American Institute of Physics.*)

sheet-like hexagonal lattices. The carbon atoms lying in the plane of a sheet are much more strongly bound than those belonging to different sheets. This fact explains the markedly different values observed for physical properties of graphite when measured in the direction of the sheet on the one hand and at right angle to the layer on the other.

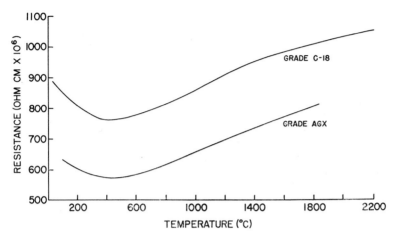

Figure 4.6. Electrical resistivity *vs.* temperature for National Carbon Company graphite grades C-18 and AGX, measured perpendicular to the direction in which molding pressure was applied. After Malmstrom, Keen, and Green, Jr.[35] (*Courtesy American Institute of Physics.*)

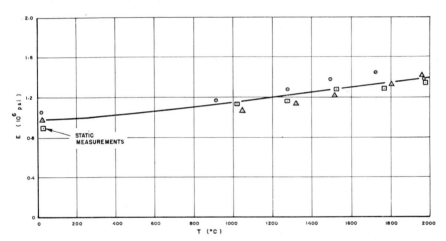

Figure 4.7. Young's modulus *vs.* temperature for National Carbon Company graphite grade ECA. After Malmstrom, Keen, and Green, Jr.[35] (*Courtesy American Institute of Physics.*)

Since the manufacturing process favors the alignment of individual crystallites, the graphite part resulting on heating to high temperature will also exhibit distinctly different values for physical properties, such as tensile strength and electrical conductivity, depending on whether they are measured in the direction of extrusion or at right angle to the direction in which pressure was applied. Large values are obtained for the two quantities just mentioned in the direction of extrusion and much smaller values at right

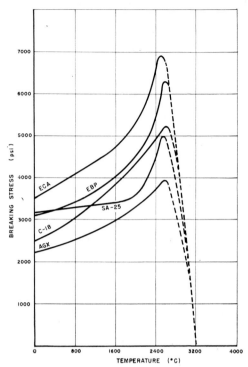

Figure 4.8. Short-time breaking strength *vs.* temperature for various grades of National Carbon Company graphites. After Malmstrom, Keen, and Green, Jr.[35] (*Courtesy American Institute of Physics.*)

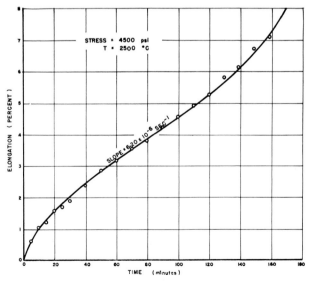

Figure 4.9. Typical creep curve for grade ECA graphite. After Malmstrom, Keen, and Green, Jr.[35] (*Courtesy American Institute of Physics.*)

angle to this direction. Similar preferred directions exist in parts molded under pressure in a die.

The high radiancy of graphite results in a substantially lower temperature of operation than that attained by other materials at equal power input. This behavior is illustrated in Figure 4.12 and Table 4.2 which give data of radiated power and vapor pressure at different temperatures for graphite, tantalum, and molybdenum. It is evident that graphite has a much superior power dissipating capacity than either molybdenum or tantalum at a given temperature. The vapor pressure of graphite is somewhat higher than that of tantalum or tungsten but lower than that of molybdenum; for a given power input where the vapor pressure of tantalum reaches 6×10^{-5} Torr at an operating temperature of 2527°C, graphite reaches a temperature of only 1200°C, and its vapor pressure is consequently lower by nearly 10 orders of magnitude. For these reasons, graphite is a favored anode material

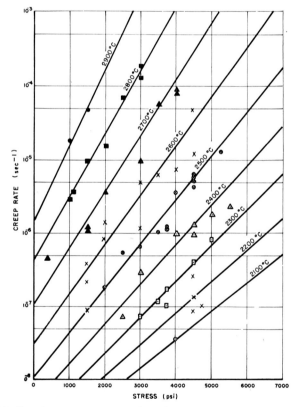

Figure 4.10. Steady creep rate as a function of stress for various temperatures measured on ECA graphite. After Malmstrom, Keen, and Green, Jr.[35] (*Courtesy American Institute of Physics.*)

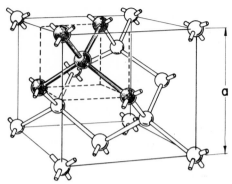

Figure 4.11. The diamond structure. After Shockley.[38] (*By permission from "Electrons and Holes in Semiconductors." Copyright 1950. D. Van Nostrand Company, Inc.*)

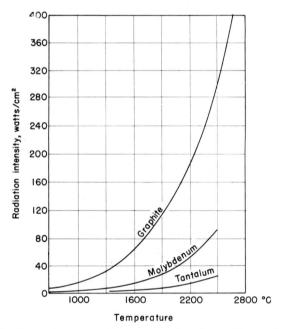

Figure 4.12. Comparison of radiation capacity of graphite, molybdenum, and tantalum. (*By permission from "Engineering Materials Handbook," C. L. Mantell, Editor. Copyright 1958. McGraw-Hill Book Company, Inc.*)[5]

in power tubes, high voltage rectifiers, and ignitrons where large overload capacities are required.

Graphite is a poor emitter of thermal electrons, as illustrated in Figure 4.13, and also gives one of the lowest yields of secondary electrons when bombarded by a beam of primary electrons (Figures 4.14 and 4.15). Sur-

TABLE 4.2. COMPARISON OF VAPOR PRESSURE OF ANODE MATERIALS
WITH RADIATED ENERGY AND TEMPERATURE*

Anode material	Total energy radiated, watts/cm²	Vapor pressure, mm Hg	Temp, °C
Graphite	253.0	7×10^{-4}	2400
Tantalum	19.0	9×10^{-6}	2400
Molybdenum	80.0	5×10^{-3}	2400
Graphite	92.0	7×10^{-8}	1800
Tantalum	6.0	6×10^{-10}	1800
Molybdenum	22.0	1×10^{-6}	1800
Graphite	24.0	3×10^{-15}	1200
Tantalum	24.2	6×10^{-5}	2527
Molybdenum	24.0	3×10^{-6}	1830

* By permission from "Engineering Materials Handbook," Ch. L. Mantell, Editor.
Copyright 1958. McGraw-Hill Book Company, Inc.[5]

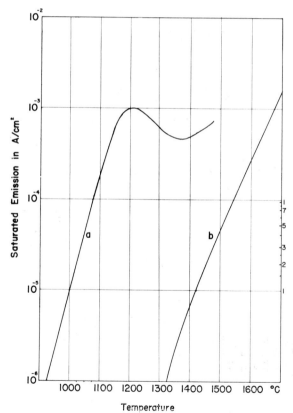

Figure 4.13. Electron emission of graphite. After Kramár.[39, 11] (*Courtesy Rudolf A. Lang Verlag, Berlin-Charlottenburg.*)

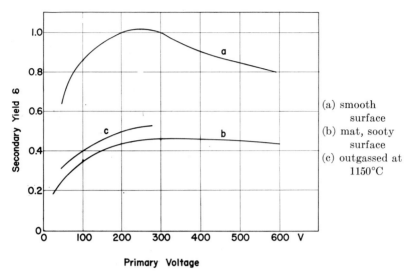

(a) smooth surface
(b) mat, sooty surface
(c) outgassed at 1150°C

Figure 4.14. Secondary electron emission yield of graphite. After De Boer, Kramár, and Espe.[11] (*Courtesy Rudolf A. Lang Verlag, Berlin-Charlottenburg.*)

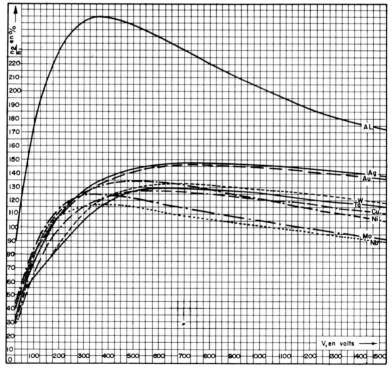

Figure 4.15. Secondary electron emission of various metals. After R. Warnecke.[40] (*Courtesy Journ. de Physique et le Radium.*)

face coatings of graphite suspensions are thus used as a means to minimize secondary electron emission from metallic elements in tubes, such as grids and beam collectors.[21, 22]

The chemical properties of carbon (Table 4.3) are characterized by high resistance to attack by all common solvents and a relatively low resistance to oxidation.

Graphite Anodes

The choice of a suitable anode material for a particular tube structure is affected by many factors which have been discussed at various times by different authors;[4, 11, 30, 46-49, 51] a list of the desirable properties of anode materials is presented in Table 4.4, and more specific data are given in Table 4.5. A compromise will have to be made in general between the desirability of certain properties and the economics of production. Receiving tubes for the entertainment industry thus generally contain anodes made of iron, aluminized iron, nickel-plated iron, and only in special cases pure nickel. Reliable tubes for critical environments may have anodes consisting of Kovar,* Monel,† or titanium. Molybdenum, tantalum, and graphite are most generally used in power tubes with glass envelopes, and OFHC‡ copper is the common material for power tubes with external anodes that are cooled either by forced air or water circulating through a cooling jacket.

Some of the advantages of graphite as an anode material have been pointed out above; a good many of its disadvantages which were prevalent in the past have been overcome in recent years. Electronic-grade graphite can now be obtained with an impurity content as low as 0.003 per cent so that the formerly objectionable content of calcium compounds is virtually eliminated.[48] Another difficulty which was frequently encountered with graphite parts in the past was the danger of having loose carbon particles released during the operation of the tube by abrasion of the graphite surface where it is in contact with metal parts, or by the action of high voltage gradients. Such loose carbon particles might then find their way to the cathode and cause poisoning of the emission, or produce noise in the tube. These difficulties have now been largely overcome. Not only is graphite now being produced from a finer and more uniform grade of carbon so that it takes on a hard surface and can be polished, but it is also possible to electroplate the surface with chromium, or apply a coating of zirconium,

* Registered Trademark of the Westinghouse Electric Corporation. Fabricated Kovar parts and assemblies are available from The Carborundum Company, Refractories Division, Latrobe, Pa.

† Registered Trademark of the International Nickel Company, Inc.

‡ Registered Trademark of American Metal Climax, Inc.

TABLE 4.3. CHEMICAL PROPERTIES OF CARBON AND ELECTROGRAPHITE

	Valence 4	Valence 2
Electrochemical equivalent:[19]	0.03111 mg/Coul.	0.06223 mg/Coul.
	32.13989 Coul/mg	16.06994 Coul/mg

A. *Reactions with gases and vapors:*

  air, dry or moist, up to 170°C: none; (direct formation of surface oxide at 25°C requires many days).[43] Carbon begins to show noticeable signs of oxidation above 350°C and graphite above 450°C although the rate of oxidation is not rapid even at 600°C; (see Figure 4.16/17.) Above 500°C, the rate of oxidation of graphite increases with time, below 475°C it decreases.[43]

  nitrogen: none up to 3000°C;[3] when heated in an inert atmosphere, such as helium, diamond will readily convert to graphite at 1800°C.[6]

  oxygen: charcoal ignites above 400°C, graphite at 700°C, diamond at about 800°C.

  hydrogen, dry: formation of CH_4 in range of 1100 to 1500°C (0.1 p.c. yield which decreases with increasing temperature).[45] In presence of catalyst (Ni), CH_4 is formed at 900°C.[3] (at 500°C)[4]

  hydrogen, wet (bubbled through water at 25°C): above 1000°C, conversion into $CO + H_2$ at about 3 p.c. yield; (yield of same reaction above 1000°C becomes 12 p.c. for water at 50°C)[45]

  water vapor: above 1000°C nearly complete conversion into $CO + H_2$;[45] negligible reaction below 800°C.[3]

  carbon dioxide: negligible below 800°C; formation of CO above 800°C.[3]

  chlorine: none up to 2300°C.[3]

  bromine: formation of interlamellar compounds at 20°C.[3]

  fluorine: formation of interlamellar compounds at 20°C.[3]

  potassium vapor: formation of interlamellar compounds at 20°C.[3]

  sulfur vapor: formation of CS_2 at 20°C.[10]

B. *Reactions with liquids:*

  water: up to 100°C none.

  dilute acid or alkali: none below boiling point.[3]

  aqua regia: none.

  HCl up to boiling point: none.

  HF (15%) up to boiling point: none; anodic etching possible, however.[11]

  H_2SO_4 (98%): causes swelling of graphite but not of carbon.[5]

  HNO_3, conc: attack; formation of mellitic acid, $C_6(COOH)_6$, hydrocyanic acid, HCN, or $CO_2 + N_2O$.[3]

  KOH (50%): dissolves graphite above 350°C.[3]

  $H_2Cr_2O_7 + H_2SO_4$: oxidation.

  20 c.c. HNO_3 (conc.) + 40 c.c. H_2SO_4 (conc.) + 20 gr $KClO_3$ dissolves 1 gr graphite with formation of graphitic acid.[4, 46]

  carbon tetrachloride: none up to boiling point.

  trichloroethylene: none.

C. *Reaction with solids:*

  Alkali hydroxides (in inert atmosphere): at fusion no attack.[3]

  Sodium sulfate: at fusion no attack.[3]

  Sodium carbonate: formation of CO at fusion.[3]

  Most metals: formation of carbides above 1500°C.[3]

  Metal oxides: formation of metal carbide and carbon oxides.[3]

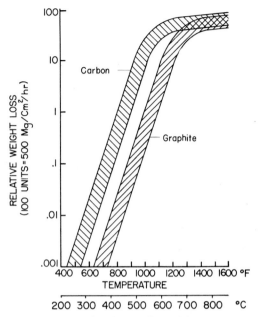

Figure 4.16. Combustion rate of carbon and graphite *vs.* temperature in terms of relative weight loss per hour. After Bemis and McKnight.[44] (*Courtesy Speer Carbon Company and International Graphite & Electrode Corporation.*)

or metallize the surface with molybdenum or a combination of molybdenum and vanadium.[52, 53]

In the past, it was not possible to weld or braze graphite to metals so that it was necessary to provide screw threads or channels through which leads could be passed and locked at the ends. In recent years, new processes have been announced by which carbon can be soldered or welded to metals so that this former difficulty also seems to have been overcome.

The mechanical strength of graphite is relatively low although it increases with temperature and reaches about twice the room temperature value at near 2400°C.[35] For this reason, relatively large wall thicknesses must be used for structural elements. Since the density of graphite is quite low, a substantial increase of wall thickness can be tolerated without greatly increasing the weight of the part. The wall thickness of anodes is usually held to the range from 60 to 80 mils but very small anodes have been made with a wall thickness as low as 16 mils; delicate grid structures have also been made from graphite.[11]

When graphite is used in contact with glass or ceramic, some thought must be given to the very strong reducing action of carbon which, at elevated temperatures, may lead to the formation of free alkali or alkaline

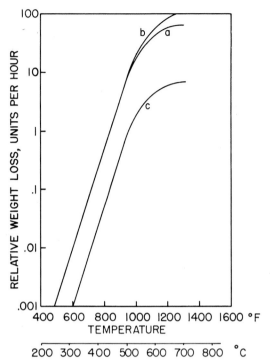

Figure 4.17. Effect of different atmospheres on the oxidation rate of graphite; a) normal air flow; b) air flow velocity doubled; c) oxygen content of air reduced to one-tenth normal at normal flow rate. After Bemis and McKnight.[44] (*Courtesy Speer Carbon Company and International Graphite & Electrode Corporation.*)

TABLE 4.4. DESIRABLE PROPERTIES OF ANODE MATERIALS

Mechanical strength at highest operating temperature
Ease of fabrication and good weldability
Ready availability and low cost
High rate of power dissipation
Ease of outgassing
Low vapor pressure
High melting point
Low thermal expansion on heating
High thermal conductivity
High electrical conductivity
Low sputtering rate
Good getter action
Suitable magnetic properties
Suitable secondary emission
Chemical inertness to filler gases or vapors
Compatibility with cathode material
Resistance to atmospheric corrosion (external anodes)
Ease of joining to ceramic or glass (external anodes)
Resistance to nuclear radiation

TABLE 4.5. PHYSICAL CHARACTERISTICS OF POWER TUBE ANODE MATERIALS

Physical property	Units	Copper	Molybdenum	Tantalum	Electrographite
Melting point[22,5]	°C	1083	2577	2997	3700[5]
Outgassing temperature	°C	800	1800–2000	2000	1800–2200
Typical operating temperature	°C	60 to 120	500	700	350
Total thermal emissivity[5]	% B.B.	2 (100°C)	9.4 (687°) 14.4 (1047°C) See Table 10.3	20 (1400°C) 25 (2000°C)	89 at all temperatures
Power dissipation	W/cm^2	0.0022 (100°C) 12 (1200°C)	0.6 (727°C) 1.4 (927°C) 3.2 (1127°C) 6.2 (1327°C) 11.3 (1527°C) 19.5 (1727°C)	7.0 (1327°C) 13.0 (1527°C) 21.5 (1727°C) 34.0 (1927°C) 51.0 (2127°C) Ref. 53a	24.0 (1200°C) 92.0 (1800°C) 253 (2400°C) Ref. 4
Thermal conductivity[16]	cal/cm²/cm/ sec/°C	0.918 (18°C)	0.346 (17°C) 0.259 (927°C) 0.159 (1627°C) Ref. 19	0.13 (20°C) 0.174 (1700°C)	0.2
Specific heat[5]	cal/g/°C	0.092 (20°C)	0.065 (20–100°C) 0.075 (475°C)	0.036 (20°C)	0.165 (20°C)
Linear thermal expansion coeff.[5]	cm/cm/°C $\times 10^{-7}$	165 (20°C)	49 (20°C)	65 (20°C)	90 (0–2500°C)
Vapor pressure[22]	Torr	10^{-8} (732°C) 10^{-6} (862°C) 10^{-5} (942°C) 10^{-4} (1032°C)	10^{-8} (1582°C) 10^{-6} (1837°C) 10^{-5} (1987°C) 10^{-4} (2167°C)	10^{-8} (1957°C) 10^{-6} (2237°C) 10^{-5} (2397°C) 10^{-4} (2587°C)	10^{-8} (1677°C) 10^{-6} (1867°C) 10^{-5} (1977°C) 10^{-4} (2107°C)
Getter action	—	none	some	good	none
Electrical conductivity[16]	micromhos-cm	0.5910 (20°C)	0.173 (27°C)	0.065 (20°C)	0.00125 (20°C)
Percent electrical conductivity of IACS (weight basis)[5]	%	100.00	10.2	16.6	1.2
Magnetic susceptibility[19]	10^{-6} cgs	−0.086 (18°C) −0.075 (500°C)	0.04 (18°C)	0.87 (18°C) 0.77 (820°C)	−3.5 (20°C) −2.0 (600°C)
Electron work function	e.v.	4.9	4.2	4.1	4.62
Apparent or bulk density[16]	g/cc	8.89 (20°C)	10.2	16.6	1.65–1.68 (AGW)
Young's modulus[5]	psi $\times 10^6$	16	40–50	27	0.7

earth metals of low work function that may cause breakdown during inverse voltage cycles in rectifier tubes. For this reason, these areas of contact between graphite and glass, or ceramic, should not be exposed to the electrical field.

Outgassing of Graphite

Owing to the porous nature of graphite, considerable quantities of gas are absorbed by this material, and parts made from it must thus be subjected to a special outgassing treatment before they are mounted in the tube. The principal gases released are CO_2, CO, N_2, and H_2; in addition, the surface will contain adsorbed gases so that the outgassing treatment must aim at the removal of both these constituents. The various gases are bound to the external and internal surfaces to varying degrees, and complete outgassing thus requires exceedingly high temperatures. According to Norton and Marshall,[54] graphite heated in vacuo at 2150°C will not release further gas on subsequent heating at higher temperature. The gas evolved in the range from 1700 to 2200°C is predominantly nitrogen. A piece of graphite which has been completely degassed in this manner will absorb oxygen on subsequent exposure to air and release this oxygen as carbon monoxide only on heating to 2150°C; it should thus be stored in an evacuated container or in a rare-gas atmosphere such as argon. A less rigorous outgassing treatment may be permissible when the operating temperature of the anode during service is kept at low values. Firing in hydrogen at 1000°C for a period of from one-half to one hour is a practice used for small graphite anodes which can then be raised to higher temperatures by induction heating on the pump. The carburizing of thoriated tungsten filaments by flashing in a hydrocarbon atmosphere must be done before the graphite anodes are mounted because the removal of absorbed hydrocarbons from the porous graphite body would require a much longer pump cycle.[11]

Less pure grades of graphite may require special treatment to remove remaining binders and volatile impurities. Air-firing by furnace- or induction-heating is used to bring the graphite part to a high temperature which is maintained while a film of burning gases remains. Some manufacturers quench the red-hot graphite part in boiling distilled water or other liquid to dislodge loosely adhering particles.[56]

In order to eliminate the release of gas from graphite anodes used in transmitting tubes containing thoriated tungsten cathodes, Espe[11] describes a method by which a layer of zirconium hydride is applied to the graphite electrode by cataphoresis and then transformed into zirconium carbide by heating in a vacuum furnace at 2000°C. A second layer of zirconium hydride is then applied cataphoretically and reduced to zirconium metal by heating to 1500°C for a period of one-quarter to one-half hour.

Special Techniques and Applications

In addition to its use as an anode material, graphite finds many other applications in the tube industry. Surface coatings of colloidal graphite suspensions are commonly used on the internal wall of cathode ray and picture tubes to remove wall charges and serve as an extended anode to provide a field-free region within which the electron beam travels.

In order to render graphite impervious to liquids and gases, "Karbate"* carbon and graphite products are produced by impregnating the more conventional products with synthetic resins and phenolic or modified phenolic type and polymerizing these resins within the normal pore structure. Porosity is reduced to a minimum in this manner, and imperviousness even to gases under pressure results.[5] These Karbate products find extensive use in the chemical industry but, owing to the presence of organic fillers, they naturally have no place within a vacuum tube. By replacing the aforementioned resins with finely divided carbon, a truly impervious graphite results which can be subjected to temperatures as high as 3000°C. This material is marketed under the trade name "Graph-I-Tite" by Graphite Specialities Corporation of Niagara Falls, New York, and as grade ATJ-82 by National Carbon Company, Division of Union Carbide Corporation, Cleveland, Ohio. While these materials are still permeable to gases to some degree, it should not be difficult to render them vacuum tight by metallizing their surface.

Electrolytically polished graphite anodes have been described by Bakker[57] who uses a bath of molten potassium hydrofluoride KHF_2 in which the graphite part is immersed and made the anode of a 130-volt supply; 15 amperes are passed for one-half hour after which time the graphite anode is as smooth as a mirror. The current density ranges from 0.1 to 1a/cm². When such anodically polished anodes are used in rectifier tubes, the danger of arc-back is greatly minimized according to the claim of the inventor.

Protective coatings for graphite have been described by Lynch, Slyh, and Duckworth[58] who apply a coating of molybdenum disilicide in the form of powder suspended in a phenolic-resin vehicle which is cured and then heated in a neutral or reducing atmosphere to 2150°C. A dense, adherent, glaze-like surface results which protects graphite in a hot, high-velocity stream of oxidizing gases such as are encountered in the use of rocket mo-

* "Karbate" is a registered trade name of National Carbon Company, Division of Union Carbide Corporation.

tors. Under oxidizing conditions, the upper temperature limit of the coating is given as 1930°C. The major phase of the matured coating is molybdenum silicon carbide.

The use of graphite in the atomic energy program has been described by Fletcher and Snyder[25] and also by Currie, Hamister, and McPherson.[59] Graphite is valuable both as a neutron moderator and as a structural component for reactors; its high neutron moderating efficiency, low neutron absorption cross-section, its extreme chemical purity, high mechanical strength, its refractory properties and its resistance to thermal shock make it particularly suited for this purpose. Like other materials, graphite suffers radiation damage on exposure to nuclear radiation which, in the case of graphite, causes primarily the displacement of carbon atoms from the graphite lattice by collisions with energetic neutrons, or with previously displaced, energetic carbon atoms. These lattice distortions bring about an expansion of the graphite parts and an increase in electrical resistivity and thermal resistivity which are dependent on neutron flux density and temperature during bombardment. The changes incurred by irradiation at a given temperature may be annealed by heating the graphite to higher temperatures; by heating to temperatures approaching graphitization temperature (over 2000°C), virtually complete recovery of properties may be realized.[60-64]

Electrographite for nuclear reactors is being produced to an exceptionally high degree of purity by a classified process, known as the "F" process, developed by United Carbon Products Company; it results in a maximum total ash content that will, in general, not exceed 10–20 ppm. Boron content is kept so low that it cannot be detected by the most sensitive spectrographical methods, according to Alsopp.[64a]

Graphite is a suitable material for molds both for metallurgical applications and the production of special glass shapes in the laboratory. A hard, dense graphite of the pitch-treated grade is recommended, and high thermal conductivity, toughness, and resistance to thermal shock are necessary.[8] The ready machinability of graphite* makes it possible to produce intricate shapes, but on repeated usage such graphite molds tend to oxidize and take on a rough surface. The techniques mentioned above for electropolishing and plating of graphite may well recommend themselves to improve the wear resistance of graphite molds. Graphite is also used extensively as a die material for the hot pressing of ceramics, cermets, and refractory materials made by powder metallurgical techniques.[65]

Furnace boats made from graphite are useful for many applications in the tube shop as well as in the factory; they should not be used, however, when decarburizing is the main object of the furnace run. When Kovar

---

* Alumina ceramic bits are recommended for this purpose.

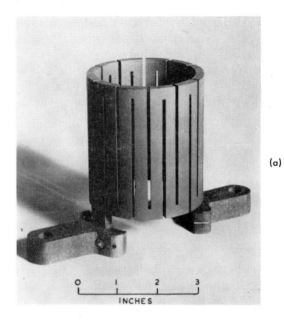

(a)

(b)

Figure 4.18. Improved Czochralski crystal pulling furnace; a) graphite heater; b) crystal, crucible, heater, and radiation shields. After Marshall and Wickham.[67] (*Courtesy Services Electronic Research Laboratory, Baldock, Herts, England.*)

parts are supported on graphite during the customary firing in wet hydrogen for the purpose of stress relief and decarburization, subsequent seals made with such parts will be full of bubbles.

The use of graphite for high-temperature furnace elements is another application of great interest. Many such furnaces have been described in the literature;[66] Figure 4.18 shows a crystal-pulling furnace described by Marshall and Wickham.[67]

REFERENCES

1. *Materials in Design Engineering*, **47**, 10 (Mar. 1958).
2. V. S. Kingswood, "Carbon in the engineering and metallurgical industries," *Metallurgia*, **48**, (Aug., Sept., Oct., Nov., Dec., 1953); Pt. I. Historical introduction and constitution of carbon allotropes, pp. 55–62; Pt. II. Industrial carbons, pp. 133–138; Pt. III. Industrial graphites, diamonds, and special mixtures, pp. 169–174; Pt. IV. Refractories, electrodes, and other metallurgical uses, pp. 221–227; Pt. V. Chemical, mechanical, and electrical uses, pp. 300–305.
3. "The Reactor Handbook," Vol. 3, Section 1, "General Properties of Materials," Chapter 1.9 "Graphite" by J. A. Slyh. United States Atomic Energy Commission, AECD-3647, Mar. 1955; (contains data up to about Aug. 1952).
4. C. L. Mantell, "Industrial Carbon," 2nd ed., D. van Nostrand Co., Inc., Princeton, 1946.
5. C. L. Mantell, Ed., "Engineering Materials Handbook," section 28, pp. 1–29, McGraw-Hill Book Co., Inc., New York, 1958.
6. I. E. Campbell, Ed., "High Temperature Technology," John Wiley & Sons, Inc., New York, 1956. Chapter IV, "Properties of Carbon and Graphite at High Temperatures" by M. S. Wright.
7. Proceedings of the 1st and 2nd Conferences on Carbon held at the University of Buffalo, Buffalo, N. Y. in 1953 and 1955. (A similar conference was held in 1957 in Buffalo.) Copyright 1956, the University of Buffalo.
7a. "Industrial Carbon and Graphite," The Macmillan Co., New York, 1958. Papers read at the conference on the industrial use of carbon and graphite held in London, England, Sept. 24–26, 1957.
8. R. E. Kirk, D. F. Othmer, J. D. Scott and A. Standen, Eds, "Encyclopedia of Chemical Technology," Vol. 3, pp. 1–34. "Carbon," by H. W. Abbott; The Interscience Encyclopedia, Inc., New York, 1949.
9. G. L. Clark, G. G. Hawley and W. A. Hamor, Eds, "The Encyclopedia of Chemistry," Reinhold Publishing Corp., New York, 1957.
10. "Encyclopaedia Britannica," Vol. 4, Encyclopaedia Britannica, Inc., 1957.
11. W. Espe, "Carbon as a material in high vacuum technique" (in German), *Vakuum-Technik*, **4**, 10–24 (Apr. 1955); *ibid.*, 34–40 (June 1955).
12. H. W. Parker, "Voltage Indicating Electron Discharge Tube," U. S. Patent 2,105,818 (Jan. 18, 1938); assigned to Rogers Radio Tubes Ltd., Toronto, Ontario.
13. H. Bruining, J. H. DeBoer and W. G. Burgess, "Secondary electron emission of soot in valves with oxide cathodes," *Physica*, **4**, 267–275 (Apr. 1937).
14. J. D. LeVan, "Fluorescent Coating," U. S. Patent 2,226,567 (Dec. 31, 1940); assigned to Raytheon Mfg. Company, Waltham, Mass.

15. F. P. Bundy, H. T. Hall, H. M. Strong and R. H. Wentorf, Jr., "Man-made diamonds," *Nature*, **176**, 51–55 (July 9, 1955).
16. D. E. Gray, Ed., "American Institute of Physics Handbook," McGraw-Hill Book Co., Inc., New York, 1957.
17. C. J. Smithells, "Metals Reference Book," 2nd ed. (2 Vols.), Interscience Publishers, Inc., New York, 1955.
18. S. Mrozowski, "Mechanical strength, thermal expansion and structure of cokes and carbons," Ref. 7, pp. 31–45.
19. C. D. Hodgman, Ed., "Handbook of Chemistry and Physics," 40th ed., Chemical Rubber Publishing Co., Cleveland, 1958/1959.
20. O. Kubaschewski and E. L. Evans, "Metallurgical Thermochemistry," 2nd ed. John Wiley & Sons, Inc., New York, 1956.
21. A. L. Marshall and F. J. Norton, "Carbon vapor pressure and heat of vaporization," *J. Am. Chem. Soc.*, **72**, 2166–2171 (May 1950).
22. R. E. Honig, "Vapor pressure data for the more common elements," *RCA Rev.*, **18**, 195–204 (June 1957).
23. L. Brewer, P. W. Gilles and F. A. Jenkins, "The vapor pressure and heat of sublimation of graphite," *J. Chem. Phys.*, **16**, 797–807 (Aug. 1948).
24. L. Brewer, "The vapor pressure and melting point of graphite," *J. Chem. Phys.*, **16**, 1165–1166 (Dec. 1948).
25. J. F. Fletcher and W. A. Snyder, "Use of graphite in the atomic energy programs," *Am. Ceram. Soc. Bull.*, **36**, 101–104 (Mar. 1957).
26. J. G. Castle, Jr., "Heat conduction in carbon materials," Ref. 7, pp. 13–19.
27. C. P. Jamieson and S. Mrozowski, "Thermal conductivities of polycrystalline carbons and graphites," Ref. 7, pp. 155–166.
28. J. P. Howe, "Properties of graphite," *J. Am. Ceram. Soc.*, **35**, 275–282 (Nov. 1952). Discussion by S. Mrozowski, pp. 282–283.
29. R. J. Thorn and O. C. Simpson, "Spectral emissivities of graphite and carbon," *J. Appl. Phys.*, **24**, 633–639 (May 1953).
30. L. L. Winter and H. G. MacPherson, "Effect of surface finish and wall thickness on the operating temperature of graphite radio tube anodes," *Proc. IRE*, **33**, 834–837 (Dec. 1945).
31. S. C. Jain and Sir K. S. Krishman, "The thermionic constants of metals and semiconductors; I. Graphite," *Proc. Roy. Soc.*, **A213**, 143–157 (June 1952).
32. H. F. Ivey, "Thermionic electron emission from carbon," *Phys. Rev.*, **76**, 567 (Aug. 15, 1949).
33. A. L. Reimann, "Thermionic emission from carbon," *Proc. Phys. Soc.*, **50**, 496–500 (July 1938).
34. S. Mrozowski, "Semiconductivity and diamagnetism of polycrystalline graphite and condensed ring systems," *Phys. Rev.*, **85**, 609–620 (Feb. 15, 1952); Errata, *ibid.*, **86**, 1056 (June 15, 1952).
35. C. Malmstrom, R. Keen and L. Green, Jr., "Some mechanical properties of graphite at elevated temperatures," *J. Appl. Phys.*, **22**, 593–600 (May 1951).
35a. P. Wagner and A. R. Driesner, "High-temperature mechanical properties of graphite; I. Creep in compression," *J. Appl. Phys.*, **30**, 148–151 (Feb. 1959).
35b. P. Wagner, A. R. Driesner and L. A. Haskin, "High-temperature mechanical properties of graphite; II. Creep in tension," *J. Appl. Phys.*, **30**, 152–154 (Feb. 1959).
36. "Materials Selector Reference Issue," *Materials in Design Engineering*, **46**, 224 (Sept. 1957).

37. C. R. Houska and B. E. Warren, "X-ray study of the graphitization of carbon black," *J. Appl. Phys.*, **25**, 1503–1509 (Dec. 1954).
38. W. Shockley, "Electrons and Holes in Semiconductors," D. Van Nostrand Co., Inc., Princeton, 1950.
39. J. Kramár, "Measurement of primary and secondary electron emission from graphite" (in Czech.), *Elektrotech. Obzor*, **43**, 95–103 (1954).
40. R. Warnecke, "Secondary electron emission of pure metals" (in French), *J. phys. radium*, **7**, 270–280 (June 1936).
41. H. Bruining, "Physics and Applications of Secondary Electron Emission," McGraw-Hill Book Co., Inc., New York, 1954.
42. A. J. Dekker, "Secondary Electron Emission," pp. 251–311 in "Solid State Physics," F. Seitz and D. Turnbull, Eds; Academic Press, Inc., New York, 1958.
43. E. A. Gulbransen and K. F. Andrew, "Reactions of artificial graphite"; 4 consecutive articles dealing with (1) Kinetics of oxidation, (2) Surface oxide formation, (3) Mechanism of oxidation at 425–575°C, (4) Reaction with carbon dioxide at 500–900°C; *Ind. Eng. Chem.*, **44**, 1034–1051 (May 1952).
44. A. S. Bemis and G. P. McKnight, "The oxidation rate of carbon and graphite," *Tech. Rep. No. 3030* (June 23, 1948). Speer Carbon Company (not published), Abstract in *International Digest*, **2**, (Dec. 1949), published by International Graphite and Electrode Corp., St. Marys, Pa.
45. B. Kopelman, "Clean-up of graphite lubricant from tungsten wire," *Sylvania Technologist*, **2**, 13–16 (Apr. 1949). .
46. W. Espe and M. Knoll, "Werkstoffkunde der Hochvakuumtechnik," Julius Springer Verlag, Berlin, 1936.
47. W. C. Kalb, "Graphite elements for electronic devices," Ref. 5, Section 28, pp. 23–25.
48. L. L. Winter and F. L. Alexander, "New graphite developments for electronic applications," *Elec. Mfg.*, **41**, 86–91 (Jan. 1948).
49. J. L. Boyer and A. P. Colaiaco, "Sealed ignitron principles extended to large tubes," Applications and Industry (AIEE), No. 25, pp. 125–129 (July 1956).
50. E. E. Spitzer, "The application of graphite as an anode material to high vacuum transmitting tubes," *Proc. IRE*, **21**, 1075–1081 (Aug. 1933).
51. R. Szymanowitz, "The emissive power of typical grid and plate surfaces," *Electronics*, **16**, 93, 178 (May 1943).
52. W. Espe, "Zirconium, its Production, its Properties and Applications in the Vacuum Industry" (in German), Füssen, 1953.
53. H. W. Abbot, "Graphite anodes in electron tubes," Ref. 4, pp. 354–365.
53a. A. H. W. Beck, "Thermionic Valves," Cambridge At The University Press. 1953.
54. F. J. Norton and A. L. Marshall, "The degassing of metals," *Trans. Am. Inst. Mining Met. Engrs.*, **156**, 351–371 (1944).
55. I. A. Eltzin and A. P. Jewlew, "Outgassing of graphite at high temperature" (in German), *Physik. Z. Sowjetunion*, **5**, 687–705 (1934).
56. T. H. Briggs, "Carbonized nickel for radio tubes," *Metals & Alloys*, **9**, 303–306, (Nov. 1938).
57. J. Bakker, "Electrolytically polished graphite anode," U. S. Patent 2,494,425 (Jan. 10, 1950).
58. J. F. Lynch, J. A. Slyh and W. H. Duckworth, "Molybdenum Disilicide Coating for Graphite," Battelle Memorial Institute; U. S. Department of Commerce, Office of Technical Services, PB 121084 (1956).

59. L. M. Currie, V. C. Hamister and H. G. McPherson, "The production and properties of graphite for reactors," Geneva Conference on Peaceful Uses of Atomic Energy, Aug. 8–20, 1955.

60. M. Burton and T. J. Neubert, "Effect of fast neutron bombardment on physical properties of graphite: a review of early work at the Metallurgical Laboratory (Argonne)," *J. Appl Phys.*, **27,** 557–567 (June 1956).

61. J. E. Hove, "Radiation damage effects on graphite," Ref. 7, pp. 125–136.

62. W. L. Kosiba, G. J. Dienes and D. H. Gurinsky, "Some effects produced in graphite by neutron irradiation in the BNL reactor," Ref. 7, pp. 143–148.

63. R. L. Carter and R. R. Eggleston, "Moderator graphite for high temperature reactors," Ref. 7, pp. 149–153.

64. J. J. Harwood, H. H. Hausner, J. G. Morse and W. G. Rauch, "The Effects of Radiation on Materials," Reinhold Publishing Corp., New York, 1958.

64a. W. E. Alsopp, "The growing role of graphite in the semiconductor industry," *Semiconductor Prod.*, **2,** 42–44 (June 1959).

65. P. Murray, D. T. Livey and J. Williams, "The Hot Pressing of Ceramics," pp. 147–171 in "Ceramic Fabrication Processes," W. D. Kingery, Ed., The Technology Press of Massachusetts Institute of Technology and John Wiley & Sons, Inc., New York, 1958.

66. M. Balicki, E. G. Kendall and W. H. Orthman, "A suspended graphite-spiral furnace," *Metal Progr.*, **60,** 72–74 (Feb. 1951).

67. K. H. J. C. Marshall and R. Wickham, "An improved Czochralski crystal pulling furnace," *J. Sci. Instr.*, **35,** 121–125 (Apr. 1958).

CHAPTER 5

IRON AND STEELS

Introduction

Knowledge of the basic properties of iron and steel is of some importance to the tube maker since these materials are used extensively. From aluminum-clad iron for receiving tube anodes, to stainless steel gun structures in travelling-wave tubes (TWT), steel housings for thyratrons, ignitrons, mercury-vapor rectifiers, alloy support rings for color masks in TV tubes, glass-sealing alloys, steel foil windows for counter tubes, etc., iron and steels are found in many different tube components.

In view of the very extensive literature on the subject, the following exposition must be brief and limited to highlights which have a special bearing on problems encountered in the manufacture of tubes. Nevertheless, a few terms commonly used in describing the strength of materials will be defined for the benefit of those who have not been exposed to them before, or who, in spite of such prior treatment, are not fully aware of their significance. The best way to fill such gaps, naturally, is to consult some of the textbooks devoted to these subjects.[1-9]

The strength of materials

The strength of materials is usually determined by applying a load (P) to the material under study and observing the resulting deformation (e). In the case of a static load, the external forces acting on the system are in equilibrium, and the deformation may take the forms of elongation, contraction, or shear. The forces which act in small domains in the interior of the body are known as stresses; they resist the deformation induced by the load and result in strain. Depending on whether the forces acting on the system take the form of thrust or traction, there are two kinds of principal stresses, i.e., pressure and tension, and the corresponding strains are compression and extension. When referred to axes oblique to the principal stresses, there are furthermore shear components of stress and strain.

As long as the elastic range of the material is not exceeded, the balance of the force reactions is governed by Hooke's law which states that stress S is proportional to total strain e, i.e.,

$$S = E \times e$$

where the proportionality constant E is charistic for the material under test and known as the *modulus of elasticity*. Depending on the type of load

174

applied, one speaks of a modulus of elasticity in tension (Young's modulus), in compression, or in shear (E_t, E_c, E_s). The readings taken with a tensile strength testing machine give the load vs. the elongation, but are generally presented as stress-strain diagrams in which the unit stress, S, is plotted as a function of unit elongation, E_t, referred, respectively, to the original cross-section, A_0, of the testpiece and its original length, l_0. The following relations thus apply:

$$S_t = P/A_0 ; \quad e_t = \epsilon_t \times l_0 ; \quad E_t = S_t/\epsilon_t$$

The fact that the cross-section of the testpiece decreases after the onset of necking is neglected in most engineering tests, but is taken into account in more refined tests where reference is made to the true tensile stress, $\bar{S} = P/A$, and true strain, $\bar{e}$, defined by the incremental change $d\bar{e} = dl/l$.

Figure 7.8 (p. 222) is an example of a conventional stress-strain diagram; following the curve from the origin, one encounters in succession the following important points:

(1) *the proportional limit;* up to this point Hooke's law applies, according to which a linear relationship exists between load and elongation in the elastic range.

(2) *the elastic limit,* just beyond the proportional limit; curvature sets in but, on release of the load, the body still returns to its original shape without suffering a permanent deformation.

(3) *the yield point,* to which corresponds the yield stress, S_y, where an increase in elongation is obtained without increase in load. It may decrease in some materials so that an upper and lower yield point can be distinguished; in the latter case, the lower yield point is quoted as S_y. In the absence of a lower yield point, S_y is determined by drawing a line parallel to the straight-line portion of the curve at a preselected off-set, usually 0.2 per cent, and calling the intercept with the measured curve the yield point. Other values of offset may be chosen, or S_y be determined by the tangent to the curve drawn parallel to a line with 1.5 times the slope of the lower part of the measured curve. The yield strength so determined is known as Johnson's Apparent Elastic Limit (Figure 7.8), but is rarely used.

(4) *the ultimate tensile strength,* S_u, also referred to as just tensile strength, which is given by the maximum of the curve, or the highest value attained.

(5) *the breaking strength* or *rupture strength* given by the end point of the curve where the material breaks; this point is generally lower than the tensile strength.

Examples of curves where the true tensile stress is plotted vs. true strain are Figures 9.7 and 9.8; in these cases, no maximum is observed when the load is referred to the decreasing instantaneous cross-section of the testpiece, rather than to the original cross-section A_0.

The general engineering data for materials quoted in handbooks refer to measurements taken at room temperature. In the construction of electron tubes and of many other critical devices, account must be taken of the fact that the strength of materials rapidly diminishes with increase in temperature. An effort has thus been made to present high-temperature data for many of the physical and mechanical properties of metals and alloys treated in the following chapters. The properties of materials are also seriously affected by the presence of impurities, by their grain size, by recrystallization and grain growth, and by phase transformations which may take place at elevated temperature. Creep—the plastic flow of a material in the presence of a continuous load applied over a long period of time—and fatigue—the deterioration of mechanical properties in the presence of repetitive loads—are also important factors that must be taken into account if a structure is to survive under adverse conditions of operation.

Extensive studies in recent years have led to the realization that "real" materials behave in a much more complex manner than had been assumed in the past when the "ideal" isotropic continuum was the basis for engineering calculations of strength properties. Imperfections in the submicroscopic structure have been shown to exist by the methods of x-ray diffraction, electron microscopy, and electron diffraction, as well as by etching techniques, or the effect of the associated strain fields. Grain boundaries, dislocations, vacancies, and particles of a second phase are examples of such imperfections, which can produce internal stresses on which the microscopic behavior of a test member under load largely depends. The stress-strain curve is thus at best a coarse representation of material properties.

The distinction between ductile and brittle materials, long used as an engineering classification, must also give way to a more subtle treatment when it is realized that all engineering materials possess inherent propensities of brittleness as well as of ductility. Under sufficiently large cyclic stresses, all materials give evidence of brittle behavior by the formation of cracks. Brittle fractures can also occur in apparently ductile materials under steady stress. The phenomenon of creep-to-rupture at high temperatures provides still another evidence of brittle behavior in circumstances which might be expected to cause large-scale yielding. At the end of the process, however, fracture occurs in brittle fashion, particularly in tests of long duration at lower stress.[10, 11]

Examples of the transition from ductile to brittle fracture on lowering the ambient temperature are given in Chapters 9 and 10. For high-purity iron and some steels, this transition takes place at $-200°C$ in a simple tensile test, while these materials fail by brittle fracture below $-15°C$ in the V-notch Charpy impact test. The type of loading thus has a marked effect on the type of failure encountered.[12]

The physical properties of pure iron[13] are tabulated in Table 5.1. Pure iron is ductile and, in its commercial form, is known as ingot iron. The question arises, how pure is pure? To avoid the discontinuous behavior of the stress-strain curve of low-carbon steel when increasing values of strain are measured, the carbon and nitrogen* content in fine-grained poly-crystalline steel must be well below 0.01 per cent and below 0.003 per cent

TABLE 5.1. THE PHYSICAL CHARACTERISTICS OF PURE IRON[4, 13]

Atomic number: 26

Atomic weight: 55.85

Isotopes: 54, 56, 57, 58

Density (gm/cc): 7.871 (19°C)

Melting point (°C): 1537 ± 1

Boiling point (°C): 3070

A_3 transformation $(\alpha \rightarrow \gamma)$; (°C): 910

A_4 transformation $(\gamma \rightarrow \delta)$; (°C): 1386 ± 5

Curie point A_2 (°C): 760

Atomic valence: 3, 2

Valence orbitals: $3d^6 4s^2$

Lattice type: b.c.c. (α); f.c.c. (γ); b.c.c. (δ).

Lattice constant (A): 2.86645 (α); 3.64 (γ); 2.94 (δ).

Atomic diameter: 2.52 A

Atomic volume (cc/gm atom): 7.10

Closest approach of atoms: 2.476 A

Heat of fusion, ΔH_m (Kcal/mole): 3.6

Heat of vaporization, ΔH (Kcal/mole):

Entropy of fusion, ΔS_m (cal/mole/deg K): 2.0

Entropy of vaporization, ΔS_v (cal/mole/deg K):

Entropy at 298.16°K, ΔS (cal/mole/deg K): 6.491

Specific heat (cal/gm/°C):

0	20	50	100	200	300	400	500	600	700	800	°C
0.104	0.106	0.109	0.114	0.125	0.133	0.144	0.159	0.180	0.220	0.200	

Thermal conductivity (cal/cm²/cm/sec/°C):

30	100	200	800	100–727	100–912	100–1245	°C
0.173	0.163	0.147	0.071	0.202	0.184	0.191	

Thermal expansion coeff. (cm/cm/°C):

−100–0	0–20	20–100	20–300	20–600	20–900	°C
104	116	121	134	147	150	× 10⁻⁷

Vapor pressure (mm Hg):[3]

$\log p = (-21{,}080/T) + 16.89 - 2.14 \log T$ (900–1812°K)

$\log p = (-19{,}710/T) + 13.27 - 1.27 \log T$ (1812–3000°K)

10^{-8}	10^{-7}	10^{-6}	10^{-5}	10^{-4}	10^{-3}	10^{-2}	10^{-1}	mm Hg
1150	1220	1290	1380	1480	1595	1740	1910	°K[14]

Spectral emissivity (25°C):[4]

0.5	0.6	1.0	2.0	3.0	4.0	5.0	7.0	micron
0.45	0.43	0.35	0.22	0.16	0.12	0.09	0.07	

Total emissivity:[3]

25	100	500	1000	1200	1400	°C
0.05	0.05		0.08	0.11	0.13	

Electrical resistivity (microhm·cm):

0	50	100	150	200	°C
8.8	11.5	14.5	17.8	21.5	

Maximum permeability: 250,000 (H_c = 0.04 oersted) Pure iron treated in hydrogen at 1350°C

Electron work function: 4.5 e.v.

Richardson constant A: 26 a/cm²deg²

* The influences of carbon and nitrogen on the properties of iron are similar in many respects.

TABLE 5.1—*Continued*

Mechanical Properties: These depend to a large extent on the degree of purity of "pure" iron, on grain size and lattice defects, and on heat treatment as shown below for typical high-purity iron furnace-cooled (F.C.), air-cooled (A.C.), and water-quenched (W.Q.) from 950°C to room and sub-zero temperatures:[13]

	20°C			−73°C			−196°C		
	F.C.	A.C.	W.Q.	F.C.	A.C.	W.Q.	F.C.	A.C.	W.Q.
Lower yield stress (10³ psi)	13.02	15.71	21.32	34.78	34.78	46.45	75.85	78.09	—
Tensile strength (10³ psi)	36.13	36.58	39.49	48.25	48.70	56.55	80.56	87.29	61.71
Elongation (% on 4√area)	61	55	52	61	63	31	0.5	2	0
Reduction of area (%)	87	90	91	87	86	54	0.5	2	0
Grain size (grains/mm)	6	7.2	8.5	—	—	—	—	—	—

Young's modulus (10⁶ psi): 28.5 ± 0.5
Poisson's ratio: 0.29

in a single crystal of iron.[9] Only then is a continuous transition from elastic to plastic yielding encountered. If carbon is added to carbon-free iron in as small an amount as 10 parts per million (ppm), the yield strength will increase by at least a factor of 2.[12] Other "impurities," in the sense suggested above, will have a similar effect on strain hardening. Typical chemical compositions of commercial iron are listed in Table 5.2.[1] Reactions of iron with chemical reagents are given in Table 5.3.

The solubility of carbon in ferrite at 20°C is about 0.006 per cent and that of nitrogen at the same temperature is less than 0.001 per cent. Both elements form solid solutions of the interstitial type with iron. If carbon or nitrogen segregate on ageing or as a result of mechanical shock, the magnetic properties of ferrite are seriously impaired. Pure iron is less subject to corrosion than are carbon steels. Gas absorption and sputtering rate for iron electrodes in gas discharge lamps are higher for impure iron. "Svea iron"* has been widely accepted for such electrodes and other applications where its high purity gives superior performance and warrants the extra cost. Armco iron† is another ferritic iron of low carbon content which finds application for magnetic shields in tube structures, and so is Core Iron‡ and "Ingot Iron"§ tubing which is also known as "Globe Iron."‖

Trademarks:
   * Swedish Iron & Steel Corporation, Westfield, N. J.
   † Armco Steel Company, Middletown, Ohio.
   ‡ Carpenter Steel Company, Reading, Pa. (The same alloy is known as Miromold when used for plastic molds.)
      § Superior Tube Company, Norristown, Pa.
   ‖ Globe Steel Tubes Division, Newport Steel Corp. Newport, Ky.

TABLE 5.2. TYPICAL CHEMICAL COMPOSITION OF COMMERCIAL IRONS[1, 29]

Description	Composition (weight percent)									μmax
	C	Mn	P	S	Si	Cu	Ni	O_2	N_2	
Armco ingot iron[29]	0.012	0.030	0.004	0.018	0.002	—	—	0.030	0.0018	7,000
After 3 hrs at 1475°C in dry H_2	0.005	0.028	0.004	0.006	—	—	—	0.003	0.0003	30,000
After 18 hrs at 1475°C in dry H_2	0.005	0.028	0.004	<0.003	—	—	—	0.003	0.0001	227,000
Electrolytic iron	0.006	—	0.005	0.004	0.005	—	0.004			
Kahlbaum iron	—	0.001	—	trace	0.015	0.004	—	—	—	
H_2-purified iron	0.005	0.028	0.004	0.003	0.0012	†	†	0.003	0.0001*	
Carbonyl iron	0.0007 0.00016	†	†	†	†			<0.01	—	
Bureau of Standards	<0.001	‡	<0.0005	0.002	0.002	<0.002	‡	0.003	0.0002	
Ferrovac-E (Vacuum Metals Corp.)§	0.01	0.001	0.001	0.003	0.01	0.001	0.015	0.01	0.0002 (H_2)	

* Total reported impurities 0.024%.

† Unable to identify; also Cr, Co, Mo, Zn.

‡ Unable to identify; also Ag, As, Au, B, Ba, Bi, Ca, Cb, Cd, Ce, Co, Cr, Ga, Ge, Hf, Hg, In, Ir, K, Li, Mg, Mn, Mo, Na, Ni, Os, Pb, Pd, Pt, Rh, Ru, Sb, Sc, Sn, Sr, Ta, Th, Ti, Tl, U, V, W, Y, Zn, Zr. Total impurity content: less than 0.010%.

§ All values given for Ferrovac-E are maximum; in addition: Pb: 0.001; As: 0.0005; Sn: 0.001; Al: 0.001; Co: 0.001; Cr: 0.001.

Table 5.3. Chemical Properties of Pure Iron

Electrochemical equivalent: Valence: 3   2

0.19291 mg/Coul.   0.28938 mg/Coul.
5.18353 Coul./mg   3.45568 Coul./mg

A. *Reactions with gases and vapors:*

dry air at room temperature: none; finely divided iron will ignite.

moist air: rapid corrosion by forming hydrated ferric oxide, Fe_2O_3 X H_2O

water vapor: $3\ Fe + 4\ H_2O \rightarrow 4\ H_2 + Fe_3O_4$; red hot iron and steam interact to form an adherent, nonporous black coating

oxygen: combustion to ferroferric oxide, Fe_3O_4

carbon monoxide: formation of iron tetracarbonyl, $Fe(CO)_4$, a gas, at 80°C; formation of iron pentacarbonyl, $Fe(CO)_5$, a yellow liquid (B.Pt. 103°C) by reaction of finely divided iron with CO at room temperature; decomposed by light, air, and moisture at R.T.; decomposes above 200°C[16]

B. *Reactions with liquids:*

H_2O: none if water is absolutely pure and free of dissolved oxygen

H_2SO_4 , cold, dilute: formation of ferrous sulfate with evolution of H_2

H_2SO_4 , hot, conc.: formation of ferrous sulfate with evolution of H_2

HCl, cold, dilute: formation of ferrous sulfate with evolution of H_2

HNO_3 , cold, dilute: dissolution

HNO_3 , hot, conc.: dissolution

HNO_3 , cold, conc.: formation of passive surface

alkalies: none, except with hot solutions of high concentration

mercury: none up to elevated temperatures

gallium: attack above 200°C on stainless steel

C. *Reactions with solids:*

alkalies: none

carbon: formation of Fe_3C, cementite, at elevated temperature

D. *Iron oxides:* removed by hydrogen or vacuum firing at 900–950°C[15]

FeO—protoxide, ferrous oxide, black; M.Pt. 1420°C, changes rapidly to Fe_2O_3 at R.T.

Fe_3O_4—magnetite, ferroferric oxide, triirontetroxide, black; decomposes at 1538°C

Fe_2O_3—hematite, sesquioxide, ferric oxide, red; M.Pt. 1565°C.

The Iron-Carbon Equilibrium Diagram[1, 17]

Apart from other alloying constituents which are present in varying amounts in the numerous types of steel, carbon is the determining element; it affects not only the predominant microstructure of the alloy but also the resulting physical characteristics of plain carbon steels. *Ingot iron,* as previously mentioned, has the lowest content of carbon and other alloying elements; it is used largely for sheets on account of its corrosion-resistant properties. *Extra soft* or *dead soft steel* contains from 0.08 to 0.12 % carbon (AISI 1010) and finds application where ductility, toughness, weldability, or ease in cold-working are desirable, and strength or stiffness is a minor consideration. *Structural grade,* or *mild steel,* contains from 0.15 to 0.25 %

carbon (AISI 1020); *medium grade* ranges from 0.25 to 0.35 % carbon content (AISI 1030) and is harder and stronger than mild steel, yet it may be hot-forged without difficulty. *Medium hard* steel contains from 0.35 to 0.65 % carbon (AISI 1040) and enters into the range where the final condition and reliability is much dependent upon the past mechanical and heat treatment. *Hard steel* ranges from 0.65 to 0.85 % carbon (AISI 1075) and is used only after it is heat-treated to a correct combination of strength and ductility. *Spring grades* range from 0.85 to 1.05 % carbon and are likewise used in a heat-treated condition as are *high-carbon tool steels* which contain from 1.05 to 1.20 % carbon; each additional 0.01 % carbon increases the ultimate strength in the annealed condition by approximately 1,000 psi, but at the expense of ductility or toughness, the latter property being expressed by the product of strength and ductility and measured in impact tests.[5] *Cast irons* contain from 2.2 to 4.5 % carbon and show little or no ductility; the ratio of compressive strength to tensile strength for gray iron is 4:1. By special treatment, *malleable iron* and ductile, nodular, or spheroidal graphite iron is obtained, the latter having a compressive to tensile strength ratio of 2:1.

The wide range of compositions between iron and carbon is represented in the iron-carbon phase equilibrium diagram (Figure 5.1). Familiarity with this diagram is a prerequisite to the understanding of the properties of steel and special glass-sealing alloys described in Chapter 13. When pure iron is heated to higher and higher temperatures, it undergoes several phase transformations; the various phases exist within a limited range of temperature and enter into solid solution with carbon in different concentrations. The terminal solid solution at the left-hand side of the diagram is known as alpha iron which crystallizes in the body-centered cubic system; α-iron becomes nonmagnetic at 769°C (Curie point); this temperature is given the designation A_2, represented by the A_2 line drawn parallel to the abscissa.

At 906°C, α-iron transforms into γ-iron which crystallizes in the face-centered cubic system.* At 1404°C, γ-iron transforms into δ-iron, which is again body-centered cubic and exists up to the temperature of 1535°C, where it melts (Point A). The liquidus is given by the line connecting points A, B, C, D. At a carbon content of 6.67 per cent, the compound cementite (Fe_3C) is formed, which has an orthorhombic crystal structure, is very hard and brittle and weakly magnetic; it loses its magnetism on heating at 200°C, as shown by the A_0 line. All irons and steels of practical interest contain less than 6.67 % carbon, and it is for this reason that only this section of the iron-carbon phase diagram is shown. A eutectic exists at Point C where

* The phase between 769 and 906°C is designated as β-iron and represents non-magnetic α-iron.

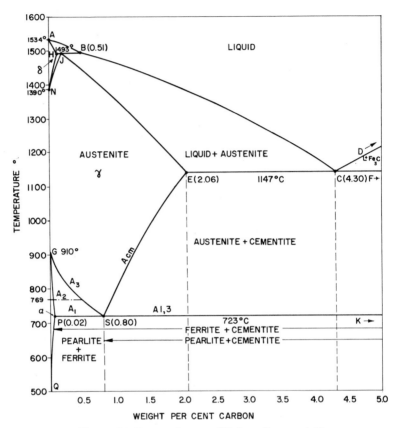

Figure 5.1. Iron-carbon equilibrium diagram.[1, 17]

molten alloy, a single phase, separates into the two phases of austenite and
cementite. The solidus line E–C lies at the temperature of 1130°C, and the
carbon content at Point C is 4.30 per cent.

A eutectoid is formed when a solid phase separates into two new solid
phases on cooling; this happens when austenite, which is a solid solution
of carbide in gamma-iron, is cooled to a temperature of 723°C where austenite is in equilibrium with α-iron and cementite (Point S); the carbon
content of the eutectoid is 0.80 per cent. Corresponding to the area where
liquid and austenite coexist (JBCE), there is an area GSP where α-iron
and austenite are in equilibrium. The line G–S has the designation A_3, and
the line P–S is known by the symbol A_1, while the symbol $A_{1,3}$ is given to
the line S–K; similarly, the line SE is given the symbol cm indicating the
limit of solubility for cementite in α-iron. The various border lines for limits
of solubility change somewhat on heating and cooling; they are affected

only slightly by the rate of heating, but very much so by the rate of cooling. A distinction is thus made when discussing transitions from one area to another by adding the suffix "c" (chauffage) for transitions on heating and the suffix "r" (refroidissement) for transitions on cooling. One then speaks of the Ar_3, Ac_2 and Ar_{cm}, Ac_{cm} lines, respectively. The letter e (equilibrium) is used to indicate extremely slow cooling, e.g., Ae_3, Ae_{cm}.

The eutectoid formed at S is known as *pearlite*, and the eutectic at point C bears the name *ledeburite*. Alloys formed to the left of points S and C bear the prefix *hypo* and those formed to the right of these critical points have the prefix *hyper*, so that one speaks of hypoeutectoid steels and hypoeutectic cast irons, and hypereutectoid steels. To clarify a few additional terms which frequently occur in describing phase transformations, it should be said that a peritectic transformation occurs at point J in Figure 5.1 when, on cooling, the two phases liquid plus δ-iron transform into the solid phase γ-iron. Where a mixture of two solid phases transforms into a new single solid phase on cooling, one speaks of a peritectoid. When one phase changes directly into another phase without any alteration in composition during the transformation, the phase change is said to be congruent. Conversely, an incongruent phase change is one which requires either a transient or a persistent composition change such as occurs in the freezing of eutectic-type alloys.

It should be emphasized that the phase diagram presented in Figure 5.1 applies only to plain carbon steels at conditions of equilibrium when sufficient time has been allowed to establish uniform temperature throughout the system and completion of the phase changes that are expected to occur at that temperature. This condition is difficult to achieve in practice and is often avoided for the purpose of carrying phases that exist at a higher temperature into lower temperature ranges by rapid cooling, or quenching, to take advantage of desirable physical characteristics resulting from such treatment. Tempering may follow a quenching treatment to partially neutralize an excessive precipitation of hard and brittle components.

Tempering refers to heating of a quenched ferrous alloy to a temperature below the transformation range and then cooling at any rate desired, while *normalizing* is heating to a temperature above the transformation range and then cooling in still air to room temperature. The heat treatment of steels is of necessity a complicated subject which requires detailed study of special texts devoted to this subject. The effects achieved by such treatment are often presented in the form of TTT diagrams, or S-curves, which give the time-temperature-transformation for austenitized steel if held at a constant temperature below the transformation range. A typical TTT diagram, such as shown in Figure 5.2, gives the time required for transformation to start, to proceed halfway (the dotted line marked 50 %), and to

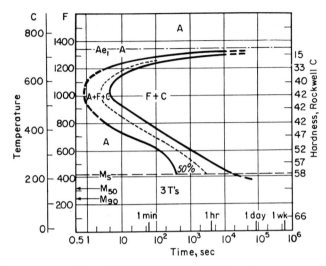

Figure 5.2(a). Typical TTT diagram.
A—austenite; F—ferrite; C—cementite. After Everhart.[18] (*Courtesy U. S. Steel Corporation.*)

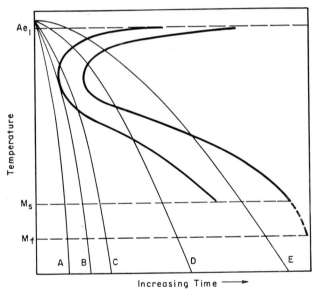

Figure 5.2(b). TTT diagram with different continuous cooling curves. After Everhart.[18] (*Courtesy National Bureau of Standards.*)

be complete at any constant temperature in the range covered by the curve. It is thus possible with the aid of such a diagram to predict the response of a steel to any type of cooling from the austenitic condition.

The diagram also shows the temperature at which austenite starts to

A-Martensite   B-Martensite (with trace of   C-Martensite (and very
                very fine pearlite,   fine pearlite)
                shown dark)

D-Fine pearlite   E-Coarse pearlite

Figure 5.2(c). Structures resulting when austenite is cooled at the rates shown in (b). After Everhart.[18] (*Courtesy National Bureau of Standards.*)

transform to martensite on rapid cooling (M_s), the temperature at which transformation is half complete (M_{50}), and the temperature at which transformation is 90 per cent complete (M_{90}). In continuous cooling, the structure will depend on the time that the steel remains in the various transformation regions, i.e., the cooling range.

Figure 5.2b has several different cooling curves superimposed on the TTT diagram, and the resulting structures are illustrated by photomicrographs in Figure 5.2c.[18, 19] Pearlite forms within the bay of the S-curve when austenite is cooled fairly slowly; it is characterized by a structure of platelets consisting alternately of ferrite and cementite (see Figure 5.2c at D and E). While pearlite always contains about 0.85 % carbon, finer-grained structures known as sorbite and troostite can be obtained by more rapid cooling, and these have widely differing carbon contents. The transformation product obtained below the nose of the S-curve is called *bainite*, which is characterized by a feather-like microstructure which at lower temperatures turns into a needle-like or acicular structure which gives great ductility, resilience, strength, and impact toughness.

When cooling below the horizontal lines shown at the bottom of the S-curve in Fig. 5.2a, b, a structure known as *martensite* results. The transformation to martensite is not time-dependent and occurs almost instantaneously. As previously stated, M_s indicates the start of the martensite transformation and M_f the finish, or completion, of this transformation. It is not possible to cool metal fast enough to prevent the martensite reaction. Martensite has the same chemical composition as the parent solid solution; all the carbon present initially in the γ-iron is still dissolved interstitially in the α-iron. Martensite is thus thermodynamically unstable and this abnormal supersaturation severely strains and distorts the α-iron cubic lattice into the body-centered tetragonal lattice of martensite. The strain thus produced is likely responsible for the unique mechanical properties of martensitic steels. The strained and distorted lattice interferes with the mobility of the structure in deformation, so plastic flow is very low and the hardness is very high. The great elastic stress locked within the martensite lattice causes steels that are wholly martensitic to break in a brittle manner under relatively light impact. Steels with martensitic microstructures retain magnetization well and are ideal for permanent magnets.[7]

The location of the critical lines shown in the iron-carbon equilibrium diagram (Figure 5.1) is notably affected by the addition of alloying elements which may shift the lines to the right or left, or up, or down. The addition of manganese or nickel generally causes a lowering of the critical range $A_{1,3}$. As the eutectoid point S is lowered and shifted, the steel may be quenched from lower temperature for hardening, and less strain will be suffered. It will also not be necessary to cool so rapidly, as the recrystallization involved in the formation of pearlite from austenite progresses more slowly at the lower temperature. By sufficient alloy addition, the steel may fully harden even on air-cooling, and one then speaks of air-hardening steel; oil-hardening and water-hardening steel are other terms that apply to particular alloys. With increasing depression of the critical range, steel may remain untransformed, or austenitic, at room temperature so that freezing to low temperatures is necessary to bring about the transformation. Most alloying elements raise the critical range; aluminum, cobalt, and copper shift the eutectoid point to the right, and chromium, tungsten, vanadium, molybdenum, and silicon shift it to the left.[7, 8]

Stainless Steels[6-8, 20-21]

Thirty-seven types of stainless steel are designated by code numbers issued by the American Iron and Steel Institute (AISI), and several hundred additional stainless alloys are commercially available under various trade designations. The Society of Automotive Engineers (SAE) and the Alloy Casting Institute (ACI), have separate number specifications for various alloys and some are covered by Aeronautical Materials Specifications (AMS). The various branches of the Armed Services have their set of specifications for alloy steels, and there are Federal specifications. Comparative tabulations of these codes are given in various handbooks; in the discussions to follow, the AISI designations will be used.

To provide the corrosion-resistant properties for which stainless steels are known, a minimum of 12 per cent chromium must be added to plain carbon steels. Chromium forms a thin, strongly adherent coating of oxide on the steel surface and very effectively prevents further oxidation. Strongly oxidizing conditions thus promote corrosion resistance. Reducing atmospheres, on the other hand, deprive the steel of the oxide film and lead to attack of the metal, especially if it is exposed to such reducing conditions for a long period of time. As it is known that carbon lowers the resistance to corrosion, carbon content of stainless steels is kept generally below 0.2 per cent. Steels of this type are known as *ferritic stainless steels*; they can be hardened to some extent by cold working but not by heat treatment and they are always magnetic. AISI Type 430, containing nominally 17 % chromium, is a representative of this series. In addition to chromium, these steels contain various amounts of manganese, silicon, phosphorus, and sulfur.

Martensitic steels also contain chromium as the main alloying element, in addition to those previously mentioned and present in smaller amounts (Table 5.4). It will be appreciated from the discussion of the martensite transformation that these steels can be hardened by heat treatment; they are always magnetic.

Austenitic steels, on the whole, contain somewhat larger percentages of chromium and in addition a fair percentage of nickel; the manganese content is of the order of 2 per cent. AISI Type 302, also known as "18-8" stainless steel, containing 18 % chrome and 8 % nickel, is a representative of this class. The critical range has been depressed to temperatures below room temperature by the addition of nickel as described earlier. As the name implies, the austenitic steel is nonmagnetic, but when these alloys are cold-worked at room temperature, some of the γ-phase is transformed to the α-phase, and an increase in magnetic susceptibility results.

The critical demand for nickel in times of national emergency has encouraged development of stainless steels, which have properties similar to those exhibited by the members of the "300" series without containing as much nickel. The "200" series is the result of these efforts.

The austenitic chromium-nickel-manganese stainless steels are nonmagnetic and cannot be hardened by heat treatment, like their counterpart the "300" series.

Application of Stainless Steels. Austenitic stainless steels of the "300" series are being used extensively in the tube industry for the construction of electron guns and other components. It is important to realize that Type

TABLE 5.4. SOME TYPICAL STAINLESS STEELS[20]

Group	AISI Type No.	Cr	Ni	C	Mn	Annealed sheets and strip *Annealed bars and plates			
						Tensile strength (psi)	Yield strength (psi)	Elongation (% in 2'')	Rockwell hardness
Hardenable chromium steels (martensitic and magnetic)	410	11.5-13.5	—	.15 max.	1 max.	65,000	35,000	25	B-80
	420	12-14	—	Over .15	1 max.	*95,000	50,000	25	B-92
	440A	16-18	—	.60-.75	1 max.	*105,000	60,000	20	B-95
	440B	16-18	—	.75-.95	1 max.	*107,000	62,000	18	B-96
	440C	16-18	—	.95-1.2	1 max.	*110,000	65,000	14	B-97
Nonhardenable chromium steels (ferritic and magnetic)	405	11.5-14.5	—	.08 max.	1 max.	65,000	40,000	25	B-75
	430	14-18	—	.12 max.	1 max.	75,000	45,000	25	B-80
	446	23-37	—	.2 max.	1.5 max.	80,000	50,000	20	B-83
Nonhardenable chromium-nickel and chromium-nickel-manganese steels (austenitic and nonmagnetic)	201	16-18	3.5-5.5	.15 max.	5.5-7.5	115,000	55,000	55	B-90
	202	17-19	4-6	.15 max.	7.5-10	105,000	55,000	55	B-90
	301	16-18	6-8	.15 max.	2 max.	110,000	40,000	60	B-85
	302	17-19	8-10	.15 max.	2 max.	90,000	40,000	50	B-85
	303**	17-19	8-10	.15 max.	2 max.	*90,000	35,000	50	—
	304	18-20	8-12	.08 max.	2 max.	85,000	35,000	50	B-80
	305†	17-19	10-13	.12 max.	2 max.	85,000	38,000	50	B-80

* Annealed bars and plates.

† Added by present author.

** Type 303 contains a minimum of 0.15% sulfur and should not be used in vacuum tubes; all other steels listed have a maximum sulfur content of 0.03 per cent.

303 contains an excessive amount of sulfur, a minimum of 0.15 and as much as 0.25 %, and for this reason it cannot be used in a vacuum tube, particularly one containing an oxide cathode. Types 302 and 304 stainless steel are in common use for electron tube components but they are not as suited as Type 305 for the reason given earlier. When Types 302 or 304 are cold-worked, their magnetic susceptibility increases, and when they are heavily cold-worked they may become fairly magnetic. Spot welding can also cause the formation of sufficient ferrite in Type 304 to produce magnetic properties; Type 305 contains more nickel and is thus free from these harmful effects.

The high degree of permeation of hydrogen through iron and steel, especially in humid atmospheres, should be borne in mind when using stainless steel for envelopes for vacuum tubes. Hydrogen diffuses through iron in its monatomic state and is thus taken up the more readily when atomic hydrogen is available at the surface, as supplied by electrolysis. For large sealed-off rectifiers made of steel, cooling with liquids which do not contain hydrogen ions is thus recommended. The permeation of hydrogen through steel increases markedly with increasing carbon content; a low-carbon steel, such as Armco iron, is thus preferred as envelope material.[15] It is also advisable to guard against gas leaks through microscopic fissures that may exist in the direction of rolling of the original ingot by arranging fabricated parts which form part of the envelope in such a way that the rolling grain does not provide a direct path from the inside to the outside of the tube.

Iron and steel are very difficult to outgas; even after heating these metals to a high temperature for several days, they continue to liberate a small amount of gas at operating temperatures in the range of several hundred degrees centigrade.[22] The gases released by iron and steel consist primarily of carbon monoxide, nitrogen, and hydrogen, and the rate of evolution increases both with increase in temperature and with decrease in the partial pressure of the evolved gases in the surrounding atmosphere. Iron contains about 10 to 50 times as much oxygen as nickel does; most of the oxygen is combined with iron in the form of FeO, and, in view of the extremely low dissociation pressure of the oxide even at 1400°K, this oxygen content is not harmful. Within the limitations mentioned above, an outgassing temperature of 1000°C is recommended for general-purpose applications.

Aluminum-clad Iron

To alleviate the critical dependence on imports of nickel, the German metal industry expended considerable effort shortly before World War II to develop a substitute that might serve for anodes in receiving tubes. The result of this effort was the introduction of "P2-Iron"; this consists of a low-carbon steel clad with aluminum containing from 1.0 to 1.5% silicon and from 0.3 to 0.6% iron by cold-rolling to a thickness of less than one mil on one side. When this clad sheet is heated in hydrogen, it takes on a black finish and becomes ductile. Heating in air or vacuum will also produce this dark surface finish, which is due to a reaction between the aluminum and the base iron, resulting in the formation of $FeAl_3$, or a more complex compound. Large tonnages of this material were produced in Europe during World War II either in the form of sheet iron coated on both sides with aluminum (P2), on one side only, the other side being coated with nickel (PN-Iron), or one side coated with aluminum and the other with a very low-carbon spheroidized iron containing 0.05% carbon (PI). Similar materials were introduced on the American market after the war and are now in common use for anodes of many types of receiving tubes. ASTM Tentative Specification F2-57T covers these materials.

It is worthy of note that in addition to the composition ranges given above for carbon and silicon, the maximum phosphorus and sulfur contents for the carbon steel base material are given as 0.040 and 0.050%, respectively, and the maximum sulfur content for nickel used to clad one side of the composite strip as 0.008%. Espe and Steinberg[22] have described in some detail the manufacturing procedures, the properties, and the applications of these composite materials. The spectral emissivity ($\lambda = 6650A$) of the converted aluminized steel surface is 0.85 compared to 0.75 for carbonized nickel. The degassing properties are stated to be excellent, and some "getting" action is suggested during the conversion of the surface when this process is performed in the tube itself by induction heating. Spot welding is somewhat difficult. One tube manufacturer reports that aluminum-coated steel cannot be used in r-f amplifier pentodes designed for 12-volt anode supply. While the reason for this behavior is not clearly established, it appears that a "surface impedance" of some sort makes for low plate resist-

TABLE 5.5. COOLING RATES OF VARIOUS PLATE MATERIALS AT 300°C.*

Test	Material	Cooling rate, °C/sec (300°C)
A	Permanickel	2.40
B	Steel—nickel-plated	2.46
C	Armco iron	2.62
D	Steel—nickel-plated, nickel-coated	3.72
E	Nickel—gas-carbonized	5.46
F	Steel—aluminum-clad	6.00
G	Permanickel—nickel-coated, carbonized	6.06
H	Steel—nickel-plated, nickel-coated, carbonized	6.58

* After Horsting et al.[23]

ance; at higher anode voltages this effect disappears, but at 12 volts the plate current vs. plate voltage characteristic does not properly saturate. When carbonized nickel is used in the cases, the difficulties disappear.*

The relative cooling rates of various plate materials were determined at 300°C by Horsting *et al.*[23] by mounting a small test cylinder to which a thermocouple was attached in a vacuum tube, heating it to 900°C and then measuring the temperature during cooling on a recording potentiometer. By drawing tangents to these curves, the cooling rates recorded in Table 5.5 were obtained. While these values do not represent absolute values but apply only to the particular experimental conditions employed in this case, the technique could be used to determine total emissivity from the following relation:

$$e_t = \frac{dT}{dt} \frac{C_p}{A\sigma(T_w{}^4 - T_t{}^4)}$$

where e_t = total emissivity of sample

$\dfrac{dT}{dt}$ = specific cooling rate

A = radiating area

σ = Stefan-Bolzmann constant

C_p = heat capacity of sample material at T_t

T_w = absolute temperature of envelope

T_t = absolute temperature of sample

It is apparent from the table that aluminum-clad steel presents a high rate of cooling which, within the reservations just made, is somewhat higher than that of gas-carbonized nickel and only slightly less than that of carbonized, nickel-coated "Permanickel."

A still further refinement along these lines aiming at uniform heat dissipation of receiving tube anodes has been recently described by Miller and Millis.[24] In cooperation with the General Electric Company Receiving Tube Division at Owensboro, Kentucky, the General Plate Division of the Metals and Controls Corporation of Attleboro, Massachusetts, has developed a 3- or 5-layer material consisting of aluminum on steel on copper which presents an improvement over their former "Aliron." A 5-ply material results when a copper core is coated on both sides with iron and aluminum. The reason for this development is of course the high thermal conductivity of copper, which will equalize any temperature gradients that might develop on ordinary "Aliron" and lead to hot spots. OFHC copper is used in conjunction with a low carbon steel (0.08 %C) and Alcoa C-22 aluminum alloy

* Personal communication from Dr. A. K. Wright.

containing 1.0 to 1.5 % silicon. The copper content of the composite material is held to a minimum of 40 % by volume for "Copper Cored Aliron" and to 60 % by volume in the "Copper Base Aliron." The thickness of the strip is 0.007 ± 0.0003 in. The thickness of the steel layers is not less than 1.7 mils and that of the aluminum is on the order of 0.5 mil. "Copper-Cored Aliron" is preferable for the amplifier types of tubes, while "Copper-Base Aliron" is preferable for rectifiers. No poisoning effect on cathode emission has been noted when copper was facing the cathode. Gas evolution was measured for the various materials at 850°C after they had been fired in hydrogen for 10 minutes at 500°C before assembly; "Copper-Cored Aliron" was lower than "Aliron," which was lower than "Copper-Base Aliron," which in turn was materially lower than gas-carbonized nickel in terms of gas evolution. Superior performance characteristics are reported after life tests on a number of different types of tubes.

Magnetic Properties of Iron and Steel

The design of magnetic circuits is necessary in some special tube applications such as permanent-magnet focussed travelling-wave tubes, Brillouin-flow electron guns, crossed-field devices, and others. Magnetic lenses play an important role in electron optics. Magnetic shielding is necessary where extraneous stray fields would interfere with desired performance characteristics of electrodynamic systems. In most cases, the magnetic materials are arranged outside the vacuum tube.

It would be outside the scope of this book to attempt a treatment of ferromagnetism or that of ferrites which have replaced conventional permanent magnets in many cases.

REFERENCES

1. "Metals Handbook," The American Society For Metals, Cleveland, Ohio, 1948.
2. "Engineering Materials Handbook," C. L. Mantell, Ed., McGraw-Hill Book Co., Inc., New York, 1958.
3. "Metals Reference Book" (2 Vols.), C. J. Smithells, Interscience Publishers, Inc., New York, 1955.
4. "American Institute of Physics Handbook," D. E. Gray, Ed., McGraw-Hill Book Co., Inc., New York, 1957.
5. "Encyclopaedia Britannica," Encyclopaedia Britannica, Inc., Chicago, 1957.
6. J. Marin, "Engineering Materials, Their Properties and Applications," Prentice-Hall, Inc., New York, 1952.
7. J. Wulff, H. F. Taylor and A. J. Shaler, "Metallurgy for Engineers," John Wiley & Sons, Inc., New York, 1952.
8. A. A. Bates, "Fundamentals of Ferrous Metallurgy," American Society For Metals, Cleveland, 1935.
9. J. E. Goldman, Ed., "The Science of Engineering Materials," John Wiley & Sons, Inc., New York, 1957.

10. C. R. Soderberg, "Mechanical properties in relation to design requirements," *Metallurgical Revs.*, **1**, Pt. 1, 31–63 (1956).

10a. S. H. Avner and H. E. Barkner, "Key to metals in design engineering," *Elec. Mgf.*, **63**, 123–146 (May 1959).

11. A. M. Freudenthal, "Internal stresses and fatique in metals," *Physics Today*, **12**, 16–19 (Feb. 1959).

12. "Relation of Properties to Microstructure," American Society For Metals, Cleveland, 1954. (Papers presented at a Seminar held in Cleveland, Oct. 17–23, 1953).

13. B. E. Hopkins, "The preparation and properties of high-purity iron," *Metallurgical Revs.*, **1**, Pt. 1, 117–155 (1956).

14. R. E. Honig, "Vapor pressure data for the more common elements," *RCA Rev.*, **18**, 195–204 (June 1957).

15. W. Espe and M. Knoll, "Werkstoffkunde der Hochvakuumtechnik," Julius Springer-Verlag, Berlin, 1936.

16. "Van Nostrand's Scientific Encyclopedia," 3d ed., D. Van Nostrand Co., Inc., Princeton, 1958.

17. M. Hansen and K. Anderko, "Constitution of Binary Alloys," 2nd ed., McGraw-Hill Book Co., Inc., New York, 1958.

18. J. L. Everhart, "Designing with heat-treated steels," Manual No. 149, *Materials in Design Engineering*, **47**, 122–136 (June 1958).

19. S. J. Rosenberg and Th. G. Digges, "Heat Treatment and Properties of Iron and Steel," NBS Circular 495 (1950).

20. J. Winlock, "What are stainless steels?" *Foote Prints*, **29**, No. 1 (1957); Foote Mineral Company, Philadelphia, Pa.

21. J. L. Everhart, "How to select a stainless steel," *Materials in Design Engineering*, **49**, 96–110 (Jan. 1959).

22. W. Espe and E. B. Steinberg, "Aluminum-clad iron for electron tubes," *Tele-Tech.*, **10**, 28–30, 72 (Feb. 1951).

22a. E. A. Gulbransen and K. F. Andrew, "Oxide nucleation and the substructure of iron," *J. Electrochem. Soc.*, **106**, 511–515 (June 1959).

23. C. W. Horsting, I. S. Solet, T. A. Sternberg and P. Avakian, "Method for determining specific cooling rates of electron tube anode materials in vacuum," *IRE Trans. Electron Devices*, **ED-6**, 119–120 (Jan. 1959).

24. E. A. Miller and W. T. Millis, "The production of copper-base Aliron and copper-cored Aliron for receiving tube applications," Metals & Controls Corporation, General Plate Division, Attleboro, Mass., 1958. (U.S. Patent 2,691,815).

25. A. Arrott and J. E. Goldman, "Fundamentals of Ferromagnetism," *Elec. Mfg.*, **63**, 109–140 (Mar. 1959).

26. F. Sterzer and W. W. Siekanowicz, "The design of periodic permanent magnets for focusing of electron beams," *RCA Rev.*, **18**, 39–59 (Mar. 1957).

27. "Materials used in radio and electronic engineering, Pt. 5, Magnetic materials," *J. Brit. Inst. Radio Engs.*, **18**, 449–464 (Aug. 1958). Contains extensive tables and references.

28. R. M. Bozorth, "Ferromagnetism," D. Van Nostrand Co., Inc., Princeton, 1951.

29. R. A. Chegwidden, "A review of magnetic materials, especially for communication systems," *Metal Progr.*, **54**, 705–714 (Nov. 1948).

CHAPTER 6

COPPER AND COPPER ALLOYS

Introduction

The prime reasons for the use of copper in electron tubes are its high electrical conductivity and its high thermal conductivity, which distinguish it from other metals; in addition, it has high resistance to corrosion. Copper is readily available at reasonable cost and can be formed and machined into all conceivable shapes, it can be plated onto other base metals to impart desirable characteristics to their surfaces and thus make it possible to use stronger materials for structural members while maintaining high electrical and thermal conductivity at the surface.

A great number of copper alloys is available for different industrial applications, and their composition is described in the metals handbooks,[1-3] several texts on copper,[4-6] catalogues issued by copper producers, and treatises sponsored by trade associations.*[7, 8] Specifications governing the various copper products are compiled in the 1958 Book of ASTM Standards, Part 2, Non-Ferrous Metals; a Copper and Copper-Alloy Specifications Index[9] is available which correlates all applicable specifications issued by professional societies, as well as Federal and military agencies.

When copper is used for vacuum tube envelopes or internal structural components, a special brand of oxygen-free, high-conductivity copper, known as "OFHC"† must be specified. A very limited number of copper alloys, such as cupro-nickel, is used for internal components; these are discussed later in this chapter. For external components, such as radiators, which are separately attached to the envelope, other grades of copper may be used. Copper finds very little application in receiving tubes, but large power tubes and the whole family of microwave tubes make most extensive use of it for anodes, cavity structures, and collectors. We will thus be mainly concerned in this chapter with the properties of OFHC copper.

OFHC Brand Copper

The American Metal Climax, Inc.[10] has published a very carefully prepared survey on the properties of this material, and copies of this attractive

---

* Copper and Brass Research Association, 420 Lexington Ave., New York 17, N. Y.; Brass and Bronze Ingot Institute, 300 W. Washington St., Chicago 6, Ill.; British Non-Ferrous Metals Research Association, London, England.

† Registered trademark, American Metal Climax, Inc.

book are available; it is profusely illustrated and contains 180 references to the literature. This study, the excellent monograph on copper by Butts,[4] and the extensive review article on applications of copper in high vacuum technique by Espe,[11] afford a complete background of literature for reference purposes. To have some of the highlights gathered together in this chapter, however, may be a convenience for the student of electron tube technology.

Table 6.1 gives the ASTM classification of coppers. The better grades of ordinary commercial copper such as electrolytic tough pitch copper (ETP), lake copper, and deoxidized or phosphorized copper have a minimum specified copper content of 99.90 per cent. The tough pitch coppers contain enough oxygen in the form of copper oxide to form voids and intergranular cracks when they are hydrogen-fired; the hydrogen combines with the remaining oxygen to form steam under very high pressure which literally tears the copper apart on a microscopic scale so that leaks result when such coppers are used for a vacuum envelope. The photomicrographs shown in Figures 6.1 and 6.2 illustrate this point.

There are two grades of OFHC copper, i.e., regular grade and "certified" OFHC. The quality of OFHC copper is governed by ASTM Specification B 170–47. When buying "certified" OFHC, one has the assurance that any particular shipment has been checked for its conformity not only with this specification but also with additional stipulations essential for electronic use. A premium must naturally be paid for this certification because analyses must be run on a sample; this extra cost is well worth while. The greatest possible care must be taken by a tube manufacturer to keep such certified OFHC, or for that matter, regular OFHC copper, apart from other commercial grades of copper that may be used for other purposes in the manufacturing operations. Very costly failures will result if lower grades of copper, including electrolytic copper, find their way into departments where tube components are fabricated.

Table 6.2 gives the composition of copper grades which are acceptable for vacuum tube components. In addition to the OFHC coppers, vacuum-cast, gas-free, high-purity copper, (GFHP), manufactured by the Vacuum Metals Corporation,* is also listed. OFHC copper is produced from electrolytic copper cathodes by continuous melting in an electric induction furnace and then cast in water-cooled copper or steel molds; a reducing atmosphere is maintained during the melting and casting operations. Any remaining traces of oxides or free oxygen dissolved in the electrolytic copper are thus eliminated by chemical action. In vacuum casting, free oxygen will be removed by the pump, and remaining oxides broken down by thermal decomposition.

* Syracuse 1, N. Y.

TABLE 6.1. CLASSIFICATION OF COPPERS
(ASTM Designation B 224–58)

Letter code	Type of copper	Notes*
CATH	Electrolytic cathode	
	Tough Pitch Coppers	1
ETP	Electrolytic tough pitch	2
FRHC	Fire-refined, high-conductivity tough pitch	2, 3
FRTP	Fire-refined tough pitch	3
ATP	Arsenical, tough pitch	4
STP	Silver bearing tough pitch	2, 3
SATP	Silver bearing arsenical tough pitch	4
CAST	Casting	
	Oxygen-Free Coppers	5
OF	Oxygen-free without residual deoxidants	2
OFP	Oxygen-free, phosphorus bearing	
OFPTE	Oxygen-free, phosphorus and tellurium bearing	
OFS	Oxygen-free, silver bearing	2
OFTE	Oxygen-free, tellurium bearing	
	Deoxidized Coppers	6
DHP	Phosphorized, high residual phosphorus	4
DLP	Phosphorized, low residual phosphorus	2
DPS	Phosphorized, silver bearing	4, 7
DPA	Phsophorized, arsenical	4, 8
DPTE	Phosphorized, tellurium bearing	4, 9

* Notes have been rearranged and extended by the author of this book.

1. Tough-pitch coppers are fire refined and given a controlled oxygen content to improve castability and mechanical strength.

2. High-conductivity copper, in the annealed condition, has a minimum electrical conductivity of 100% I.A.C.S. (p. 200) Types ETP, FRHC, STP, OF, and OFS are high-conductivity coppers; DLP can be so classified if agreed upon between supplier and purchaser.

3. Low-resistance lake copper is included under Types FRHC and STP.

4. High-resistance lake copper is included under Types ATP, SATP, DHP, DPS, DPA, DPTE, and FRTP.

5. Copper which has been refined by electrolytic deposition and is free from cuprous oxide; produced without the use of metallic or metalloidal deoxidizers.

6. Copper cast in the form of refinery shapes, free from cuprous oxide through the use of metallic or metalloidal deoxidizers.

7. Silver is added to raise the softening temperature and increase the creep resistance; electrical conductivity drops close to 0.15 per cent for each ounce per ton silver tenor.

8. Addition of arsenic (0.25 to 0.50 per cent) increases corrosion resistance and also the recrystallization temperature; not acceptable for use in vacuum.

9. Addition of tellurium, about 0.5 per cent, greatly increases machinability (free-cutting copper) without decreasing electrical conductivity to any extent; not acceptable for use in vacuum.

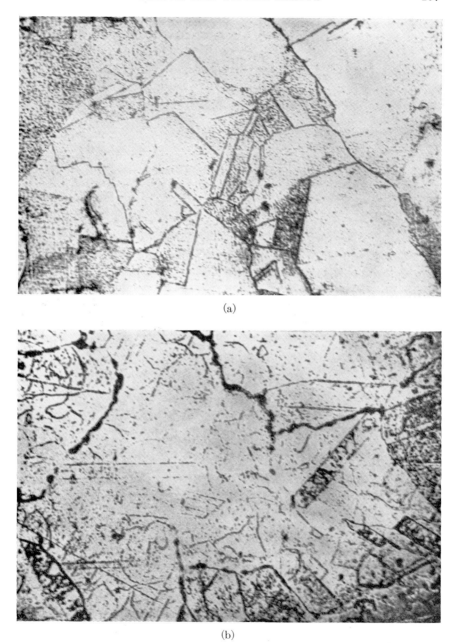

(a)

(b)

Figure 6.1. Photomicrographs of copper taken to detect inclusions of Cu_2O. a) "good" copper, magnification 250×; b) "bad" copper, magnification 405×. (*By permission from "Microwave Magnetrons," edited by George B. Collins.*[12] *Copyright 1948, McGraw-Hill Book Company, Inc.*)

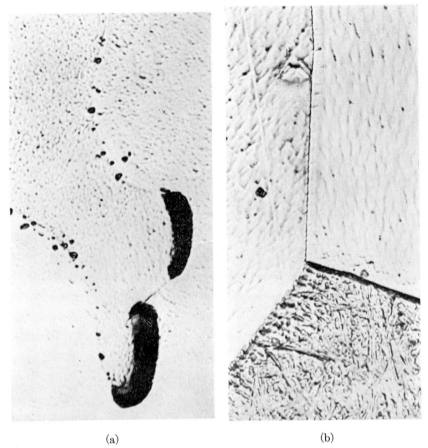

(a)   (b)

Figure 6.2. Photomicrographs of copper. a) OFHC ingot (1000×); b) gas-free high-purity copper (1000×). After Stauffer et al.[13] (*Reprinted by permission, The American Chemical Society and National Research Corporation.*)

Another high-conductivity copper, known as "PDCP Copper,"* is also obtained from electrolytic copper but not by remelting. The desired shapes of bar, rod, and strip are produced from pressed compacts of nodules of electrolytic copper cathodes by exposing them to very high pressure at elevated temperature in a reducing atmosphere. PDCP copper compares favorably in its analysis with that of certified OFHC, but the latter has a higher ductility.

Electrolytic tough-pitch copper generally contains from 0.03 to 0.06 per cent oxygen, OFHC copper has an oxygen content of 0.0002 per cent,

* Phelps Dodge Copper Products Corporation, New York, N. Y.

TABLE 6.2. CHEMICAL COMPOSITION OF VACUUM TUBE
COPPERS (IN WEIGHT PERCENT)

OFHC copper[10]	Fe: 0.0005; S: 0.0025; Ag: 0.0010; Ni: 0.0006; Sb: 0.0005; As: 0.0003; Se: 0.0002; Te: 0.0001; Pb: 0.0006; Sn: 0.0002; Mn: 0.00005; Bi: 0.0001; O_2 : 0.0002; Cu: Bal.
OFHC copper[10] (Certified grade) (ASTM B170–47)	P: 0.0003 max.; S: 0.0040 max.; Zn: 0.0003 max.; Hg: 0.0001 max.; Pb: 0.0010 max.; Cu + Ag: 99.96 min.
Vacuum-cast copper (GFHP)*	N_2 : <0.0001; O_2 : <0.0001; H_2 : <0.0001; Fe: <0.002; Ni: <0.0005; As: 0.001 max.; Pb: 0.0001 max.; Ag: 0.003 max.; S: 0.0001 max.; Bi: tr.; Sn: tr.; Zn: tr.; Cu: Bal.

* Vacuum Metals Corporation, Division of Crucible Steel Company of America, Syracuse 1, N. Y.

GFHP copper less than 0.0001 per cent and PDCP coalesced copper a similarly low oxygen content to make it suitable for glass-to-metal seals and resist hydrogen embrittlement.[4] It is particularly important that copper intended for glass-to-metal seals be low in phosphorus so that the oxide scale will be firmly adherent. The extra specifications for certification call for a maximum phosphorus content of 0.0003 per cent.[11]

Several tests are available to ensure that the quality of a given lot of copper comes up to the required standard. In the hydrogen bend test (ASTM Specification B 170–47), a strip of copper sheet, not thicker than one-sixteenth inch, is chemically cleaned and fired in dry hydrogen at 850°C for 30 minutes and then quickly removed from the furnace and quenched in water. The sample, if oxygen-free copper, should be flexible and not break when clamped between jaws having edges with a radius 2.5 times the diameter of the wire, or the thickness of the strip, and bent through 90° and back to its original position at least four times, the bends being performed in opposite directions. Copper suitable for seal making, when heated in air at 820°C for 30 minutes and subsequently plunged into cold water, should be coated with a film of black matt oxide, lying on the surface of red cuprous oxide, which adheres very tenaciously to the metal. A loose oxide film indicates unsatisfactory material, arising from the presence in the copper of deoxidizers which reduce the cuprous oxide to spongy copper.[14] A more refined test to detect the presence of cuprous oxide is that by microscopic examination of a polished and etched sample as described by Collins.[12] The possibility exists, however, that other compounds may be found which look like oxide inclusions under the microscope but nevertheless are not harmful. It is thus more general practice in the industry to rely on the hydrogen bend test and correlate results from it with actual test seals to glass; this will give a reliable check on the quality of the copper.

It is also possible to distinguish high-purity copper from other grades by its electrical resistivity. The International Electrotechnical Commission defined in 1913 the International Annealed Copper Standard (IACS) according to which a copper wire of a density equal to 8.89 grams/cc has a resistance of 0.15328 ohm at 20°C for a specimen one meter long and weighing one gram. If the conductivity of the IACS is taken as 100 per cent, various types of commercial high-conductivity copper generally fall between 100.5 and 101.8 per cent; OFHC copper has a conductivity on this scale equal to 102 per cent, while deoxidized copper with a residual phosphorus content ranging from 0.015 to 0.035 per cent will result in a conductivity range of 80 to 90% IACS.[4] As little as 0.05 per cent arsenic will lower the electrical conductivity by about 14 per cent, and the same amount of iron will reduce it by about 19 per cent.[15] Corresponding figures for other commercial copper grades are entered in Table 6.3.

The physical characteristics of pure copper are given in Table 6.4. Some comparative stress-strain relations for tough-pitch and OFHC copper appear in Table 6.5 after Butts,[4] and comparative yield-strength data for the same materials are given in Table 6.6. Figure 6.3 presents the tensile strength of OFHC copper as a function of percent reduction and temperature on progressive reannealing after Yokelson and Balicki;[20] the same authors have investigated the uniform elongation of OFHC copper as a

TABLE 6.3. COMPARISON OF SEVERAL TYPES OF COPPER WITH RESPECT TO TENSILE PROPERTIES AND ELECTRICAL CONDUCTIVITY AT 21°C (70°F) AND CREEP STRENGTH AT 150, 200, AND 260°C (300, 400, AND 500°F)[4]

ASTM Designation	Temper		Tensile strength at 70°F, psi	Yield strength at 0.5 per cent extension under load at 70°F, psi	Creep strength, stress, psi, for creep rate of 0.01 per cent per 1000 hr			Electrical conductivity at 70°F, per cent IACS
	Annealed, avg. grain size, mm	Drawn, reduction, per cent			300°F	400°F	500°F	
ETP	0.025		35,100	7,200	2,950	1,300	350	100.9
OF	0.025		34,500	7,900	3,600	1,500	400	101.3
DLP	0.013		36,500	12,000	7,200	2,100	700	100.1
DHP	⎧0.015		34,800	8,600	5,100	2,550	650	89.0
	⎨0.032		33,300	5,850	5,400	2,650	900	89.0
	⎩0.070		32,200	4,550	7,200	4,000	2,000	88.6
DPA	0.045		35,000	6,100	8,400	5,200	2,600	45.3
ETP		84	55,400	50,000	9,400	2,100		99.1
OF		84	54,500	49,500	8,300	1,750		99.5
DLP		84	57,500	54,000	21,000	5,200	600	98.3
DHP		84	56,400	52,000	33,500	2,500*	1,000*	88.5
DPA		84	60,900	55,500	40,000	27,500	2,000†	46.0

* By extrapolation of log stress-log creep-rate curve.
† Produces third stage of creep, accelerating creep rate.

TABLE 6.4. PHYSICAL CHARACTERISTICS OF PURE COPPER[3, 16]

Atomic number: 29
Atomic weight: 63.54
Isotopes: 63, 65
Density (gm/cc): 8.93 (theoretical)
        8.9436 (GFHP)

Atomic valence: 1.2
Valence orbitals: $3d^24s^1$
Lattice type: f.c.c. (A1)
Lattice constants: a = 3.6147 ± 0.0020 A
Atomic diameter: 2.551 A
Atomic volume (cc/gm atom): 7.09

Melting point (°C): 1083 ± 0.1
Boiling point (°C):[17] 2578
Heat of fusion, ΔH_m (Kcal/mole): 3.110; (48.9 cal/gm)
Heat of vaporization, ΔH_v (Kcal/mole): 72.8
Entropy of fusion, ΔS_m (cal/mole/°K): 2.29
Entropy of vaporization, ΔS_v (cal/mole/°K): 25.4
Entropy at 298.16°K, ΔS (cal/mole/°K): 7.97
Specific heat (20°C), (cal/gm):[4] 0.092; for solid from $0 \rightarrow t°C$: $0.092 + 0.0000250t$
Thermal conductivity (20°C), (cal/cm²/cm/sec/°C):[4] 0.934 (for 101% IACS) (temperature has very little effect)
Thermal expansion coeff. (20°C), (cm/cm/°C): 165×10^{-7}
    $0 \rightarrow 300°C: L_t = L_0[1 + (16.23t + 0.00483t^2) \times 10^{-6}]$ cm
    $0 \rightarrow 1000°C: L_t = L_0[1 + (16.733t + 2.626 \times 10^{-3}t^2 + 9.1 \times 10^{-7}t^3) \times 10^{-6}]$ cm
Vapor pressure (Torr):[2]
    $\log p = (-17{,}870/T) - 10.63 - 0.236 \log T - 0.16T$; (298–1356°K)
    $\log p = -17{,}650 - 13.39 - 1.273 \log T$; (1356–2870°K)

10^{-8}	10^{-7}	10^{-6}	10^{-5}	10^{-4}	10^{-3}	10^{-2}	10^{-1}	Torr
1005	1065	1135	1215	1305	1415	1545	1700	°K[17]

Spectral emissivity:[4]

λ	500	550	600	650	700	mμ
1000°C:	40.4	31.3	18.5	11.2	8.7	%
1125°C:	38.7	29.3	20.5	14.8	11.8	%

Total emissivity (at 100°C):[2] 0.02
             (at 1200°C): 0.12
Electrical resistivity (20°C), (microhm·cm):[18] 1.647 (99.999% Cu)
Temperature coeff. of resistivity (microhm·cm/°C):[18] 0.0043
Magnetic susceptibility (c.g.s.):   18°C = -0.086×10^{-6}
                         1080°C = -0.077×10^{-6}
                         1090°C = -0.054×10^{-6}
Electron work function (e.v.): 4.6 (Table 15.3)
Richardson constant A(a/cm²deg²): 16.7 (at melting point)[19]
Mechanical Properties: (see also Tables 6.3, 6.5, 6.6 and Figs. 6.3, 6.4)
Poisson's ratio:[4] 0.33 ± 0.01

function of percent reduction and temperature of exposure reached on progressive reannealing as shown in Figure 6.4. Table 6.7 gives the chemical properties of pure copper and its reaction with solids, liquids, and gases.

It has been demonstrated by Landauer[26] and Rutter and Reekie[27] that isotropically cold-worked copper displays an increase in its electrical resistivity which amounts to about 2 per cent compared with the d-c resis-

TABLE 6.5. SOME COMPARATIVE STRESS-STRAIN RELATIONS OF
TOUGH-PITCH AND OXYGEN-FREE COPPER[4]

	Tough-pitch copper		Oxygen-free copper	
	Hard	Annealed	Hard	Annealed
Modulus of elasticity, million psi	16.95	15.82	17.54	16.20
0.0002% offset—stress, psi				
Initial	8,300	1,150	8,300	1,400
Strained*	13,400	3,300	15,000	3,300
0.002% offset—stress, psi				
Initial	12,850	1,900	15,400	1,950
Strained*	21,500	4,720	24,800	4,500
0.0002% permanent set—stress, psi				
Initial	5,000		5,500	
Strained†	21,000		21,000	
0.002% permanent set—stress, psi				
Initial	13,500		14,200	
Strained†	34,800		38,200	
Yield strength (0.5% strain), psi	46,000	5,500	47,000	5,000
Tensile strength, psi	46,900	31,500	47,500	30,900
Elongation in 2 in., %	14.8	53.0	20.5	60.0
Reduction of area, %	58.5	71.4	86.4	92.1

  * Stress for stated offset after prestraining to 0.5 per cent extension.

  † Stress for stated permanent set after prestressing to produce a permanent set
of 0.10 per cent.

TABLE 6.6. SOME COMPARATIVE YIELD-STRENGTH DATA FOR
TOUGH-PITCH AND OXYGEN-FREE COPPER[4]

	Electrolytic copper	OFHC copper
0.5% total strain		
Stress at 0.5% strain	46,000 psi	47,000 psi
Offset at 0.5% strain	0.229%	0.232%
Resulting permanent set	0.212%	0.222%
0.1% set		
Stress for 0.1% permanent set	44,300 psi	45,000 psi
0.1% offset		
Stress	43,700 psi	44,600 psi
Total strain	0.359%	0.355%
0.2% offset		
Stress	45,700 psi	46,800 psi
Total strain	0.473%	0.468%

tivity of fully annealed copper. This small decrease in conductivity will
rarely have any practical importance. The corresponding decrease in r-f
conductivity, however, is much more serious, especially at high frequencies
when a large part of the r-f current flows in a thin skin.

    Machining processes are known to destroy the perfection of the crystal
lattice and thus result in surface layers which have a much lower conductivity. Thorp[28] has investigated this effect on hobbed cavities at a wave

length of 8 mm. The copper used had the following analysis: Cu: 99.95 per cent plus, S: 0.002 per cent, Fe: 0.001 per cent, Ag; 0.001 per cent, Sb: 0.0007 per cent, As: 0.0002 per cent. The conductivity of copper of this purity, which is equivalent to OFHC copper, is 5.917×10^5 mhos/cm (102 % IACS). Hobbed cavities with extremely smooth surfaces showed a ratio of d-c conductivity to r-f conductivity $\sigma/\sigma' = 0.58$ without hydrogen cleaning and 0.57 with hydrogen cleaning, these figures representing average measurements on six cavities made with an accuracy of $\pm$ 1 per cent. An annealing treatment in hydrogen at 500°C for a period of from one to two hours caused the σ/σ' value to rise to 0.64. When hobbed cavities were etched by immersing them for 30 seconds in either nitric acid or a mixture of phosphoric and acetic acid, or by deplating them in sulfuric acid, the r-f conductivity reached 78 per cent of the d-c conductivity without annealing treatment. When etched cavities were annealed in hydrogen, 98 per cent of the d-c conductivity was achieved. The skin depth at 8 mm is 3.5×10^{-5} cm; the etching treatment removed about 10^{-4} cm of the surface.

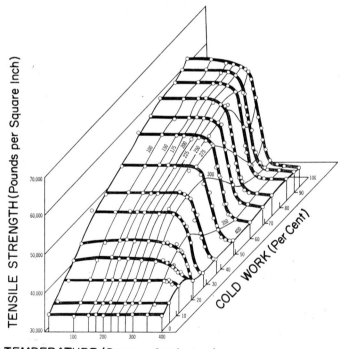

Figure 6.3. Tensile strength of OFHC copper as a function of percent reduction and temperature on progressive reannealing; heating rate employed, 10.8°C per minute. After Yokelson and Balicki.[20] (*Courtesy Quinn-Brown Publishing Corp.*)

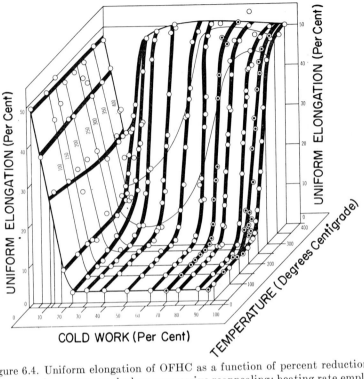

Figure 6.4. Uniform elongation of OFHC as a function of percent reduction and temperature of exposure reached on progressive reannealing; heating rate employed, 10.8°C per minute. After Yokelson and Balicki.[20] (*Courtesy Quinn-Brown Publishing Corp.*)

"The r-f conductivity of copper cavities can also be improved by an oxidation and reduction process. The hobbed cavity is silver plated, heated in hydrogen at 780°C, cooled and reheated to 700°C, first in air and then in hydrogen. This treatment first forms a copper-silver layer. The copper content of this layer is selectively oxidized, and a surface layer of copper oxide is built up because copper diffusing into the silver from the base is oxidized on reaching the surface. On heating in hydrogen, the copper oxide is then reduced and a copper layer is formed on the cavity surfaces. Microscopic studies have shown that the thickness of the copper layer is several times greater than the skin depth. This type of processing increased σ/σ' from 0.56 to 0.85 of the d-c value. Annealing produced no further increase, which suggested that the copper layer was strain-free. Chemical analysis showed that the surface layer was almost pure copper; it consists of globules; the surface path was thus increased slightly by this processing as compared with the hobbed surface; the calculated reduction of σ/σ' due to this was 0.24 which was sufficient to account for the observed departure from unity."[28]

The hobbing of cavities is an example of cold-working which results in strain-hardening effects. Hot-working, on the other hand, implies the elastic and plastic deformation of metal above the recrystallization temperature, and work-hardening effects are not observed when the metal is cooled to room temperature. There is a danger that metals will crack excessively

TABLE 6.7. CHEMICAL PROPERTIES OF PURE COPPER

Electrochemical equivalent:[21]   0.3294 mg/coul for Cu^{++} (3.0360 coul/mg)
   0.6588 mg/coul for Cu^{+} (1.5180 coul/mg)

A) *Reactions with gases and vapors:*

dry air at room temperature:[22] none

dry air at 100°C:[22] formation of invisible protective oxide, Cu_2O

dry air at 200° to 600°C: formation of mixed oxides, $Cu_2O + CuO$; oxidation colors: brown-orange, rose-red, violet, steel-blue, brass-yellow, red, greenish-gray, gray, black.

moist air at 20°C: practically none in absence of CO_2 ; formation of 2 $CuCO_3$· $Cu(OH)_2$ in presence of CO_2 .

sulfurous atmosphere at 20°C: tarnishing to a purplish color in 1 to 2 weeks when concentration of reactive sulfur corresponds to 1 vol. H_2S in 35×10^6 vols. of air. Formation of copper basic sulfate $CuSO_4·3 Cu(OH)_2$ (verdigris or green patina).

steam at 500°C: very slight oxidation

hydrogen: solubility increases with temperature (see Fig. A4)[23] oxide films will form at about 100°C at a dew point of $-20°C$.[24]

alkali-metal vapors: none

B) *Reactions with liquids:*

water at 20°C: practically none

salt water at 20°C: slow corrosion

dry CCl_4 : practically none

moist CCl_4 : some corrosion

dry trichloroethylene: practically none

moist trichloroethylene: some corrosion

HCl, unaerated, dilute or concentr., cold: practically none

HCl, unaerated, dilute or concentr., warm: very slight attack

H_2SO_4 , unaerated, dilute or concentr., cold: practically none

H_2SO_4 , unaerated, dilute or concentr., warm: very slight attack

HNO_3 , dilute, cold or warm: dissolution, especially in 25% concentr.

HNO_3 , conc.: passivation

Aqua Regia (1 pt HNO_3 + 3 pts HCl): dissolution

HF: none

HF + HNO_3 (1:1): rapid dissolution

NH_4Cl, warm, dilute, with access of oxygen: dissolution

NH_4OH: rapid dissolution

Na(OH) or K(OH) solutions: slight attack

Cyanides: rapid dissolution

Hg: amalgamation and stress corrosion

TABLE 6.7—(*Continued*)

C) *Reactions with solids:*
   sulfur: corrosive attack (beware vulcanized rubber and sulfur-bearing hydro-carbon oils!)

D) *Oxides of copper:*
   Cu_2O—cuprous oxide, red, octahedral or cubic; d = 6.0; M.P. = 1235°C; insoluble in water, dissolves in NH_4Cl

   CuO—cupric oxide, black, tetragonal, cubic, triclinic; d = 6.4, decomposes at 1026°C; insoluble in water, dissolves in NH_4Cl, KCN, and acids

   $CuO_2 \cdot H_2O$—monohydrated copper dioxide, brownish black; insoluble in water, dissolves in acids, insoluble in alcohol

E) *Cleaning solutions, etching and polishing:*[11, 2, 25]

   I. *Removal of heavy oxide:*

   a. HNO_3 (d = 1.40 gm/cc)—400 cc ⎱ pour H_2SO_4 slowly into HNO_3 , not
      H_2SO_4 (d = 1.83 gm/cc)—300 cc ⎰ vice versa!
      HCl (d = 1.16 gm/cc)—5 cc   Pour acids into water, not vice versa!
      H_2O—295 cc
      Immerse part in bath at R.T.   Wear gloves and goggles when
      Rinse in flowing water.   handling acids!

   b. HNO_3 (65%)—1000 cc ⎱ immerse parts for 2–3 sec and rinse in flowing
      HCl (37%)—10 cc   ⎰ water immediately.

   II. *Bright dip:*

   a. HNO_3 (d = 1.40 gm/cc)—250 cc   immerse part and rinse in free
      H_2SO_4 (d = 1.83 gm/cc)—600 cc   flowing water very thoroughly,
      HCl (d = 1.16 gm/cc)—20 cc   then rinse in solution of:
      H_2O—130 cc $NaCN$—15 to 30 gm; H_2O—1000 cc

   b. HNO_3 (65%)—500 cc ⎱ see note under Ia ⎧ rinse in water, distilled water,
      H_2SO_4 (conc.)—500 cc ⎰   ⎨ methyl alcohol, dry in warm
                                            ⎩ air.

      HCl (37%)—10 cc   immerse part for 2–3 sec and rinse in flowing dis-
      Soot—5 gm   tilled water. Transfer to plating bath while
                            parts are wet if plating is to follow.

   III. *Matt dip:* HNO_3 (d = 1.4 gm/cc)—650 cc   heat bath to 80°C and im-
        H_2SO_4 (d = 1.83 gm/cc)—350 cc   merse parts, rinse and dry
        $ZnSO_4$ (tech.)—120 gm   as under IIb above.

   IV. *Electrolytic polishing:*

	Current density	Time
a. HPO_3—630 cc		
H_2O—370 cc		
Bath temp.—20°C	0.02 to 0.05 a/in²	5 min
b. HPO_3—580 cc		
H_2O—420 cc	0.5 to 0.7 a/in²	10–15 min
Bath temp.—20°C		

on hot-working; such a condition is called "hot shortness." Copper exhibits this effect at times, especially in the presence of impurities. Small quantities of lead, bismuth, and sulfur are especially harmful in this respect; the purer the copper the more easily it can be hot-worked with a minimum of cracking.

Cracking which occurs as a result of internal and external stresses while the metal is exposed to a corrosive environment is called "stress corrosion." Pure copper is not susceptible to stress corrosion. Copper alloys and deoxidized copper such as phosphorized copper may show this effect in the presence of ammonia or ammonium compounds and also when in contact with mercury or solutions of mercury salts.

When various shapes of copper anodes are produced by spinning of OFHC copper disks, special precaution in regard to cleanliness must be observed. If the surfaces are not clean, impurities may be entrapped and "plowed under" during the spinning operation. Subsequent hydrogen firing may produce a shiny surface, but heat treatment on the pump results in severe discoloration when impurities diffuse to the surface. Even under clean conditions, oxide films are known to form rapidly at room temperature. After rupture of the oxide at points of critical plastic flow, adhesion to the stylus occurs, and the resulting deformation in the surface layers is sufficiently severe for oxide particles to be included. On further sliding, successive layers of oxide are broken up and entrapped. Moore and McG. Tegart[29] have investigated these effects and taken photomicrographs of the surface, which clearly demonstrate the severe tearing of the surface layers. With lubricated sliding, no evidence of oxide inclusions was found. The lubricant used consisted of a 10 percent solution of oleic acid in paraffin oil. If the increase in r-f resistivity which results from the cold-working of the surface is to be avoided, the measures recommended by Thorp should be applied. Cocks[30] has recently commented on the debris formed by sliding contacts.

Copper-Base Alloys

Of the many compositions which fall in this category, only a few find application for structural components to be used within the tube envelope. We are here concerned with alloys that consist mainly of copper and contain up to 30 per cent additions of other metals. The reader is referred to Chapter 7 for alloys where these proportions are reversed and copper itself is the smaller additive.

Cupro-nickel[31, 32] is commercially available in two compositions, i.e., 90 Cu–10 Ni and 70 Cu–30 Ni, but other compositions can be obtained on special request. A 5 percent cupro-nickel has thus been used for shadow masks in color kinescopes and a nonmagnetic 45/55 Cu/Ni alloy is used for cathode ray tube deflection systems. The physical characteristics of cupro-nickels are tabulated in Table 6.8. It should be noted that the typical analysis of these alloys permits a maximum content of 1.0 per cent zinc and 0.05 per cent lead. Freedom from these two undesirable elements should be specified for vacuum tube application. Cupro-nickels are characterized by their superior hot strength, higher yield point, and recrystalliza-

Commercial designation:	Cupro-Nickel, 30%	Cupro-Nickel, 20%	Cupro-Nickel, 10%
Nearest ASTM specifications:	B111–58, B122–55T, B171–58	B111–58, B122–55T	B111–58, B171–58
Nominal composition, per cent	Ni: 30, Cu: 70	Ni: 20, Cu: 80	Ni: 10, Fe: 1.3, Cu: 88.7
Commercial limits, per cent	Pb: 0.05 max. Fe: 0.4–0.7 Zn: 1.0 max. Mn: 1.0 max. Ni: 29.0–33.0 Cu: 65.0 min.	Fe: 0.5 Mn: 0.6 Ni: 21 Cu: Bal.	Pb: 0.05 max. Fe: 0.5–2.0 Zn: 1.0 max. Mn: 1.0 max. Ni: 9.0–11.0 Cu: 86.5 min.

Physical Properties:			
Liquidus (°C—°F)	1240 (2264°F)	1200 (2192°F)	1150 (2102°F)
Solidus (°C—°F)	1170 (2138°F)	1150 (2102°F)	1100 (2012°F)
Density (gm/cc—lb/cu. in.)	8.94 (0.323)	8.94 (0.323)	8.94 (0.323)
Coeff. therm. exp.			
(20–300°C) × 10⁷	162.0/°C	163.8/°C	171.0/°C
(68–572°F) × 10⁷	90/°F	91/°F	95/°F
Therm. conductivity			
(20°C) (cal/cm²/cm/sec/°C)	0.07	0.087	0.091
(68°F) (Btu/sq ft/ft/hr/°F)	17.	21.	22.
Specif. heat			
(20°C) (cal/gm/°C)	0.09	0.09	0.09
(68°F) (Btu/lb/°F)	0.09	0.09	0.09
Electr. resistivity (20°C) (microhm-cm)	37.	27.	15.
Electr. conductivity % IACS	4.6	6.4	9.1
Young's modulus (tension)			
(10⁶ psi)	22.0	20.	18.0
(kg/mm²)	15,500	14,100	12,700
Modulus of rigidity (10⁶ psi)	8.3	7.5	6.8
(kg/mm²)	5,800	5,200	4,800
Mechanical Properties:			
Tensile strength, 1000 psi			
Annealed strip*	54–60	45–51	44
Half hard strip	73	—	—
Hard strip	80	—	—
Annealed tube*	54–60	49	44
Light-drawn tube	75	80	60
Yield strength (0.5% ext.), 1000 psi			
Annealed strip*	20–22	—	15
Half hard strip	68	—	—
Hard strip	73	—	—
Annealed tube*	25	14	16
Light-drawn tube	—	75	57
Elongation (2 in.), %			
Annealed strip*	40–45	27	40
Half hard strip	12	—	—
Hard strip	5	—	—
Annealed tube*	45	40	42
Rockwell hardness			
Annealed strip*	B 37–50	—	B 10
Half hard strip	B 80	—	—
Hard strip	B 85	—	—
Annealed tube*	B 36–45	B 25	B 15
Light-drawn tube	B 85	B 81	B 72

* Properties of annealed materials vary with grain size.

tion temperature; for commercial applications, their high resistance to corrosion is another attractive feature. Cupro-nickels can be readily formed and joined to other metals by brazing and welding; carbon-arc welding, however, is not recommended.

Chrome copper containing from 0.2 to 0.6 per cent chromium is soft and ductile in the as-received condition, and its electrical conductivity is low. By a suitable heat treatment at about 500°C for two hours or more, the chromium precipitates as a separate phase, and both mechanical properties and electrical conductivity are markedly improved. Tensile strength is

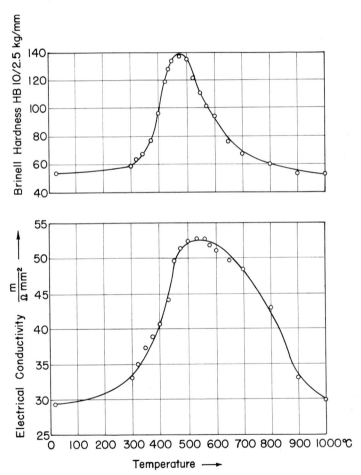

Figure 6.5. Brinell hardness and electrical conductivity of a 0.48 percent chrome-copper alloy after homogenizing and age-hardening for 5 hours in the temperature range from 20 to 1000°C. After Petri and Vosskühler.[33] (*Courtesy Verband Deutscher Elektrotechniker* [*VDE*].)

doubled, elongation reduced to about one-third, hardness more than doubled, and electrical conductivity increased from 45 to 85 per cent IACS.[3]

Petri and Vosskühler[33] have reported on the properties of chrome copper, and their paper contains references to the recent literature. Figure 6.5,

TABLE 6.9. PHYSICAL AND MECHANICAL PROPERTIES OF CHROME-COPPER[33, 31]

(containing 0.6 pct. chrome, being homogenized, quenched, precipitation-hardened, and work-hardened—compared to electrolytic copper)

	Chrome-Copper		Electrolytic Copper	
Physical properties:				
Melting point (°C)	1076		1083	
Density (gm/cc)	8.92		8.92	
Specific heat (0–20°C) (cal/gm/°C)	0.092		0.092	
Temperature coeff. of thermal expansion				
0 to 100°C (10^7/°C)	158.		168.	
0 to 300°C (10^7/°C)	170.		175.	
Electrical conductivity (20°C) (Fig. 6.9)				
(m/ohm. mm²)	∼50.		>56.	
(μmho. cm⁻¹)	0.5		>0.56	
% IACS	86.2		101.	
Thermal conductivity (20°C) (cal/cm²/ cm/sec/°C)	∼0.8		>0.9	
Magnetic susceptibility (× 10^{-6})	0.03		−0.09	
Young's modulus (tension) (10^6 psi)	19.		17.	
Mechanical properties:[31] (amount of chrome content not specified)				
Yield strength (0.5%) (psi)				
Rod, 1 in. dia.				
hard-drawn	57,000		40,000–45,000	
soft	15,000		8,000–10,000	
heat-treated, hard	61,000		—	
heat-treated, soft	45,000		—	
Tensile strength (psi)				
Rod, 1 in. dia.				
hard-drawn	62,000		45,000–48,000	
soft	35,000		32,000	
heat-treated, hard	72,000		—	
heat-treated, soft	63,000		—	
Elongation, % (2 in.)				
Rod, 1 in. dia.				
hard-drawn	20.		15–16	
soft	40.		45–55	
heat-treated, hard	25.		—	
heat-treated, soft	25.		—	
Rockwell hardness (Fig. 6.9)	B	F	B	F
Rod, 1 in. dia.				
hard-drawn	70		47–50	
soft		50		35–40
heat-treated, hard	77		—	—
heat-treated, soft		65	—	—

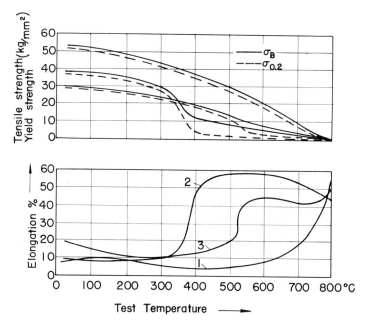

Figure 6.6. Tensile strength, ultimate strength, and elongation of 0.6%-chrome-copper (curve 1), electrolytic copper SE-Cu F37 (curve 2), and phosphor deoxidized copper SF-Cu F30 (curve 3) in the temperature range 20 to 800°C. After Petri and Vosskühler.[33] (*Courtesy Verband Deutscher Elektrotechniker [VDE].*)

taken from this paper, shows the increase of hardness and electrical conductivity during an age-hardening treatment at various temperatures for a period of five hours. Figure 6.6 shows tensile strength, ultimate strength, and elongation of chrome copper (0.6 per cent) which have been age-hardened and subsequently exposed to various test temperatures; corresponding properties of electrolytic copper and copper deoxidized by phosphorus are also shown.

Figure 6.7 shows how the electrical conductivity decreases with increasing test temperature both for electrolytic copper and chrome copper, and Figure 6.8 portrays the change in Brinell hardness with increasing temperatures up to 800°C for these two materials after they have been annealed for five hours in a range of temperatures from 100 to 800°C. The electrolytic copper had been work-hardened by cold-forming. The benefit of this process is lost for electrolytic copper above 200°C, while age-hardened chrome copper can be exposed to high temperature of the order of 400°C without any noticeable annealing effect. This property makes chrome copper most attractive for vacuum tube components.

Copper alloys containing 1.1 per cent nickel and 0.22 per cent phosphorus

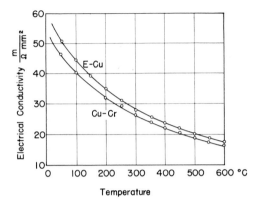

Figure 6.7. Electrical conductivity of electrolytic copper and ∼0.6% chrome-copper in the temperature range 20 to 800°C. After Petri and Vosskühler.[33] (*Courtesy Verband Deutscher Elektrotechniker [VDE].*)

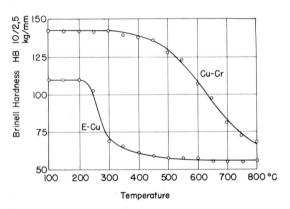

Figure 6.8. Effect of a 5-hr annealing treatment at temperatures ranging from 100 to 800°C on hardness at room temperature after cooling for ∼0.6%-chrome-copper and electrolytic copper. After Petri and Vosskühler.[33] (*Courtesy Verband Deutscher Elektrotechniker [VDE].*)

are known under the trade name "Phosnic" *; similarly, alloys containing 1.0 per cent nickel, 0.2 per cent phosphorus, and 0.5 per cent tellurium have the trade name "Telnik."* Both these alloys have been used for internal components in the construction of magnetrons. The presence of phosphorus and tellurium, respectively, would suggest that such components have to be maintained at a low temperature during operation to prevent harmful effects of the high-vapor pressure components.

Finally, it should be pointed out that a substantial increase in tensile

* Registered trade names by Chase Brass & Copper Company.

strength, creep strength, and hardness can be obtained with various metals, including copper, by *internal oxidation*. If small percentages of additives which have a greater affinity for oxygen than the parent metal are uniformly dispersed throughout the parent metal, a heat treatment at a few hundred degrees below the melting point in an atmosphere with a controlled oxygen content will bring about the preferred oxidation of the additive by diffusion from an oxide surface layer. These oxides will retard grain growth and thus increase the recrystallization temperature. For copper, internal oxidation is carried out at 950°C, and the additives may be 0.5 per cent aluminum, 0.2 per cent beryllium, or 0.3 per cent silicon. In contrast to the hardening effect obtained by cold-working or precipitation-hardening, that resulting from internal oxidation is not destroyed to any great extent by subsequent heat treatment.[34]

Special Processes

The low yield point of fully annealed OFHC copper makes it possible to effect a cold joint between two mating copper surfaces when these are pressed against each other under high pressure. Copper tubes serving as exhaust tubulations can thus be pinched off by means of cutting shears which have been provided with rounded jaws. This operation is quite straightforward for small tubes, but can be applied to tubulations of as much as one-half inch diameter. A pinch-off tool has been described by Neher and Johnston[35] and more recently by Neher and Prakash.[36] Pinch-off seals can also be performed with gas pressures of several hundred psi inside and—what is most useful to the experimentalist—these seals can be depinched according to the authors just mentioned. Furthermore, by either not quite closing the pinch-off, or just slightly depinching, controlled gas leaks can be achieved. In commercial production, automatic pinch-offs are made by hydraulically operated jaws. Perfect cleanliness of the internal surfaces is essential, and the reliability of the seal can be improved by preheating the copper. Hermetic seals on copper housings for power transistors are effected in the same manner.

The strength of copper envelopes can be materially improved by shot-peening, an operation which exposes the metal surface to a blast of small steel shot or spheres. The story is told that a second source of supply was to be established at one time for a power tube with a water-cooled anode. All specifications were thus furnished by the original producer, A, to the second producer, B. During the high-temperature bakeout on the pump, the copper anodes oxidize severely, and this black oxide scale must of course be removed before mounting the tube in its cooling jacket. No specification had been forwarded as to the method of cleaning the anode. While the tubes made in plant B performed satisfactorily when tested on the pump, it was found that the anodes collapsed when the tubes were mounted in the cooling jacket and the water pressure applied. It turned out that the removal of the black oxide scale from the anode was achieved in plant A by shot blasting whereas in plant B it was done by chemical cleaning. The thickness of the copper anode was so marginal that the strengthening effect of shot-peening made the tubes survive in plant A while they failed in plant B.

The present author on one occasion had a copper housing for a cyclotron resonance tube of unusual shape[37] made by electroforming. In general, this procedure results in vacuum-tight structures, but the one referred to had a large number of very small leaks. By shot-peening the envelope, many of these leaks were closed; those remaining were sealed by coating the outside surface of the copper housing with copper oxide powder and pass it through a hydrogen furnace; this caused the copper oxide to be reduced to copper and permitted the copper to flow over the surface.

The permissible power dissipation of copper anodes depends on the type of cooling employed and also on the wall thickness. For water cooling of smooth surfaces values of 50 to 60 watts/cm² are common, whereas with axially, tangentially, or spirally grooved anodes 100 watts/cm² can be obtained. If the cooling water is supplied under pressure, the dissipation can be increased to values ranging from 500 to 1000 watts/cm². Under ordinary conditions, for an inlet water temperature of about 15°C, the water consumption runs to about 1 meter³/minute/kilowatt.

Air cooling of power tubes is generally facilitated by providing fins which increase the surface area. Normally one aims at a surface temperature somewhere near 200°C. The required volume of air is of the order of 1 m³/minute/kilowatt dissipated at a loading of 50 to 60 watts/cm² and an anode temperature of 180°C.[11]

The machining of OFHC copper requires some special precautions on account of the great toughness of the metal. Dalzell[38] recommends the following procedures:

"In preparing the metal for further machining in volume production carbide-tipped standard slitting or high-speed steel saws are recommended. For cutting with carbide-tipped tools, a top rake angle of 20 to 30 degrees and a 5- to 8-degree side-clearance angle are best; cut at 250 to 300 feet per minute.

"Precision-ground taps should be used for internal threading, maintaining close tolerances on the pitch diameters of the tap. In some cases standard gun taps can be used. External threading can be done with self-opening die heads on which the chasers have a 15-degree radial hook to facilitate chip clearance. (Landis, Geometric or Jones and Lampson tapping heads have been used with success.) Coolants must be free of sulfur to avoid contamination. (Paragon Lard Oil, Cutrite, and sulfur-free Acorn No. 10 cutting oils give good results; others can be used.) Spiral milling cutters are preferred, four flute-fast spiral-end-mills producing the best results for end milling."

REFERENCES

1. "Metals Handbook," American Society For Metals, Cleveland, Ohio, 1948.
2. C. J. Smithells, "Metals Reference Book" (2 Vols.), Interscience Publishers, Inc., New York, 1955.
3. Charles L. Mantell, Ed., "Engineering Materials Handbook," Sect. 7: Copper and Copper-Base Materials; McGraw-Hill Book Co., New York, 1958.
4. A. Butts, "Copper, the Science and Technology of the Metal, its Alloys and Compounds," Reinhold Publishing Corp., New York, 1954.
5. O. W. Ellis, "Copper and Copper Alloys," American Society For Metals, Cleveland, Ohio, 1948.
6. R. A. Wilkins and E. S. Bunn, "Copper and Copper-Base Alloys," McGraw-Hill Book Co., Inc., New York, 1943.
7. "Copper and Its Alloys in Engineering and Technology," The Copper Development Association, London, 1954.
8. C. Upthegrove and H. L. Burghoff, "Elevated-Temperature Properties of Coppers and Copper-Base Alloys," American Society For Testing Materials, Philadelphia Pa., 1956.
9. Copper & Copper-Alloy Specifications Index, Publication B-34, The American Brass Company, Waterbury Conn., 1954.
10. The American Metal Climax, Inc., "OFHC Brand Copper," 1957.
11. W. Espe, "Kupfer als Werkstoff der Hochvakuumtechnik," Pt. 1, *Nachrichtentechnik*, **6**, 355–364 (Aug. 1956); Pt. 2, "Kupfer-Glas-Verschmelzungen," *ibid.*, 401–408 (Sept. 1956).
12. G. B. Collins, "Microwave Magnetrons," Radiation Laboratory Series, Vol. 6, p. 696, McGraw-Hill Book Co., Inc., New York, 1948.
13. R. A. Stauffer, K. Fox, and W. O. DiPietro, "Vacuum melting and casting of copper," *Ind. Eng. Chem.*, **40**, 820–825 (May 1948).
14. J. H. Partridge, "Glass-to-Metal Seals," Society of Glass Technology, Sheffield, England, 1949.
15. S. L. Archbutt and V. E. Prythench, "Effect of impurities in copper," *Brit. Non-Ferrous Metals Research Assoc.* (London), *Research Monograph No. 4*, (1937).
16. "American Institute of Physics Handbook," D. E. Gray, Coord. Ed., McGraw-Hill Book Co., Inc., New York, 1957.
17. R. E. Honig, "Vapor pressure data for the more common elements," *RCA Rev.*, **18**, 195–204 (June 1957).
18. F. Pawlek and K. Reichel, "The influence of additives on the electrical conductivity of copper" (in German), *Z. Metallkunde*, **47**, Pt. 1, 347–356 (June 1956); *ibid.*, F. Pawlek, K. Viessmann and K. Wendt, (Pt. 2) pp. 357–363.
19. V. G. Bolshov and L. I. Dobretsov, "Thermionic emission from copper at the melting point," *Compt. rend. acad. sci. U.S.S.R.*, **98**, 193–196 (Sept. 11, 1954).
20. M. V. Yokelson and M. Balicki, "Progressive work-hardening and reannealing of five brands of high-conductivity copper," *Wire and Wire Products*, **30**, 1179–1287 (Oct. 1955).

21. "Handbook of Chemistry and Physics," 40th ed., Chemical Rubber Publishing Co., Cleveland, 1958/59.
22. K. R. Dixit and V. V. Agashe, "Study of the oxides of copper formed in air" (in English), *Z. Naturforsch.*, **10a**, 152–153 (Feb. 1955).
23. E. Waldschmidt, "Desorption and gas permeation of metals used in the construction of vacuum tubes" (in German), *Metall*, **8** (19/20), 749–758 (Oct. 1954).
24. "Brazing Manual," Committee on Brazing and Soldering, American Welding Society, Reinhold Publishing Corp., New York, 1955.
25. "Tube Laboratory Manual," 2nd ed., Research Laboratory of Electronics, Massachusetts Institute of Technology, Cambridge, Mass., 1956.
26. R. Landauer, "Conductivity of cold-worked metals," *Phys. Rev.*, **82**, 520–521 (May 15, 1951).
27. J. W. Rutter and J. Reekie, "The effect of cold working on the electrical resistivity of copper and aluminum," *Phys. Rev.*, **78**, 70–71 (Apr. 1, 1950).
28. J. S. Thorp, "R.F. conductivity in copper at 8mm wavelengths," *Proc. Inst. Elec. Engrs.*, **101**, Pt. 3, 357–359 (Nov. 1954).
29. A. J. W. Moore and W. J. McG. Tegart, "Rupture of oxide films during repeated sliding," *Australian J. Sci. Research* (A)**4**, 181–184 (June 1951).
30. M. Cocks, "Wear debris in the contact between sliding metals," *J. Appl. Phys.*, **29**, 1609–1610 (Nov. 1958).
31. J. L. Everhart, "Engineering coppers," *Materials & Methods*, **38**, 123–138 (Manual No. 100) (Dec. 1953).
32. J. L. Everhart, "Cupro-nickels offer corrosion resistance and hot strength," *Materials in Design Engineering*, **47**, 114–120 (May 1958).
33. H. G. Petri and H. Vosskühler, "Wrought copper-chrome alloys as materials for the electrical industry" (in German), *Elektrotech. Z.* (A)**76**, 380–385 (June 1, (1955).
34. J. L. Meijerling, "Increase of hot strength of alloys by internal oxidation" (in German), "Plansee Proceedings 1955, pp. 405–410, F. Benesovsky, Ed., Metallwerk Plansee G.M.B.H. Reutte, Tyrol and Pergamon Press Ltd., London, 1956.
35. H. V. Neher and Alan R. Johnston, "Techniques useful in evacuating and pressurizing metal chambers," *Rev. Sci. Instr.*, **25**, 517–518 (May 1954).
36. H. V. Neher and S. Prakash, "Metal system for chemical reactions and for studying properties of gases and liquids," *Rev. Sci. Instr.*, **28**, 267–270 (Apr. 1957).
37. W. H. Kohl, "Construction of a Sealed-Off, All-Metal Cyclotron Resonance Tube," Tech. Rept. No. 23, (Aug. 15, 1954), Electronics Research Laboratory, Stanford University, Stanford, Calif. (Declassified 1957).
38. R. C. Dalzell, "Copper in electronic tubes," *Electronics*, **22**, 164–170 (Apr. 1949).

CHAPTER 7

NICKEL AND NICKEL ALLOYS

Introduction

Nickel and its alloys are the most favored materials for the construction of almost all components of receiving tubes and power tubes of small and medium output range. Cathodes, grid laterals and side rods, anodes, shields, getter flags and supports, all these tube components can and in many cases are being made of nickel and nickel alloys owing to their favorable properties. Nickel not only is available in grades of controlled purity at reasonable cost, but it can be easily fabricated into all conceivable shapes and is readily spotwelded to itself and other metals, or brazed. The mechanical properties of nickel and its alloys are adequate for most applications, it can be readily outgassed, and its high resistance to corrosion permits storing for prolonged periods without tarnishing. Nickel is magnetic at room temperature; this property may militate against its use in certain applications.

Nickel-clad iron and nickel-plated iron were introduced before World War II and reached a position of great importance during the war when nickel was difficult to procure. Aluminum-clad iron was developed at the same time, as described in Chapter 5. These materials are now being used for receiving-tube anodes on a fairly large scale.

Nickel anodes, pure or clad, are usually carbonized to increase their thermal emissivity and thus permit larger power dissipation, as discussed later in this chapter. Anodes which operate at 800°C, or higher, are made of more refractory materials, such as molybdenum, tantalum, or graphite, which are described in separate chapters. The danger of depositing nickel films by sublimation during the outgassing treatment on the pump, or when nickel parts are used as electrodes or shields in too close proximity to cathodes operating at high temperatures, should be kept in mind.

Nickel alloys for oxide-coated cathodes are described in Chapter 15 and those used for glass-to-metal seals in Chapter 13. The properties of nickel have been the subject of many publications.[1-12] Special attention should be given to the many technical bulletins available from the International Nickel Company.[3-5] Jackson and Jenkins[6] discuss at some length the considerations which govern the selection of the most suitable grade of nickel for various components of electron tubes.

Table 7.1 lists the approximate percent compositions of nickel and nickel-base alloys. Tables 7.2 and 7.2a give the physical characteristics and mechanical properties of pure nickel, and Table 7.3 gives the chemical properties of pure nickel. A number of the physical constants of nickel and

TABLE 7.1. PERCENT COMPOSITIONS OF NICKEL AND NICKEL-BASE ALLOYS

Material	Ni*	Cu	Fe	Cr	Mo	Si	Mn	C	S	Al	Ti	Others
"A" Nickel (Commercial)†	99.0 min	0.25 max	0.40 max			0.35 max	0.35 max	0.15 max	0.01 max			
"A" Nickel (Electronic Grade)†	99.00 min	0.15 max	0.20 max			0.15 max	0.35 max	0.15 max	0.008 max		0.01–0.05	
Low-carbon nickel	99.00 min	0.25 max	0.40 max			0.35 max	0.35 max	0.02 max	0.01 max			
Duranickel†	93.00 min	0.25 max	0.60 max			1.00 max	0.50 max	0.30 max	0.01 max	4.00–4.75	0.25–1.0	Mg 0.20–0.50
Permanickel†	97.00 min	0.25 max	0.60 max			0.15	0.50 max	0.40 max	0.01 max		0.20–0.60	Mg 0.01–0.10
"202" Nickel†	94.0 min	0.20 max	0.20 max			0.02–0.06	0.20 max	0.10 max	0.008 max		0.02 max	W 3.50–4.50
"220" Nickel†	99.00 min	0.10 max	0.10 max			0.01–0.05	0.20 max	0.08 max	0.008 max		0.01–0.05	Mg 0.01–0.08
"225" Nickel†	99.00 min	0.10 max	0.10 max			0.15–0.25	0.20 max	0.08 max	0.008 max		0.01–0.05	Mg 0.01–0.08
"330" Nickel†	99.00 min	0.10 max	0.10 max			0.03 max	0.30 max	0.10 max	0.008 max		0.005 max	Mg 0.01–0.10
"D" Nickel	93.70 min	0.25 max	0.75 max			0.04 max	4.25–5.25	0.20 max	0.015 max			
"E" Nickel†	97.00 min	0.25 max	0.75 max			0.04 max	1.75–2.25	0.20 max	0.015 max			
MONEL†	63.0–70.0	Bal.	2.50 max			0.50 max	2.00 max	0.30 max	0.024 max			
MONEL "403"†‡	55.0–60.0	Bal.	1.00 max			0.75 max	1.25–2.25	0.30 max	0.024 max			
"R" MONEL†	63.0–70.0	Bal.	2.50 max			0.50 max	2.00 max	0.30 max	0.025–0.060			
"K" MONEL†	63.0–70.0	Bal.	2.00 max			1.00 max	1.50 max	0.25 max	0.01 max	2.0–4.0	0.25–1.00	
"KR" MONEL†	63.0–70.0	Bal.	2.00 max			1.00 max	1.50 max	0.20–0.30	0.01 max	2.0–4.0	0.25–1.00	
INCONEL†	72.0 min	0.50 max	6.0–10.0	14.0–17.0		0.50 max	1.00 max	0.15 max	0.015 max			Cb 0.70–1.20 (includes Ta)
INCONEL "X"†‡	70.0 min	0.50 max	5.0–9.0	14.0–17.0		0.50 max	1.00 max	0.08 max	0.01 max	0.40–1.00	2.00–2.75	W 5.0
Hastelloy A‡	57.0		20.00		20.0	1.00	2.00	0.12				
Hastelloy B‡	65.0		5.00		28.0	1.00	1.00	0.12				
Hastelloy C‡	55.0		5.00	16.5	17.0	1.00	1.00	0.12				
Hastelloy D‡	85.0	3.00				10.0	1.00	0.12		1.00		
Illium G§	56.0	6.50	6.50	22.5	6.4	0.65	1.25	0.20				
Nimonic 75†	77.9	0.05	0.50	20.5		0.45	0.45	0.10	0.007	0.15	0.35	
Nimonic 80A†	74.5	0.05	0.55	20.5		0.20	0.55	0.05	0.007	1.25	2.40	
Nimonic 90†	57.0	0.05	0.45	20.5		0.20	0.50	0.05	0.007	1.65	2.60	Co 16.9
80 Ni 20 Cr alloy, wrought	78.0		1.00 max	19.0		1.00	2.50 max	0.25 max	0.03 max			
60 Ni 15 Cr alloy, wrought	60.0		Bal.	15.0		1.00	3.00 max	0.25 max	0.03 max			

* Including cobalt
† Trademark, The International Nickel Company, Inc.
‡ Trademark, Haynes Stellite Company
§ Trademark, Burgess-Parr Company

TABLE 7.2. PHYSICAL CHARACTERISTICS AND MECHANICAL
PROPERTIES OF PURE NICKEL[1]

Atomic number: 28   Atomic valence: 2, 3

Atomic weight: 58.69   Valence orbitals: $3d^84s^2$

Isotopes: 58, 60, 61, 62, 64   Lattice type: f.c.c. (A1)

Lattice constant:[10] 3.52394 A (25°C)
(99.99% Ni)

Density (gm/cc): 8.908 at 20°C (theoret.)   Atomic diameter:[10] 2.49 A

       8.907 at 23°C—cast   Atomic volume (cc/gm atom):[2] 6.59

       8.901–8.903 (25°C)—   Closest approach of atoms: 2.486 A

       cold swaged, annealed

Melting point (°C): 1453 (fixed point, ITS 1948)

       1440 ± 5 ("A" Nickel)

Boiling point (°C):[13] 2839

Heat of fusion, ΔH_m (Kcal/mole):[10] 4.2

Heat of vaporization, ΔH_0 (Kcal/mole):[10] 91.0

Entropy of fusion, ΔS_m (cal/mole/°K):[10] 2.4

Entropy of vaporization, ΔS_v (cal/mole/°K):[10] 29.6

Entropy at 298.16°K, ΔS (cal/mole/°K):[14] 7.12

Specific heat (20°C), (cal/gm/°C): see Fig. 7.1

Thermal conductivity (cal/cm²/cm/sec/°C): see also Fig. 7.2

100	200	300	400	500	°C
0.198	0.175	0.152	0.142	0.148	

Thermal expansion coeff. (cm/cm/°C):[16] average from 25°C to

100	300	600	900	°C	(see also Fig. 7.3)
133	144	155	163	× 10⁻⁷	

Vapor pressure (mm Hg):[8, 17] $\log p = -22{,}100/T + 10.75 - 0.131\ T$ (1000–1728°K)

                $\log p = -18{,}000/T + 8.17$ (1728–2500°K)

10^{-8}	10^{-7}	10^{-6}	10^{-5}	10^{-4}	10^{-3}	19^{-2}	10^{-1}	Torr
1185	1260	1330	1415	1520	1630	1770	1940	°K[13]

Spectral emissivity:[10] $\lambda = 0.655\mu$ $e_\lambda = 0.355$ (22°C)

                      1.0   0.27

                      3.0   0.12   for variation with

                      5.0   0.06   temperature see ref. 18

                      9.0   0.04

Total emissivity:

25	100	500	1000	°C
0.045	0.06	0.12	0.19	(Black body = 1.0)

Electrical resistivity (microhm·cm): (see also Figs. 7.4, 7.5)

	−200	−100	0	20	100	200	400	600	800	1000	°C
R_t :	0.49	2.82	6.141	6.844	10.3	15.8	30.6	37.2	42.8	48.3	
R_t/R_o :	0.08	0.46	1.00	1.11	1.68	2.57	4.99	6.06	6.97	7.86	

Temperature coeff. of resistivity:[3] 0.0067/°C (0–100°C)

Magnetic transformation temp.: 353°C (Curie Point) (see Fig. 7.6)

Magnetic saturation value: 6,394 gauss (0°K) 6,084 gauss (15°C)

Permeability: 2,000 to 3,000 (H = 1 oersted)

Electron work function: 5.0 e.v. (see Table 15.3)

Richardson constant A: 50 a/cm²deg²

Mechanical Properties: (see also Figs. 7.7–7.10)

     Modulus of elasticity in tension (20°C) (10⁶ psi):[3] 30

     Modulus of elasticity in torsion   (10⁶ psi):[3] 11

     Poisson's ratio:[3] 0.31

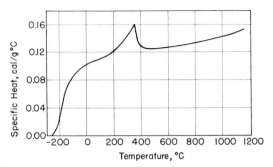

Figure 7.1. Specific heat of high-purity nickel. After J. G. Thompson.[1] (*Courtesy National Bureau of Standards.*)

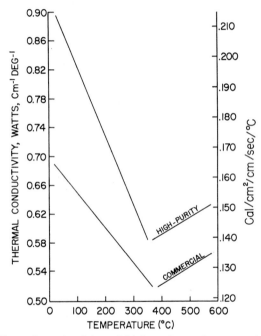

Figure 7.2. Thermal conductivity of high-purity and commercial-purity nickel. After Van Dusen and Shelton.[15] (*Courtesy National Bureau of Standards.*)

nickel-base alloys are presented in Table 7.4 and their mechanical property ranges are given in Table 7.5. Some of the ASTM Specifications on nickel which apply in the manufacture of electron tubes are presented in Table 7.6.

Commercial Wrought Nickel and Powder

Carbonyl nickel powder, produced by the Mond Nickel Co., Ltd., is the purest powder available; it can be sintered into a bar and rolled to thin

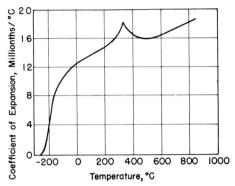

Figure 7.3. Thermal expansion of pure nickel. After Thompson.[1] (*Courtesy National Bureau of Standards.*)

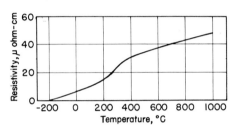

Figure 7.4. Electrical resistivity of high-purity nickel. After Thompson.[1] (*Courtesy National Bureau of Standards.*)

strip. In this form, it is marketed as "HPM nickel" and used for hydrogen thyratron parts and as a reference standard for cathodes and anodes in experimental studies of the behavior of other nickels.[27]

Nickel produced by electrodeposition, according to a process developed by Wesley[28] at the International Nickel Company Laboratory, also is of high purity but will normally contain slightly less than 0.10 % cobalt which has no harmful effect in vacuum tubes. This electrolytic nickel is the melting stock used in producing most wrought nickel and nickel alloys.

499 nickel, well known as a passive cathode nickel of high purity (see Table 15.11), is made by melting the electrolytic cathode, deoxidizing with 0.35 % carbon, rolling to intermediate gauges, and removing the carbon by prolonged treatment in moist hydrogen according to a process developed by Wise and Schaefer.[3]

INCO* Low-carbon nickel has a maximum carbon content of 0.02 per cent and is therefore soft and ductile owing to its low rate of work hardening. This property makes this material suited for spinning and cold-coining operations, but it is not recommended for deep drawing where a special grade of "deep drawing" "A" nickel is preferred.

* Trademark, The International Nickel Company, Inc.

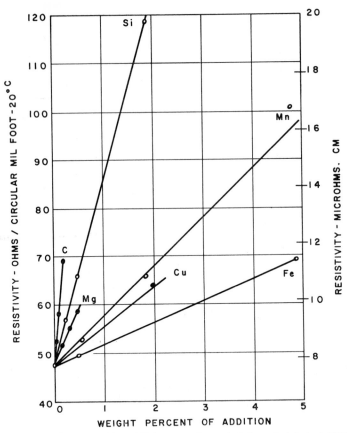

Figure 7.5. Effect of alloying additions on the resistivity of nickel at 20°C. After Wise and Schaefer.[3] (*Courtesy Reinhold Publishing Corporation.*)

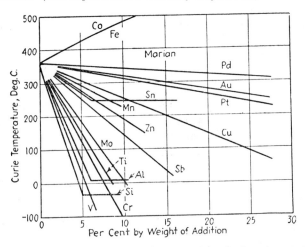

Figure 7.6. Effect of single alloying additions on the Curie point of nickel. After Wise and Schaefer.[3] (*Courtesy Reinhold Publishing Corporation.*)

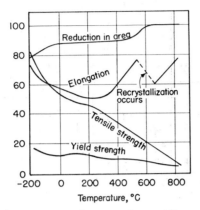

Figure 7.7. Effect of temperature, from −196 to 834°C, on the mechanical properties of annealed 99-85-percent nickel. After Jenkins and Digges.[19] (*Courtesy National
Bureau of Standards.*)

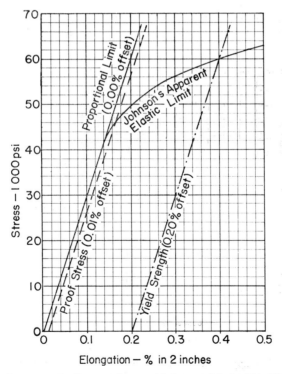

Figure 7.8. Stress-strain diagram for a cold-drawn nickel rod.[4] (*Courtesy The International Nickel Company, Inc.*)

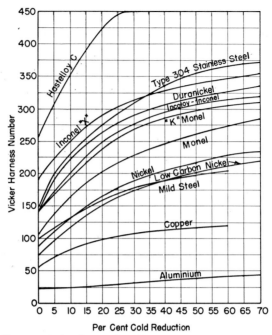

Figure 7.9. Increase in hardness of various metals with cold working.[4] (*Courtesy The International Nickel Company, Inc.*)

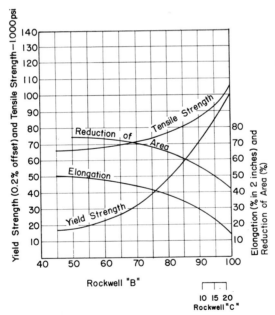

Figure 7.10. The approximate relationship of tensile properties to hardness for hot-rolled, forged, and cold-drawn nickel.[4] (*Courtesy The International Nickel Company, Inc.*)

TABLE 7.2a. MECHANICAL PROPERTY RANGES OF "A" NICKEL[4]

Form and temper	Tensile strength, 1000 psi	Yield strength (0.2% offset), 1000 psi	Elongation in 2 in., per cent	Brinell hardness (3000 kg)	Rockwell hardness, B
Wire					
Cold-drawn					
Annealed	55–85	15–50	50–30	—	—
No. 0 temper	80–95	—	—	—	—
No. 1 temper	70–95	40–75	40–20	—	—
Regular temper	105–140	105–135	15–4	—	—
Spring temper	125–145	105–135	15–2	—	—
Rod and bar					
Cold-drawn					
Annealed	55–80	15–30	55–40	90–120	45–70
As-drawn	65–110	40–100	35–10	140–230	75–98
As-rolled	60–85	15–45	55–35	90–150	45–80
Forged, hot-finished	65–90	20–60	55–40	100–170	55–85
Plate					
Hot-rolled					
Annealed	55–80	15–40	60–40	90–140	45–75
As-rolled	55–85	20–50	55–35	100–150	55–80
Sheet					
Annealed	55–75	15–30	55–40	—	70 max.
Hard	90–115	70–105	15–2	—	90 min.
Strip					
Annealed	55–75	15–30	55–40	—	64 max.
Spring	90–130	70–115	15–2	—	95 min.
Tubing					
Cold-drawn					
Annealed	55–75	20–30	60–40	—	70 max.
Hard, stress-relieved	65–110	40–90	35–15	—	75–98
Condenser and evaporator					
Annealed	55–75	15–30	60–40	—	65 max.
Stress-relieved	65–90	40–75	35–20	—	75–92
Castings					
Nickel, as cast	50–65	15–30	30–15	90–130	45–72
"G"* nickel, as cast	50–60	25–35	25–15	90–125	45–70
"S"* nickel, as cast	70–100	50–70	6–2	185–250	89–100
annealed and aged	75–105	55–75	6–2	200–280	92–104

Electronic "A" * nickel* is produced by melting electrolytic cathodes and deoxidizing with fractional percentages of silicon, manganese, titanium and a trace of magnesium which reacts with any sulfur that is present, or which may be acquired during processing. While electronic "A" nickel is suitable for many tube applications, it is better practice to use one of the passive

* Trademarks, The International Nickel Company, Inc.

TABLE 7.3. CHEMICAL PROPERTIES OF NICKEL

Electrochemical equivalent: 0.30409 mg/coul

3.28846 coul/mg

A) *Reactions with gases and vapors:*

dry air at room temperature: none

dry air above 400°C: slow oxidation (visible, protective film of NiO at 400°C)

clean moist air at room temperature: practically none

sulfurous atmosphere at 20°C; relative humidity $> 70\%$: formation of $NiSO_4$ film

steam, up to 425°C: none; at red heat: $Ni + H_2O \rightleftharpoons NiO + H_2$

hydrogen: none; for data on sorption, desorption, and permeation see Figures A4
and A6

nitrogen: none

ammonia: none

dry chlorine: none up to $\sim 540°C$

wet halogens, SO_2, NH_3: corrosion

dry CCl_4: none

moist CCl_4: corrosion; blue and yellow spots develop on surface.

Trichloroethylene: none

SO_2: onset of reaction at about 460°C to form nickel sulfide, Ni_3S_2

reaction complete at about 700°C; may reverse at higher temperatures

B) *Reactions with liquids:*

water at 20°C: practically none; corrosion is less than 0.001 in. penetration per
year (ipy) when exposed on one side only

salt water at 20°C: very little corrosion; less than 0.005 ipy; some pitting

neutral and alkaline salt solutions, cold or hot: corrosion less than 0.005 ipy

alkalies, cold or hot: practically none (0.0001 ipy)

H_2SO_4, cold: less than 0.05 ipy for concentrations up to 80% (b.wt.)

max. corrosion at about 5 p.c. acid concentr. b.wt. and decreases
uniformly with increasing concentr. up to 80%

hot: corrosion above 25 p.c. acid concentration (0.05 to 0.1 ipy)

HCl, cold, dilute: air-free 0.005 ipy; air-saturated 0.10 ipy

cold, conc.: air-free 0.06 ipy; air-saturated 0.08 ipy

hot, dilute, or conc.: severe attack above 2 p.c. conc. (b.wt.)

HNO_3, cold, dilute: rapid dissolution

HPO_3, pure, free of oxidizing impurities such as ferric compounds: 0.015–0.04 ipy

cold, dilute (commercial grade): slow dissolution

hot, concentr. (commercial grade): rapid dissolution

HF, dilute (20–110°C): 0.010–0.110 ipy

anhydrous (20–150°C): 0.002 ipy

$HF + HNO_3$: rapid dissolution

acetic acid, 20°C, air-saturated: max. rate 0.4 ipy at 85% conc.

0.01 ipy in 0.1% conc.

oxide-coated cathodes can be stripped of the coating by boiling in
10 p.c. solution of acetic acid

Mercury: no amalgamation up to 370°; stress-relief anneal as a safeguard against
cracking; do not remove oxide

Molten metals: do not use in contact with Al, Sn, Pb, Bi, Sb, Zn

C) *Reactions with solids:*

Tantalum—forms brittle alloy with nickel near 1400°C when Ta content > 40 p.c.

Zirconium—forms eutectic with nickel above 1000°C

TABLE 7.3—*Continued*

D) *Nickel oxides:*

NiO—nickel monoxide,[17, 20-23] olive green to greenish yellow, or grayish black; somewhat harder than Ni[24]

d = 7.45; M.P. = 1960°C; soluble in acids and NH$_4$OH; readily reduced in hydrogen; reacts with Al$_2$O$_3$ at about 900°C to form nickel spinel[25]

	400	500	800	900	1000°C	
Color:	black	gray	gray-green	greenish	yellow	
NiO%:	99.15	99.61	99.91	100	100	Mellor, Vol. 15(1936)[26]
sp. gr.:	5.668	5.745	6.265	6.305	6.310	ϵ_λ (5500–6650):

$$.89 \ (1000°C)$$
$$.69 \ (1450°C)$$

Higher oxides of variable composition can be produced by electrolysis of aqueous solutions.

E) *Cleaning solutions, etching and polishing:*

HNO$_3$ (conc)—33 c.c. immerse in solution, rinse in water and methyl alcohol
H$_2$O   —67 c.c.   in succession, air-dry
HCl (conc) —10 c.c.

electrolytic cleaning: H$_2$SO$_4$ (50% b.vol.); current density: ~1a/cm^2
time: 30 sec to 2 min; use nickel cathode, work as anode

Note: Many polishing and etching solutions are listed in two tables of Ref. 1, pp. 12–13.

The Jewitt-Wise reagent consists of equal volumes of 10% ammonium persulfate and 10% potassium cyanide and is recommended for etching of metallographic specimens after careful polishing with flat silk crepe and very fine alumina as the abrasive for the last stage.

nickels, especially when the components in question operate at elevated temperature.

"A"* nickel is the commercial wrought nickel and differs from the electronic "A" nickel in regard to the limits of the deoxidizing elements (Table 7.1). The present author would not recommend its use for internal tube elements.

"330"* nickel differs from the grades described above in containing slightly more magnesium and substantially no titanium; while this nickel was originally designed to be used for anodes, as it is, Sylvania Electric Products Inc. utilized selected lots of 330 nickel for oxide-coated cathodes under the code Sylvania "A" nickel some ten years ago; N4 nickel is now the Sylvania code for selected 330 nickel, and RCA uses the code N109. The recently announced "230" nickel (INCO) meets this situation by giving the selected "330" nickel for cathode use a special number and making it to the closer tolerance to start with. "330" nickel is also widely used for magnetostriction transducers although 4% cobalt nickel offers some advantages for this application.

"D"* nickel is characterized by its higher manganese content which ranges

* Trademarks, The International Nickel Company, Inc.

TABLE 7.4. PHYSICAL CONSTANTS OF NICKEL AND NICKEL-BASE ALLOYS[2]

Material	Density, gm/cc	Melting point, °C	Mean specific heat (20–400°C) cal/gm/°C	Thermal expansion coefficient (0–100°C), cm/cm/°C $\times 10^7$	Thermal conductivity (0–100°C), cal/cm²/cm/sec/°C	Electrical resistivity (0°C), μ ohm.cm	Tensile modulus of elasticity, 10^6 psi	Torsional modulus of elasticity, 10^6 psi
"A" Nickel (Commercial)	8.89	1435–1446	0.13	129.6	0.145	9.46	30	11
Low-carbon nickel	8.89	1435–1446	0.13	129.6	0.145	8.30	30	11
Duranickel	8.24	1400–1438	0.104	129.6	0.047	43.12	30	11
Permanickel	8.74	1400–1438	0.106	129.6	0.138	15.69	30	11
"D" nickel	8.78	1426	0.13	133.2	0.115	18.26	30	11
"E" nickel	8.86	1426	0.13	133.2	0.115	14.11	30	11
Monel	8.83	1300–1450	0.127	136.9*	0.062	48.14	26	9.5
"R" Monel	8.84	1300–1350	0.13	136.9*	0.062	48.14	26	9.5
"K" Monel	8.46	1315–1350	0.127	140.4	0.045	58.10	26	9.5
"KR" Monel	8.46	1315–1350	0.127	140.4	0.045	58.10	26	9.5
Inconel	8.43	1393–1426	0.109	115.2	0.036	102.	31	11
Inconel "X"	8.31	1393–1426	0.105	127.9*	0.030	124.5	31	11
Hastelloy A	8.80	1300–1330	0.094	109.8	0.037	126.7	27	
Hastelloy B	9.24	1320–1350	0.091	100.8	0.027	135.	30	
Hastelloy C	8.94	1270–1305	0.092	113.4	0.030	132.8	28	
Hastelloy D	7.80	1110–1120	0.109	109.8	0.050	113.1	28	
Illium G	8.58	1255–1338	0.105	122.4	0.029	123.3	26	
Nimonic "75"	8.35	1390–1420	0.110*	160.0†	0.032	108.9	30	
Nimonic "80A"	8.25	1360–1389	0.103*	158.0†	0.029	123.8	31	
Nimonic "90"	8.27	1360–1389		170.0†	0.030	114.9	31	
80 Ni 20 Cr Alloy, wrought	8.36	1232	0.104	176.4‡	0.036	107.9	31	
60 Ni 15 Cr alloy, wrought	8.24	1350	0.107	169.2‡	0.032	112.1		

* 20–100°C
† 20–900°C
‡ 20–982°C

from 4.25 to 5.25 per cent. The strength and base hardness of "D" nickel, when fully annealed, are slightly above those of "A" nickel. The annealing temperature is also higher, and greater hardness is retained after degassing when this material is used as a structural part in a vacuum tube. The high manganese content imparts some tolerance to attack by sulfur compounds at elevated temperatures. For this reason, it has been used for supports sealed into glass where embrittlement by sulfur in the heating flame is a factor. However, the resulting oxidation is somewhat greater than with "A" nickel or "E"* nickel, so that the latter is more generally used under

* Trademark, The International Nickel Company, Inc.

TABLE 7.5. MECHANICAL PROPERTY RANGES* OF NICKEL AND NICKEL-BASE ALLOYS[2]

Alloy	Available forms†	Yield strength, 1,000 psi 0.2 % offset	Tensile strength, 1,000 psi	Elongation, % in 2 in.	Reduction in area, %	Hardness		Impact standard, izod
						Rockwell	(3,000 kg) Brinell	
"A" Nickel	ABCDEFG	15–135	50–145	60–2	75–50	45B–104B	90–230	120
Duranickel	ACE	30–175	90–240	55–2	65–15	75B–46C	135–380	120–25
"D" Nickel	ACE	25–125	75–140	50–2	75–60	60B–100B	110–230	
Monel	ABCDEFG	25–130	65–140	50–2	75–50	<60B–27C	110–250	120–75
"K" Monel	ABCDEF	40–190	90–210	45–2	70–25	75B–40C	140–340	90–20§
"KR" Monel	AC	40–125	90–180	45–13		75B–37C	140–350	
"R" Monel	AC	25–100	70–110	50–45	70–50	60B–100B	110–240	99–96
Inconel	ABCDEFG	25–175	70–185	50–2	70–30	65B–34C	120–300	120–70
Inconel "X"	ABCDEFG	50–240	110–275	45–2	60–20	80B–47C	150–437	40
Hastelloy B	ABCDEFG	55–68	75–140	55–6	50–30‡	92B–21C	190–240	62–10
Hastelloy C	ABCDEFG	52–60	73–140	50–5	54–20‡	92B–22C	190–245	40–8
Hastelloy D	G		110–125	1		46C–49C	452–496	1–2
Illium G	G		60–73	4–9.5	8–11		160–210	40§
Type 80 Ni 20 Cr	ABCDEFG	50–190	95–200	35–0	55–0	85B–30C	150–320	
Type 60 Ni 15 Cr	ABCDEFG	40–160	80–175	35–0.5	70–40	83B–24C	120–250	

* Lower values for annealed or hot-finished condition; higher values for cold-worked or age-hardened condition.

† Forms: A, rods and bars over 0.5 in. diameter; B, forgings; C, wire, less than 0.5 in. diameter; D, sheet; E, strip; F, tubing; G, castings.

‡ Wrought forms only.

§ Charpy.

TABLE 7.6. SELECTED ASTM SPECIFICATIONS ON NICKEL

F 1–57T	Clear Nickel-Clad and Nickel-Plated Steel Strip for Electron Tubes
F 2–57T	Aluminum-Clad Steel Strip and Nickel-Steel-Aluminum Strip for Electron Tubes
F 3–57T	Clear Nickel Strip for Electron Tubes
F 4–57T	Carbonized Nickel Strip and Carbonized Nickel-Plated and Nickel-Clad Steel Strip for Electron Tubes
F 239–57T	Nickel Alloy Cathode Sleeves for Electronic Devices
F 175–50	Nickel Wire, Round, for Lamps and Electronic Devices
F 290–57T	Round Wire for Use as Electron Tube Grid Laterals and Verticals
F 128–56T	Sleeves and Tubing for Radio Tube Cathodes
F 278–55T	Sublimation Characteristics of Metallic Materials by Electrical Resistance
B 39–22	Nickel
B 160–58T	Nickel Rod and Bar
B 161–58T	Nickel Seamless Pipe and Tube
B 162–58T	Nickel Plate, Sheet, and Strip

these circumstances. The electron emission from "D" nickel, even when it is contaminated with barium, is lower than that of "A" nickel, so that it is useful for grid wires which may become contaminated with barium from the cathode. The electrical resistivity of "D" nickel is 18.26 microhm·cm at 0°C (110 ohms/circular mil foot). When "D" nickel is drawn to sizes suitable for winding grid laterals, trade names such as "Mangrid" and "Magnonickel" wire are used.

"E"* *nickel* contains from 1.75 to 2.25 per cent manganese and has therefore mechanical properties which are intermediate between those of "A" nickel and "D" nickel. Its corrosion resistance at moderate temperature is comparable to that of "A" nickel. "E" nickel is widely used for support wires in incandescent lamps and also for grid laterals under the trade name "Mangrid-E" wire.

*Duranickel** alloy is an age-hardenable wrought nickel-aluminum alloy with mechanical properties between those of "K" Monel* age-hardenable nickel-copper alloy and Inconel "X"* age-hardenable nickel-chromium alloy. The properties of the alloy in the soft condition may be increased by cold work, and this may be supplemented by the ageing treatment. In the annealed and aged condition, Duranickel alloy exhibits low relaxation and thus is useful for spring parts subjected to relatively high stress for prolonged times at temperatures as high as 350°C, or, at low stress and short exposure times, as high as 400°C. The alloy is slightly magnetic at room temperature in the soft condition and magnetic after age-hardening. The corrosion resistance of Duranickel alloy is comparable to that of "A" nickel. For the attainment of the best surface condition, ageing in dry hydrogen is recommended, but, even in this gas, a thin, tenacious aluminum oxide film is formed which must be removed prior to welding or soldering. The electrical resistivity of this material is about 45 microhm·cm (270 ohms/circular mil foot) at 20°C.

*Permanickel** alloy is the original age-hardenable, high-nickel alloy developed for applications where high strength and corrosion resistance are required. This alloy requires a different annealing and ageing treatment than Duranickel and has different physical characteristics. Permanickel alloy is magnetic at room temperature in all conditions and has a lower electrical resistivity than Duranickel alloy. The mechanical properties of the two materials are about the same, and the resistance to corrosion of Permanickel alloy is comparable to that of "A" nickel. Permanickel alloy has a somewhat lower resistance to relaxation at elevated temperatures and should be used in place of Duranickel alloy only when higher electrical conductivity and magnetic properties are essential. After ageing, the surface must be cleaned prior to welding or soldering, a condition that applies to all age-hardenable nickel alloys. The electrical resistivity of Permanickel

---

* Tradenames, The International Nickel Company, Inc.

alloy is about 16.6 microhm·cm at 0°C (100 ohms/circular mil foot at 32°F).

Monel* nickel-copper alloy is the typical representative of a series of wrought nickel-copper alloys which combine high strength, ductility, weldability, and excellent corrosion resistance; its composition is about two-thirds nickel and one-third copper. The strength of Monel nickel-copper alloy can be increased by mechanical working, although it cannot be age-hardened by thermal treatment. Monel is somewhat magnetic at room temperature; its permeability will vary to some degree with variations in composition and ambient temperature. Its electrical resistivity is about 48 microhms·cm (290 ohms/circular mil foot at 32°F).

Monel "403"*[29] low-permeability nickel-copper alloy has a slightly lower nickel content, contains less iron and more manganese than Monel nickel-copper alloy. The permeability of Monel "403" alloy in any of the commercial forms, sizes, and tempers furnished will not exceed a value of 1.1 at room temperature and a field strength of 200 oersteds; a typical value at room temperature is 1.004. Normal processing operations, such as hot-rolling, forging, cold-drawing, or cold-rolling, annealing, stress-relieving, etc., have little, if any, effect on the permeability of this material. The alloy has substantial strength at elevated temperatures and is comparable in this respect to stainless steel as shown in Figure 7.11. The thermal expansion

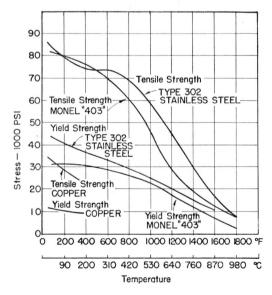

Figure 7.11. Tensile strength and yield strength of annealed Monel "403" as a function of temperature compared to stainless steel 302 and copper.[29] (*Courtesy The International Nickel Company, Inc.*)

---

* Tradenames, The International Nickel Company, Inc.

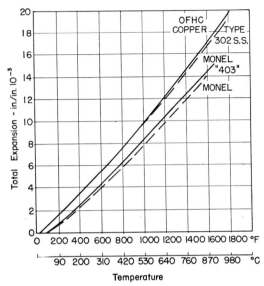

Figure 7.12. Thermal expansion of Monel "403," "OFHC" Copper, and Type 302 Stainless Steel.[29] (*Courtesy The International Nickel Company, Inc.*)

of Monel "403" is comparable to that of stainless steel and OFHC copper, as shown in Figure 7.12. It is thus practical to construct assemblies from these various materials without running into the danger of mechanical distortion on heating.

Alloys of somewhat higher ratio of copper-to-nickel, such as Monel "401" alloy, Constantan, etc. also find use for similar purposes in vacuum tube construction. However, precautions should be taken to ensure that these alloys are free from volatile impurities such as zinc or cadmium.

Because of freedom from formation of refractory oxides, which form on some of the other nonmagnetic alloys, the nickel-copper materials are readily brazed, welded, or soldered and are comparable to elemental nickel in this respect.

"R" *Monel** freely machinable alloy differs from Monel alloy mainly in having a higher sulfur content; for this reason, it cannot be used for tube structures.

"K" *Monel** age-hardenable nickel-copper alloy contains aluminum and possesses the excellent corrosion-resistant properties of Monel nickel-copper alloy combined with greater strength and hardness. The alloy develops a strength level ordinarily found only in heat-treated alloy steels. "K" Monel alloy is nonmagnetic at temperatures as low as $-100°C$. The permeability at room temperature is of the order of 1.0015 at field strengths from 10 to

* Tradenames, The International Nickel Company, Inc.

300 oersteds. Hot strength is good up to near 600°C, but where creep at maximum temperature is of controlling importance, Inconel or Inconel "X" is recommended. Owing to the presence of aluminum and titanium in the alloy, a thin oxide film is likely to form even on heating in fairly dry hydrogen; this oxide film must be removed before welding or brazing operations are performed. The electrical resistivity of "K" Monel at 0°C is 58.1 microhm.cm (350 ohms/circular mil foot).

"KR" Monel differs from "K" Monel in having a slightly higher carbon content to improve its machinability by a thermal treatment in the unaged condition for the purpose of precipitating small amounts of graphitic carbon. Parts may be machined in the annealed or cold-drawn condition and subsequently age-hardened. Like "K" Monel, "KR" Monel is nonmagnetic, and its physical and mechanical properties, after ageing, are comparable to those of annealed and aged "K" Monel.

"Inconel" nickel-chromium alloy is nonmagnetic and resistant to oxidation at elevated temperatures and not attacked by a wide variety of inorganic and organic compounds as well as many heat-treating atmospheres. The alloy work-hardens more rapidly than nickel or Monel alloy, as shown in Figure 7.9. The permeability of Inconel alloy at 20°C is approximately 1.007, and at −100°C it is 1.1. The electrical resistivity at 20°C is about 98 microhm·cm (590 ohms/circular mil foot).

Inconel "X" alloy is a wrought, nonmagnetic, age-hardenable modification of Inconel alloy, developed primarily for gas turbines and jet engines in which high rupture strength and low creep rates under high stress at temperatures up to 815°C are essential. For springs subjected to relatively high stresses, the soft, or mildly cold-worked and aged, material shows low relaxation for prolonged times at temperatures up to 540°C. For minimum creep at the highest temperatures, cold work must be avoided. In the heavily cold-worked and aged condition the alloy has a tensile strength of about 250,000 psi. In this condition, the alloy has low relaxation up to about 400°C and offers useful characteristics at higher temperatures for short-time exposure. The permeability at room temperature is about 1.003 and the Curie temperature is approximately −175°C. Its electrical resistivity at 20°C is about 120 microhm·cm (740 ohms/circular mil foot).

It would lead us too far afield to enumerate the many other nickel alloys containing chromium, molybdenum, silicon, copper, and iron in various proportions. The composition of some of these is given in Table 7.1, and the reader is referred to handbooks and trade bulletins for further information.

Nickel Alloys for Grids. Very special properties are required of the fine wires employed for grids; some of these are incompatible, so that compromises must be made and the optimum grid wire will not be the same for widely different types of tubes. The first requirement is that the wire possess reasonably good mechanical properties and great uniformity so that it can be wound into uniform grids with little shrinkage and will withstand stretching and other processing steps without difficulty. Subsequently the grid should retain its shape despite heating and should emit a minimum number of electrons, even after it is contaminated with barium from the cathode; it must do all of these things at a cost that is appropriate for the class of tube involved.

The low manganese-nickel alloys are widely used for grids in small tubes, as in Permanickel. Chromium-nickel and molybdenum-nickel alloys are employed where better strength properties are needed and where the decreased thermal conductivity is acceptable. At higher temperatures, platinum-clad molybdenum, or platinum-clad tungsten, are best suited; pure molybdenum and tungsten are used for still higher temperatures. The coating of platinum reduces the grid emission, not only because of the high work function of platinum but also because of its ability to blot up and sequester considerable quantities of thorium or barium that might come from the cathode. At lower temperatures, nickel alloys may be coated with gold or with palladium to accomplish the same result. Gold works well as long as the grid is not heated too hot during manufacture or use. Palladium is more tolerant and platinum permits even higher processing and operating temperatures (see Chapter 8). A number of the more important grid alloys are listed in Table 7.7.

Special Materials and Processes

Carbonized nickel is extensively used for receiving tube anodes but has been replaced by carbonized nickel-plated cold-rolled steel and nickel-clad steel and, more recently, by aluminum-clad iron, which takes on a dark color on firing at about 700°C in vacuum and thus does not require a carbonizing treatment. (See Chapt. 5). The total emissivity of bright nickel is about 0.16 at 727°C whereas for carbonized nickel it is 0.85.

According to Briggs[30] "the carbonization of nickel is accomplished through formation of a very thin green oxide by heating the nickel in air to about 925°C, then almost immediately placing it in another furnace at the same temperature in a hydrocarbon-gas atmosphere. The nickel oxide is reduced and may act as a catalyst and crack the gas into its carbon and hydrogen components. The carbon deposits on the active nickel surface. The oxidation and reduction of the nickel surface itself tends to open up the grain boundaries and generally roughen the nickel surface. Other roughening is frequently used, such as by mechanical or chemical means, or an earlier carbonization and oxidation."

The quality and adherence of the carbon coating on the nickel base metal

TABLE 7.7. NICKEL ALLOYS FOR GRID LATERALS (L) AND SIDERODS (S)

Materials*	Suppliers	Use	Composition (Wt. Pct.)	M. Pt. (°C)	Sp. Gr. (g/cc)	Resistivity (microhm·cm) 20°C	(microhm·cm) 800°C	Tensile Strength 20°C a-annealed h-hard	(kg/cm²) 850°C
Permanickel*	INCO	L,S	See Table 7.1	14				5,250–10,500(a) 11,200–18,200(h)	
Permagrid*	WBD	L,S	See Table 7.1						
"D" Nickel*	INCO	L,S		1426	8.78	18.26	—	4,200–7,700(a) 8,750–12,250(h)	—
Gridnic-E*	DHC	L,S	See Table 7.1			20.0	57.9	5,270	2,530
Mangrid*	WBD	L,S				18.3	43.9	6,050	—
Permacarb†	WBD	L,S							
Gridnic A*	DHC	L	Ni: 50.5, Bal: Fe	1425	8.25	43.2	115.9	4,950	—
Gridnic C*	DHC	L	Fe: 1.0, Mn: 1.75, Cr: 15.0, Bal: Ni	1390	8.53	94.3	99.4	7,740	1,760
Gridnic D*	DHC	L	Cr: 20.0, Bal: Ni	1400	8.41	108.0	114.7	9,200	850
Gridnic F*	DHC	L	Ti: 2.25, Fe: 7.5, Co: 17.0, Bal: Ni	1450	8.59	35.0	100.	2,770	—
Gridnic T*	DHC	L	Ni: 98.0 min.	1450	8.75	16.6	48.2	7,030	—
"E" Nickel*	INCO	S	See Table 7.1	1426	8.86	14.11	—	—	—
"A" Nickel* (Electronic gr.)	INCO	S	See Table 7.1	1440	—	—	—	4,200–6,650(a) 8,050–11,200(h)	—
"330" Nickel*	INCO	S	See Table 7.1						
HB Alloy (Hastalloy B)	Sylvania	L	See Table 7.4						

* Names listed are Registered Trademarks of the respective companies:
INCO—International Nickel Co., Inc., 67 Wall Street, New York 5, N. Y.
WBD—Wilbur B. Driver Company, 1875 McCarter Highway, Newark 4, N. J.
DHC—Driver Harris Company, 201 Middlesex Street, Harrison, N. J.
† Carbonized Mangrid
(See Chapter 8 for plated grid wires; WBD supplies silver-plated Mangrid and Permagrid with a 5 pct. by weight coating.)

may be tested by exposing a sample to a hydrogen atmosphere in a furnace at 1000°C for 1 to 2 minutes, or by heating it for 30 minutes in a vacuum furnace at from 1100 to 1300°C. Good material will show little or no damage in color under this test, while poor material will be partially or entirely carbonized. A variety of different finishes are available from commercial suppliers; anodes may be carbonized on both sides, or on one side only; the excess carbon may be removed leaving either a dull black, or a polished carbon surface. Any oxide remaining on the nickel, or oxygen released from the nickel itself at elevated temperature, will react with carbon to form CO. It has been found that passive nickel, such as Type 499, will release less CO than carbonized "330" nickel.

High-purity nickel: Nickel for spectroscopic standards has been made by chemically purifying a nickel solution and electrodepositing the nickel on a surface from which it can be stripped. This process avoids the contamination that will result from melting under most conditions. Other methods of conversion into rod can be employed but, in general, the method just mentioned has proved most suitable and was used by Wesley[28] of the International Nickel Company Laboratory in the production of nickel having an extraordinarily high purity which makes it suitable for a spectroscopic standard. The electrical and various other properties of this material have been determined and reported by Wise and Schaefer.[3]

Vacuum cast nickel is available from the Vacuum Metals Corporation* under the code Nivac-P and will be produced to order by electron beam melting in vacuum by Temescal Metallurgical Corporation.† A series of extremely high-purity nickels, containing controlled fractional percentages of single additions, has been reported by K. M. Olsen[31, 32] of the Bell Telephone Laboratories; he selected the high-purity carbonyl nickel as the base. Using such nickel for oxide coated cathodes, the emission activity obtained was twice that available from HPM nickel.

Rolled-powder nickel in the form of sheet and wire is being produced on an experimental scale in various laboratories by compacting carbonyl nickel powder or reduced nickel powder by rolling and sintering. This process offers the advantage of close control over the resulting purity of the product and the amount of purposely added activating agents in the case of cathode nickels. Lund[33] of the University of British Columbia, Vancouver, Canada has recently reported on his work on this process and Fig. 7.13 shows the ultimate tensile strength and the elongation as a function of percent reduction in the thickness for the finest powder used after the green strip was sintered 15 minutes at 1232°C, cold-rolled 50 per cent, annealed 25 minutes at 870°C, and then rerolled by the amount indicated on the abscissa.

* P. O. Box 977, Syracuse 1, N. Y.
† 1201 South 47th Street, Richmond, California.

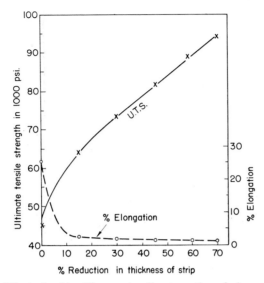

Figure 7.13. Effect of cold rolling on tensile strength and elongation of densified strip. F-100 strip, sintered 15 min. at 1230°C, cold rolled 50 per cent, annealed 25 min. at 870°C, then rerolled by amounts indicated. After Lund.[33] (*Courtesy The American Institute Mining, Metallurgical and Petroleum Engineers.*)

Outgassing of Nickel: Summaries of the gas properties of nickel can be found in the well-known book by Dushman[34] and in review articles by Espe[26] and Waldschmidt.[35] (Figures A3–6 in the appendix contain a number of graphs from Waldschmidt's paper.) Depending on its method of fabrication, nickel may contain very substantial amounts of gases of which hydrogen, carbon dioxide, and carbon monoxide are the principal constituents released during outgassing; these gases do not exist in the molecular state within the nickel lattice, but combine from hydrogen, carbon, and oxygen atoms at the surface during outgassing, and, in turn, dissociate from the molecular state into atomic components when sorbed by the metal from the surrounding atmosphere. The permeation of hydrogen through nickel increases rapidly with rising temperature (Figure A6), and the amount of hydrogen dissolved also increases with increasing temperature (Figure A4), rising from 111 to 419 micromoles/100 grams in the temperature range from 300 to 900°C.[36] The solubility of hydrogen in nickel is greater than it is in iron, molybdenum, silver, platinum, or copper (Figure A4).

Solubilities of hydrogen in nickel-iron alloys are intermediate between those observed for either nickel or iron alone. Owing to the high rate of diffusion of hydrogen in nickel,[37] this metal can be readily purged by hydrogen-firing at relatively low temperatures, of the order of 500°C, although firing near 1000°C is common practice. Any hydrogen remaining in the nickel is then readily released during a vacuum-firing treatment, or during bake-out on the pump. The removal of carbon monoxide from nickel, in the sense stated above, is a slow process and requires temperatures of the order of 1000°C. It is desirable, therefore, to limit the amount of carbon monoxide to be formed by using nickel of a low oxygen and carbon content.[5]

An abnormal enrichment of nickel with hydrogen has been reported by Morrison and Lander[20], who find that nickel tubing used as a cathode in a glow discharge in a hydrogen atmosphere will take up a very much larger amount of hydrogen when the surface is covered by a visible film of nickel oxide or a thin white film of barium oxide than is the case for clean nickel. The oxide film was maintained during the discharge by providing for an adequate partial pressure of water vapor. Dry hydrogen was used for measurements on nickel coated with barium oxide. The concentrations of hydrogen observed in the presence of oxide films not only were substantially higher than those observed with pure nickel, but also increased with decrease of temperature from near 200°C to near 100°C. For equal numbers of atoms striking the surface, the increase in concentration near 100°C amounts to about four orders of magnitude. The transport mechanism in both surface films is believed to have been proton migration in imperfect hydroxides. The energetic hydrogen ions penetrate the outer surfaces efficiently and are then trapped in the interior by surface barriers which amount to about 0.35 ev for both nickel oxide and barium oxide on nickel.

REFERENCES

1. J. G. Thompson, "Nickel and its Alloys," United States Department of Commerce, National Bureau of Standards, Circular 592 (1958); U. S. Government Printing Office, Washington 25, D. C. Price 60 cents (87 pp.).
2. F. E. Allen, "Nickel and Nickel-Base Alloys," Chapter 10, in "Engineering Materials Handbook," C. L. Mantell, Ed., McGraw-Hill Book Co., Inc., New York, 1958.
3. E. M. Wise and R. H. Schaefer, "The properties of pure nickel," *Metals & Alloys*, **16**, 424–428; 891–893; 1067–1071 (Sept., Nov., Dec. 1942).
4. The International Nickel Company, Inc., New York, Bull. T-15 (7th ed.), "Engineering Properties of Nickel," 1957.
5. E. M. Wise, "Nickel in the radio industry," *Proc. Inst. Radio Engrs.*, **25**, 714–751 (June 1937).
6. K. Jackson and R. O. Jenkins, "Nickel in electronics," *Metallurgia*, **47**, 277–282 (June 1953).
7. "Metals Handbook," American Society For Metals, Cleveland, 1948.
8. C. J. Smithells, "Metals Reference Book" (2 Vols.), Interscience Publishers Inc., New York, 1955.
9. "The Reactor Handbook," Vol. 3, Section 1; United States Atomic Energy Commission, AECD-3647 (March 1955).
10. "American Institute of Physics Handbook," D. E. Gray, Ed., McGraw-Hill Book Co., Inc., New York, 1957.

11. "Van Nostrand's Scientific Encyclopedia," 3d ed., D. Van Nostrand Company, Inc., Princeton, 1958.

12. "Inco Nickel Alloys for Electronic Uses," The International Nickel Company, Inc., New York, 1959.

13. R. E. Honig, "Vapor pressure data for the more common elements," *RCA Rev.*, **18**, 195–204 (June 1957).

14. O. Kubashewski and E. Ll. Evans, "Metallurgical Thermochemistry," John Wiley & Sons, Inc., New York, 1956.

15. M. S. Van Dusen and S. M. Shelton, "Apparatus for measuring thermal conductivity of metals up to 600°C," *J. Research Natl. Bur. Standards*, **12**, 429–440 (RP 668) (Apr. 1934).

16. F. C. Nix and D. MacNair, "The thermal expansion of pure metals: copper, gold, aluminum, nickel, and iron," *Phys. Rev.*, **60**, 597–605 (Oct. 15, 1941).

17. H. L. Johnston and A. L. Marshall, "Vapor pressures of nickel and nickel oxide," *J. Am. Chem. Soc.*, **62**, 1382–1390 (June 1940).

18. H. Lund and L. Ward, "The spectral emissivities of iron, nickel, and cobalt," *Proc. Phys. Soc.*, (**B**)**65**, 535–540 (July 1952).

19. W. D. Jenkins and T. G. Digges, "Effect of temperature on the tensile properties of high-purity nickel," *J. Research Natl. Bur. Standards*, **48**, 313–321 (RP2317) (Apr. 1952).

20. J. Morrison and J. J. Lander, "The concentration of hydrogen in nickel under hydrogen ion bombardment," *J. Electrochem. Soc.*, **105**, 145–148 (Mar. 1958).

21. F. J. Morin, "Electrical properties of NiO," *Phys. Rev.*, **93**, 1199–1204 (Mar. 15, 1954).

22. E. A. Gulbransen and K. F. Andrew, "High-temperature oxidation of high-purity nickel between 750 and 1050°C," *J. Electrochem. Soc.*, **104**, 451–454 (July 1957). (Disc. **105**, 363–364 (June 1958).

23. E. A. Gulbransen and K. F. Andrew, "The kinetics of oxidation of high-purity nickel," *J. Electrochem. Soc.*, **101**, 128–140 (Mar. 1954).

24. M. Cocks, "The role of atmospheric oxidation in high-speed sliding phenomena II," *Am. Soc. Lubrication Engrs*, **1**, 101–107 (Apr. 1958).

25. H. R. Thirsk and E. J. Whitmore, "An electron diffraction study of the surface reaction between nickel oxide and corundum," *Trans. Faraday Soc.*, **36**, 565–574 (Apr. 1940).

26. W. Espe, "Methods and techniques of metal degassing" (in German), *Vak.-Technik*, **5**, 39–53 (May 1956); *ibid.*, 69–82 (June 1956).

27. B. Wolk, "Studies of the effect of anode materials on oxide-coated cathode performance," *Sylvania Technologist*, **12**, 41–45 (Apr. 1959).

28. W. A. Wesley, "Preparation of pure nickel by electrolysis of a chloride solution," *J. Electrochem. Soc.*, **103**, 296–300 (May 1956).

29. Basic Data on Monel "403", a low-permeability nickel-copper alloy. The International Nickel Company, Inc., New York (Mar. 15, 1958).

30. T. H. Briggs, "Carbonized nickel for radio tubes," *Metals & Alloys*, **9**, 303–306 (Nov. 1938).

31. K. M. Olsen, "Superpurity nickel melted under controlled atmospheres," *Metal Progr.*, **72**, 105–109 (Sept. 1957).

32. K. M. Olsen, "The effect of trace elements on the tensile, electrical resistance and recrystallization properties of high-purity nickel," *Trans. ASM* (1960).

33. J. A. Lund, "Roll-compacting produces pure nickel strip," *J. Metals*, **10**, 731–734 (Nov. 1958).

34. S. Dushman, "Scientific Foundations of Vacuum Technique," John Wiley & Sons, Inc., New York, 1949.

35. E. Waldschmidt, "Gas release and permeation of metals used in the construction of vacuum tubes" (in German), *Metall*, **8,** 749–758 (Oct. 1954).

36. M. H. Armbruster, "The solubility of hydrogen at low pressure in iron, nickel and certain steels at 400 to 600°C," *J. Am. Chem. Soc.*, **65,** 1043–1054 (June 1943).

37. M. L. Hill and E. W. Johnson, "The diffusivity of hydrogen in nickel," *Acta Metallurgica*, **3,** 566–571 (Nov. 1955).

CHAPTER 8

PRECIOUS METALS: SILVER, GOLD, AND THE PLATINUM FAMILY

Introduction

The precious metals play an important role in the electron tube industry not as structural materials by themselves, but as brazing filler metals for the joining of metals and as thin films to impart desirable properties to the surfaces of other metals used within the tube. For general applications, the precious metals are widely used in the form of corrosion-resistant coatings, for high-temperature thermocouples, high-temperature furnace windings, electrical contacts, and highly reflective surfaces, such as mirrors in optical systems. Platinum crucibles of considerable size are used for the melting of optical glass and in other critical chemical processes, where contamination would result from the use of more conventional containers. In the production of fiber glass for electrical insulation and other purposes, platinum trays, or bushings, with hundreds of small orifices are used through which the molten glass passes to form threads.

The precious metals and their alloys which are used for brazing are listed in Table 12.1 (p. 360). The use of pure platinum cathodes is mentioned in Chapter 15 (p. 563). Gold diffusion seals are described in Chapter 12 (p. 382), and the application of gold films to metals used in glass-to-metal seals is described in Chapter 13 (p. 458). Having thus relegated the description of many of the principal applications of the precious metals to other chapters, it remains to describe the physical characteristics and chemical properties in the present one; this is done in Tables 8.1 and 8.2. Additional information on the precious metals is easily available in references 1 to 6. The *Platinum Metals Review*[6] is especially recommended as a current source of information and a guide to the international literature on all possible applications, including electronics, where platinum, palladium, rhodium, iridium, osmium, and ruthenium play a part.

Suppression of Primary Electron Emission

One of the difficulties which hampers the successful operation of high-frequency tubes is the thermal emission of electrons from control grids and screen grids when barium, barium oxide, or thorium have been deposited onto them by evaporation from the cathode; this is an unavoidable effect which takes place in all tubes which contain oxide cathodes or dispenser

241

TABLE 8.1. PHYSICAL CHARACTERISTICS OF PRECIOUS METALS[7-14]

Property	Unit	Ag	Au	Pt	Pd	Rh	Ir	Os	Ru
Atomic number		47	79	78	46	45	77	76	44
Atomic weight		107.880	197.0	195.09	106.4	102.91	192.2	190.2	101.1
Isotopes		107, 109	—	190, 192, 194, 195, 196, 198	102, 104, 105, 106, 109, 110	103	191, 193	184, 186, 187, 188, 189, 190, 192	96, 98, 99, 100, 101, 102, 104
Atomic valence		1	3, 1	2, 4	2, 4	3, 4	3, 4, 6	4, 6, 8	3, 4, 6, 8
Valence orbitals		$4d^{10}5s$	$6s$	$4f^{14}5d^9 6s$	$4d^{10}$	$4d^8 5s$	$4f^{14}5d^7 6s^2$	$4f^{14}5d^6 6s^2$	$4d^7 5s$
Lattice type		f.c.c. (A1)	f.c.c. (A1)	f.c.c. (A1)	f.c.c. (A1)	f.c.c. (A1)	f.c.c. (A1)	c.p.h. (A3)	c.p.h. (A3)
Lattice constants	Angstroms	4.086	4.0781	3.9237	3.8902	3.8044	3.8389	a = 2.72; c = 4.314	a = 2.70; c = 4.27
Atomic radius	Angstroms	1.4415	1.439	1.3845	1.3725	1.35	1.3545	1.350	1.335
Atomic volume	cc/gm atom	10.28	10.2	9.102	8.89	8.273	8.58	8.46	8.33
Closest approach of atoms	Angstroms	2.882	2.878	2.769	2.745	2.684	2.709	2.670	2.644
Density (20°C)	gm/cc	10.492	19.29	21.45	12.0	12.41	22.54	22.5	12.3
Melting point	°C	960.5	1063	1769	1552	1960	2442	2700	2450
Boiling point	°C	1950	2600	4300	~2200	>2500	>4800	>5300	4900
Specific heat (20°C)	cal/gm	0.056	0.031	0.032	0.058	0.059	0.032	0.031	0.031
Thermal conductivity	c.g.s.	1.0	0.71	0.17	0.17	0.36	0.35	—	—
Thermal expansion coeff. (0–100°C)	cm/cm/°C $\times 10^{-7}$	197	142	89	117	85	65	66	96
Vapor pressure temp. at which p(Torr) = 10^{-8}	°K	852[7]	1045[7]	1560[7]	1034[13]	1550 est.[7]	1720 est.[7]	—	—
10^{-6}		961	1180	1755	1179	1745 est.	1950 est.	—	—
10^{-4}		1105	1355	2015	1371	1980 est.	2220 est.	—	—
10^{-2}		1305	1605	2350	1637	2300 est.	2580 est.	—	—
Spectral emissivity (%)	at 0.650 μ	5.5[5]	14 (1000°C)[5]	33[7]	33[7]	29[7]	30[7]	—	—
	100°C	2[5]	2[5]	5[5]	—	—	—	—	—
	500°C	3	3	10	—	—	—	—	—
Total emissivity (%)	1000°C	—	—	15	—	—	—	—	—
Electrical resistivity (20°C)	ohm·cm $\times 10^{-6}$	1.59	2.44	10.6	10.7	4.7	5.3	9.5	9.5

242

Property	units								
Temp. coeff. of resistance (0-100°C)	ohm/°C	0.0038	0.004	0.003927	0.0038	0.0046	0.004	0.0042	0.0042
Magnetic susceptibility	$\times 10^{-6}$	-0.20	-0.15	$+1.10$	$+5.4$	$+1.11$	$+0.15$	$+0.05$	$+0.50$
Electron work function	e.v.	4.5	4.9	5.32	4.99	4.80	5.40	4.7	(4.52)
Richardson constant A	a/cm^2/°K^2	—	—	32	60	33	63	—	—
Secondary emission coeff. δ		1.5	1.5	1.8	>1.3	—	—	—	—
Mechanical Properties:[7]									
Proportional limit annealed (a)	psi $\times 10^3$			2-5	4				
Ultimate tensile strength	psi $\times 10^3$	18 (a)	19 (a)	42 (h) 20-24 (a)	55 (h) 20-25 (a)	365 (h),138 (a)	290 (h),80 (a)		
Young's modulus (tension)	psi $\times 10^6$	11	11	22	16	40	74	(81)	(60)
Elongation annealed	% on 2 in.	52	45	24-30	30-40	35	9		
Hardness (annealed)	V.P.H.	50	50	110	40	100	370 (melted)	800 (melted)	455 (melted)

Ag:[5] log $p_{\mathrm{Torr}} = (-14{,}710/T^{\circ}_{\mathrm{K}}) + 11.66 - 0.755 \log T \;(298\text{--}1234^{\circ}\mathrm{K})$

Pt:[5] log $p_{\mathrm{Torr}} = (-27{,}100/T^{\circ}_{\mathrm{K}}) + 9.40\,(298\text{--}2042^{\circ}\mathrm{K})$

Au:[5] log $p_{\mathrm{Torr}} = (-19{,}820/T^{\circ}_{\mathrm{K}}) + 10.81 - 0.306 \log T - 0.167T\,(298\text{--}1336^{\circ}\mathrm{K})$

Pd:[13] log $p_{\mathrm{Torr}} = (-16{,}860 \pm 85/T^{\circ}_{\mathrm{K}}) + 8.30 \pm 0.04$

TABLE 8.2. CHEMICAL PROPERTIES OF PRECIOUS METALS

	Ag	Au	Pt	Pd	Rh	Ir	Os	Ru
Electrochemical equivalent	1.11793 mg/Coul. 0.89451 Coul./mg	0.68117 mg/Coul. 1.46805 Coul./mg	0.50578 mg/Coul. 1.97716 Coul./mg	0.27642 mg/Coul 3.61762 Coul./mg	0.26661 mg/Coul. 3.75085 Coul./mg	0.50026 mg/Coul. 1.99896 Coul./mg	0.49611 mg/Coul. 2.01567 Coul./mg	0.26347 mg/Coul. 3.79548 Coul./mg
A) *Reactions with gases and vapors:*								
dry air at room temperature	none	none	none	none	none	none	none	none
oxidation in dry air at	200		>1000 (slightly)	750	1100 → Rh_2O_3	>1000 → IrO_2	200 → OsO_4	600°C
sulfurous atmosphere	tarnish at R.T. (AgS_2)	none	none	none	none			none
oxygen	copious diffusion 600°C	none	none up to 1400°C no permeation up to 1425°C[44] permeation >700°C	absorption—hot absorbs >900 × its vol. permeation at 100–300°C				
hydrogen	none	none						
nitrogen								
chlorine				attack when hot				
sulfur dioxide	attack	attack	none at 1000°C	attack when hot	attack			attack
B) *Reactions with liquids:*								
HCl	dil. surface only conc. slow attack	none	none	hot: dissolves slowly	hot, conc: none	none	none	none
H_2SO_4	hot, <60%: none hot, 80%: dissolves	none	none	hot: dissolves slowly	hot, conc: attack	none	none	none
HNO_3	dissolves	none	none	hot, conc: dissolves	hot, conc: none	none	none	none
HF	hardly any	none	none	none	none	none	none	none
H_2SeO_4	dissolves	dissolves	dissolves		none			
aqua regia	dissolves	dissolves	attack	dissolves	none	none		none
fused alkali hydroxides	none	attack		attack			slow attack	
fused alkali carbonates	none		none					

244

fused alkali cyanides	none	dissolves in presence of air	attack	attack	attack	attack	attack
fused KHSO₃				dissolves			
fused (NaOH + NaNO₃)				attack			
Hg	amalgamates	dissolves	none (wets)				
C) Reactions with solids:							
carbon				graphite dissolves in Pd several hundred degrees below M.P. of Pd	none at high temp.		
silicon			eutectic at 830°C				
phosphorus			eutectic at 588°C		none at high temp.		
lead			attack				
tantalum			alloys	intermetallic compound			
tungsten							
MgO							
D) Oxides:	Ag_2O—brown Ag_2O_2—black	Au_2O—gray-violet Au_2O_3—d. br.-black		PdO—black Pd_2O_3—brown PdO_2—black	IrO_2 Ir_2O_3	OsO Os_2O_3 OsO_4 M.P. 40°C	Ru_2O_3—black RuO_4—gold-yell. RuO_2—green

cathodes. The work function of the grid wires is then lowered by substantial amounts so that these grids become electron emitters when their temperature is raised by heat radiation from the hot cathode, or by electron bombardment.[14-17] When the grid bias is applied through a high resistance, a small amount of grid emission can reduce the bias sufficiently to cause the tube to run away, so to speak, because, once the control grid is bombarded by electrons, its temperature will rise and the primary emission increase farther and farther, thus causing a higher and higher potential at the grid and producing more bombardment by electrons from the cathode until the grid is destroyed. This situation is particularly critical in close-spaced grids which are apt to run quite hot and are also quickly covered with evaporation products from the cathode. The successful operation of such tubes thus depends on the extent to which grid primary emission can be suppressed.

A large number of different types of treatment of the grid surfaces has been suggested throughout the years, and many proprietary processes are being used and carefully guarded. The applied coating should have a high work function by itself and be able to absorb the activating agents so that the latter are not able to build up low-work-function surface films. The surface coating on the grid wire should be chemically stable at elevated temperature, have a low vapor pressure, and adhere tightly to the wire so that it is not damaged during the fabrication of the grid. It also should have a low diffusion rate and should not form low-melting alloys with the grid metal. Very few, if any, of the now commercially used coatings satisfy all these conditions, regardless of the claims made for their excellence. Some coatings are better for oxide cathodes and others are preferred for thoriated tungsten emitters. The type of processing used on the pump will also have a bearing on the choice of the grid coating. The maximum temperature at which a given coating can effectively operate is a critical factor and seriously limits the ambient temperature to which even ceramic envelope tubes can be exposed.

One of the earliest techniques for the suppression of primary grid emission consisted of the application of a film of graphite, or carbon, to the surface. While such a coating is quite effective, not only in the suppression of primary emission, but also in greatly lowering the secondary emission from the grid, it is difficult to get a hard and smooth coating unless pyrolytic carbon films are used. Champion[18] has more recently reported on studies in which a colloidal suspension of graphite was applied to molybdenum; he concludes that such coatings may be satisfactory for screen grids. Controlled amounts of barium and barium oxide were evaporated onto the graphite-coated molybdenum surface, and the emission therefrom measured at various temperatures. Below 900°C, the emission actually increased with time corresponding to activation of the surface, while at temperatures above 900°C the emission decayed rapidly to a negligibly small value. It is suggested that barium oxide is being reduced to barium by the carbon during the initial period of decay which takes place at a faster rate than that following when the remaining free barium is evaporated from the surface. Considering the fact that screen grids usually operate at a temperature of 600 to 700°C, the decrease of primary emission in time above 900°C would thus not be effective, and the much lower value of the emission from a fully activated carbon-coated molybdenum surface compared with that of molybdenum by itself would have to be relied upon. No data are given for the performance of actual tubes in which the grids were treated in this manner.

Gold plating of grid wires is by far the most widely used technique for the suppression of primary emission in the presence of oxide-coated cathodes. The beneficial effect of such coatings has been known since 1930 according to Baker[19] who has described carefully controlled experiments with gold-plated molybdenum and gold-plated manganese-nickel wires to which a coating of gold resinate was applied by a continuous process and then heated in air to 500°C to produce a thin layer of gold. In addition to tests performed in specially constructed tubes in which two straight filaments were located on opposite sides of an oxide-coated cathode, large-scale factory trials were also run on triodes and tetrodes which were life tested for periods of 600 hours and, in one case, up to 2600 hours. Uncoated 5 % manganese-nickel wire showed a much smaller amount of grid primary emission than uncoated molybdenum wire both at 450 and at 590°C. All gold-coated wires tested during these experiments showed no primary emission up to 600°C when a test limit of 0.2 ma/cm² was applied. A coating thickness of at least one micron was required for effective suppression. Micrographs of wires which had been used at different temperatures for various periods of time disclosed that, in the case of manganese-nickel wires, diffusion of the gold into the body of the wire takes place above 450°C, but no such diffusion was observed with gold-coated molybdenum. While these gold-coated wires have been shown to be effective in suppressing grid emission up to temperatures in the range of 550 to 600°C, as mentioned above, the safe temperature from the point of view of gold evaporation is given as 500 to 550°C. When misaligned grid wires are bombarded by electrons and run excessively hot, gold is evaporated and will rapidly poison the emission from the cathode.

"It should be recognized that the melting point of the interface between nickel and gold is rather low, 960°C, and it is probable that transient melting can occur during processing steps. In the case of palladium-clad nickel, the melting temperature is considerably higher, about 1250°C, so that no trouble will be encountered; it is also possible to interpose a layer of palladium between the gold and the nickel to achieve a higher melting point.

"In considering gold coatings, the possible presence of sulfur in some of these, both electrodeposited and fired types, must be kept in mind, as sulfur would be highly detrimental to cathode activity."*

As Baker[19] points out in his paper, it is very difficult to lay down definite temperature limits because so many factors enter into play. Some of the figures which have come to the present author's attention as upper limits for the safe operating temperature of gold-plated grids are substantially lower than those given by Baker. The method of fabrication used by Baker is not plating in the proper sense of the word which usually implies electrolytic deposition from a bath. Rhodium has also been used for the suppression of grid primary emission in the presence of oxide-coated cathodes, and it is claimed that more uniform coatings can be obtained than is the case with gold. Silver was tested by Baker and found to be unreliable although it did prevent primary emission in some cases.

Etter[28] has recently reported on the most suitable method of cleaning molybdenum wire prior to plating with nickel and gold and finds that cathodic treatment at room temperature in 65 to 75% (b.vol.) sulfuric acid for 20 seconds at 6v was effective in removing all contaminants, including oxides of mercury which were present on some wires. (Some vendors use mercury pools for electrical contacts during annealing of the hot-drawn wire.) The electro-cleaned wire is fired in dry hydrogen at a temperature of 900 to 1050°C for at least five minutes to remove all absorbed gases; a film of nickel corresponding to not less than 0.1, nor more than 0.4 per cent by weight of the wires is then laid down by plating in a conventional nickel chloride bath. After thoroughly rinsing in demineralized water, the wire is transferred to the final cyanide gold plating bath, rinsed again and hydrogen fired near 1000°C to flow the gold into a bright lustrous surface.

According to information from other sources, the cathodic cleaning in H_2SO_4 described above, is not applicable to tungsten wire; electrolytic etching in a 20 percent solution of KOH for 30 seconds, or longer, by applying 7.5v ac, using a graphite electrode, was found effective at Stanford in preparing tungsten or molybdenum parts for subsequent nickel and gold plating.

Russell[22a] described the step plating recommended by Etter in a patent disclosure according to which the strike is produced to a thickness of from 10^{-5} to 10^{-4} in. on a molybdenum base metal, such as a grid wire, by using a gold electrode submerged in a solution of potassium gold cyanide, potassium cyanide, and potassium hydroxide. The wire is then heated in form-

---

* Personal communication from Dr. E. M. Wise of the International Nickel Company, Inc., Development and Research Division.

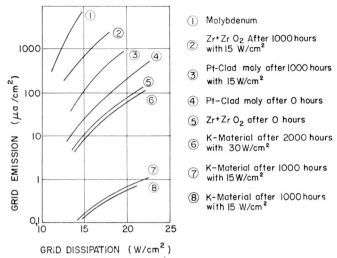

Figure 8.1. Comparison of various types of surface films on molybdenum wire for the suppression of primary electron emission. After Dorgelo.[24] (*Courtesy Société Française Des Ingénieurs Du Vide.*)

ing gas at near 1200°C for about five minutes, and a thicker layer of gold then plated onto the first one.

Freeman and Briggs[22b] have recently reviewed the various procedures which have been evaluated in industrial and government laboratories where electroplating on molybdenum was studied. Both, compositions and procedures are described for plating a variety of metals.

In the presence of thoriated tungsten emitters, the members of the platinum family have been found most effective as grid coatings. While grids made from platinum wire show negligible grid emission even at high operating temperatures, the hot strength of platinum is inadequate. Platinum-clad tungsten wire, containing 25 to 30% platinum by weight, or a 0.6 mil coating on a 10-mil-dia. wire, is commercially available from Baker Platinum Division, Engelhard Industries, Inc.[23]* Thorium deposited on the platinum surface diffuses into the platinum so that the high work function of platinum is not impaired. Platinum-clad molybdenum wire is also being used but such wires sag seven times as fast as do platinum-clad tungsten wires at 1200°C according to a statement by the supplier. Tungsten-platinum alloys, containing 4% tungsten have also been used, especially for high-temperature operation.[2]

Dorgelo[24] of the Philips Laboratories in Eindhoven has reported on the effectiveness of various types of grid coatings for the suppression of primary emission, and Figure 8.1 is reproduced from his paper. The K-mate-

* 113 Astor St., Newark 2, N. J.

rial is essentially a platinum surface which is separated from the molybdenum base by an intermediate layer of very fine carbon particles. These different layers are sintered at appropriate temperatures and result in a surface which has all the advantages of platinum and, in addition, a high thermal emissivity (85 % B.B.). No harmful chemical or physical change has been observed after running such K-grids at 1600°K for several thousand hours. Even at a grid loading of 40 W/cm², the emission measured after 1000 hrs was less than the initial value obtained from a platinized molybdenum surface. If Pt is replaced by gold, similar results are observed in the presence of barium contamination from oxide-coated cathodes or dispenser cathodes.

In addition to the aforementioned precious metals, zirconium, titanium, silicon, boron carbide, tungsten carbide, alumina, titania, and various combinations thereof, sometimes with precious metals, have been described in the patent literature.[25]

The superior properties of titanium as a grid material with negligible primary and secondary emission have been described by Espersen and Rogers,[26] and more recently by Champion.[27] It is reported by Espersen and Rogers that titanium has the lowest grid emission of all materials investigated in the presence of an impregnated Philips cathode. Other grid materials tested were plain tungsten, plain molybdenum, plain zirconium, molybdenum wire coated with zirconium, calcium, and magnesium, manganese nickel, gold-plated molybdenum, and titanium dioxide. In the presence of thoriated tungsten cathodes, titanium grids also were found to suppress grid emission better than any other material. Champion,[27] in pursuing his earlier work on grid coatings suitable for the suppression of primary emission, studied titanium wire grids onto which barium and barium oxide were separately deposited and the emission obtained therefrom compared with that of tungsten treated in a similar way. He confirmed the observations by Espersen and Rogers in many respects but does not concur in the assumption that barium reevaporates from titanium at temperatures as low as 327°C. When barium was deposited on tungsten and titanium wires at different rates while the wires were at a temperature of 700°C, the primary emission from titanium was always about two orders of magnitude lower than that measured from tungsten wires. For a deposition rate of one monolayer per minute, which corresponds to the rate of evaporation of barium from an oxide-coated cathode when the latter is run under very onerous conditions, the emission from titanium amounted to 0.18 ma/cm² while for tungsten it was 15 ma/cm² after a period of 10 minutes. At higher temperatures up to 1000°C, the emission from titanium was very substantially lower, being less than 0.00002 ma/cm² both at 850 and 1000°C, while the emission from tungsten first increased and then settled down to a value just slightly lower than that measured at 700°C. Similar results were obtained for the evaporation of barium oxide. The possible poisoning effect of hot titanium wires in the proximity of oxide-coated cathodes was also investigated by Champion. The conclusion was reached that it is generally necessary to limit the operating temperature of titanium to 900°C to avoid poisoning the emission from an oxide cathode. When a shield was interposed between the titanium wire and the cathode, gas released from the titanium at temperatures between 900 and 1100°C had only a negligible poisoning effect.

High-temperature Thermocouples

There is a continuous need in our rapidly advancing technology to measure higher and higher temperatures with accuracy. Thermocouples made from combinations of refractory metals, and particularly those of the platinum family, serve this purpose, as shown in Figure 8.2, which is taken from a summary review of this subject by Sanders.[29] The reader is referred to this very excellent article for additional references to the literature, in addition to those separately listed at the end of this chapter.[30-34] A thermocouple which has pure platinum as one leg and an alloy consisting of 10 per cent rhodium and platinum for the other leg is referred to as the Pt/ Pt-10 Rh couple which serves as a standard for temperature measurements between the freezing point of antimony (630.5°C) and the gold point (1063.0°C). For industrial applications, this couple can be used continuously without special precautions in air up to about 1500°C, and the maximum temperature for intermittent use is usually given as 1700°C. A Pt/ Pt-13 Rh couple is used at times; it gives a slightly higher thermal emf, but the difference in performance is slight. At temperatures above 1500°C, the standard Pt/Pt-10 Rh couple is subject to a number of harmful effects which interfere with its stability. It has been shown by recent investigations, that platinum evaporates at a rate which is four times as high as that for rhodium; a migration of rhodium, the mechanism of which has not been fully established, also takes place at high temperature, and recrystallization and grain growth cause embrittlement which lead to eventual mechanical failure of the wires. To reduce harmful reactions at the surface of the wires when operating the couple in various types of furnace atmospheres, for example, it is common practice to protect the couple by a surrounding protective tube generally made from ceramic, and the most favorable choice of a ceramic material that does not interact with the material from which the couple is made presents another serious problem.

High-temperature thermocouples, for the purpose of this review, are those giving useful service at temperatures above 1500°C. A couple consisting of Pt-20 Rh/Pt-40 Rh has been calibrated up to 1884°C, and a max-

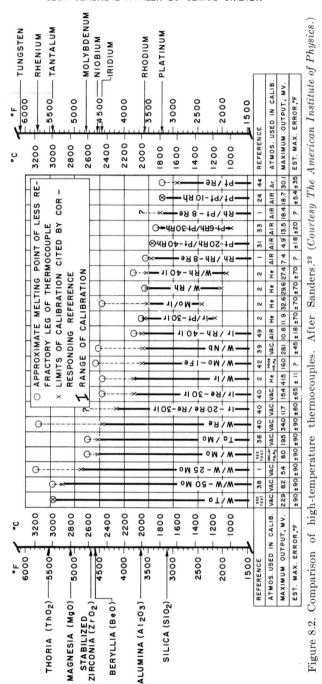

Figure 8.2. Comparison of high-temperature thermocouples. After Sanders.[29] *(Courtesy The American Institute of Physics.)*

imum variation of measurement is stated to be $\pm 10°C$ at $1800°C$.* Recrystallized alumina was found to be a satisfactory material for the sheath. For still higher temperatures, tungsten is utilized as one of the thermal elements which is coupled with molybdenum, tantalum, tungsten-molybdenum alloys, iridium, rhenium, and others which are described in the review by Sanders. The present author has used a W/Mo couple with great satisfaction in a high-temperature furnace calibrated up to $1900°C$; other workers have used this particular couple up to $2400°C$. The W/Ta thermocouple has been calibrated to $3000°C$, the highest temperature for all known combinations although the thermoelectric output undergoes a maximum near $2000°C$ which precludes accurate measurements in this region. A W/Re couple is useful up to $2400°C$ where about 33 mv is obtained. The highest known output for metallic pairs in the high-temperature range is obtained from W/Ir thermocouples which give 40 mv at $2100°C$.

"A more recent development in the thermocouple field has been the introduction of the all-noble-metal couple with a high thermal emf approximating that of Chromel-Alumel.

"The iridium vs. iridium/rhodium couple can be used in air to $2000°C$ for limited periods; it is usable continuously in vacuum and neutral atmospheres, such as nitrogen and helium.

"The iridium vs. tungsten couple has been used to $2,100°C$ in vacuum or inert atmosphere."†

Miscellaneous Applications

Precious metals and alloys are also used for a variety of instruments and in microwave gear, especially for surface coatings. Table 8.3 gives the properties of such materials used for precision wire-wound potentiometers after Willis[35] with two new materials added.

Electronic components are plated with gold, or platinum group metals, where the maintenance of a clean unoxidized surface is required. These metals are also substantially free from the tendency to develop whiskers. The latter are particularly troublesome with the low-melting base metals where whiskers cause short circuits between closely spaced conductors.[36] Thin silver plate and, occasionally, gold plate may be applied to parts to facilitate subsequent soft soldering, particularly after long storage.

Relays and switches handling low currents and low voltages are best surfaced with platinum, palladium, or gold. Silver is useful for higher currents and higher voltages, but its tendency to develop sulfide films which

---

* Introduced by Johnson, Matthey & Company, Inc. available from Sigmund Cohn Corp., Mount Vernon, N. Y.

† Personal communication to the author from Hanovia Liquid Gold Division, Engelhard Industries, Inc., East Newark, N. J.

TABLE 8.3. PROPERTIES OF NOBLE METAL RESISTANCE MATERIALS*

	Resistivity at 20°C		Temperature coefficient of resistance per °C (0 to 100°C)	Ultimate tensile strength as fine wire, psi × 10³†	
	Microhm-cm.	Ohms per circ. mil. ft.		Annealed	Hard drawn
10% Rhodium-platinum	19	114	0.0017	67.2	168.
10% Iridium-platinum	24.5	147	0.0013	78.4	179.2
20% Iridium-platinum	32	192	0.00085	100.8	235.2
10% Ruthenium-platinum	42	252	0.00047	112.	201.6
5% Ruthenium–15% rhodium-platinum	31	186	0.00070	45.6	246.4
8% Tungsten-platinum	62	372	0.00028	134.4	212.8
5% Molybdenum-platinum	64	384	0.00024	134.4	201.6
40% Silver-palladium	42	252	0.00003	53.8	156.8

* After Willis.[35]

† Converted from tons/sq. in. given in the original on the basis of 1 ton/sq. in. = 2,240 psi.

have nonlinear resistance characteristics render it undesirable in the low-current, low-voltage field.

Where contacts are operated in the presence of organic vapors emanating from insulating materials, the rate of wear is sharply increased when the contacts handle fairly high voltages. Where the contact is employed in the "dry" circuit, organic films may develop which can cause occasional failure to close. Gold is least sensitive in this respect, although it is somewhat disturbed, but the platinum metals are disturbed to a greater extent. Where this problem is important, a thin layer of gold may be applied to the palladium to handle the "dry" circuit situation. When the contacts handle appreciable energy, the organic film is no problem. Where electrical contacts are required to withstand rubbing, special combinations may become necessary. These often utilize one of the hard palladium-silver-copper-gold alloys, or rhodium electroplate for one of the elements. In potentiometers, individual attention is required to develop the proper combination between the wire and slider to meet the torque, jitter, and other requirements.

A peculiar difficulty is experienced when silver is used in contact with fibrous insulation. "Silver migration"[37-40] results when appreciatable voltage exists between two silver electrodes and is particularly troublesome where humidity is high. Under these circumstances, little silver threads grow from one of the electrodes and ultimately result in considerable leakage. This effect seems to be limited to silver, as gold and platinum are free from it, and the more reactive metals, such as copper, do not show it. Copper, however, when made the anode in contact with the usual organic insulating materials, and in hot, humid atmospheres, may corrode, causing destruction of fine-wire windings and connections.*

REFERENCES

1. E. M. Wise, "The Platinum Metals," Chapter 15 in "Modern Uses of Nonferrous Metals," 2nd ed., AIME, 1953.

1a. E. M. Wise and R. Vines, "Platinum Metals and their Alloys," The International Nickel Company, Inc., New York, 1941.

2. E. M. Wise, "The platinum metals: a review of their properties and uses," *J. Electrochem. Soc.*, **97**, 57C–64C (Mar. 1950).

3. E. M. Wise, "Precious Metals," in "Metals Handbook," The American Society For Metals, Cleveland, Ohio, 1948.

4. C. A. Hampel, Ed., "Rare Metals Handbook," Reinhold Publishing Corp., New York, 1954 (2nd ed. in preparation).

5. C. J. Smithells, "Metals Reference Book" (2 Vols.), Interscience Publishers, Inc., New York, 1955.

6. *Platinum Metals Review*, a quarterly survey of research on the platinum metals and of developments in their applications in industry, published by Johnson, Matthey & Co., Limited, Hatton Garden, London, E.C.1. England.

7. R. E. Honig, "Vapor pressure data for the more common elements," *RCA Rev.*, **18**, 195–204 (June 1957).

8. D. E. Davies, "Oxide films on silver at high temperatures," *Nature (London)*, **179**, 1293–1294 (June 22, 1957).

9. W. S. Graff and H. H. Stadelmaier, "Higher oxides of silver," *J. Electrochem. Soc.*, **105**, 446–449 (Aug. 1958).

10. G. A. Alers and J. R. Neighbours, "Elastic constants of silver and gold," *Bull. Amer. Phys. Soc.*, Ser. 2, **3**, 70 (Jan. 29, 1958).

11. G. Reinacher, "Creep properties of platinum metals and alloys" (in German), *Metall*, **10**, 597–607 (1956).

12. J. W. Edwards, R. Speiser and H. L. Johnson, "High-temperature structure and thermal expansion of some metals as determined by x-ray diffraction data. I. Platinum, tantalum, niobium, and molybdenum," *J. Appl. Phys.*, **22**, 424–428 (Apr. 1951).

13. J. F. Haefling and A. H. Daane, "The vapor pressure of palladium," *Trans. Met. Soc. AIME*, **212**, No. 1, 115–116 (Feb. 1958).

14. I. E. Mouromtseff and H. N. Kozanowski, "Grid temperature as a limiting factor in vacuum tube operation," *Proc. IRE*, **24**, 447–454 (Mar. 1936).

14a. F. J. Norton, "Nondiffusibility of oxygen through platinum," *J. Appl. Phys.*, **29**, 1122 (July 1958).

15. H. E. Sorg and G. A. Becker, "Grid emission in vacuum tubes," *Electronics*, **18**, 104–109 (July 1945).

16. H. B. Michaelson, "Variations of grid contact potential and associated grid currents," *J. Franklin Inst.*, **249**, 455–473 (June 1950).

17. S. D. O'Neill, "The influence of the internal correction voltage on the proper ratings of receiving-type tubes," *Sylvania Technologist*, **10**, 71–77 (July 1957).

18. J. A. Champion, "The suppression of screen-grid emission by carbon," *Brit. J. Appl. Phys.*, **7**, 395–399 (Nov. 1956).

---

* The material for the last four paragraphs was kindly supplied by Dr. E. M. Wise of the International Nickel Company, Inc.

19. B. O. Baker, "Gold as a grid emission inhibitor in the presence of an oxide-coated cathode," *Brit. J. Appl. Phys.*, **4**, 311–315 (Oct. 1953).

20. A. H. W. Beck, "Thermionic Valves," p. 322, Cambridge University Press, 1953.

21. C. E. Fay, "High-vacuum oxide cathode pulse modulator tubes," *Bell System Tech. J.*, **26**, 818–836 (Dec. 1947).

22a. A. G. Russell, "Methods of Plating Articles," U.S. Patent 2,816,066 (Dec. 10, 1957); assigned to Western Electric Company, Inc., New York.

22b. R. R. Freeman and J. Z. Briggs, "Electroplating on Molybdenum Metal," Tech. Rep. Sept. 1958, Climax Molybdenum Company, New York, N. Y.

23. Baker and Company, Newark, N. J., "Platinum-clad tungsten," *Rev. Sci. Instr.*, **26**, 645 (New Materials Section). (June 1955).

24. E. G. Dorgelo, "Technological aspects of UHF triode design" (in French), *Le Vide*, **12**, No. 67, 3–8 (Jan/Feb 1957).

25. V. J. De Santis and F. L. Hunter, "Method of Forming Protective Coatings for Metallic Surfaces," U.S. Patent 2,711,980 (June 28, 1955); assigned to International Telephone & Telegraph Corporation.

26. G. A. Espersen and J. W. Rogers, "Studies on grid emission," *IRE Trans. Prof. Group on Electron Devices*, ED-3, 100–107 (Apr. 1956).

27. J. A. Champion, "The grid emitting properties of titanium," *Brit. J. Appl. Phys.*, **9**, 491–495 (Dec. 1958).

28. R. W. Etter, "Cathodic Electrocleaning of Molybdenum Wire Prior to Gold Plating," ASTM Symposium on Cleaning of Electronic Device Components and Materials, Philadelphia, Oct. 13–14, 1958. ASTM Special Technical Publication No. 246, 129–135 (1959).

29. V. D. Sanders, "Review of high-temperature immersion thermal sensing devices for in-flight engine control," *Rev. Sci. Instr.*, **29**, 917–928 (Nov. 1958).

30. H. E. Bennett, "Noble Metal Thermocouples," Johnson, Matthey & Co., Ltd., London, 1958, 2nd ed.

31. H. E. Bennett, "The care of platinum thermocouples," *Platinum Metals Rev.*, **2**, No. 4, 120–123 (Oct. 1958).

32. I. E. Campbell, Ed., "High-Temperature Technology," pp. 357–376, John Wiley & Sons, Inc., New York, 1956.

33. A. U. Seybolt, "Experimental Metallurgy," John Wiley & Sons, Inc., New York, 1953.

34. A. G. Metcalf, "The use of platinum thermocouples in vacuo at high temperatures," *Brit. J. Appl. Phys.*, **1**, 256–258 (Oct. 1950).

35. K. J. Willis, "The design of precision wire-wound potentiometers," *Platinum Metals Rev.*, **2**, No. 3, 74–82 (July 1958). (Besides data reproduced in Table 8.4, this article also contains a useful nomogram for precious metal resistance wires, correlating resistivity, diameter of wire, and ohms/yd.)

36. S. M. Arnold, "The growth of metal whiskers on electrical components," Proc. 1959 Electronic Components Conf., Philadelphia, Pa., pp. 75–82.

37. L. H. Germer, "Physical processes in contact erosion," *J. Appl. Phys.*, **29**, 1067–1082 (July 1958).

38. H. W. Hermance and T. F. Egan, "Organic deposits on precious metal contacts," *Bell Syst. Tech. J.*, **37**, 739–776 (May 1958).

39. H. J. Keefer and R. H. Gumley, "Relay contact behavior under non-eroding circuit conditions," *Bell Syst. Tech. J.*, **37**, 777–814 (May 1958).

40. S. W. Chaikin, "Study of Effects and Control of Surface Contaminants on Electrical Materials," Stanford Research Institute, Menlo Park, California; Rept. No. 3 (July 15, 1958). Contr. No. DA-36-039-sc-74965.

CHAPTER 9

TUNGSTEN

Introduction

Tungsten is now officially called wolfram* but, on account of the firmly established use of the older term, the more familiar name will be used throughout this chapter. This highly refractory metal is of the greatest importance to the electron tube industry; the bulk of the ore used for its production is imported from foreign countries, principally Korea, Burma, Portugal, and Australia, and to a lesser extent from the South American countries Brazil, Argentina, Bolivia; tungsten is thus one of the strategic materials.† About 85 per cent of all the tungsten ore processed in the United States finds its way into the production of alloy steel and cemented or sintered carbides for dies and tools; the remainder is fabricated into lamp filaments, grid wire, and filaments for power tubes and receiving tubes. Anticathodes for x-ray tubes, helices for travelling-wave tubes, lead wires, and welding electrodes are other applications.

The preferred position with tungsten occupies among the commercially available metals is due to its high melting point and its comparatively high mechanical strength at elevated temperatures. Tungsten also combines strength with ductility to a greater degree than any other metal. The operating temperature of tungsten in various applications ranges from 2000 to 3000°C.

The extreme refractoriness of tungsten makes it necessary to employ for its fabrication procedures different from those that are common for the molding and shaping of ordinary metals. It is not possible to melt tungsten in a furnace and pour it into molds, because furnace materials which would withstand such high temperatures are not available. The techniques of powder metallurgy are thus used to produce solid ingots of tungsten. According to a process developed by Coolidge in 1909, tungsten powder is compressed under pressures of the order of 25 tons/sq. in. and then presintered into porous bars in a hydrogen furnace at temperatures ranging from 1000 to 1250°C. Further sintering takes place in hydrogen by

---

* Recommendation by the International Union of Pure and Applied Chemistry.

† Two types of tungsten ore are used as source material for the production of tungsten, i.e. wolframite and scheelite. In the United States, practically all non-sag tungsten wire is made from wolframite, which is imported, while tungsten for the steel industry is made from scheelite, of which a great amount is mined in the United States.

passing several thousand amperes through the bar and thus raising its temperature to near its melting point; the maximum temperature reached during sintering is about 3000°C.

As recrystallization sets in at about 1500°C, this treatment results in a coarse crystalline structure and a densification which is accompanied by linear shrinkage of the bar by about 17 per cent. The bar is now quite strong but very brittle; it is then made ductile by a specialized forging process, called "swaging," which takes place at an elevated temperature, initially at about 1500°C, in a series of passes through sets of dies that permit hammers to strike from 3000 to 15,000 blows per minute from all sides, closer each time to the axis, thus gradually reducing the diameter; the temperature is gradually lowered as this treatment proceeds. The originally randomly oriented grains are elongated in the axial direction during swaging of the rod, and a fibrous structure results which is easily apparent on fracture. Figure 9.1[1] shows an electron micrograph of a 0.010-in.-dia. wire, as drawn from 0.040-in.-dia. swaged rods; wire can be drawn by the use of tungsten carbide and diamond dies, and ribbon can be hot-rolled from wire. Drawing temperatures are gradually reduced from 1000 to 400°C as the wire becomes progressively finer in size; graphite is used as a lubricant.[2-4]

An excellent treatise on the metallurgy of tungsten, its properties and applications, is that by Smithells[5]; Li and Wang[6] have described history, geology, oredressing, metallurgy, chemistry, analysis, applications, and economics of tungsten; a condensed summary of these items is contained in a bulletin by Reed.[7] Additional information is available in books on powder metallurgy,[8, 9] general metallurgy,[10, 11] and rare metals.[12] The ASTM specifications listed in Table 9.1 apply to the use of tungsten in its various shapes in the electronic industry. In the United States, tungsten, in its various fabricated shapes may be purchased from the companies listed below.* Some of these suppliers specialize in the fabrication of very fine wires and ribbons, while others supply heavy rods and tungsten sheet. The manufacture and fabrication of tungsten is still to a large extent an

---

* Cleveland Tungsten, Inc., 10200 Meech Ave., Cleveland 5, Ohio
  Elmet Division, North American Philips Co., Inc., Lisbon Rd., Lewiston, Maine
  Fansteel Metallurgical Corp., 2200 Sheridan Rd., North Chicago, Illinois
  General Electric Co., Lamp, Wire and Phosphors Dept., 21800 Tungsten Road, Cleveland 17, Ohio
  H. Cross, Inc., 15 Beekman St., New York 7, N. Y.
  Kulite Tungsten Co., 1040 Hoyt Ave., Ridgefield, N. J.
  The Rembar Co., Inc., 67 Main St., Dobbs Ferry, N. Y. ,
  Sylvania Electric Products Inc., Chemical & Metallurgical Div., Towanda, Pa.
  Union City Filament Corp., 540 39th St., Union City, N. J. (Callite Bldg.)
  Westinghouse Electric Corporation, Lamp Div., Bloomfield, N. J.

Figure 9.1. Electron micrograph of cold-worked tungsten wire drawn to 10 mil diameters; 19,600 ×, Parlodion-carbon replica shadowed with platinum. After Nelson.[1] (*Courtesy Sylvania Electric Products Inc., Metallurgy Research Laboratory.*)

TABLE 9.1. ASTM SPECIFICATIONS FOR TESTING TUNGSTEN
WIRE AND WIRE PRODUCTS

F 113–41	Bend Testing of Wire for Radio Tubes and Incandescent Lamps
F 155–50	Test for Temper of Strip and Sheet Metals for Electronic Devices (Spring Back Method)
F 157–50	Testing Wire for Supports used in Electronic Devices and Lamps
F 180–50	Test for Density of Fine Wire and Ribbon for Electronic Devices
F 203–50	Test for Strength of Welded Joints of Lead Wires for Electronic Devices and Lamps
F 204–50	Test for Surface Flaws in Tungsten Seal Rod and Wire
F 205–56T	Tentative Method of Test for Diameter by Weighing of Fine Wire Used in Electronic Devices and Lamps
F 219–50	Testing Fine Round and Flat Wire for Electronic Devices
F 269–52T	Tentative Method of Test for Sag of Tungsten Wire
F 288–57T	Tentative Specifications for Tungsten Wire for Electronic Devices and Lamps (under 20 mils in diameter)
F 290–57T	Tentative Specifications for Round Wire for Use as Lateral Winding Wire in Electron Tube Grids.

art, and some suppliers have mastered this art better than others when it comes to the fabrication of unusual shapes.

It is of some importance to come to an agreement with the manufacturer on acceptable size tolerances and elongation expected under a given load. The applicable ASTM specifications should be made the basis of acceptance tests. On account of the difficulty of fabrication, unusual shapes of tungsten, be they large or small, are necessarily expensive, and some consultation with the supplier is desirable before a design is carried too far.

Tungsten is bought in units of kilograms for both rods and wires, and lengths are measured in meters. Fine wires, up to 0.030 in. diameter, are designated in terms of weight per specified length of 200 mm, where the weight, W, is expressed in milligrams. The value of W depends on the density of the tungsten processed by any one manufacturer, and it is necessary to obtain this information on the basis of which orders are to be placed. In general, the following relation applies:

$$W = 0.1034 \, Dd^2$$

where D = density in grams/cc and d = diameter in mils.

Using $D = 19.17$, according to ASTM Specification F 288–57T,

$$W = 1.943 \times d^2 \; (\text{mg}/200 \; \text{mm})$$

Physical and Chemical Characteristics of Tungsten

The physical characteristics of tungsten are tabulated in Table 9.2, and the chemical properties are listed in Table 9.3. As tungsten is principally used in the form of wire, its properties are dependent to a large extent on the purity of the wire, the presence or absence of additives, the prior mechanical and thermal treatment during manufacture and fabrication, and the temperature of operation. Many of the special circumstances which affect the properties of tungsten will be described later in this chapter. Chapter 13 should be consulted for problems arising in connection with glass-to-metals seals.

The mechanical properties of drawn wires given in Table 9.2 are supplemented in Table 9.4. Figure 9.2 gives a graphical representation of the tensile strength of tungsten wire as a function of diameter; it is apparent from this semi-log plot that the tensile strength increases exponentially as the diameter of the wire decreases from a value of 2 mm. Curve B in the same figure shows the decrease in tensile strength that occurs when the wire is annealed at the stage in the drawing operation where its diameter has been reduced to 0.13 mm and the subsequent increase in tensile strength when this annealed wire is drawn to smaller sizes. The effect of the annealing temperature on the tensile strength of fine, drawn tungsten wire is shown by the curves in Figure 9.3. Annealing below 600°C produces a very slight

TABEL 9.2. PHYSICAL CHARACTERISTICS OF TUNGSTEN[13, 14]

Atomic number: 74
Atomic weight: 183.92
Isotopes: 180, 182, 183, 184, 186, 187
Density: 19.3 gm/cc (0.697 lb/cu in.)
Melting point: 3395 ± 15°C
Boiling point: 5530°C [12]
Heat of fusion: 61 cal/gm

Atomic Valence: 2, 4, 5, 6
Valence orbitals: $5d^4 6s^2$
Lattice type (β-tungsten): b.c.c. (A2)
Lattice constant a_0 : 3.1647A (25°C)
Atomic volume: 15.848 A^3 (9.53 cc/g. atom)
Closest approach of atoms: 2.7407 A
Atomic radii: 1.41 (coordination No: 12)
1.37 (coordination No: 8)

Thermal-neutron-absorption cross-section: 19.2 ± 1.0 barns/atom
Vapor pressure:[15]

10^{-8}	10^{-7}	10^{-6}	10^{-5}	10^{-4}	10^{-3}	10^{-2}	10^{-1}	Torr
2340	2480	2640	2820	3030	3280	3570	3915	°K

Specific heat (cal/gm/°C): 0.032 (20°C)
0.036 (1000°C)
Enthalpy (cal/gm): 1102 (25°C)
Entropy (cal/mole/°C): 8 (condensed phase at 25°C)
41.5 (gaseous phase at 25°C)
Electrical resistivity (microhm·cm): 5.5 (20°C)
25.5 (750°C)
40 (1200°C)
85 (2400°C)
Temperature coeff. of resistivity: 5.1 × 10^{-3}/°C (0 to 170°C)
Coeff. of linear thermal expansion (cm/cm/°C): 44.4 × 10^{-7} (27°C)
51.9 × 10^{-7} (1027°C)
72.6 × 10^{-7} (2027°C)
Thermal conductivity (cal/sec.cm.°C): 0.46 (−183°C)
0.40 (0°C)
0.39 (100°C)
0.28 (1250°C)

	500	1000	1500	2000	2500	3000°K
Spectral emissivity (0.665μ):[5]	0.466	0.456	0.445	0.435	0.425	0.415
Spectral emissivity (0.467μ):	0.498	0.486	0.476	0.469	0.462	0.455
Total emissivity:	0.042	0.105	0.192	0.259	0.301	0.334
Total radiation intensity: (W/cm²)	0.015	0.600	5.54	23.65	67.2	154.5

(See also Ref. 16, 17)

	2000	2200	2400	2600	°K (T_b)
Thermal yield of electrons (ma/W):	0.042	0.348	2.01	8.55	
Surface yield of electrons (ma/cm²):	1.0	13.3	116	716	

Electron work function: 4.55 e.v.
Richardson constant $A_0 \epsilon^{-\alpha/k}$: 70 a/cm²/°K² (for A_0 = 40 a/cm²/°K²)[18]
Magnetic susceptibility: −0.28 × 10^{-6}
Mechanical properties:
Density (gm/cm³): presintered at about 1500°C: 10 to 15
sintered at 3000°C: 16.5 to 17.5
swaged 18 to 19
drawn 18 to 19.3
most probable lattice density 19.3
reference value for wire table 19.17

TABLE 9.2.—*Continued*

Hardness (Vickers Dismond No.—VDN; Rockwell C—RC)

Sintered bar, 9 × 9 mm	255 VDN	
Swaged to 8 mm	400	"
Swaged to 5 mm	407	"
Reheated to 2700°C	392	"
Swaged to 3.5 mm	474	"
Swaged to 2.7 mm	483	"
Swaged to 1.8 mm	488	"
Sheet 0.04 in. thick	45 RC	
Sheet 0.01 in. thick	67	"
Rod 0.25 in. dia.	37	"
Rod 0.10 in. dia.	40	"

Ultimate tensile strength:[19, 20] (See also Table 9.4)

Wire   0.6 mm dia. (24 mils)

400°C	120–160 kg/mm²	170,000 to 227,000 psi	
800°C	80–100	"	113,000 to 142,000 "
1200°C	40–60	"	57,000 to 85,000 "
1800°C	10–30	"	14,000 to 42,000 "

Young's modulus of elasticity: 50×16^6 psi

Modulus of torsion (single crystal) 150,000–22,000 kg/mm²

Poisson's ratio:[21] independent of temperature: 0.17

for a single crystal: 0.284

High-temperature tensile strength of tungsten single crystals (values probably represent optimum for pure tungsten)[22]

1500	1750	2000	2250	°C
10,700	8,250	5,800	3,400	psi

increase in strength, but above this temperature the tensile strength falls rapidly, and in the fully recrystallized condition the value is only one-tenth of that for the fibrous drawn wire. This behavior is an important consideration in the design of tungsten springs.

The very marked effect of mechanical and thermal history on the tensile strength of tungsten wire is illustrated in Fig. 9.4 after Goucher.[35] Drawn wire, curve (A), has the highest tensile strength; if the same wire is heated for one minute to 3000°K, long crystals are developed which occupy the full cross-section of the wire and cause a much lower tensile strength as shown by curve (B). Curve (C) for Pintsch single-crystal wire containing 2 per cent thoria indicates a tensile strength about three times that of pure tungsten crystals at low temperature. All three curves show a marked drop of tensile strength with increase in temperature.

For the study of the physical properties of tungsten, single-crystal wires are particularly suited.[35-42] Fonda[43] has made measurements on the hot tensile strength of several types of commercially produced tungsten wire as well as on Pintsch wire; these are reproduced in Figure 9.5. Type 218 wire, developed by the General Electric Company for gas-filled lamps, is

TABLE 9.3. CHEMICAL PROPERTIES OF TUNGSTEN

Electrochemical equivalent: 0.3178 mg/Coulomb
  (for valence 6)   3.147 Coulomb/mg

A) *Reactions with gases and vapors:*

    Air, oxygen, nitrogen, hydrogen, chlorine at room temperature: none

    Fluorine at room temperature: forms volatile fluoride

    Air above 400°C: onset of oxidation; slight tarnish at 300°C

    Air above 500°C: rapid oxidation

    Water vapor above 500°C: rapid oxidation

    Dry chlorine above 250°C: formation of hexachloride

    Nitrogen up to 2000°C: none; but there are three energy levels of absorption at temperatures up to 1700°C[23]

    Nitrogen absorbed in tungsten: formation of dinitride at 2300°C

    Carbon monoxide: formation of W_2C_4 at 1000°C

    Carbon dioxide: oxidation at 1200°C

    Hydrocarbon vapors: carbide formation above 1200°C (increase of emissivity; carbides decompose at 2430°C)

    Hydrogen: none; very low absorption below 1200°C

    Oxygen: formation of WO_3 at low pressure at 530°C

B) *Reaction with liquids and molten salts:*

    Mercury: none

    Water, hot or cold: none; at red heat, rapid oxidation ($WO_3 + W_2O_5$)

    HCl, H_2SO, HF, cold, dilute or conc.: practically none

    HCl, H_2SO_4, hot, dilute or conc.: slight attack

    HF, warm, dilute or conc.: none

    H_2SO_4, hot, conc.: formation of blue liquid, SO_2, and intermediate tungsten oxides[6]

    HNO_3, warm: very slight solubility and formation of WO_3

    HF + HNO_3 (4:1 by vol.) hot: rapid dissolution

    Aqua regia, warm: slight solubility and superficial oxidation

    Aqueous ammonia: none

    NH_4Cl, $NH_4(OH)$, $K(OH)$, $Na(OH)$: none in aqueous solutions

    Molten $K(OH)$ or Na_2CO_3 with access of air: slow oxidation

    Molten $K(OH)$ or Na_2CO_3 plus KNO_3 or KNO_2 or $KClO_3$ or PbO_2: rapid attack

C) *Reactions with solids:*

    Carbon and graphite: carbon absorption from 850°C to 1410°C
                           carbide formation from 1410 to 1600°C

    Alkaline earth carbonates: formation of $R_3WO_6 + CO + CO_2$ (in vacuo)[24]

    Strontium oxide: reduction from 375°C to 1275°C (in vacuo)[25]

    Magnesia: reduction above 1000°C[26]

    Zirconia: decomposition above 2300°C[27]

    Thoria: slight reduction above 2200°C[27]

    Molybdenum: sintering above 2000°C[27]

    Beryllia: unstable above 2000°C[27]

    Alumina: reduction above 2000°C[26]

D) *Cleaning solutions:*

    1. Boil in 20% $Na(OH)$ for 15 min.

    2. 5 pts. HNO_3 + 3 pts. H_2SO_4 + 2 pts. H_2O (by vol.) followed by rinse in chromic acid and water

TABLE 9.3.—*Continued*

3. 305 gm $K_3Fe(CN)_6$ + 44.5 $Na(OH)$ + 1000 ml. H_2O: very rapid attack suitable for removal of tungsten from assemblies containing stainless steel and copper; when immersed for 24 hrs. at 90°C, 25 mil.-dia. tungsten wire was thus removed. (E. R. L. Stanford University)
4. Molten $NaNO_2$–$NaNO_3$ at 340°C: rapid etching
5. Boiling solution of 5 p.c. solution of 27% H_2O_2 : slow etching
6. Electrolytic with tungsten as anode in 20% $Na(OH)$: rapid attack
7. Electrolytic with tungsten as anode in 250 gm $K(OH)$ + 0.25 gm $CuSO_4$ (or $CuCl_2$) + 1000 ml. H_2O: uniform etching
8. Removal of graphite coating from wires:[28, 29]
9. Electrolytic polishing: anodic in 0.1 N $Na(OH)$ at 0.045 a/sq. in.[30, 31]
10. Pointing tungsten wires electrolytically:[32, 33]

E) *Oxides of Tungsten:*
  WO_3—Tungsten trioxide—yellowish green; M.P. 1478°C; d = 7.16[34]
  W_2O_5—Tungsten hemipentoxide—blue (W_4O_{11})
  WO_2—Tungsten dioxide—brown; M.P. 1580°C; forms at 700°C; d = 12.11
  Vapor pressure of WO_2 + W :[34a]

1324	1375	1507	1593	1595	1603	1658	°K
0.565	3.04	78.51	151.85	177.69	259.84	979.64	microns

  Vapor pressure of WO_3 :[34a]

1314	1340	1388	1464	1503	1560	1581	°K
0.735	0.846	8.094	31.27	56.07	580.94	629.2	microns

TABLE 9.4. MECHANICAL PROPERTIES OF DRAWN TUNGSTEN WIRE*

Wire diam.		Tensile strength			Modulus of elasticity		Modulus of rigidity	
mm	Mils	Kg/mm²	Tons/in.²	Psi	Kg/mm²	Psi	Kg/mm²	Psi
Sintered bar		13	9.24	18,486				
5	197.5	40	28.44	56,880				
3	118.5	75	53.33	106,650				
2	79	100	71.10	142,200				
1	39.5	140	99.54	199,080			13,000	18,486,000
0.5	19.75	185	131.54	263,070			15,200	21,614,000
.3	11.85	220	156.42	312,840	9,000	12,798,000	16,000	22,752,000
.15	5.925	270	191.97	383,940	26,000	38,172,000	16,800	23,889,600
.10	3.95	300	213.10	426,200	31,500	44,793,000	17,200	24,458,400
.05	1.975	345	245.60	490,590	33,200	47,210,400	17,800	25,311,600
.03	1.185	385	273.74	547,470	34,000	48,348,000	18,400	26,164,800
.02	0.790	425	302.18	604,350				
.015	.5925	470	334.17	668,340				

* After Smithells.[5] (*Courtesy Chapman & Hall, Ltd., London.*)

a "non-sag," doped wire which permits the growth of long-grained crystals; this type of wire is now made by various suppliers and commonly used for heaters in receiving tubes and cathode ray tubes. Sodium oxide, potassium oxide, calcium chloride, aluminum oxide, and silicon oxide in amounts

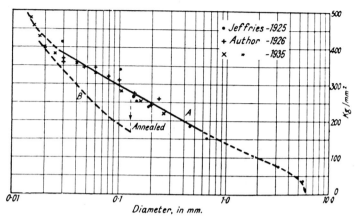

Figure 9.2. Tensile strength of tungsten wire; (A) Normal drawing; (B) Intermediate anneal at 0.13 mm. After Smithells.[5] (*Courtesy Chapman & Hall, Ltd., London.*)

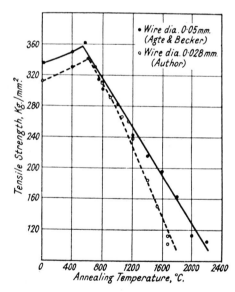

Figure 9.3. Effect of annealing on the tensile strength of pure tungsten wire. After Smithells, Agte, and Becker.[5] (*Courtesy Chapman & Hall, Ltd., London.*)

totaling about 1 per cent are added to the tungsten powder, and the mixture is sintered in the usual way. "E" wire contains 1.5 per cent of thoria and has a fine-grain structure. The Pintsch wire used in this experiment also contained 2 per cent of thoria.

The successful growth of tungsten single crystals is extremely sensitive to the presence of just the right amount of impurities, and most of the

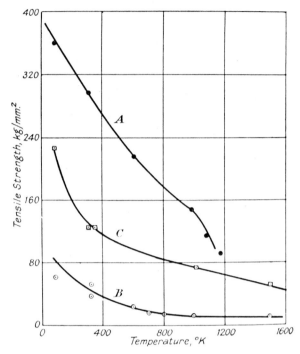

Figure 9.4. Tensile strength *vs* temperature for (A) Drawn tungsten wire; (B) Drawn tungsten wire recrystallized; (C) Pintsch single crystal wire. After Smithells.[5] (*Courtesy Chapman & Hall, Ltd., London.*)

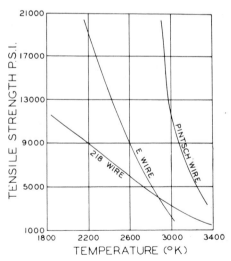

Figure 9.5. Hot tensile strength of tungsten filaments. After Fonda.[43] (*Courtesy General Electric Company.*)

single-crystal wires have been grown from type-218 wire. Gifford and Coomes[30] have demonstrated that single crystals can be grown much more successfully, and with wires from any source, if a torsion strain is first imposed on the filaments before they are heated to a temperature of about 2000°K for a number of hours, or subjected to a temperature discontinuity which is moved along the length of the wire at a fixed rate. Wires ranging in diameter from 3 to 10 mils, and being 19 inches long, were given twists up to 20 turns per inch, and this treatment resulted in single crystals well over 2 inches long. These results could be produced either with tungsten or molybdenum wire. An interesting result of this treatment is the presence of a screw pattern on the wire which cannot be removed by etching or polishing and corresponds to the number of twists imposed on the wire before its thermal treatment; the spiral can be made visible on a surrounding luminescent screen owing to the unusually high electron emission which originates at the "screw" dislocation.

The tensile and creep properties of bulk tungsten, machined into standard test bars from sintered rod, were recently investigated by Pugh.[44] Figure 9.6 gives true stress vs true plastic strain (flow curves) for tungsten recrystallized at 2900°F (1594°C) for one hour. The ultimate tensile strength vs temperature is plotted in Figure 9.7, where values obtained by Bechtold

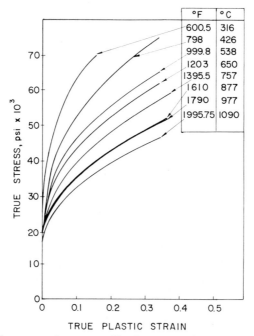

°F	°C
600.5	316
798	426
999.8	538
1203	650
1395.5	757
1610	877
1790	977
1995.75	1090

Figure 9.6. Flow curves for recrystallized tungsten. After Pugh.[44] (*Courtesy American Society For Testing Materials.*)

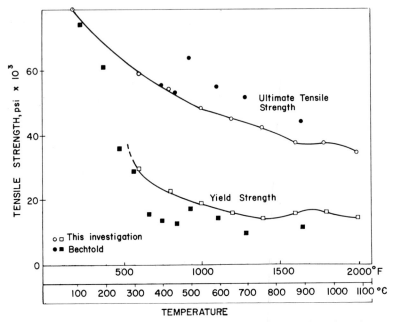

Figure 9.7. Ultimate tensile strength and yield strength as a function of temperature for recrystallized tungsten. After Pugh.[44] (*Courtesy American Society For Testing Materials.*)

in an earlier investigation are also indicated. The corresponding curve for unrecrystallized tungsten, annealed one hour at 1000°C and having the fibrous structure of drawn wire, is presented in Figure 9.8. Figure 9.9 permits comparison of the different values for elongation as a function of temperature obtained for recrystallized and unrecrystallized tungsten (treated at the temperatures stated above). Figure 9.10 gives curves for the temperature dependence of the ultimate tensile strength of tungsten, molybdenum, and chromium, where temperature is expressed as percentage of the respective melting point of the metal under test; test conditions were identical in all three cases. Observe that the contribution to strength caused by the fibrous (cold-worked) structure is considerable for both tungsten and molybdenum, but more significant for tungsten at the lower temperatures. The comparison is obscured at higher temperatures by the strain-aging effect in both metals. In the recrystallized condition, the three metals compare quite favorably on the homologous temperature scale. All the short-time tensile properties evaluated by Pugh are summarized in Table 9.5.

Table 9.6 gives a number of properties of tungsten which depend solely on temperature, and Fig. 9.11 shows the trend of emissivities of tungsten

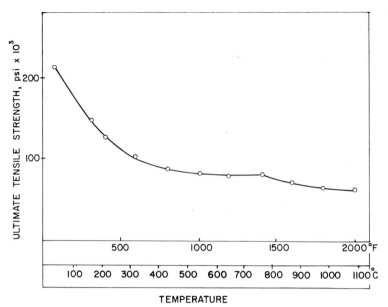

Figure 9.8. Ultimate tensile strength as a function of temperature for unrecrystallized tungsten. After Pugh.[44] (*Courtesy American Society For Testing Materials.*)

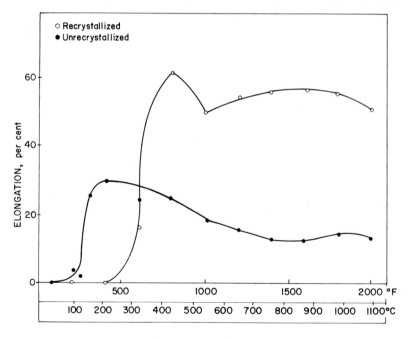

Figure 9.9. Elongation as a function of temperature for recrystallized and unrecrystallized tungsten. After Pugh.[44] (*Courtesy American Society For Testing Materials.*)

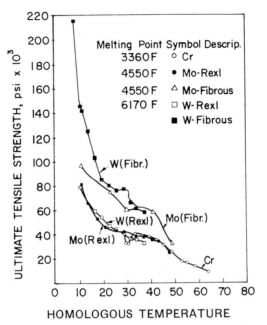

Figure 9.10. A comparison of strength for chromium, molybdenum, and tungsten. Homologous temperature is testing temperature in per cent of the melting point. After Pugh.[44] (*Courtesy American Society For Testing Materials.*)

vs temperature, as listed in Table 9.6. More recent measurements have been published by Larrabee.[16]

Tungsten and Oxygen

The principal oxides of tungsten are listed in Table 9.3; the reactions which take place when these oxides are reduced in hydrogen are indicated in Table 9.7, according to Smithells.[5] The lowest temperature at which complete reduction of the oxides is practical is thus 700°C. The oxidation of tungsten has most recently been investigated by Webb, Norton, and Wagner[46] who find the following behavior:

"Two oxide layers form during the oxidation of tungsten between 700°C and 1000°C. The outer layer is porous, powdery, yellow tungstic oxide, WO_3, and the inner layer is a dense, thin, dark-blue, tightly adherent oxide of uncertain composition. The oxidation reaction follows initially the parabolic rate law, but eventually there is a transition to the linear rate law. The rate of formation of the inner oxide is presumably inversely proportional to its thickness. The inner oxide seems to transform to the outer oxide at a constant rate. Upon combining the rate laws of the two individual processes, an overall rate equation covering the whole range is

TABLE 9.5. TENSION TEST PARAMETERS FOR TUNGSTEN*

Treatment	Temperature, deg. Fahr.	Yield strength 0.02 offset, per cent	Ultimate tensile strength, psi	Elongation, per cent	Strain hardening coefficient, m	Strain rate sensitivity exponent, n	Slope of σ — ϵ curve at $\epsilon = 0.1$ psi
Annealed 1 hr at 2900 F	202		79 600				
	600	28 800	59 700	16.4	0.244		157 000
	798	22 000	54 100	62.4	0.299	0.0104	160 000
	1000	17 900	47 200	51.0	0.288	0.0061	164 000
	1203	15 200	44 500	55.3	0.292	0.0065	127 000
	1395	13 000	41 200	57.1	0.308	0.0053	129 000
	1610	14 500	36 600	57.9	0.327	0.0072	116 000
	1790	14 400	36 500	56.8	0.304	0.0066	111 000
	1995	12 900	33 500	52.0	0.306	0.0038	81 000
Annealed 1 hr at 1830 F	80		215 000	0.2			
	206		145 000	3.3			
	309		146 000	26.4			
	405		125 400	30.0			
	599		103 000	24.5			
	798		85 100	24.5			
	1007		80 800	18.2			
	1195		76 579	16.0			
	1408		77 900	13.6			
	1600		66 200	13.5			
	1803		61 500	15.5			
	2000		58 969	14.5			

* After Pugh.[44]

obtained. The thickness of the inner layer tends to a limiting value when the rate of its formation is equal to the rate of transformation to the outer layer."

Reference to earlier work on the oxidation of tungsten may be found in this article. Tungsten oxides do not volatilize to any significant extent in a dry atmosphere of oxygen up to 1000°C and in a good vacuum only above 800°C, according to Gulbransen and Wysong.[47] The controlled oxidation of tungsten is of considerable importance in electron tube technology. High electron emission has been observed from barium films adsorbed on oxygenated tungsten, and this phenomenon has a bearing on the mechanism of operation of impregnated tungsten matrix cathodes (See Chapter 15). Tungsten-to-glass seals rely on the presence of a well-adhering oxide layer (See Chapter 13). Conversely, the electron emission from clean tungsten is adversely affected by the presence of very small amounts of oxygen.[48-50]

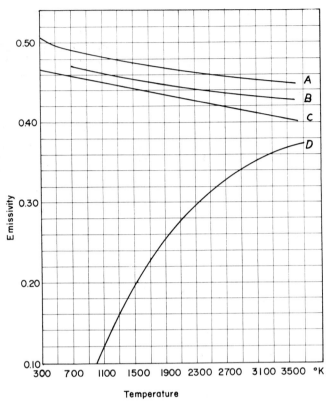

Figure 9.11. Emissivities of tungsten. A, Normal spectral emissivity for λ = 0.467 microns; C, Normal spectral emissivity for λ = 0.665 micron; B, Average normal luminous emissivity; D, Total emissivity. After Smithells.[5] (*Courtesy Chapman & Hall, Ltd., London.*)

The Applications of Tungsten

Electron Emission from Pure Tungsten. When heated to a temperature of 2300°K or more, tungsten is a copious emitter of electrons and does not require any activation other than outgassing by a preliminary flashing at temperatures of the order of 2600°K for about thirty minutes to prevent gas evolution at still higher temperatures if these should be encountered in operation.[51] In order to ensure an adequate life of the emitter, the diameter of the filament must be of adequate size, and the operating temperature must be kept at a reasonable value. As the power required to heat the filament to the necessary temperature increases with the increase of the filament diameter, one might be tempted to keep the diameter as low as possible. As the endpoint of life owing to burn-out is reached when the diameter of the filament has been reduced by 6 per cent, a careful balance must be arrived at between power consumption, filament diameter, and operating temperature.

It has been customary for many years to refer the endpoint of life of a tungsten filament to the reduction in diameter by evaporation when this quantity reaches 10 per cent of the original diameter. In order to determine the number of hours required to bring about this reduction in diameter, accurate data on the rate of evaporation of tungsten at a given temperature must be available. Unfortunately, published values show a wide scatter as evident from Table 9.8, taken from a recent paper by Bloomer[52], who studied this long-standing controversy and resolved it by careful analysis of the early literature data. The evaporation rates published by Jones and Langmuir[53] should not be used as a basis for calculation of filament lives, because these figures are in error for reasons explained by Bloomer. The figures given by these same authors for currents and voltages at various temperatures are satisfactory. Reimann's[54] figures for evaporation rates of tungsten are found in agreement with life test data when the end-of-life point is defined by a 6-percent reduction of the filament diameter. Zwicker's[55] data give different values.

Table 9.9 gives the specific characteristics of an ideal tungsten filament, 1 cm long and 1 cm in diameter, according to Jones and Langmuir, corrected to agree with the 1927 temperature scale.[5] In order to obtain the values of resistance, voltage, current, or power, for filaments of given diameters other than 1 cm, and different lengths, it is only necessary to set up the dimensional equations with the aid of factors given in the second line at the top of Table 9.9. To give an example, one finds that it takes 1526 amperes to heat a 1 cm-dia. wire to 2500°K, if end-cooling is neglected. From the relation $(A/d)^{3/2} = 1526$, one obtains the value $A = 42.2$ amperes for a 0.040-in.-dia. wire. In a similar manner, all other transformations can be performed.* Figure 9.12 gives the data of Table 9.9 in graphical representation according to Spangenberg.[56] In practical designs of tungsten emitters, such as are used in power tubes, it is necessary to apply corrections to the values obtained from Table 9.9 in order to take account of thermal losses occurring at the leads, and, conversely, to allow for back-heating of the filament which may occur owing to reflected radiation from surrounding structures.[57-66]

Another important consideration in the design of tungsten filaments, particularly those which carry a heavy current, is the presence of magnetic forces caused by the passage of these currents. Electrostatic forces acting on the filaments in the presence of high voltages also tend to distort the filaments and must be guarded against.[67, 68] The fact that the filament

---

* It must be borne in mind, however, that emission densities, rates of evaporation, and other surface effects are given for pi cm² in the Jones and Langmuir table.

TABLE 9.6.—PROPERTIES OF TUNGSTEN.*

Temperature. Degr. K. T.	(1) Colour temperature. Degr. K. T_c.	(2) Brightness temperature. $S_{0.665\mu}$.	(3) Radiation temperature. T_R.	(4) Spectral emissivity. $e_{0.665\mu}$.	(5) Spectral emissivity. $e_{0.467\mu}$.	(6) Average luminous emissivity. e_v.	(7) Colour emissivity. e_c.	(8) Total emissivity. e_t.	(9) Normal brightness. Candles per cm.²	(10) Total radiation intensity. Watts per cm.²	(11) Luminous efficiency lumens per watt.	(12) Rate of evaporation gm./cm.²/sec. m.	(13) Vapour pressure, baryes.	(14) Atomic heat. cals. per gm. atom/degree C_p.	(15) Relative lengths at different temperatures.	(16) Resistivity. Microhm. cm. ρ.
300	—	—	—	0.470	0.505	—	—	0.024	—	0.00110	—	—	—	6.03	1.0000	5.65
400	—	—	—	0.468	0.501	—	—	0.034	—	0.00495	—	—	—	6.05	1.0005	8.00
500	—	—	—	0.466	0.498	—	—	0.042	—	0.015	—	—	—	6.09	1.0010	10.48
600	—	—	—	0.464	0.495	—	—	0.052	—	0.0385	—	—	—	6.14	1.0014	13.07
700	—	—	—	0.462	0.492	—	—	0.062	—	0.0850	—	—	—	6.20	1.0018	15.75
800	—	—	—	0.460	0.490	—	—	0.074	—	0.173	—	—	—	6.24	1.0023	18.51
900	—	—	—	0.458	0.488	—	—	0.089	—	0.333	—	—	—	6.30	1.0028	21.35
1000	1006	966	581	0.456	0.486	0.464	0.396	0.105	0.000126	0.600	0.000693	—	—	6.36	1.0032	24.26
1100	1108	1058	659	0.454	0.484	0.463	0.393	0.121	0.00107	1.01	0.00344	—	—	6.43	1.0036	27.23
1200	1210	1149	738	0.452	0.482	0.462	0.391	0.138	0.00631	1.63	0.0126	—	—	6.52	1.0041	30.26
1300	1312	1240	819	0.450	0.480	0.460	0.388	0.156	0.0276	2.54	0.0355	—	—	6.67	1.0046	33.29
1400	1414	1330	905	0.448	0.478	0.459	0.386	0.174	0.0104	3.82	0.0899	—	—	6.80	1.0052	36.37
1500	1517	1420	991	0.445	0.476	0.457	0.383	0.192	0.333	5.54	0.199	—	—	6.95	1.0057	39.50
1600	1619	1509	1080	0.443	0.475	0.456	0.381	0.207	0.94	7.74	0.395	—	—	7.10	1.0063	42.67
1700	1722	1597	1167	0.441	0.473	0.455	0.378	0.222	2.30	10.58	0.724	—	—	7.25	1.0069	45.88
1800	1825	1684	1254	0.439	0.472	0.454	0.376	0.236	5.15	14.15	1.19	—	—	7.40	1.0075	49.12
1900	1929	1771	1342	0.437	0.470	0.453	0.373	0.248	10.40	18.45	1.94	—	—	7.55	1.0081	52.40
2000	2033	1857	1428	0.435	0.469	0.452	0.370	0.259	20.00	23.65	2.84	1.75×10^{-12}	1.32×10^{-8}	7.70	1.0088	55.71
2100	2137	1943	1514	0.433	0.467	0.450	0.367	0.269	35.9	29.85	4.08	1.58×10^{-12}	1.22×10^{-7}	7.85	1.0094	59.05
2200	2242	2026	1601	0.431	0.466	0.449	0.364	0.278	61.0	37.2	5.52	1.25×10^{-11}	9.89×10^{-7}	8.00	1.0101	62.42
2300	2347	2109	1688	0.429	0.464	0.448	0.362	0.286	100.1	45.7	7.24	7.82×10^{-11}	6.32×10^{-6}	8.15	1.0108	65.82

2400	2452	2192	1775	0.427	0.463	0.447	0.359	0.294	156.0	55.7	9.39	4.36×10^{-10}	3.52×10^{-5}	8.30	1.0116	69.25
2500	2557	2274	1859	0.425	0.462	0.446	0.356	0.301	234.0	67.2	11.72	2.03×10^{-9}	1.71×10^{-4}	8.45	1.0124	72.71
2600	2663	2356	1945	0.423	0.460	0.444	0.353	0.309	345	80.6	14.34	8.79×10^{-9}	7.57×10^{-4}	8.60	1.0132	76.20
2700	2770	2437	2031	0.421	0.459	0.443	0.350	0.315	495	95.6	17.60	3.17×10^{-8}	2.77×10^{-3}	8.75	1.0140	79.71
2800	2878	2516	2116	0.419	0.458	0.442	0.347	0.321	690	112.5	20.53	1.12×10^{-7}	9.99×10^{-3}	8.90	1.0149*	83.25
2900	2986	2595	2202	0.417	0.456	0.441	0.345	0.329	950	132.5	23.64	3.45×10^{-7}	3.18×10^{-2}	9.05	1.016*	86.81
3000	3094	2673	2286	0.415	0.455	0.440	0.343	0.334	1270	154.5	27.25	9.69×10^{-7}	9.09×10^{-2}	9.20	1.017*	90.40
3100	3202	2750	2371	0.413	0.454	0.438	0.341	0.337	1640	177.5	30.95	2.66×10^{-6}	2.51×10^{-1}	9.35	1.018*	93.9
3200	3311†	2827	2455†	0.411	0.452	0.437	0.338†	0.341†	2105	203	34.70	6.67×10^{-6}	8.06×10^{-1}	9.50	1.019*	97.4
3300	3422†	2903	2538†	0.409	0.451	0.436	0.335†	0.344†	2685	232	38.90	1.60×10^{-5}	1.55	9.65	1.020*	101.1
3400	3533†	2978	2621†	0.407†	0.450†	0.435†	0.332†	0.348†	3370	264†	43.20	3.55×10^{-5}	3.49	9.80	1.021*	104.9
3500	3646†	3053	2704†	0.405†	0.449†	0.434†	0.329†	0.351†	4220	300†	47.15	7.57×10^{-5}	7.55	9.95	1.023*	108.5
3655‡	3817†	3165	—	0.402†	0.447†	0.433†	0.324†	0.354†	5740	360†	53.10	2.28×10^{-4}	23.3	10.18	—	114.2*

* After Smithells.[5]
† These values are extrapolated.
‡ Melting-point.

TABLE 9.7. STAGES IN THE REDUCTION OF TUNGSTIC OXIDE[5]

Temperature, °C	Appearance	Approximate Composition
400	Green-blue	$WO_3 + W_4O_{11}$
500	Intense blue	$WO_3 + W_4O_{11}$
550	Violet	W_4O_{11}
575	Purple-brown	$W_4O_{11} + WO_2$
600	Chocolate-brown	WO_2
650	Brown-black	$WO_2 + W$
700	Gray-black	W
800	Gray	W
900	Metallic gray	W
1000	Coarse metallic	W

TABLE 9.8. A SELECTION OF PUBLISHED EVAPORATION RATES FOR TUNGSTEN AT VERY HIGH TEMPERATURES $(GM/CM^2/SEC)$[52]

Temp. °K	Zwicker[55]	Jones and Langmuir*[53]	Wahlin and Whitney[45]	Reimann[54]
2800	8.33×10^{-8}	1.12×10^{-7}	5.9×10^{-8}	7.20×10^{-8}
2900	3.09×10^{-7}	3.45×10^{-7}	2.0×10^{-7}	2.36×10^{-7}
3000	1.05×10^{-6}	9.69×10^{-7}	6.4×10^{-7}	7.15×10^{-7}

* The values in this column have been obtained by dividing the Jones and Langmuir figures by pi.

increases in length on heating must be allowed for. Adding up these many requirements for a reliable filamentary emitter poses a problem of no small magnitude to the tube engineer.

Pure tungsten emitters can be operated near current saturation, but it is customary to allow a reserve of about 10 per cent so that the filaments are designed for a peak emission of about 110 per cent of that required in service.

The many possible geometrical arrangements for filamentary cathodes must naturally be adapted to the requirements of a specific design; they vary from spring-loaded single hair-like filaments used in battery-operated receiving tubes to spring-loaded, V-shaped hair-pins, W-shaped structures, single, or double-helical filaments, catenary designs,[69, 70] freely supported squirrel cage structures, or filament baskets of various designs.[71-73]

Figure 9.13 illustrates a variety of such cathode structures. Self-supporting structures are generally preferred in large power tubes because the introduction of springs or spring-activated supports invariably leads to complications that result in premature failures.[74, 75]

Figure 9.14 is a graph of percentage of normal life and electron emission vs operating temperature of the filament. The intersection of the two curves corresponds to the rated filament voltage which is indicated as 100 per cent, and the corresponding life of the filament also is indicated as 100 per cent. It is evident that a 5-percent increase in filament voltage, which

TABLE 9.9. SPECIFIC CHARACTERISTICS OF IDEAL TUNGSTEN FILAMENTS*
(For a wire 1 cm in length and 1 cm in diameter)

T, °K	W', $\dfrac{W}{ld}$ watts per cm²	$\dfrac{R' \times 10^6}{\dfrac{Rd^2}{l} \times 10^6}$, ohm. cm	A', $\dfrac{A}{d^{3/2}}$, amps per cm³/²	$V' \times 10^3$, $\dfrac{V\sqrt{d}}{l} \times 10^3$, volts per cm¹/²	I', $\dfrac{I}{ld}$, amp per π cm²	M, $\dfrac{M}{ld}$, g per π cm² per sec, evaporation	$\dfrac{R'_T}{R'_{293}°}$, $\dfrac{R_T}{R_{293}°}$
273	....	6.37	....		....	....	0.911
293	0.0	6.99	0.0	0.0	....	....	1.00
300	0.000100	7.20	3.727	0.02683	....	....	1.03
400	0.00624	10.26	24.67	0.2530	....	....	1.467
500	0.0305	13.45	47.62	0.6404	....	....	1.924
600	0.0954	16.85	75.25	1.268	....	....	2.41
700	0.240	20.49	108.2	2.218	....	....	4.93
800	0.530	24.19	148.0	3.581	....	....	3.46
900	1.041	27.94	193.1	5.393	....	....	4.00
1,000	1.891	31.74	244.1	7.749	3.36×10^{-15}	1.16×10^{-33}	4.54
1,100	3.223	35.58	301.0	10.71	4.77×10^{-13}	6.81×10^{-30}	5.08
1,200	5.210	39.46	363.4	14.34	3.06×10^{-11}	1.01×10^{-26}	5.65
1,300	8.060	43.40	430.9	18.70	1.01×10^{-9}	4.22×10^{-24}	6.22
1,400	12.01	47.37	503.5	23.85	2.08×10^{-8}	7.88×10^{-22}	6.78
1,500	17.33	51.40	580.6	29.85	2.87×10^{-7}	7.42×10^{-20}	7.36
1,600	24.32	55.46	662.2	36.73	2.91×10^{-6}	3.92×10^{-18}	7.93
1,700	33.28	59.58	747.3	44.52	2.22×10^{-5}	1.31×10^{-16}	8.52
1,800	44.54	63.74	836.0	53.28	1.40×10^{-4}	2.97×10^{-15}	9.12
1,900	58.45	67.94	927.4	63.02	7.15×10^{-4}	4.62×10^{-14}	9.72
2,000	75.37	72.19	1,022	73.75	3.15×10^{-3}	5.51×10^{-13}	10.33
2,100	95.69	76.49	1,119	85.57	1.23×10^{-2}	4.95×10^{-12}	10.93
2,200	119.8	80.83	1,217	98.40	4.17×10^{-2}	3.92×10^{-11}	11.57
2,300	148.2	85.22	1,319	112.4	1.28×10^{-1}	2.45×10^{-10}	12.19
2,400	181.2	89.65	1,422	127.5	0.364	1.37×10^{-9}	12.83
2,500	219.3	94.13	1,526	143.6	0.935	6.36×10^{-9}	13.47
2,600	263.0	98.66	1,632	161.1	2.25	2.76×10^{-8}	14.12
2,700	312.7	103.22	1,741	179.7	5.12	9.95×10^{-7}	14.76
2,800	368.9	107.85	1,849	199.5	11.11	3.51×10^{-7}	15.43
2,900	432.4	112.51	1,961	220.6	22.95	1.08×10^{-6}	16.10
3,000	503.5	117.21	2,072	243.0	44.40	3.04×10^{-6}	16.77
3,100	583.0	121.95	2,187	266.7	83.0	8.35×10^{-6}	17.46
3,200	671.5	126.76	2,301	291.7	150.2	2.09×10^{-5}	18.15
3,300	769.7	131.60	2,418	318.3	265.2	5.02×10^{-5}	18.83
3,400	878.3	136.49	2,537	346.2	446.0	1.12×10^{-4}	19.53
3,500	998.0	141.42	2,657	375.7	732.0	2.38×10^{-4}	20.24
3,600	1,130	146.40	2,777	406.7	1,173	4.86×10^{-4}	20.95
3,655	1,202	149.15	2,838	423.4	1,505	7.15×10^{-4}	21.34

* After Jones and Langmuir.[53] Emission density I' and evaporation rate M' are given for an area of π cm².

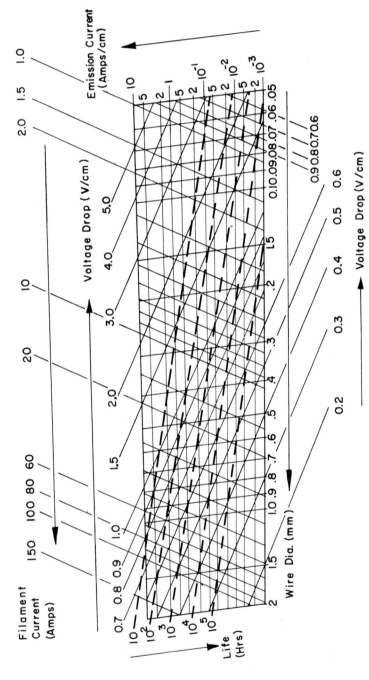

Figure 9.12. Characteristics of ideal tungsten filaments, one centimeter long, according to data by Jones and Langmuir.[53] Adapted from curves given by Spangenberg,[56] but dashed lines for filament life were recalculated on the basis of recent findings by Bloomer[52] according to which end-of-life point occurs after six percent reduction of filament diameter by evaporation. Data by Reimann[54] were used for rates of evaporation.

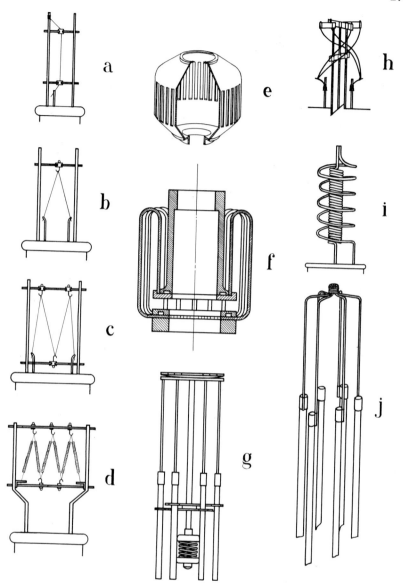

Figure 9.13. Representative types of filamentary cathodes.

roughly corresponds to a temperature rise of 40°C, will reduce the life expectancy by almost one-half, and a 10-percent voltage increase will cut the filament life by a factor of 4.[76] In order to preserve the life of power tubes when equipment is in a stand-by condition, the National Electrical Manufacturers Association (NEMA) and the Joint Electron Devices

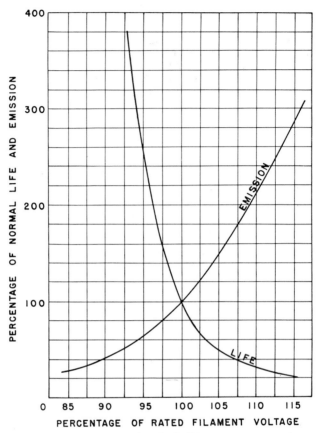

Figure 9.14. Electron emission and cathode life vs temperature for tungsten filaments. After Frankel.[76] (*Courtesy Machlett Laboratories, Inc.*)

Engineering Council (JEDEC)* have prepared recommendations giving the amount by which the operating filament voltage should be reduced during stand-by conditions for various types of filamentary cathodes, and the voltage reduction to be applied for various periods of stand-by condition.

Thoriated Filaments.[77] Thoriated filaments are prepared by adding from 0.5 to 2.0% thoria to the tungsten. Usually, the addition is made in the form of a water-soluble thorium compound to a slurry of tungstic acid in water. In this manner, intimate mixture of the constituent compounds is accomplished. The dried, thoria-doped WO_3 is then reduced to metal in hydrogen. The method generally adopted is to begin this reduction at

* Formerly JETEC.

about 550°C and complete it in the range of 780–1100°C, according to the particle size required[2] (see Table 9.7). Thoria is not reduced at these temperatures and is uniformly distributed throughout the tungsten powder; during the subsequent sintering treatment at substantially higher temperatures, described previously, thoria still remains distributed throughout the tungsten bar from which thoriated filaments are produced by swaging and drawing.

By "flashing" such filaments *in vacuo* to a temperature variously given as high as 2500°K for a period of from 30 to 60 seconds, some of the thoria is reduced to metallic thorium. As the melting point of thorium is 2118°K, any thorium on the surface of the filament is thus evaporated. By reducing the filament temperature to near 2100°K for a period of about thirty minutes, metallic thorium formed in the interior of the filament is given a chance to diffuse to the surface and there form a monatomic film. The filament may then be operated in service at a temperature ranging from 1800 to 2200°K, depending on the particular application, and an emission yield of approximately 3 a/cm² can be obtained.

A most significant contribution to the understanding of the activation of thoriated tungsten filaments has recently been published by Schneider.[78] By developing methods for the quantitative chemical analysis of the constituents of thoriated tungsten, both uncarbonized and carbonized (see below), the thermal emission obtained from such filaments could be correlated with the methods used in their preparation and the chemical composition resulting from it. Many of the trial-and-error methods practiced in the past have thus become unnecessary. Tests were performed on 0.60-mm-dia. filaments, 25 cm long, which had a combined (ThO_2 + Th) content by weight equal to 2.09 per cent in the as-received condition. Filaments were flashed at a fixed temperature for a given time and then chemically analyzed; with the aid of several groups of filaments, each mounted separately in a vacuum tube, the temperature range of 1700 to 2900°K was covered. Figure 9.15 gives Schneider's results, which he describes as follows:

"Curve I gives the measured thoria remaining in each filament of one group after 5 min. at the temperature indicated by the abscissa. Curve IV gives the measured amounts of thorium metal in each filament. Curve II gives the calculated total amounts of thorium metal produced in each filament by reduction; each ordinate of this curve is 2.09 % by weight (the original total content of thoria plus thorium) minus the proper ordinate of Curve I. The difference between Curves II and IV represents thorium metal which evaporated. Comparison of Curves I, II, and IV shows that treatment for 5 min. below about 2150°K produces thorium metal without causing appreciable evaporation.

"Curves III and V give the measured thorium metal content of filaments

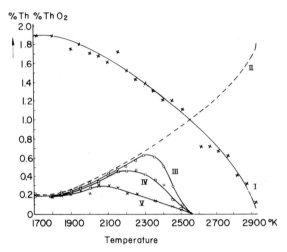

Figure 9.15. Reduction of ThO_2 to Th in uncarbonized samples as a function of duration and temperature of heating. Curve I. Measured weight percent of ThO_2 retained. Curve II. Amount of Th formed. This was calculated by subtracting the ordinate of Curve I from 2.09%. Curve III. Measured content of Th metal after 1 min of heating. Curve IV. Measured content of Th metal after 5 min of heating. Curve V. Measured content of Th metal after 10 min of heating. After Schneider.[78] (*Courtesy The American Institute of Physics.*)

treated for 1 min. or 10 min., respectively. The thoria content was measured but is not shown because it was substantially the same as shown by Curve I for the filaments treated for 5 min. These results suggest that above about 2000°K, all the thoria which *can* be reduced, is reduced in less than 1 min. and that additional treatment tends to evaporate the available thorium metal. Smithells has also found that tungsten will not reduce all thoria to thorium even at 2800°K for 24 hr. His analyses, which seemed qualitative, led him to suggest the formation of thorium-tungsten bronzes of the form $Th(WO_3)_n$ with $n = 3$ to 10, approximately. However, we did not observe any bronzes.

"Emission measurements indicate the behavior of thorium on the tungsten surface. Figure 9.16 shows results of a typical test. The filament was first operated at 1800°K for 10 min. and emission measured at 1-min. intervals. Emission increased almost exponentially during this 10-min. period. Increasing the temperature to 1900°K, and measuring the emission again at 1-min. intervals, causes the specific emission to decrease with time. Increasing the temperature to 2100, 2300, and 2500°K, each for a similar 10-min. interval, decreases the emission permanently. This decrease is more rapid at high temperatures. If it is assumed that emission in these systems is a function only of the total amount of thorium metal on the filament

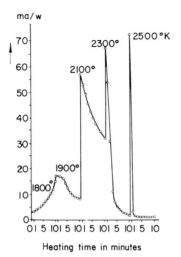

Figure 9.16. Emission efficiency of uncarbonized filament as function of heating temperature and time. After Schneider.[78] (*Courtesy The American Institute of Physics.*)

surface, we conclude that, above about 1800°K, thorium diffuses rapidly to the surface and that, above about 1900°K, the evaporation is more rapid than diffusion.

"Study of both Figures 9.15 and 9.16 suggests that the irreversible loss of emission on heating above 2000°K represents depletion of the thorium metal, and that good practice in handling commercial uncarbonized filaments requires heat activation for less than 1 min. at temperatures below about 2250°K, with subsequent operation at about 1800°K to conserve the available thorium metal. This conclusion is justified by the evidence in Fig. 9.15 that all of the thoria reducible by a filament is reduced in not over 1 min."

Plain thoriated filaments are sensitive to poisoning by oxygen and sputtering by gaseous ions which will remove the thorium from the surface of the filament and thus revert its properties to those of pure tungsten. These difficulties are alleviated by carburizing* the thoriated filaments.

Carburized thoriated tungsten filaments[79-88] are produced from plain thoriated tungsten filaments but subjecting the formed and mounted filaments to a heat treatment in a hydrocarbon atmosphere consisting of benzene, acetylene, naphthalene, or xylene vapors which are usually carried to the treating chambers by a stream of hydrogen under controlled flow conditions. When heating a filament in this atmosphere to a temperature as high as 2500°K, the hydrocarbon is decomposed at the hot filament surface to

---

* The term "carbonizing" is also used in the literature but is not strictly correct because elemental carbon is fed into the filament from an external source.

form tungsten carbide, W_2C, which diffuses into the tungsten. The details of the process will vary from case to case as a compromise has to be made between the creation of a relatively thick carbide shell on the filament, which is desirable, and the embrittlement of the filament which results from this treatment. Figure 9.17 shows a photograph of the cross-section of a carburized, thoriated tungsten filament and also some curves indicating what life may be expected for different percentages of carburization as a function of wire diameter. In practice, the percentage of the wire cross-section which is transformed into carbide ranges from 15 to 50 per cent of the total cross-sectional area; great care has to be taken in processing to avoid longitudinal and radial cracks in the carbide shell.

Schneider[78] also studied carbonized thoriated filaments by chemical analysis after various periods of flashing in a benzene-hydrogen atmosphere of different concentrations and correlated the measured composition with the observed electron emission.

"Figure 9.18 shows the reduction of thoria in carbonized filaments as a function of temperature. Comparison of Figures 9.15 and 9.18 show that reduction of thoria is complete at 2600°K in carbonized thoria compared to 2900°K in uncarbonized; again the heating time is relatively unimportant. Very little reduction of thoria occurs below about 2300°K, probably because very little thorium evaporates below 2300°K, as suggested by Figure 9.19. Every sample of Figures 9.18 and 9.19 was carbonized for 2 min. at 1900°K using a constant flow of 0.42 g of benzene in 10 l of hydrogen.

"Six filaments were then carbonized at different temperatures but for constant time (2 min), with emission shown in Fig. 9.20. Note that the emission, always measured at 1930°K, increases significantly for carbonizing temperatures of 2100°K to 2200°K but decreases seriously when carbonizing temperature reaches 2400°K.

"Curve I of Figure 9.21 shows the percentage change of resistance for these 6 filaments, as a function of carbonizing temperature, and Curve II gives the weight-percent of elemental carbon. Note that above 2300°K, very little change in resistance occurs, but that the content of elemental carbon increases rapidly. Up to 2200°K, the specific resistance increases in proportion to the amount of carbon present. The emission also reaches its maximum at about 2200°K, as Fig. 9.20 shows. Apparently a chemical change occurs for carbonizing temperatures above about 2200°K, and impairs emission. This undesirable chemical change occurs at lower temperatures for either a lengthier carbonizing period, or for higher benzene content in the hydrogen.

"Figure 9.22 gives analytical results for this group of filaments all carbonized for 2 min. with a benzene content of 0.42 g per 10 l of hydrogen. This shows that:

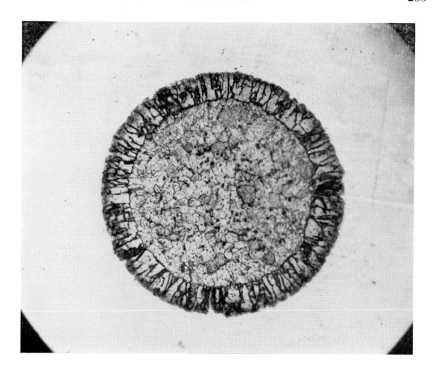

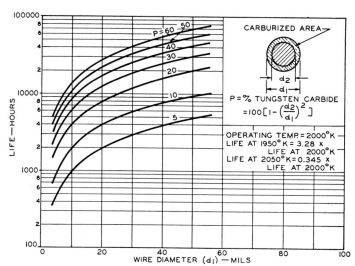

Figure 9.17. Cross-section of a carburized thoriated tungsten filament and curve showing life for different thicknesses of carbide shell. After Ayer.[85] (*Courtesy American Institute of Electrical Engineers.*)

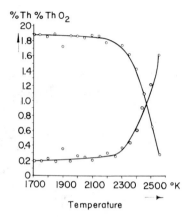

Figure 9.18. Reduction of ThO_2 to metallic Th in carbonized thoriated tungsten filaments as a function of temperature. Heating time = 2 min. Curve I. Measured percent by weight of ThO_2 remaining. Curve II. Amount of Th produced, calculated by subtracting ordinate of Curve I from 2.09% by weight. After Schneider.[78] (*Courtesy The American Institute of Physics.*)

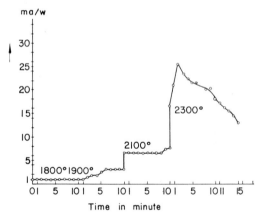

Figure 9.19. Emission efficiency of a typical carbonized filament as a function of heating temperature and heating time. After Schneider.[78] (*Courtesy The American Institute of Physics.*)

"(a) W_2C content increases up to 2200°K and then decreases rapidly.

"(b) W content decreases with increasing temperature and disappears above 2200°K.

"(c) ThO_2 behaves similarly.

"(d) Th content increases with temperature at least up to 2400°K.

"(e) WC, ThC_2, and C are first observed at 2200°K and their content increases with temperature, at least up to 2400°K.

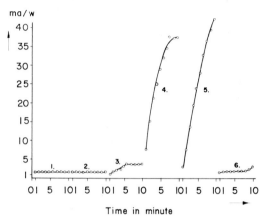

Figure 9.20. Emission efficiency of 6 carbonized filaments as a function of testing time. Filament No. 1, carbonized at 1600°K; filament No. 2, carbonized at 1800°K; filament No. 3, carbonized at 1900°K; filament No. 4, carbonized at 2100°K; filament No. 5, carbonized at 2200°K; filament No. 6, carbonized at 2400°K. After Schneider.[78] (*Courtesy The American Institute of Physics.*)

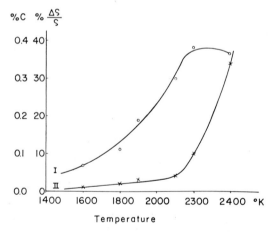

Figure 9.21. Curve I: percentage increase of specific resistance as a function of carbonizing temperature. Curve II: Corresponding content of elemental carbon by weight percent. After Schneider.[78] (*Courtesy The American Institute of Physics.*)

"(f) The emission efficiency, indicated by Fig. 9.20 resembles the curve of W_2C.

"From these results, we conclude that formation of WC and C causes a sharp decrease of emission for carbonizing temperatures above about 2200°K, probably because ThC_2 forms by reaction with elementary Th. Experiments with a synthetic ThC_2 sample showed it to be inactive thermionically."

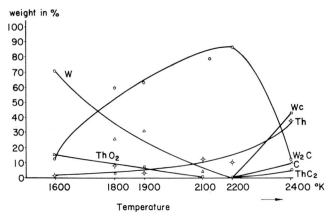

Figure 9.22. Composition of outer tenth of filament as a function of carbonizing temperature. Each filament was carbonized for 2 min in atmosphere of 0.42 g of C_6H_6 in 10 l of H_2. (Note: the ordinate scale is high by a factor of 10 for ThO_2. Th, and ThC_2; it is high by a factor of 20 for C.) After Schneider.[78] (*Courtesy The American Institute of Physics.*)

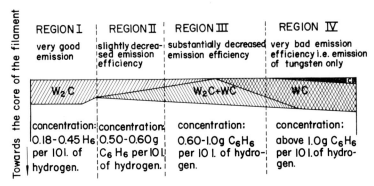

Figure 9.23. Effect of benzene concentration during carbonizing on structure and emission of filaments. Region I. Retarding effect of laminated W_2C maintains equality of rates between diffusion and evaporation of elementary thorium. Emission efficiency is high and stable. Life is much longer than for noncarbonized filaments. Region II. Retarding effect is increased because of some formation of WC. Diffusion is slowed so surface layer of Th is less dense than in Region I, decreasing emission efficiency slightly. Region III. WC becomes a major component and greatly decreases diffusion, causing further reduction of emission efficiency. Region IV. Formation of complete layer of WC and elemental carbon. This prevents emission characteristic of Th layer because: (a) diffusion of Th is very much retarded; (b) formation of poorly emitting ThC_2. After Schneider.[78] (*Courtesy The American Institute of Physics.*)

The effects of vapor concentration during carburization and that of its duration are illustrated in Fig. 9.23.

"When the benzene content is below 0.18 g per 10 l of H_2, the emission resembles that of noncarbonized filaments (Figs. 9.15 and 9.16) regardless of time and temperature of carbonizing. Tests showed that the carbide shell was too thin to prevent rapid evaporation of thorium; the emission increases rapidly to its maximum value but drops rapidly after a few minutes of heating.

"To investigate duration of carbonizing, several sets of filaments were carbonized at 2000°K and at various benzene concentrations; for each set, a given concentration of benzene was employed and the individual filaments were carbonized for a period between 2 and 10 min. Within this interval, duration above 2 min. decreases emission only slightly; the effect is too small to justify detailed presentation. The carbide shell penetrates deeper with increased exposure to benzene and the filaments become very brittle.

"The following chemical reactions are significant for thermionic emission:

$$ThO_2 + W \rightarrow Th$$

$$ThO_2 + W_2C \rightarrow Th$$

$$Th + WC \rightarrow ThC$$

$$Th + C \rightarrow ThC_2$$

$$W + C \rightarrow W_2C$$

$$W_2C + C \rightarrow WC$$

"Various secondary reactions are also conceivable, such as solution of various constituents in each other, or reactions of one or more constituents with products of the above reactions.

"These results, together with those published by others, lead to the following conclusions relating preparation and performance:

For uncarbonized filaments:

"(a) Below about 2900°K, only a fraction of the ThO_2 can be reduced by tungsten; the reaction first proceeds rapidly and then ceases, leaving unreduced thoria. Additional heating merely drives away the thorium metal produced.

"(b) Above about 2900°K, all the thoria is reduced to thorium which rapidly leaves the filament.

For carbonized filaments:

"(a) Carbonizing below about 2200°K gives desirable emission characteristics. The surface layer consists of a monatomic film of thorium metal on a matrix of W_2C; this film is more stable at higher temperatures than on pure tungsten and can be replenished from the reservoir of thorium inside. This diffusion is relatively easy through the laminated structure of the W_2C.

"(b) Carbonizing above about 2200°K gives undesirable emission characteristics. The surface layer then becomes a mixture of thorium metal and thorium carbide on solid WC, having graphite inclusions. The high carbon content of the wire causes the formation of ThC_2 which is a poor electron emitter. The WC is not porous and thus prevents diffusion of internal thorium to the surface."[78]

Carburization reduces the rate of thorium evaporation from the filament to approximately one-sixth of that for an uncarburized filament at the same temperature and thereby insures a much longer life in service. The small amount of thorium which evaporates during service life is replaced by diffusion of fresh thorium from the interior of the filament; this is facilitated by the presence of carbon in the form of tungsten carbide. The useful life of the filament comes to an end when the supply of thorium has been depleted.

The termination of life of a carburized, thoriated tungsten filament thus depends on a mechanism which is completely different from that of a pure tungsten filament. Evaporation of tungsten is not a factor in the determination of the endpoint of life of a carburized thoriated filament, because it operates at a very much lower temperature, anywhere between 1800 and 2200°K, where the rate of evaporation is negligible. For the same reason, it is not necessary to reduce the filament voltage in stand-by operation. A life of 30,000 hours is now not uncommon. The thermal yield of electron emission is of the order to 300 ma/w at 2000°K, and the surface yield of electron emission is about 3 a/cm² (peak emission).

It is customary to design thoriated tungsten filamentary cathodes with a safety factor of 2 to 5, so that saturated emission is never drawn in service. Until the end of World War II, thoriated tungsten emitters were not used in the presence of high fields exceeding a few thousand volts per cm, and emission currents were held below one ampere. Refinements in processing of the tubes have made it possible in recent years to produce reliable power tubes and rectifiers for inverse voltages up to 200 kv and current ratings of several amperes. Another important and fairly recent advance is the production of thoriated tungsten sheet so that indirectly heated cathode structures can be made in the form of drawn cups and other configurations.[89]

Non-sag Filaments. The fibrous structure of pure tungsten wire, which results from the processes of swaging and drawing during its manufacture, will give way to equi-axed crystals when the wire is heated to about 1000°C (Figure 9.24). The size of the crystal grains will increase with increasing temperature, and there is a critical range from 2600 to 2800°C where de-

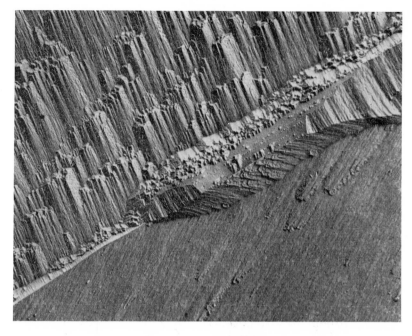

Figure 9.24. Electron micrograph of "flashed" tungsten wire drawn to 10 mil diameter; 7,810×. Parlodion-carbon replica shadowed with platinum. After Nelson.[1] (*Courtesy Sylvania Electric Products Inc., Metallurgy Research Laboratory.*)

velopment of large grains is most pronounced (Figure 9.25).[90] Equilibrium of grain growth is usually established in 10 to 15 minutes, and prolonged heating does not appear to alter the structure. Such crystal grains may assume sufficient size to extend across the full diameter of the wire, and slip may occur along the crystal boundaries at right angles to the axis of the wire, leading to hot spots and burnouts. This effect is known as "offsetting," and is illustrated in Figure 9.26 in diagrammatic form. It would of course be very harmful if such offsetting was likely to occur at any time during life; fortunately, measures can be taken to prevent this.

The admixture of thorium oxide to tungsten, which has been described above as a measure to obtain increased electron emission, was originally introduced by Langmuir[77] to prevent excessive crystal growth in tungsten filaments used for incandescent lamps. Various other additives, which have the beneficial effect of reducing excessive grain growth, have been used since that time. The mechanism of this effect[91-93] is not at all well understood, particularly since many of the additives are volatilized during the

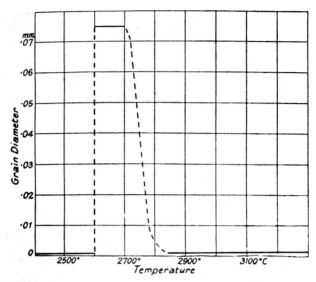

Figure 9.25. Effect of temperature on the grain size of tungsten bars. After Jeffries.[90]

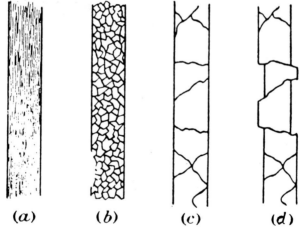

(a)   **(b)**   **(c)**   **(d)**

Figure 9.26. Changes in the structure of pure tungsten filaments heated by alternating current. After Smithells.[5] (*Courtesy Chapman & Hall, Ltd., London.*)

sintering process. Only about 0.01 per cent Si and Al can still be detected in a processed filament. Nevertheless, these small amounts appear to be adequate to influence recrystallization in the desired manner.

Meijerling and Rieck[92] have recently proposed several mechanisms by which the effect of the additives can be better understood. Reid[94] has pointed out that improper use of phosphorus as a getter in lamps can seriously interfere with the desired grain growth by reducing the additives in tungsten. Speir and Wanmaker[93] have shown that the additives also have a distinct influence on the particle size of tungsten powder produced by reduction of WO_3 with hydrogen. Addition of potassium silicate and potassium silicotungstate results in a marked growth of the tungsten particles, while calcium nitrate or magnesium sulfate tend to give a small particle size.

Figure 9.27 illustrates how grain growth is retarded in tungsten rod by the admixture of 0.75 per cent of thoria; the rod was flashed in hydrogen for two minutes at 2700°C. Different types of additives, such as alkali oxides, alumina, and silica, bring about exaggerated grain growth; these are used for wires from which coiled lamp filaments are made. Crystals,

(a)   (b)

Figure 9.27. Metallurgical sections of tungsten rod, annealed at 2700 C for 2 minutes (×100). (a) Pure tungsten; (b) Tungsten containing 0.75% ThO_2. After Smithells.[5] (*Courtesy Chapman & Hall, Ltd., London.*)

several millimeters or even centimeters long, are developed in such coils after a few seconds of flashing and remain substantially unchanged after long periods of heating above the recrystallization temperature. Such coils remain ductile after recrystallization and have many properties of the single-crystal wires (Pintsch wires). The strain introduced in the wire during coiling increases the likelihood of exaggerated grain growth, while straight wires do not show the desired long grain growth as easily. There is evidence, however, that grain growth is favored in straight filaments of the order of .040- to .050-in. dia. by the presence of strain existing between the inner and outer crystals and resulting from the drawing process.[5]*

To summarize the rather complex situation which exists in regard to the proper selection of suitable tungsten wire for various applications, one should bear in mind that tungsten filaments made for the lamp industry are not necessarily suited for heater wire or electron emitters. The intended application of the wire should thus always be clearly stated in any purchase order. Statistical investigations have disclosed that wire under 35 mils in diameter is not very likely to sag.

The procedure described in ASTM Specification F269–58T for testing the sag of tungsten wire consists in heating a hairpin filament at a constant rate to a true temperature of $2600°K$ in 1 minute, holding the wire at that temperature for 5 minutes, and then lowering the temperature at a constant rate in 1 minute. During this treatment, which is carried out in a hydrogen atmosphere, a weight is attached to the hairpin at its apex by means of a tungsten wire hook, the weight being 3 pounds for a wire diameter from 30 to 35 mils, 4 pounds for a wire from 35 to 40 mils diameter, and 6 pounds for wires from 45 to 55 mils in diameter. The hairpin filament has been mounted in a suitable fixture so that its plane is vertical. After the heat treatment, which is known as flashing, or setting, the weight is removed, and the hairpin turned by $90°$ so that it is in a horizontal plane. The flashing treatment is then repeated according to the same schedule as described above, and, after the filament has again reached room temperature, it can be determined from a previously determined zero position how much the apex of the wire has moved above or below the horizontal plane.

It is the purpose of this flashing of tungsten filaments to develop a fibrous, or long-grained, structure with the grains aligned parallel to the wire axis. The grains should be from six to ten times as long as they are wide, and there should be between 25 and 40 grains per millimeter when a cross-section of the wire is inspected under a metallurgical microscope.[95] The rate at which the current is raised to the flashing temperature of the wire has a pronounced effect on the result obtained.

---

* Note the effect of torsion strain, mentioned above on p. 267.

Fabrication and Processing of Tungsten

While some methods of fabrication and a few processes relating to the treatment of tungsten have been described above, the following pages will be devoted to a description of the variety of operations that may properly be considered under this topic. It has already been said that tungsten is available in the form of rods, and these can be centerless-ground when necessary. Ribbon can be hot-rolled from wire, but 2 inches is about the maximum width available; sheet can be purchased in sizes measuring 6 in. x 15 in. x 0.005 in and 8 in. x 20 in. x 0.025 in. Strips measuring 2 in. x 10 in. x 0.060 in. have been used as septums in cyclotron deflection chambers. Strips 2 in. wide x 0.100 in. thick, and 18 in. long are available. The preparation of thin tungsten fibers has been described by Bockris and Parsons.[96]

An ingenious process by which ribbon grids with the configuration shown in Figure 9.28 could be fabricated in very minute sizes is described by Reed[97], according to suggestions by engineers of the Sperry Gyroscope Corporation and contributions by members of the Bell Telephone Laboratories.

"The principal steps in the preparation of the ribbon grid are illustrated in Figure 9.29. Copper-plated ribbons of tungsten and iron—the tungsten 0.3 mil thick and the iron 3 mils thick—are wound and brazed into a tight spiral as shown in Figure 9.29a. Upon removal of the mandrel, the brazed spiral is face-ground on both sides to a thickness of perhaps 10 mils and

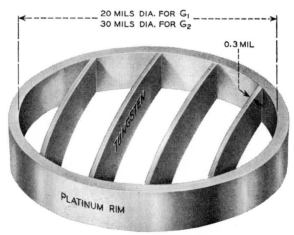

Figure 9.28. Sketch showing basic configuration of grid used in final version of M1805. The tungsten vanes, which present a thickness of 0.3 mil to the electron stream but are 3 to 4 mil deep parallel to the electron flow, are butt-brazed into the outer platinum rim. Their initial curvature serves to define the direction of expansion during operation at elevated temperatures. After Reed.[97] (*Courtesy The American Telephone and Telegraph Company.*)

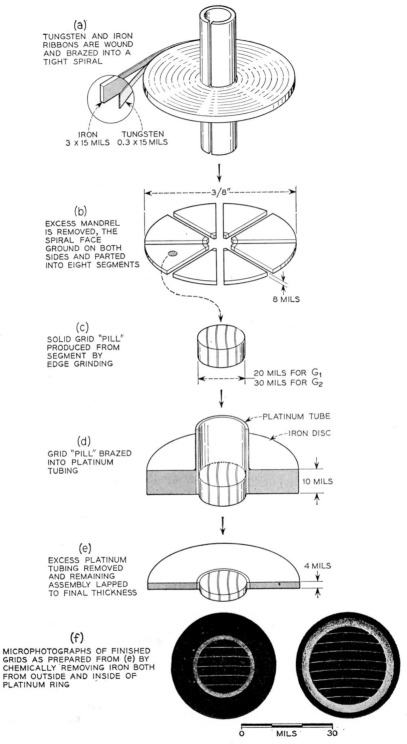

(a)
TUNGSTEN AND IRON
RIBBONS ARE WOUND
AND BRAZED INTO A
TIGHT SPIRAL

IRON
3 x 15 MILS

TUNGSTEN
0.3 x 15 MILS

3/8"

(b)
EXCESS MANDREL
IS REMOVED, THE
SPIRAL FACE
GROUND ON BOTH
SIDES AND PARTED
INTO EIGHT SEGMENTS

8 MILS

(c)
SOLID GRID "PILL"
PRODUCED FROM
SEGMENT BY
EDGE GRINDING

20 MILS FOR G_1
30 MILS FOR G_2

PLATINUM TUBE
IRON DISC

(d)
GRID "PILL" BRAZED
INTO PLATINUM
TUBING

10 MILS

(e)
EXCESS PLATINUM
TUBING REMOVED
AND REMAINING
ASSEMBLY LAPPED
TO FINAL THICKNESS

4 MILS

(f)
MICROPHOTOGRAPHS OF FINISHED
GRIDS AS PREPARED FROM (e) BY
CHEMICALLY REMOVING IRON BOTH
FROM OUTSIDE AND INSIDE OF
PLATINUM RING

0   MILS   30

Figure 9.29. Basic steps in the fabrication of a ribbon grid. After Reed.[97] (*Courtesy The American Telephone and Telegraph Company.*)

chromium-plated, the chromium serving as a thin barrier layer against subsequent brazes. The ground and plated spiral is then parted into several segments as shown in Figure 9.29b. Each segment is edge-ground to form a small, solid "pill" with a diameter corresponding to the inside diameter of the desired grid as indicated in Figure 9.29c. The grid pill is inserted and brazed into a short length of tightly fitting, thin-walled platinum tubing which, for ease of handling, has previously been brazed into an iron disk; this is shown in Figure 9.29d. This entire assembly is then machine-lapped on both sides as in Figure 9.29e to a thickness of 3 to 4 mils, i.e., to a thickness equal to the desired depth of the final grid. It merely remains to remove the iron both from outside and inside the platinum by etching. In the early stages of development, the etchant used was hot concentrated hydrochloric acid. Grids made in this manner, however, were not satisfactory because the acid did not completely remove the metallic deposits from the laterals. In addition to excessive electron interception, there was danger of these etching residues vaporizing at the high operating temperature. Deposition on the smooth cavity walls would cause increased RF losses while deposition on the insulation would cause electrical leakage. Moreover, hydrochloric acid also tended to attack the brazing fillets and thereby often gave rise to loose laterals.

"A much more elegant process of iron removal was evolved by D. E. Koontz of the Chemical Department of the Laboratories. This process has consistently resulted in a high yield of ribbon grids of excellent quality. Briefly, it operates as follows: if iron is placed in a solution of aqueous copper chloride, the surface layer of iron goes into solution and is replaced by metallic copper. Ordinarily this reaction stops when the surface has been completely covered. The only way of maintaining this reaction is to continuously remove the deposited copper in order to expose the underlying metal to further attack. In Koontz's process, this is achieved by immersing the specimen of Figure 9.29c in an ultrasonically agitated copper-chloride solution to which has been added a quantity of 'Carborundum' powder. The action of the suspended powder is twofold. It grinds off the surface layer of copper, as it is being formed, thereby providing the necessary condition for the complete dissolution of iron and it is quite effective in freeing the ribbon grid from any burrs which may have been raised in preceding lapping and grinding operations."

The forming of filaments, or the winding of coils from wire, is generally done in accordance to the following rules. Pure tungsten wire, from the smallest size up to 10-mil dia., can be wound cold on a mandrel of the same diameter as the wire, but it is customary to use a mandrel ratio 2:1; for wire diameters ranging from 10 to 15 mils, the minimum mandrel diameter should be three times the wire diameter; for wires from 15 to 20-mil dia., the mandrel diameter should be 4 times the wire diameter (mandrel ratio 4:1). Wires larger than 20 mils in dia. should not be wound cold. With the application of heat, all sizes of pure tungsten can be coiled on a mandrel of the same diameter as the wire, and the temperature required will naturally depend on the wire size, larger wires requiring higher temperatures which may range anywhere from 300 to 1000°C. Even a slight increase in temperature above room temperature will at times greatly facilitate the winding of wires.

Thoriated tungsten wire, from the smallest size up to 10-mil dia., can be wound cold on a mandrel not less than 1.5 times the wire diameter. Thoriated wires from 10 to 20 mils in diameter can be wound cold on mandrels having a diameter five to ten times that of the wire; larger thoriated wires should be wound hot according to the recommendations made for pure tungsten filaments.

These general recommendations must be adapted to the particular wire on hand, and the optimum conditions be determined by trial and error. The writer recalls an occasion where a fairly heavy tungsten rod, approximately $\frac{1}{16}$-in. dia., had to be wound into a fairly tight helix; it was found by experiment that this could be done successfully either at a white heat or at a fairly moderate, almost dull red heat; if the helix was formed in an intermediate temperature range, it turned out to be extremely brittle, while at the very low, or the very high temperatures, quite satisfactory coils could be obtained.

Tungsten springs are frequently used to hold tungsten filaments taut. The considerations entering into the design of tungsten springs have been described by Blodgett and Langmuir.[98] Springs are at times made from molybdenum, but it should be emphasized that molybdenum and tungsten show slight adherence to each other owing to sintering at 2000°C, and more so at higher temperatures.[27]

An alloy of tungsten and tantalum is available on special request from Fansteel Metallurgical Corporation under the trade name "Tantaloy." While this material has unusual elastic properties at elevated temperature, it is difficult to manufacture, very costly, and its use therefore discouraged by the manufacturer. Further data on "Tantaloy" are given on p. 351. Inconel "X" is a good substitute in many cases (See Chapter 7).

The winding of helices for travelling-wave tubes is a particularly critical operation because such a high degree of accuracy is required of the finished product; the pitch of the helix should be as uniform as possible along the length of the helix, and deviations should not exceed 0.5 mil. In general, tungsten helices are wound on an arbor of accurate dimensions made from stainless steel or molybdenum. It is important to apply sufficient tension to the wire during winding; the strain introduced in the wire during the winding operations is released by firing the helix in a hydrogen atmosphere at about 900°C while it is still on the mandrel. Depending on the material chosen for the mandrel, allowance must be made for the differential thermal expansion between the mandrel material and that from which the wire is made. Stainless stell mandrels are fired in wet hydrogen prior to use in order to produce a coating of chrome oxide, which prevents binding or sintering of the helix onto the mandrel and facilitates its removal from the helix after it has been set by heat treatment. Molybdenum mandrels may be removed from the helix by dissolving them in a hot solution of nitric acid, sulfuric acid, and water (50:30:2 vol. pts). Iversen[99] has described a procedure for winding travelling-wave tube helices of great accuracy and obtained pitch uniformity within 0.3 mil.

As an example of the delicate nature which such helices for travelling-wave tubes may assume, the dimensions of an experimental tape helix for a millimeter-range backward-wave oscillator may be quoted from a recent paper by Blattner and Sterzer[99a] who used tungsten tape 0.002 x 0.0045 in. wound at 109 T.P.I. to an internal dia. of 0.021 in. for a length of several inches. To obtain tape without camber is a major difficulty, and recourse had to be taken to edge grinding on several occasions at the Stanford Tube Laboratory.

Heaters for indirectly heated cathodes are generally made of tungsten wire and deserve the greatest care in their fabrication. The wire is usually of the doped or non-sag variety, such as GE Type-218 wire, in order to retain ductility and prevent recrystallization. Heaters for receiving tube cathodes are either of the folded type in which straight wire is formed to take on the shape of a hairpin, an M, or a multiple thereof. The tools used for producing the folds of the wire must be carefully rounded in order to avoid splitting of the wire, and the rules stated above for the forming of wires should be observed.

Alloys of tungsten and molybdenum are used at times for heater wires because they have a much higher electrical resistivity than either one of the constituents by itself; such alloy wire is also formed into various shapes more easily. Figure 9.30 gives the graphs for the resistivity and the temperature coefficient of resistivity for various alloy compositions. The resistivity of the alloys rises to a maximum at about 45 per cent molybdenum content; a 50:50 tungsten-molybdenum alloy wire is being manufactured by RCA under the tradename "Dowmo," and by Sylvania under the tradename "50/50 molybdenum-tungsten." Experience with W/Mo alloy heater wire has been unfavorable especially on account of erratic burnout; nevertheless, the material is still being used in isolated cases.

Heater wire should be designed to operate at an average temperature of 1450°K in order to ensure a satisfactory life; much higher values have been

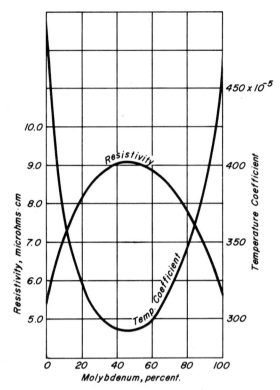

Figure 9.30. Resistivity and Temperature coefficient of tungsten-molybdenum alloys. After Smithells.[5] (*Courtesy Chapman & Hall, Ltd., London.*)

in use until it was realized by systematic tests that a great gain in life could be had by dropping the heater operating temperature by a few hundred degrees from previously used values which ranged from 1600–1800°C. During the activation of the cathode on the pump, the temperature of the heater naturally reaches much higher values for short periods of time. For an oxide-coated, directly heated filamentary cathode, the operating temperature is less than 1300°K.

Heaters for indirectly heated cathodes must be insulated to prevent shorting of adjacent legs and also to prevent electrical contact to the surrounding cathode; a coating of alumina is used for this purpose, and the method of coating has been described by Bidgood and Kent.[100] Suitable heater coating mixtures either for drag-coating, spray-coating, or cataphoric application can be purchased.* Alumina 38-500 has particles up to

* Levigated alundum, Type R500 or R900, is widely used and purchased from Norton Company, Refractories Division, Worcester, Mass.

about 40 microns in diameter with an average of 15 to 18 microns; alumina 38-900 has particles up to 24 microns with an average of 7.5 to 8.5 microns. An average particle size of 15 to 16 microns was found to give the most satisfactory results for suspensions used in continuous-coating operations, and 38-500 and 38-900 are therefore blended to give the desired size range.

If heaters are sprayed, rather than coated by passing the wires through a cup containing the coating solution, either R500 or R900 alumina is used by itself, and not the mixture. A typical coating suspension for heater wires may contain 54.5 per cent 38-500 alundum, 22.8 per cent aluminum nitrate and 23.5 per cent water. After a preliminary baking operation to dry the coating and give some adherence adequate for handling, the coated wire is rapidly passed through a hydrogen furnace at a temperature of approximately 1650°C; wet hydrogen is generally used for this operation. The thickness of the coating rarely exceeds 2 mils. The desired shapes of the heater are then produced by winding the coated wire on a drum which has carefully rounded and raised metal strip inserts which protrude from the surface of the drum so that the wire, when it is being wound on this surface, is slightly kinked, and the coating partially chipped off in this process.

When the drum is completely covered with closely wound heater wire, a sharp-edged wheel is used to cut the several turns by passing it through a groove provided in the surface of the drum. The diameter of the drum is chosen so that one turn around its surface provides one heater, and the number of metal inserts along the surface of the drum equals the number of desired bends. The final shape of the heater has to be formed by hand with the aid of tweezers, which are used to press two adjacent heater legs close to each other where the bend is indicated by the kink produced on the metal insert of the winding drum. Spade winding has to a large extent replaced drum winding. Some observations on the practical aspects of electrophoretic deposition of heater coating, or for that matter of emissive coating, have been made by Kinney and Festa[101] and also by Troelstra.[102]

It might appear on first thought that the coating of heaters is a straightforward proposition, particularly since this technique has been in use for such a long time. Actually, there are many problems as yet unsolved,[103] and the Armed Services have sponsored very extensive investigations by various tube manufacturers to do fundamental research on the causes for heater wire-coating breakdown in operation, and to develop improved heater-wire-coating methods and materials.[104, 105]

When the heater is positive with respect to the cathode sleeve by more than a few volts, say 100 v, breakdown caused by "electrolysis" of the insulating coating is a more serious danger than for the opposite polarity. Negative oxygen ions are drawn to the tungsten wire where they cause oxidation; the oxide thus formed dissolves in the alumina and produces an aluminum tungstate which has a lower resistance than pure alumina. After a time, determined by the voltage V_{kf} and the temperature of the heater, the insulation will suddenly break down, and a short circuit, or fusing of the heater to the sleeve, may result. If the cathode is positive with respect to the heater, the nickel sleeve becomes oxidized, but this reaction proceeds about ten times as slowly as for tungsten. To avoid both effects, workers at the Philips Laboratories in Holland have found it beneficial to coat the inside of the cathode sleeve with alumina.[106] Several manufacturers in the United States also apply such coatings to the inside of the sleeve; coating the inside with aluminum metal and then oxidizing it is one practical method.

As very small amounts of impurities can be responsible for substantial leakage currents, alumina as furnished by the supplier may require additional heat treatment before being suited as coating material for critical applications. A small carbon content in the form of graphite to the extent of a fraction of a per cent can be very offensive. Norton alumina has a total alkali impurity content of 0.1 per cent by weight, maximum, while Linde B alumina has an alkali content of 0.001 per cent; these alkali impurities are driven out of the coating in a reasonably short time by flashing the heater; in testing the two types of coating material, no correlation could be found between the alkali content and the leakage level in the tube.[107]

The presence of longitudinal cracks, seams, or fissures in tungsten wire is most harmful to reliable service in most applications and thus must be guarded against. Conventional tensile tests do not disclose the presence of such faults, because the fissures run parallel to the direction of stress. White[108] has described a method of test for detecting longitudinal fissures in fine wire. One end of the wire sample is attached to a given load, and the other end is pulled over an inclined wedge that is carefully polished and rounded at the edge; the wire is thus subject not only to a 90°-bend but at the same time to a rotation about its axis owing to the inclination of the wedge. After suffering this bend, the wire is then straightened again and subjected to tension which, in 5 to 10 per cent of the specimens tested, will give low values of tensile strength, whereas flawless wire, when subjected to this same treatment, will be consistently high in tensile strength.

On larger wires, particularly on seal rod, fissures and cracks are easily detected by making a glass bead seal and observing it under a low-power microscope according to ASTM Method of Test F204-50. Faulty wire will sometimes disclose a line of small bubbles at the interface between metal and glass. Such bubbles seem to occur when the cracks are sufficiently wide to entrap carbon or organic material.

Seamless tungsten tubing is not a regular commercial item, but it can be produced by vapor plating, electrodeposition, or hydrostatic pressing, and sintering of powder. The deposition from the vapor phase was first used by Van Arkel, Geiss,[21] and Van Liempt;[109] a summary description of the process is given by Smithells[5] and Powell, Campbell, and Gonser[110] in their respective books. Extensive work on vapor-deposited coatings of tungsten and molybdenum on alloy steels has been done at the Department of Metallurgy of M.I.T.[111] and at Battelle Memorial Institute for Project RAND. Quoting from one of the earlier disclosures originating from the N.V. Philips Gloeilampenfabrieken in Eindhoven:[112]

"The method consists in depositing the metal by electrochemical means or by thermal decomposition on a core and then dissolving the core away chemically. By this means small seamless tubes can be made from W, Mo, C, Tp, Ti, Zr, Hf, and others. W can be deposited from WCl_6 vapor at 2000°C on a Mo core. The rate of deposition is 5 to 25 microgram per minute, and there is practically no diffusion between the metals. The Mo core is then dissolved in 85 per cent HNO_3 plus 15 per cent concentrated H_2SO_4 at 90°C. The specific gravity of the W tubes is about 19.22 and the tubes are vacuum-tight. Tubes from 1 mm diameter x 3 cm long x 0.1 mm wall thickness to 12 mm diameter x 35 cm long x 1 mm wall thickness can be made. A single crystal W tube can be made by depositing on a single crystal Mo core. Very thin tubes can be made by depositing from a WCl_6 and H_2 mixture on a copper core and melting out the Cu core. The tubes can also be drawn to smaller size before removing the copper core."

Tungsten and other refractory metals can also be deposited on a suitable core from the vapor phase of the appropriate carbonyl in an atmosphere of CO_2, according to a process developed by Commonwealth Engineering Company of Dayton, Ohio, under the name of "Gas Plating."[113]

"Tungsten carbonyl $W(CO)_6$ exists in the form of white orthorhombic crystals which decompose at 150°C without melting. The vapor phase deposits on any object held at the proper temperature in a metallic form. 'Gas Plating' dates back to the discovery by Ludwig Mond, in 1890, that metallic nickel can be obtained from the decomposition of nickel carbonyls, a process which bears his name. In its improved form, gas plating is applied to the plating of conductors or nonconductors of intricate shapes onto which coatings of considerable thickness and density can be deposited in much shorter periods of time than conventional electroplating permits. Continuous wire coating has also been perfected. If the core mandrel is dissolved by chemical means, tubing naturally results. Alloy coating is also possible."

The production of tungsten tubing by hydrostatic pressing of powder contained between an inner and outer rubber hose was first described by Fehse.[114] Hoffman and Scheel[115] more recently replaced the rubber by lead pipes one of which is contained in a steel pipe that serves as the inner or outer liner depending on whether the hydraulic fluid (glycerin) is applied from the outside or inside. Pressures of the order of 14,000 kg/cm^2 (100 tons/sq.in.) were applied, and the tube, after removal from the mold, was sintered in hydrogen at temperatures ranging up to 1900°C. Wall thickness as low as 0.2 mm was achieved, and this could be varied to produce heavier walls at the ends of the tube, if desired. A process for making small metal tubes with diameters ranging from one millimeter to 0.1 mm, or less, has been described by Gezelius[116], who deposits the metal on silver-coated nylon fibers which can later be removed.

A protective coating in the form of a porcelain enamel has been described by Horsfall,[117] who extends the usefulness of tungsten into fields where operation in air is required at elevated temperatures up to 1650°C. The batch of the enamel consists of the following ingredients:

9 parts by weight $ZrO_2 \cdot SiO_2$

1.5 parts by weight Al_2O_3

0.5 parts by weight Co_3O_4

0.02 parts by weight $H_2MoO_4 \cdot H_2O$

0.3 parts by weight Dextrose

to which a few drops of formaldehyde are added to prevent fermentation while in storage. The tungsten rod to be coated is cleaned by flashing in a helium atmosphere and then coated with the enamel and fired again according to a prescribed schedule. A firmly adherent coat of enamel is said to result.

Radiation damage

Makin and Mrs. Gillies[118] recently investigated the effect of neutron irradiation on the mechanical properties of molybdenum and tungsten in the form of 0.040-in.-dia. wire of commercial purity. The specimens were irradiated for 6 months in a reactor at approximately 100°C in a flux at 6×10^{12} slow neutrons/cm^2/sec, the total dose of slow neutrons being 5×10^{19} neutrons/cm^2 (nvt*). Tensile tests were then performed at a strain rate of 8.2×10^{-5}/sec. A stain rate of 8.2×10^{-5}/sec was used in all the experiments which were carried out at 100° and 200°C both before and after irradiation. At 100°C, both the irradiated and unirradiated material fractured without any plastic extension. The fracture stress of the irradiated specimens was about 152,000 lb/in^2 and that of the unirradiated

---

* The symbol nvt refers to the integrated neutron flux through the sample where n = number of neutrons/cm^3, v = velocity in cm/sec, t = time in seconds, so that nvt has the dimension neutrons/cm^2.

137,000 lb/in², an increase due to irradiation of 15,000 lb/in². At 200°C both the irradiated and unirradiated specimens were ductile. The yield stress was slightly decreased by irradiation, but there was no significant difference in the ultimate tensile strength of the irradiated and unirradiated specimens.

The ductile-to-brittle transition temperature (see p. 320) was increased from 118 to 126°C after irradiation.

REFERENCES

1. R. C. Nelson, "The utilization of tungsten for high-purity applications," *Sylvania Technologist*, **10**, 78–83 (July 1957).

2. J. G. Wistreich, "The fundamentals of wire drawing," *Met. Revs.*, **3**, No. 10, 97–142 (1958).

3. R. B. Reid, "Microscopic studies of tungsten wire," *Sylvania Technologist*, **5**, 75–76 (July 1952).

4. L. Delisle, "Electron micrographs of tungsten," *Metal Progr.*, **56**, 670–671 (Nov. 1949).

5. C. J. Smithells, "Tungsten," 3rd ed. Chapman & Hall, Ltd., London, 1952.

6. K. C. Li and Chung Yu Wang, "Tungsten," 3rd ed., Reinhold Publishing Corp., New York, 1955.

7. E. L. Reed, "Tungsten," United States Atomic Energy Commission, AECD-2700, Sept. 15, 1947.

8. P. Schwartzkopf, "Powder Metallurgy," Macmillan Co., New York, 1947.

9. C. G. Goetzel, "Treatise on Powder Metallurgy," Vols. 1–3, Interscience Publishers, Inc., New York, 1950.

10. B. Stoughton, A. Butts and A. M. Bounds, "Engineering Metallurgy," 4th ed., McGraw-Hill Book Co., Inc., New York, 1953.

11. G. E. Doan, "The Principles of Physical Metallurgy," 3rd ed., McGraw-Hill Book Co., Inc., New York, 1953.

12. C. A. Hampel, Ed., "Rare Metals Handbook," Reinhold Publishing Corp., New York, 1954.

13. The Reactor Handbook, Vol. 3, Section 1, General Properties of Materials, United States Atomic Energy Commission, Mar. 1955 (AECD-3647).

14. "American Institute of Physics Handbook," McGraw-Hill Book Co., Inc., New York, 1957.

15. R. E. Honig, "Vapor pressure data for the more common elements," *RCA Rev.*, **18**, 195–204 (June 1957).

16. R. D. Larrabee, "The spectral emissivity and optical properties of tungsten," Report on 17th Annual Conference Physical Electronics, Massachusetts Institute of Technology, Cambridge, Mass. (Mar. 21–23, 1957), pp. 61–64. Also: *J. Opt. Soc. Amer.*, **49**, 619–625 (June 1959).

17. J. C. De Vos, "A new determination of the emissivity of tungsten ribbon," *Physica*, **20**, 690–714 (1954); "Relation between brightness, temperature, true temperature and colour temperature of tungsten. Luminance of tungsten," *ibid.*, 715–720.

18. D. A. Wright, "A survey of present knowledge of thermionic emitters," *Proc. Inst. Elec. Engrs.*, **100**, Pt. III, 125–139 (May 1953).

19. R. Kieffer and W. Hotop, "Pulvermetallurgie und Sinterwerkstoffe," J. Springer-Verlag, Berlin, 1943.

20. P. Schwartzkopf and R. Kieffer, "Refractory Hard Metals," Macmillan Co., New York, 1953.

21. W. Geiss, "The elastic constants of tungsten as a function of temperature," Holländ, *Z. Physik*, **3**, 322–327 (1923).

22. I. E. Campbell, Ed., "High-Temperature Technology," John Wiley & Sons, Inc., New York, 1956.

23. G. Ehrlich, "The interaction of nitrogen with a tungsten surface," *J. Phys. Chem.*, **60**, 1388–1400 (Oct. 1956).

24. M. A. Cayless and B. N. Watts, "Reactions occurring during decomposition of alkaline earth carbonates on tungsten," *Brit. J. Appl. Phys.*, **7**, 351–354 (Oct. 1950).

25. G. E. Moore, H. W. Allison, and F. Morrison, "The reduction of SrO by tungsten in vacuum," *J. Chem. Phys.*, **18**, 1579–1586 (Dec. 1950).

26. G. E. Moore, "Reduction of magnesium oxide by tungsten in vacuum," *J. Chem. Phys.*, **9**, 427–431 (May 1941).

27. P. D. Johnson, "Behavior of refractory oxides and metals, alone and in combination, in vacuo at high temperatures," *J. Am. Ceram. Soc.*, **33**, 168–171 (May 1950).

28. B. Kopelman, "Clean-up of graphite lubricant from tungsten wire," *Sylvania Technologist*, **2**, 13–16 (Apr. 1949).

29. G. Mesnard and R. Uzan, "Some preliminary treatments of tungsten filaments for electron tubes" (in French), *Le Vide*, **30**, 896–904 (Nov. 1950).

30. F. Gifford and E. A. Coomes, "Torsion-induced recrystallization of highly refractory filaments," The 1956 Field Emission Symposium, Notre Dame, June 11–13, 1956 (Tech. Rept. Contract No. Nonr 1623 (00,NR372–731), June 4, 1956).

31. K. Sedlatschek and D. A. Thomas (M.I.T.), "The effect of surface treatment on the mechanical properties of tungsten," *Powder Met. Bull.*, **8**, No. 1/2, 35–40 (June 1957).

32. W. G. Pfann, "An electrolytic method for pointing tungsten wires," *Trans. Am. Inst. Mining Met. Engrs.*, **175**, 606–609 (1948).

33. W. P. Dyke, J. K. Trolan, W. W. Dolan, and G. Barnes, "The field emitter: Fabrication, electron microscopy, and electric field calculations," *J. Appl. Phys.*, **24**, 570–576 (May 1953).

34. A. J. Hegedus, T. Millner, J. Neugebauer and K. Sasvari, "Thermo- and x-ray analytical contribution to the reduction of tungsten trioxide" (in German), *Z. anorg. allgem. Chem.*, **281**, 64–82 (Oct. 1955).

34a. P. E. Blackburn, M. Hoch and H. L. Johnston, "The vaporization of molybdenum and tungsten oxides," *J. Phys. Chem.*, **62**, 769–773 (July 30, 1958).

35. F. S. Goucher, "Further studies on the deformation of tungsten single crystals," *Phil. Mag.*, **2**, 289–309 (July 1926).

36. F. S. Goucher, "On the strength of tungsten single crystals and its variation with temperature," *Phil. Mag.*, **48**, 229–249 (Aug. 1924).

37. F. S. Goucher, "Studies on the deformation of tungsten single crystals under tensile stress," *Phil. Mag.*, **48**, 800–819 (Nov. 1924).

38. A. A. Brown, L. J. Neelands and H. E. Farnsworth, "Thermionic work function of the (100) face of a tungsten single crystal," *J. Appl. Phys.*, **21**, 1–4 (Jan. 1950).

39. R. P. Johnson and W. Shockley, "An electron microscope for filaments: Emission and absorption by tungsten single crystals," *Phys. Rev.*, **49**, 436–440 (Mar. 15, 1936).

40. M. H. Nichols, "The thermionic constants of tungsten as a function of crystallographic direction," *Phys. Rev.*, **57**, 297–306 (Feb. 15, 1940).

41. C. S. Robinson, Jr., "Rate of crystal growth in drawn tungsten wires as a function of temperature," *J. Appl. Phys.*, **13**, 647–651 (Oct. 1942).

42. G. D. Rieck, "The texture of drawn tungsten wires," *Philips Research Repts.*, **12**, No. 5, 423–431 (Oct. 1957).

43. G. R. Fonda, "Burn-out of incandescent lamps," *Gen. Elec. Rev.*, **32**, 206–212 (1929).

44. J. W. Pugh, "Tensile and creep properties of tungsten at elevated temperatures," *Am. Soc. Testing Materials Proc.*, **57**, 906–915 (1957); Disc. p. 916.

44a. J. W. Pugh, "The temperature dependence of preferred orientation in rolled tungsten," *Trans. Am. Inst. Mining Met. Engrs.*, **212**, 637–642 (Oct. 1958).

44b. G. L. Davis, "Recrystallization of tungsten wires," *Metallurgia*, **58**, 177–184 (Oct. 1958).

45. H. B. Wahlin and L. V. Whitney, "Positive and negative thermionic emission from tungsten," *Phys. Rev.*, **50**, 735–738 (Oct. 15, 1936).

46. W. W. Webb, J. T. Norton and C. Wagner, "Oxidation of tungsten," *J. Electrochem. Soc.*, **103**, 107–111 (Feb. 1956).

47. E. A. Gulbransen and W. S. Wysong, "Thin oxide films on tungsten," *Trans. Am. Inst. Mining Met. Engrs.*, **175**, 611–644 (1948).

47a. R. C. Griffis, "Equilibrium reduction of tungsten oxides by hydrogen," *J. Electrochem. Soc.*, **106**, 418–422 (May 1959).

48. A. L. Reimann, "Electron Emission," Chapman & Hall, Ltd., London, 1934.

49. J. H. De Boer, "Electron Emission and Adsorption Phenomena," Cambridge University Press, 1935.

50. W. B. Nottingham, "Thermionic Emission," Tech. Rept. 321 (Dec. 10, 1956), Res. Lab. Electronics, Massachusetts Institute of Technology, Cambridge, Mass. See also: "Handbuch d. Physik," Vol. 21, 1956.

51. F. J. Norton and A. L. Marshall, "The degassing of metals," *Trans. Am. Inst. Mining Met. Engrs.*, **156**, 351–371 (1944).

52. R. N. Bloomer, "High-temperature properties of tungsten which influence filament temperatures, lives, and thermionic-emission densities," *Proc. Inst. Elect. Engrs.*, **104**, Pt. B, 153–157 (Mar. 1957).

53. H. A. Jones and I. Langmuir, "The characteristics of tungsten filaments as functions of temperature," *Gen. Elec. Rev.*, **30**, 310–319 (1927).

54. A. L. Reimann, "The evaporation of atoms, ions, and electrons from tungsten," *Phil. Mag.*, **25**, 834–848 (June 1938).

55. C. Zwicker, "Characteristics of tungsten and the candle-power of the black body," *Arch. néerl. sci.* (Socies III A), **9**, 207 (1925). Also: *Kgl. Akad. Amsterdam Proc.*, **28**, 499–502 (May 1925).

56. K. R. Spangenberg, "Vacuum Tubes," McGraw-Hill Book Co., Inc., New York, 1948.

57. I. Langmuir, S. McLane and K. B. Blodgett, "The effect of end losses on the characteristics of filaments of tungsten and other materials," *Phys. Rev.*, **35**, 478–503 (1930).

58. I. Langmuir and J. B. Taylor, "Heat conductivity of tungsten and cooling effect of leads upon filaments at low temperature," *Phys. Rev.*, **50**, 68–87 (July 1, 1936).

59. J. W. Clark and R. E. Neuber, "End-cooling of power tube filaments," *J. Appl. Phys.*, **21**, 1084–1087 (Nov. 1950).

60. W. E. Forsythe and A. G. Worthing, "The properties of tungsten and the characteristics of tungsten lamps," *Astrophys. J.* **61**, 146–185 (Apr. 1925).

61. W. E. Forsythe and E. M. Watson, "Resistance and radiation of tungsten as a function of temperature," *J. Opt. Soc. Amer.*, **24**, 114–118 (Apr. 1934).

62. W. E. Forsythe and E. Q. Adams, "Radiation characteristics of tungsten and tungsten lamps," *J. Opt. Soc. Amer.*, **35**, 108–113 (Feb. 1945).

63. W. J. Pohl, "Mutual heating in transmitting-valve filament structures," *Proc. Inst. Elec. Engrs.*, **103**, 224–230 (Mar. 1956).

64. N. J. Gross and Z. J. Atlee, "High-vacuum tube rectifiers—Physical factors influencing their design," *J. Appl. Phys.*, **8**, 540–543 (Aug. 1937).

65. J. J. Volmer, "Filament design for high-power transmitting valves," *Proc. IRE*, **26**, 1399–1407 (Nov. 1938).

66. T. N. Dansett, "Some factors affecting transmitting valve life," *Brit. J. IRE*, **15**, 588–592 (Nov. 1955).

67. A. A. Halacsy, "Practical calculation of magnetizing force," *Proc. Inst. Elec. Engrs.*, **97**, Pt. 1, No. 104, 37–42 (Mar. 1950).

68. R. E. Peierls, "Use of the electrolytic tank for magnetic problems," *Nature*, **158**, 831–832 (Dec. 1946).

69. J. W. Skehan and B. K. M. Magnusson, "Cathode Structure for Electron Discharge Devices," U.S. Patent 2,422,142 (June 10, 1947); assigned to Machlett Laboratories, Inc.

70. J. W. Skehan, "Filament Structure for Electrical Discharge Devices," U.S. Patent 2,422,141 (June 10, 1947).

71. W. H. Kohl, "Resnatron Filament Basket," U. S. Patent 2,693,544 (Nov. 2, 1954); assigned to Collins Radio Company.

72. W. H. Kohl, "Resnatron Filament Basket," U. S. Patent 2,750,361 (Aug. 14, 1956); assigned to Collins Radio Company.

73. A. M. Hardie, "Squirrel-cage filament structures," *Wireless Engr.*, **30**, 196–204 (Aug. 1953).

74. H. S. Thomas, "The motion of idealized vacuum tube filaments under shock," *J. Appl. Phys.*, **24**, 1341–1342 (Nov. 1953).

75. H. D. Doolittle, "The design of high-vacuum tubes for industrial heating applications," *Machlett Cathode Press*, **9**, No. 1, 10–13, 26–27 (Winter 1951–52).

76. B. S. Frankel, "Industrial use of electron tubes," *Machlett Cathode Press*, **1**, No. 2, 10–15, 26–29 (Spring 1952).

77. I. Langmuir, "Thoriated tungsten filaments," *J. Franklin Inst.*, **217**, 543–569 (May 1934).

78. P. Schneider, "Thermionic emission of thoriated tungsten," *J. Chem. Phys.*, **28**, 675–682 (Apr. 1958).

79. M. R. Andrews and S. Dushman, "Diffusion of carbon through tungsten and tungsten carbide," *J. Phys. Chem.*, **29**, 462–472 (Apr. 1925).

80. B. T. Barnes, "Properties of carbonized tungsten," *J. Phys. Chem.*, **33**, 688–691 (May, 1929).

81. C. W. Horsting, "Carbide structures in carburized thoriated tungsten filaments," *J. Appl. Phys.*, **18**, 95–102 (Jan. 1947).

82. H. J. Dailey, "Designing thoriated tungsten filaments," *Electronics*, 107–109 (Jan. 1948).

83. Z. J. Atlee, "Thoriated tungsten filaments in rectifiers," *Elec. Eng.*, **68**, 863 (Oct. 1949).

84. R. B. Ayer, "Use of thoriated-tungsten filaments in high-power transmitting tubes," *Proc. IRE*, **40**, 591–594 (May 1952).

85. R. B. Ayer, "High-power industrial vacuum tubes having thoriated tungsten filaments," *AIEE Trans.*, **72**, Pt. 1, 121–125 (May 1953).

86. C. Kirka, "Life considerations of thoriated tungsten filament," Machlett Cathode Press, **11**, No. 1, 10–13, 27–28 (1954).

87. E. G. Dorgelo, "High-power transmitting valves with thoriated tungsten cathodes," *Philips Tech. Rev.*, **14**, 226–234 (Feb. 1953).

88. D. K. Das, "Some reactions involving W, C, Th, and ThO_2," Report on 16th Annual Conf. on Physical Electronics, Massachusetts Institute of Technology, March 21–23, 1957, Cambridge, Mass.

89. M. J. Slivka and R. E. Manfredi, "A long-life cathode for high-power UHF transmitting tubes," *IRE Convention Record*, **4**, Pt. 3, 58–63 (1956).

90. Z. Jeffries, "Grain-size determination and standardization," *Met. Chem. Eng.*, **16**, 503–504 (May 1, 1917).

91. R. A. Swalin and the late A. H. Geisler, "The recrystallization process in tungsten as influenced by impurities," *J. Inst. Metals*, **86**, (3), 129–134 (Nov. 1957).

92. J. L. Meijerling and G. D. Rieck, "The function of additives in tungsten for filaments," *Philips Tech. Rev.*, **19**, No. 4, 109–117 (1957/58).

93. H. L. Spier and W. L. Wanmaker, "Influence of additives on particle size of tungsten powder prepared by reduction with hydrogen from tungsten trioxide," *Philips Research Repts.*, **13**, No. 2, 149–156 (Apr. 1958).

94. R. B. Reid, "Phosphorus contamination of tungsten," *Sylvania Technologist*, **10**, No. 2, 53 (Apr. 1957).

95. Federal Telephone and Radio Corp., "Report on 'Non-Sag' Properties of Tungsten," presented to ASTM, Aug. 18, 1948.

96. J. O'M. Bockris and D. F. Parsons, "Preparation of thin tungsten fibres and their use in place of quartz," *J. Sc. Instr.*, **30**, 340 (Sept. 1953).

97. E. D. Reed, "A tunable, low-voltage reflex klystron for operation in the 50 to 60-kmc band," *Bell System Tech. J.*, **34**, 563–599 (May 1955).

98. K. B. Blodgett and I. Langmuir, "The design of tungsten springs to hold tungsten filaments taut," *Rev. Sc. Instr.*, **5**, 321–333 (Sept. 1934).

99. A. H. Iverson, "Precision helix winding and a mechanism of loss variation," *IRE Trans. Electron Dev.*, **ED-3**, 205–206 (Oct. 1956). Also: "A coupled-helix winding machine," Proc. 3rd Natl. Conf. Tube Techniques, Sept. 12–14, 1956, New York University Press, 1958; *IRE Trans. Electron Dev.*, **ED-5**, 317 (Oct. 1958).

99a. D. J. Blattner and F. Sterzer, "Two backward-wave oscillator tubes for the 29,000-to-74,000 megacycle frequency range," *RCA Rev.*, **19**, 584–597 (Dec. 1958).

100. E. S. Bidgood and G. H. Kent, "Cataphoresis and alundum coatings," *Trans. Electrochem. Soc.*, **87**, 321–329 (1945); Disc. **88**, 225–227 (1945).

101. G. F. Kinney and J. V. Festa, "Some practical aspects of electrophoretic deposition," *Sylvania Technologist*, **10**, 48–52 (Apr. 1957).

102. S. A. Troelstra, "Applying coatings by electrophoresis," *Phil. Tech. Rev.*, **12**, 293–303 (1950/1951).

103. G. H. Metson, E. F. Rickard and F. M. Hewlett, "Some experiments on the breakdown of heater-cathode insulation in oxide-cathode receiving valves," *Proc. Inst. Elec. Engrs.*, **102**, Pt. B, No. 5, 678–683 (Sept. 1955).

104. Air Force Contract 19(604)-1734 with Sylvania Electric Products Inc., "Heater-cathode leakage investigation."

105. Air Force Contract 19(604)-1744 with CBS-Hytron, "The development of improved heater wire coating methods and materials." These reports can be

obtained from ASTIA (Armed Services Technical Information Agency) by companies working on government contracts and able to establish a "need-to-know."

106. K. Rodenhuis, H. Santing and H. J. M. Van Tol, "The life and reliability of valves," *Philips Tech. Rev.*, **18**, No. 7, 181–192 (1956/57).

107. J. G. Buck, Sylvania Electric Products, Inc., First Quarterly Report, (Feb. to May 1, 1956), Contract AF 19(604)-1734.

108. D. W. White, "A mechanical test for detecting longitudinal fissures in wires," *Metal Progr.*, **54**, 837–841 (Dec. 1948).

109. J. A. M. Van Liempt, "The production of seamless tubes from materials of high melting point," *Metallwirtschaft*, **11**, 357–359 (1932).

110. C. F. Powell, I. E. Campbell and B. W. Gonser, "Vapor-plating," John Wiley & Sons, Inc., New York, 1955.

111. L. M. Shetky, H. S. Spacil and J. Wulff, "Vapor-deposited coatings," Dept. of Metallurgy, Massachusetts Institute of Technology, DA Project No. 593-08-024; PB No. 121725, Final Report, August 1, 1955.

112. British Patent 342,648 (Sept. 1939).

113. U. S. Patents 2,332,309; 2,344,138; 2,475,601; The Commonwealth Engineering Company of Ohio; "Metal plating from carbonyl gases," *Chem. Engr.* **56**, 118–119 (Oct. 1949).

114. W. Fehse, "Tungsten tube furnace for very high temperatures" (in German), *Z. Tech. Phys.*, **5**, 473–475 (Oct. 1924).

115. W. Hoffman and W. Scheel, "Lead as a means for the production of tungsten tubes by powder metallurgy technique" (in German), *Z. Metallkunde*, **45**, 512–513 (Aug. 1954).

116. R. J. E. Gezelius, "Making small metal tubes by electrodeposition on nylon fibres," *Rev. Sc. Instr.*, **21**, 886 (Oct. 1950).

117. J. C. Horsfall, "A high-temperature porcelain enamel for tungsten," *Am. Ceram. Soc. Bull.*, **29**, 314–315 (Sept. 1950).

118. M. J. Makin and (Mrs.) E. Gillies, "The effect of neutron irradiation on the mechanical properties of molybdenum and tungsten," *J. Inst. Metals*, **26** (2), 108–112 (Oct. 1957).

CHAPTER 10

MOLYBDENUM

Introduction

Molybdenum shares a preferred position as a structural material for electron tubes with tungsten and tantalum because these three materials have exceedingly high melting points, reasonable strength at high temperatures, and low vapor pressures. Nevertheless, the properties of these three refractory metals are sufficiently different from each other that each has its special field of usefulness where neither of the other two could successfully compete on the basis of cost, availability in a desired shape or size, or as a result of its deficiency in certain physical characteristics.

Molybdenum is much less expensive than tungsten but its hot strength is not as great; nevertheless, grids for power tubes are generally made from molybdenum wire which has sufficient ductility to permit cold drawing. On the other hand, molybdenum is rarely used as a heater wire for indirectly heated cathodes and never as an electron emitter in spite of the fact that the work function of molybdenum is lower than that of tungsten. In order to draw a desired amount of electron emission from a molybdenum surface, it would be necessary to operate this metal much closer to its melting point than is the case for a tungsten surface. While the temperature for tungsten would be higher, it would be far enough removed from the melting point of tungsten to keep the rate of evaporation of tungsten within bounds. In the case of molybdenum, the rate of evaporation at the equivalent temperature to give the desired emission would be prohibitively high.

Molybdenum has the advantage over tungsten of being more readily fabricated into sheets of large size and drawn into cups and other shapes. It is thus widely used as a material for anodes in microwave tubes and power tubes where large amounts of power must be dissipated, and the temperature of the anode is quite high in operation. Heat shields, corona shields, and miscellaneous supporting structures are also frequently made of molybdenum. Helix structures in traveling-wave tubes and cathode support structures for impregnated matrix cathodes are other examples for the application of molybdenum.

Molybdenum is frequently used in high-temperature electric furnaces as a heater element and for heat shields, but a neutral atmosphere must be provided to prevent the formation of oxides. Molybdenum is a suitable material for welder tips on spot welders and for thermocouple protection tubes. The glass industry employs large amounts of molybdenum for electrodes in glass tanks. One of the most important applications of molybdenum is its use as an alloying element in steel. As a minor additive to nickel, molybdenum greatly contributes to the mechanical strength of cathode sleeves for receiving tubes for critical applications (See Chapter 15). Molybdenum by itself, or in combination with other metals, or ceramics, has a great potential usefulness in the construction of gas turbines for guided missiles and rockets, but the protection of these materials against oxidation at high temperature remains a major problem.

Like tungsten, molybdenum ingots are made by powder metallurgical techniques from molybdenum powder of high purity and small particle size. The powder is pressed in steel dies under pressures of the order of 20 tons per square inch to form bars varying from 0.5 to 2.0 sq in. in section and 12 to 18 in. long. The average weight of these ingots ranges from seven to 14 lb.; ingots six inches in diameter and four feet long weighing 1500 lb have been produced recently.

These bars are sintered in hydrogen at a maximum temperature of 2340°C by passing several thousand amperes through the bar; sometimes the pressed compact is baked or presintered by heating in a dry hydrogen atmosphere at about 1000°C before the final sintering at the higher temperature takes place. The sintered bars are then swaged at 1250°C, or higher, or hot-forged, and finally converted by working to sheet or wire. During swaging, the temperature is continuously reduced to insure that the material is worked below its recrystallizing temperature. For wire manufacture, drawing commences at about 2 mm diameter and at a temperature of about 750°C, using carbide dies and a graphite lubricant; from about 0.3 mm diameter on to smaller sizes, diamond dies replace carbide dies. Further drawing, down to 0.015 mm diameter, may be carried out at approximately 400°C, or cold.*

A modified procedure of producing molybdenum metal by powder metallurgical techniques was introduced by the Westinghouse Electric Corporation in 1947. It differs from the conventional practice by sintering the compacted metal powder at considerably lower temperatures, of the order of 1500 to 1700°C. Water-saturated hydrogen is used instead of dry hydrogen. The presence of water vapor induces crystallization and accelerates sintering of the molybdenum particles into dense workable ingots in about two or three hours. Density values up to 10 gm/cm³ have been obtained as com-

---

* Purity of the metal is an essential condition for successful working of molybdenum. The presence of as little as 0.04 per cent carbon makes drawing to fine wire almost impossible.[33]

pared with the more usual 9.6 to 9.7 gr/cm³ resulting from the conventional powder metallurgy technique. As the sintering operation takes place at so much lower temperatures, it is possible to use conventional high-temperature furnaces and produce parts to the final shape required without the need of additional machining. Hydrostatic pressing may be used for the production of larger sections.

Fabricated molybdenum is available in many different shapes and sizes. Forgings can be obtained up to 2½ in diameter; pipes 2 in. dia. with a 0.250-in. wall are available in three-foot lengths, and tubes with thin walls, of the order of one inch dia., in six-foot lengths. Seamless tubing is being produced in diameters from 1 inch to 0.010 in., the wall thickness running approximately 20 per cent of the outside diameter; the available lengths range from about four feet for 0.250-in.-dia. tubing to three feet for 0.063-in. dia. Molybdenum wires are made to a standard tolerance of ±1½% of diameter and ±3% of milligram weight down to 0.001 in. diameter.

The physical and chemical characteristics of molybdenum are summarized in Tables 10.1 and 10.2. For a more detailed study of many of these properties the reader is referred to the references listed at the end of the chapter. Table 10.3 gives true temperature and brightness temperature, spectral and total emissivity, current and voltage parameters corresponding to those established for tungsten by Jones and Langmuir, and electrical resistivity as a function of temperature after Coomes.[30]

Mechanical Properties

"The tensile properties of molybdenum are dependent upon the amount of hot and cold work, the amount, kind, and distribution of impurities, the annealing temperature, and very probably the interactions between these variables.

"In general, the yield and tensile strengths (in the direction of working) are increased as the amount of working increases. The yield and tensile strengths are decreased with an increase in annealing temperature, but annealing above 2500°F (1371°C) may (although not always) cause low ductility at room temperature. This type of embrittlement is usually accompanied by a change from a fibrous structure to a recrystallized (equiaxed grain) structure. It appears that purity is a significant determinant of response to annealing, but the particular elements responsible for the recrystallization embrittlement and the concomitant effect of working have not yet been determined."[3]

This statement sharply puts into focus the many uncertainties encountered when the mechanical properties of a given piece of molybdenum are to be correctly appraised. These properties may vary distinctly depending

TABLE 10.1. PHYSICAL CHARACTERISTICS OF MOLYBDENUM

Atomic number: 42
Atomic weight: 95.95
Atomic valence: 2, 3, 4, 5, 6
Valence orbitals: $4d^5 5s^1$
Isotopes (stable): 92, 94, 95, 96. 97, 98, 100 [10]
Density: 10.2 gm/cc (0.369 lb/cu in.)[10] 9.01^{11}
Melting point: $2620 \pm 10°C^{10}$ 2577^{12-14}
Boiling point: $5560°C^{10}$ $5687°C^{15}$ $4827°C^{12-14}$
Heat of fusion: 50 cal/gm[1, 2] 70^{16}
Heat of vaporization: 1340 cal/gm[2]
   Lattice type: b.c.c. (A2) (up to 2123°C)[1]
   Lattice constant: 3.1403 A (20°C)[1]
   Atomic volume: 9.4 cc/gm atom[16]
   Atomic radius: 1.36 A (coordination No.: 8)[1]
   Closest approach of atoms: 2.720^{16}
Thermal-neutron-absorption cross section: $2.4 \pm .02$ barns/atom[3]
Specific heat:

-257	-181.5	0	100	475	°C [10]
0.0004	0.0300	0.0589	0.065	0.0750	cal/gm/°C

Vapor pressure:[14]

10^{-8}	10^{-7}	10^{-6}	10^{-5}	10^{-4}	10^{-3}	10^{-2}	10^{-1}	1	10	Torr
1855	1970	2110	2260	2440	2650	2900	3200	3570	4040	°K

$\log p_{Torr} = (-31{,}060/T) - 0.2 \log T + 9.41^{12}$ Range: 298°K to M.P.
Enthalpy $(H_T - H_{25°C})$[3]

Temp. °C:	127	527	927	1327
cal/mole:	610	3105	5825	8740

Entropy $(S_T - S_{25°C})$[3]

Temp. °C:	127	527	927	1327
cal/mole:	1.76	6.07	8.82	10.91

Coefficient of linear thermal expansion (cm/cm/°C)

-173	-23	27	500	1000	1500	2000[3]	25–100	25–500	°C[10]
28	50	51	51	55	62	72	49	55	$\times 10^{-7}$

(see also Ref. 17)
Thermal conductivity[3]

Temp. °C:	-183	-78	0	1473	2173
cal/cm/sec/°C:	0.44	0.33	0.32	0.26	0.17

Electrical resistivity[3, 18]

Temp. °C:	0	27	727	1127	1527	1927	2327	2622
Microhm. cm	5.17	5.78	23.9	35.2	47.2	59.5	71.8	81.4

Temperature coefficient of resistivity: $5 \times 10^{-3}/°C$ (0 to 170°C)[19]
Surface yield of electrons (ma/cm²):

	2000	2200	2500	°K
	4	40	800	

Electron work function: 4.1 e.v.
Richardson constant $A_0 \epsilon^{-\alpha/k}$: 55 a/cm²/deg²
Magnetic susceptibility: $+0.04 \times 10^{-6}$ (c.g.s.)
Spectral emissivity (0.66μ):

	1000	1700	2500	°C
	0.378	0.353	0.332	

See Table 10.3

TABLE 10.1—*Continued*

Mechanical Properties:[3]
  Density (gm/cm³):
    powder, bulk density: 3.0
    cold-pressed bar: 6.0
    sintered bar: 9.8
    rolled sheet, or drawn wire   ≤10.3
    arc-cast   10.2
  Hardness: Varies over a wide range depending on amounts of cold work, recrystallization and temperature. Values for annealed polycrystalline molybdenum obtained by Engl, Katz, and Folmar[20] are given below:

Temp. °C:	−189.5	−88.5	+20	520	1243	1663	1857
Diamond cone:	373	237	159.2	89.1	40.6	19.5	12.6

  Modulus of elasticity: 40 to 50 × 10⁶ psi at 21°C[2]
  Modulus of rigidity:[2]
    17 × 10⁶ psi at 24°C
    16.1 × 10⁶ psi at 593°C
  Poisson's ratio:[1a]
    0.324 at 27°C
    0.321 at 871°C

TABLE 10.1a. *Effect of Prior History on the Room Temperature Tensile Properties of Molybdenum**

Condition	Structure, grain/mm²	Upper yield point, lb/in²	Ultimate tensile stress, lb/in²	Reduction in area, %
		Arc-cast molybdenum		
As cast	—	43,000	45,000	0–1
Hot-forged and recrystallized	200	60,000	73,600	8
Cold-reduced 35% and recrystallized	170	53,000	77,000	8
Cold-reduced 90% and recrystallized	1200	49,000	70,000	72
		Sintered molybdenum		
As sintered	5400	72,000	72,000	0
Cold-reduced 35% and recrystallized	170	54,000	77,500	8
Cold-reduced 90% and recrystallized	1650	65,000	76,500	72

TABLE 10.1b. *Effect of Rolling Temperature on the Tensile Properties of Work-Hardened Sintered Molybdenum**

Rolling temperature, °C	Hardness, VPN	Yield stress, lb/in²	Ultimate tensile stress, lb/in²	Redction in area, %
800	252	106,000	108,000	36
950	236	100,000	102,000	42
1100	238	100,000	103,000	16
1300	224	87,500	88,000	3

* After Northcott.[1]

315

TABLE 10.2. CHEMICAL PROPERTIES OF MOLYBDENUM

Electrochemical equivalent: 0.16580 mg/coul.

6.03125 coul./mg

A) *Reactions with gases and vapors:*

Air, oxygen, nitrogen, hydrogen, carbon monoxide, carbon dioxide at room temperature: none; tarnishing in moist air

Air or oxygen at 200°C: onset of slow oxidation

Air or oxygen above 400°C: ready formation of MoO_3[21]

Water vapor at 700°C: rapid oxidation

Nitrogen: dissolves in Mo slowly at 600°C and very rapidly at 1200°C resulting in brittle compound[22]

nitride formation above 1500°C[23]

Carbon monoxide: carbonization sets in at 1400°C

Carbon dioxide: oxidation above 1200°C

Hydrogen: none up to M.P.

Hydrocarbon vapor: partial carbide formation at 1100°C[23]

complete carbonization at 1300 to 1400°C[23]

Sulfur dioxide: oxidation to MoO_2 at 600°C

Dry fluorine: attack at room temperature[2]

Dry chlorine: reaction above 250°C[2]

Dry bromine: reaction above 250°C[2]

Dry iodine: none at 800°C[2]

Nitrous oxide and nitric oxide: oxidation to MoO_3 at 600°C

Ammonia: none

Hydrogen sulfide: MoS_2 forms at 1200°C[2]

B) *Reactions with liquids:*

Water: very slight attack at room temperature

Mercury: no amalgamation; solubility of Mo: 2×10^{-7}

H_2SO_4	dilute, at 20°C: very slight attack
	dilute, at 100°C: slow attack
	conc., at 20°C: slow attack
	conc., at 110°C: slow attack
HCl	dilute, at 20°C: very slight attack
	dilute, at 110°C: slow attack
	conc., at 20°C: very slight attack
	conc., at 110°C: slight attack
HNO_3	25 per cent, at 20°C: *rapid attack*
	conc., at 20°C: formation of protective film of MoO_3
	conc., at 100°C: *rapid attack*
Aqua Regia	dilute or conc., at 20°C: none
	dilute or conc., at 100°C: *rapid attack*
HF	dilute or conc., cold or warm: slight attack
$HF + HNO_3$	(50:50 by vol.) at 20°C: *rapid attack*
H_3PO_4	(10 per cent) at 20°C: attack
	at 100°C: *rapid attack*
$NH_4(OH)$	solution at 20°C: very slight attack
Na(OH), or K(OH)	(10 per cent solution), cold or hot: none
	fused salts: *rapid attack*

KNO_3, KNO_2, NaO_2, K_2CO_3, $Na_2CO_3 + KNO_3$, KCl_3, PbO_2 : *violent reaction*

TABLE 10.2—*Continued*

C) *Reaction with solids:*

Carbon and graphite: partial carbide formation at 110°C

complete carbonization at 1300 to 1400°C[45, 46]

Dry sulfur: attack at 600°C

Magnesia: reaction above 1600°C[24]

Zirconia: reaction above 2200°C[24]

Thoria: reaction above 1900°C[24]

Beryllia: reaction above 1900°C[24]

Alumina: none up to 1900°C (see Table 2.18)

Tungsten: reaction above 2000°C[24]

D) *Cleaning solutions, etching and polishing:*

Removal of oxides by cathodic treatment it dil. H_2SO_4 at approx. 100 a/sq. ft.[21]

Immersion in 90 p.c. KOH + 10 p.c. $NaNO_2$ (hot) removes oxides and reduces thickness[25]

Uniform etching: a) 1000 ml H_2O + 250 gm K(OH) + 0.25 gm $CuSO_4$ (or $CuCl_2$) anodic treatment

b) $NH_4(OH) + H_2O_2$

Rapid etching: a) dilute $NaNO_2$ or K(OH)—anodic

b) 1000 ml H_2O + 305 gm $K_3Fe(CN)_6$ + 44.5 gm Na(OH)

c) 50 pts HNO_3 + 30 pts H_2SO_4 + 20 pts H_2O; use at 90°C

Etching prior to resistance welding or brazing with tantalum foil:

96 pts conc. H_2SO_4 + 3.5 pts HF + 0.5 pts conc. HNO_3 + 18.0 gm/liter Cr_2O_3-immerse 10 sec. at 90°C

Electrolytic polishing: 1 pt. H_2SO_4 + 7 pts. methyl alcohol—anodic at about 16 a/sq. in. for about 30 sec.[26]

E) *Oxides of Molybdenum:*[27-29]

MoO_2 : Mo-dioxide: lead-gray; stable with metal substrate from 300 to 700°C; d = 6.47; slightly soluble in hot, conc. H_2SO_4

MoO_3 : Mo-trioxide: whitish-yellow; volatile above 600°C; M.P. 795°C; d = 4.69; forms eutectic with MoO_2 melting at 778°C; vapor pressure at 500°C: 10^{-5} Torr; at 800°C: 10 Torr; at 1150°C: 1 atm; sublimation is significant below 700°C

Mo_2O_3 : Mo-sesquioxide, black

Mo_2O_5 : Mo-pentoxide, violet-blue

$MoO_2 \cdot 4MoO_3 \cdot xH_2O$: blue, soluble in alcohol[25]

Mo_4O_{11} : stable solid at 607°C

Vapor pressure of MoO_3 :[27a]

808	850	880	904	940	958	°K
0.148	1.154	12.145	22.22	153.6	392.6	micron

on the process used in its manufacture,* the amount of hot working and annealing, the temperature at which the characteristics are measured, and the measuring technique. In forming-operations which require intermediate annealing treatments, it has been a common experience to encounter embrittlement, if certain time-temperature limits are exceeded during

* Arc-melted molybdenum is severely embrittled by as little as 0.0025 per cent oxygen.[31]

TABLE 10.3. THERMAL, OPTICAL, AND ELECTRICAL PROPERTIES OF MOLYBDENUM*

T, °K	T_B, °K	$e_{0.642\mu}$	e_t	A'	$V' \times 10^3$	ρ, μohm.cm
1000	960	.396	.094	236	7.08	23.5
1200	1142	.388	.119	344	12.81	29.2
1400	1320	.380	.144	471	20.80	34.9
1600	1494	.372	.171	618	32.4	41.0
1800	1664	.364	.190	771	46.0	46.8
2000	1830	.356	.209	942	63.5	52.8
2200	1994	.350	.228	1130	84.5	59.0
2400	2152	344	.248	1330	110.2	65.1
2600	2300	.399	.266	1542	141.0	71.6
2800	2460	.334	.280	1761	175.2	78.0

T = True temperature.
T_B = Brightness temperature.
A', V' = Current and voltage parameters corresponding to those used by Jones
and Langmuir for tungsten (see Table 9.9).
ρ = electrical resistivity.
* After Coomes.[30]

annealing. A typical recrystallization time-temperature curve for 0.002-in. rolled molybdenum sheet is shown in Figure 10.1, according to Harwood.[2] A more detailed analysis of the recrystallization behavior of both powder metallurgically sintered and arc-cast molybdenum was carried out by Bechtold,[5] whose results are given in Figure 10.2 for arc-cast materials; the results found for sintered molybdenum were very similar.

The arc-cast sample was obtained as a 1¼-in.-square, hot-forged billet which was annealed for three hours at 1650°C to obtain a completely recrystallized initial structure of about 10 grains/mm² prior to final rolling. After annealing, the billet was reheated to 1000°C and rolled in grooved rolls with several reheats at this temperature, and samples with 17, 33, 59, and 89 per cent total reduction in area were obtained. The examination of samples taken at various stages of the rolling process showed no evidence of recrystallization during rolling. Samples cut from each test piece were treated for various times at temperatures between 1000 and 1750°C in dry purified hydrogen.

"Figure 10.2 shows the relationship between time, temperature, and deformation for the beginning and completion of recrystallization. As with other metals, the temperature at which recrystallization occurs, depends upon the time at temperature and the amount of prior deformation. The temperatures and times below and to the left of the curves for the beginning of the recrystallization give the limiting conditions for cold-working molybdenum. If molybdenum is rolled, forged, swaged, or in any other way deformed under conditions of temperature, time, and amount of deformation, so that the beginning of the recrystallization curves is not exceeded, elon-

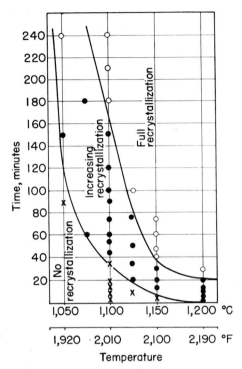

Figure 10.1. Typical recrystallization-time-temperature data for 0.002-in. rolled molybdenum sheet. After Harwood.[2] (*Courtesy McGraw-Hill Publishing Co., Inc.*)

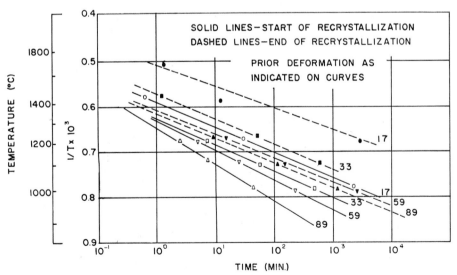

Figure 10.2. Time-temperature relation for recrystallization range of molybdenum. After Bechtold.[5] (*Courtesy American Society For Metals.*)

gated work-hardened grain structures are obtained. According to the current definition for hot working, temperatures and times above and to the right of the end of the recrystallization curves give the conditions for hot-working molybdenum."[5]

While the effect of time on the grain size after recrystallization is significantly different for arc-cast and sintered molybdenum, it is possible to obtain almost identical grain structures in most materials by carefully controlling the annealing conditions. Bechtold and Scott[6] prepared specimens in this manner and determined the mechanical properties over a range of temperatures. Figure 10.3 shows the results obtained for powder metallurgy molybdenum tested at a strain rate of 2.8×10^{-4} per second. Comparing the curves for fracture stress and total reduction in area, a marked change in the tensile properties of molybdenum is apparent which occurs at about $-25°C$. The "transition temperature" is defined as that temperature at which the total reduction in area attains a value half-way between the maximum and minimum values. For arc-cast molybdenum the transition temperature is found at $+5°C$. Below the transition temperature, fracture occurs with very little reduction in area and it is thus called brittle fracture;

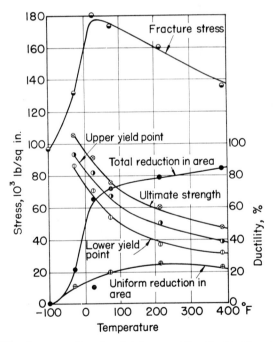

Figure 10.3. Tensile properties of molybdenum. After Bechtold and Scott.[6] (*Courtesy Electrochemical Society.*)

above the transition zone, where substantial reduction in area is indicated, the material is ductile.

"An abrupt transition from ductile to brittle behavior is not a unique characteristic of molybdenum. Iron and ferritic iron-base alloys show a similar behavior at a much lower temperature, near −150°C, and tungsten, tantalum, chromium, and other metals that have a body-centered cubic crystal structure will undoubtedly exhibit this behavior when tested under comparable conditions. An abrupt transition from ductile to brittle fracture has not been observed in metal and alloys that have a face-centered cubic crystal structure such as copper, aluminum, and austenitic stainless steels. The reasons for this behavior of body-centered cubic metals have not been determined but many of the factors which affect the temperature at which this transition occurs have been identified. Increased strain rate, stress conditions that restrain the flow of the metal, or an increase in the grain size will raise the transition temperature. Strain hardening induced by rolling, forging, or drawing, lowers the transition temperature in the direction of metal flow, or at least results in retaining some ductility below the transition temperature. However, the ductility normal to the direction of flow is reduced by strain hardening. Nonmetallic impurities, such as carbon, oxygen, and nitrogen, that form interstitial solid solutions probably raise the transition temperature."[6]

Figure 10.4 compares the tensile strength of molybdenum over a range of temperatures with that of other heat-resistant metals according to Bech-

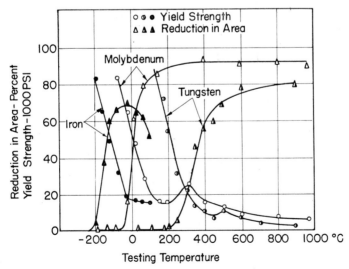

Figure 10.4. Effect of temperature on tensile properties of annealed ingot iron, molybdenum, and tungsten. After Bechtold.[34] (*Courtesy American Society For Metals.*)

told.[34] Pugh[32] has carried out a detailed analysis of the tensile properties of molybdenum at temperatures ranging up to 1100°C and suggests that a strengthening phenomenon, such as strain ageing, depending on temperature and strain, is responsible for the very attractive high-temperature properties of molybdenum. Test bars were prepared from arc-melted 4-in.-dia. ingots, extruded and swaged to 0.345-in. dia. and annealed for four hours at 1400°C which produced a recrystallized structure having an average of 500 grains per square millimeter. Short-time constant-rate tests were made at two strain rates, 0.2 and 0.02 inches per inch per minute, and constant-load creep rupture tests were conducted in an argon atmosphere at 870, 980, and 1095°C. Figures 10.5 and 10.6 give mechanical properties of as-swaged and recrystallized molybdenum from this extensive investigation.

Tensile requirements for "Molybdenum wire under 20 mils in diameter" are covered in ASTM Specification F 289–56T. Additional data for wires from 0.001 in. to 0.050-in. dia. are contained in Specification F 290–54T entitled "Round wire for use as electron tube grid laterals and verticals."

Fabrication of Molybdenum

Forged or rolled billets of molybdenum can be subsequently rolled into rods, bars, rounds, sheets, strips, or directly extruded into tubing by the Ugine-Séjournet process developed in France, which employs glass as a lubricant between the die and the workpiece.[2] Drawing, spinning, and ma-

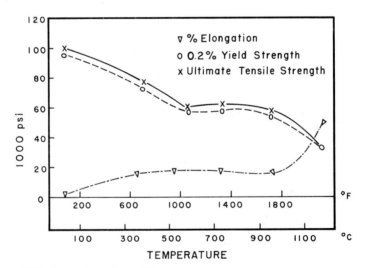

Figure 10.5. Strength and ductility vs temperature for as-swaged molybdenum. After Pugh.[32] (*Courtesy American Society For Metals.*)

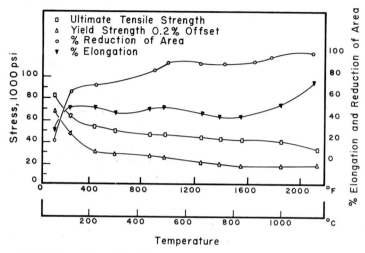

Figure 10.6. Strength and ductility vs temperature for recrystallized molybdenum. After Pugh.[32] (*Courtesy American Society For Metals.*)

chining operations can be applied to molybdenum, and it can be joined by the methods of welding and brazing (Chapter 12).

In all forming operations careful attention must be given to the transition from the brittle to the ductile state, which occurs near or below room temperature, and to the onset of recrystallization delineated by the curves shown in Figure 10.1. Many forming operations which result in cracks when conducted at room temperature are entirely feasible and readily performed at temperatures even only slightly above room temperature. It has been reported that the forming of molybdenum wire which was difficult in an air-conditioned room was done easily when the work was placed under a heat lamp. Cross-rolled* molybdenum sheet less than 0.020-in. thick can be bent 180° in any direction around a radius equal to the thickness of the material (1-T bend radius). Between 0.020- and 0.040-in. sheet thickness, working should take place within the temperature range of 200–325°F (93–163°C), and, for heavier stock, temperatures from 900–1000°F (482–538°C) should be employed, and dies be heated to these temperatures. Similar recommendations also hold for blanking, punching, or shearing. Straight, cold-rolled sheet has a tendency to fail by brittle fracture when bent along a line at 45° to the rolling direction.†

* Rolling molybdenum sheet from ingot can be done in different ways and is described by the following terms: (1) *Straight rolling*: All conducted parallel to the original longitudinal axis of the ingot. (2) *Cross rolling*: Rolling in two perpendicular directions, i.e. alternate rolling parallel to the longitudinal axis of the ingot and at

In drawing molybdenum, the number of draws should be held to a minimum to avoid the possibility of cracking. Bell and Hillier,[36] and Duckworth[37] have described a new drawing technique by which it was possible to form 0.010-in. sheet into cylindrical cups with a length-to-diameter ratio of over two to one without the need for annealing of the metal either before or during the drawing operations. As long as deep-drawing tools were used which called for the cup to be drawn right through the die, splits occurred along the walls of the cup at the first and second draw and extended on further drawing so that it was difficult to produce cups whose length was as great as the diameter. Splitting always occurred when the molybdenum wrinkled, or was subjected to compression, which always happened during the last stages of the drawing operation with the normal type of tool. When special tools were designed to keep the material under tension while being drawn, no failures occurred up to the sixth draw and only 10 per cent of the samples failed on the seventh draw. Fansteel has recently announced the availability of deep-drawn molybdenum anodes with a rolled rim at the open end to minimize corona in high-voltage applications. The cups are drawn from 0.015-in. sheet and are $2\frac{3}{4}$ in. deep and $1\frac{1}{2}$ in. in dia. Aluminum bronze is used in all drawing dies which are heated with strip heaters and lubricated with castor oil.[38] Additional information on the fabrication of molybdenum is given in references 33, 39–41.

For turning and milling as well as for cutting, tapping, or threading, various authors recommend the use of sulfur-base cutting oil lubricants. If the parts so treated are to be used within a vacuum tube, sulfur-base oils should be avoided and a suitable substitute be used, as harmful effects to the operation of cathodes will otherwise result. As a matter of fact, a sulfur-free soluble oil will do a much better job on grinding molybdenum with much less need for frequently dressing the wheel.[42]

Special Processes

The great importance of small percentages of impurities on the mechanical properties of molybdenum has been repeatedly pointed out. Apart from oxide inclusions and dissolved oxygen, the formation of oxide films on the

---

right angles to the ingot; sufficient passes are made in one direction to reduce the sheet thickness about 25 per cent before changing the rolling direction. (3) *Compression rolling*: During the rolling operation, the sheet is rotated 10 to 20 degrees between each successive pass. A reference direction is arbitrarily selected for compression-rolled sheet and all manipulation of the specimen is based on this direction.[34]

† For severe sheet-forming operations, Fansteel Metallurgical Corporation supplies Molybdenum "D" sheet which is annealed, cross-rolled, and treated to impart maximum ductility. Fansteel Molybdenum "G" wire is recommended for severe wire-forming operations for grids, hooks, and support members; it contains small controlled quantities of cobalt and has superior mechanical properties.[35]

surface of molybdenum is of great importance in the use of this material for tube components. Such films form in air, or oxygen, at relatively low temperatures of the order of 200°C (Table 10.2), and they will have a marked effect on contact potential between grid and cathode when molybdenum is used for grid laterals, lead to cathode poisoning if these films are later decomposed by electron bombardment, and impair the vacuum.

Gulbransen and Wysong[28] have investigated thin oxide films on molybdenum in oxidizing and reducing atmospheres and in high vacua at elevated temperatures. It was found that the oxides of molybdenum are essentially nonprotective to the base metal and that the rate of oxidation follows the well-known parabolic law up to 450°C, where deviations from this law set in. The stable oxides formed are MoO_2 and MoO_3, and the rate of formation depends much more markedly on the gas pressure than is the case for the oxides of tungsten. The oxides are volatile at relatively low temperatures, but are stable in high vacua at 10^{-6} Torr up to 1000°C; MoO_2 may be formed at such high vacuum and high temperature; it then tends to inhibit further reaction. At pressures as low as 300 microns at 1000°C, the volatile oxide MoO_3 is rapidly formed. A previously formed oxide film will begin to evaporate in a vacuum of 10^{-6} Torr when heated to 415°C, but at 400°C the rate of vacuum oxidation overcomes the evaporation phenomena and increases with increasing temperature. The reduction of molybdenum oxides in hydrogen is difficult to carry to completion. Three equations govern the possible reactions:

$$(1) \quad MoO_2(s) + 2H_2(g) \gtrless Mo(s) + 2H_2O(g)$$

$$(2) \quad MoO_3(s) + 3H_2(g) \gtrless Mo(s) + 3H_2O(g)$$

$$(3) \quad MoO_3(s) + H_2(g) \gtrless MoO_2(s) + H_2O(g)$$

Gulbransen and Wysong state that, from a thermodynamic point of view, reactions (2) and (3) above are favorable both in dry and wet hydrogen, while reaction (1) is feasible if the water-vapor concentration is maintained below the equilibrium value. Oxide films formed on molybdenum during a two-hour exposure to oxygen at a pressure of 7.6 cm and a temperature of 400°C were completely reduced when the sample was exposed to a hydrogen atmosphere at 2.2 cm pressure and a temperature of 550°C. Figure 10.7 gives plots of the equilibrium pressure ratio log pH_2O/pH_2 vs temperature for the three reactions. The decomposition pressures of MoO_3 and MoO_2 as a function of temperature are shown in Figure 10.8; they are negligibly small for practical considerations.

The *outgassing of molybdenum* has been studied by Norton and Marshall,[43] who found it necessary to heat the metal to 1760°C (true temperature) in a vacuum of 10^{-6} Torr for a time depending on the thickness of the metal

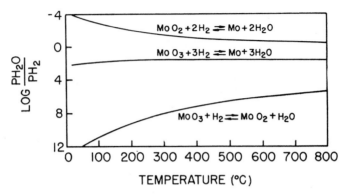

Figure 10.7. Equilibrium pressure ratio H_2O/H_2 vs temperature for hydrogen reduction of molybdenum oxides. After Gulbranson and Wysong.[28] (*Courtesy American Institute of Mining, Metallurgical and Petroleum Engineers.*)

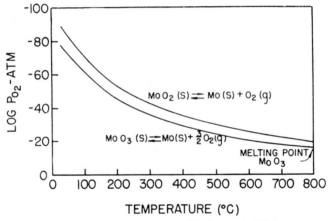

Figure 10.8. Decomposition pressure for MoO_3 and MoO_2 vs temperature. After Gulbranson and Wysong.[28] (*Courtesy American Institute of Mining, Metallurgical and Petroleum Engineers.*)

($\frac{1}{2}$ to 1 hour). The gases given off were nitrogen (over 60 per cent), carbon monoxide (15 to 36 per cent), carbon dioxide (3 to 65 per cent), and hydrogen in a negligible amount. Molybdenum parts which have been outgassed in this manner may be stored in dry air at atmospheric pressure without absorbing gas from the air if they are wrapped in cellophane or paper bags and not handled. Only a monatomic surface film is absorbed during storage and is readily given off after a short heating *in vacuo*. Hydrogen firing at atmospheric pressure is also a suitable degassing process because the absorbed hydrogen is readily given off *in vacuo* at relatively low

TABLE 10.4. ANALYSIS OF GASES RELEASED BY MOLYBDENUM[43]

	Time of degassing at 1760°C, (min)	Amount of gas per gm sample, mm³ (N.T.P.)	Gas composition (%)		
			N₂	CO	CO₂
Filed clean and washed in benzol	70	7.8	35	65	
Caustic dipped	24	4.4	79	16.5	4.5
Electrolyzed in conc. H₂SO₄	20	3.3	88.5	10.5	1

temperatures. The purity of the hydrogen used in the furnace has a marked effect on the amount of gas left in the metal; the furnace atmosphere should be free of N_2, CO, CO_2. Norton and Marshall found that molybdenum from different sources responded to outgassing quite uniformly, but noted a marked difference in the time of treatment required and in the amount of gas given off depending on the method of prior cleaning of the metal. Table 10.4 thus reproduces results obtained for 0.070-in. samples.

The outgassing of molybdenum anodes is of critical importance in the manufacture of voltage regulator tubes, which are generally filled with one of the noble gases, such as helium. In order to obtain stable operation of the tube, it is necessary that the filler gas have an impurity content of less than 1 ppm, or less than can be detected spectroscopically by a factor of 10 to 100. Extreme measures are thus necessary to obtain this degree of purity of the filler gas and maintain it in operation.

It has been found that the impurity content of the gas can be decreased by sputtering metal from the electrodes within the tube, and molybdenum was found to be most suited for this purpose. Todd, Drennan, and Kleinschmidt[44] investigated this technique, which had been suggested earlier by Penning and Moubis.[45] In order to clean the filler gas by sputtering action, it is of course essential that a minimum of gas be given off by the molybdenum electrodes. By separately degassing the molybdenum electrodes for at least six hours at a temperature of about 1900°C and a pressure of 5×10^{-5} Torr, or less, the time required for conditioning the VR tube by sputtering was reduced by a factor of 20 to 60. The authors recommend that the molybdenum parts should be heated to the high temperature just mentioned in a few minutes rather than in a few seconds. They warn that vacuum-firing should not be extended for too many hours, or the tube be treated on the pump for a very long time, because back diffusion of oil from the evacuating pumps, even at a theoretical back pressure of 10^{-11} Torr, may cause oil to impinge on the hot electrodes and thus result in formation of molybdenum carbide. Unsatisfactory tubes showed evidence of such carbide formation on the electrodes when analyzed.[46, 47]

Efforts to protect molybdenum against oxidation at elevated temperature in ordinary atmosphere by plating, cladding, or vapor deposition have been most extensive but not entirely successful, so far.[48] This activity is naturally directed toward the application of molybdenum for jet aircraft, which is beyond the scope of this book. In so far as molybdenum is an important component in ceramic-to-metal seals, serious thought must be given, however, to the protection of the metallizing layer if it is exposed to moderately high temperatures of the order of several hundred degrees centigrade in humid atmospheres. More will be said about this in Chapter 14.

When sealing molybdenum to aluminosilicate glasses or to fused silica (see p. 426), the excessive oxidation at the required high sealing temperatures is a serious handicap. Molybdenum disilicide coatings are capable of protecting the base metal for several hours at 1400°C, according to Rawson,[49] who found that seals to several aluminosilicate glasses can be made successfully. A tendency toward formation of bubbles at the glass-metal interface could be greatly minimized by heating the silicided material in hydrogen above the siliciding temperature, i.e. 1000°C.

Nickel-plated molybdenum disks, in diameters from $\frac{1}{8}$ to $\frac{3}{4}$ in., are available for semiconductor devices, where such plated disks are inserted between the copper leads and the silicon or germanium wafer and brazed to form the final assembly. Molybdenum sheet clad with platinum, nickel, or copper is used in some electronic devices.[33]

Radiation Damage

The physical characteristics of molybdenum are materially affected by exposure to nuclear radiation. An increase in tensile strength and yield point by 50 per cent on exposure to thermal neutrons (10^{20} nvt) at 80°C ambient temperature is reported by Varley.[50] Young's modulus did not increase up to 5×10^{18} nvt. Bruch, McHugh, and Hockenbury[51] of the Knolls Atomic Power Laboratory tested arc-cast molybdenum rods, swaged to $\frac{1}{2}$-in. dia., after an exposure to radiation in a reactor for 22 days at from 1.9×10^{20} to 5.9×10^{20} thermal nvt at 90°C. There was no visible change in microstructure as a result of the irradiation. The hardness, which originally was 264 VPN, or 99.2 R_B, increased by 35 BHN regardless of the position of the specimen in the horizontal plane of the reactor. Prior to irradiation, the material had a sharp yield point and considerable ductility. After irradiation, it was completely brittle, and each specimen fractured in two places. Irradiation changed the transition temperature (see p. 321) from approximately -30 to about $+70°C$—an increase of 100°C. The transition temperature of the irradiated material corresponds to that of unirradiated material having a grain count of 200 rather than the actual value of 5000 grains per square millimeter in the transverse direction. As no changes in structure could be detected microscopically, the authors concluded that radiation embrittlement was caused by submicroscopic changes.

REFERENCES

1. L. Northcott, "Molybdenum," Academic Press Inc., New York, 1956.
1a. "The Metal Molybdenum," Proceedings of a Symposium sponsored by The Office of Naval Research, held at Detroit, Michigan, Sept. 18–19, 1956. Published by American Society For Metals, Cleveland, Ohio, 1958; J. J. Harwood, Technical Editor.
2. J. J. Harwood, "Molybdenum, our most promising refractory metal," *Product Eng.*, **23**, 121–132 (Jan. 1952).
3. United States Atomic Energy Commission, "The Reactor Handbook," Vol. 3, Section 1, "General properties of materials" (AECD-3647), Mar. 1955.
4. R. M. Parke, "Molybdenum, a new high-temperature metal," *Metal Progr.*, **6**, 81–96 (July 1951). Contains extensive bibliography.
5. J. H. Bechtold, "Recrystallization applied to control of the mechanical properties of molybdenum." *Trans. Am. Soc. Metals*, **46**, 1449–1469 (1954).
6. J. H. Bechtold and H. Scott, "Mechanical properties of arc-cast and powder metallurgy molybdenum," *J. Electrochem. Soc.*, **98**, 495–504 (Dec. 1951).
7. J. Gelok, "Molybdenum—practical structural material," *Westinghouse Eng.*, 156–159 (Sept. 1947).
8. R. M. Parke and J. L. Harn, "The melting of molybdenum in the vacuum arc," *Trans. Am. Inst. Mining Met. Engrs.*, **171**, 416–430 (1947).
9. N. L. Deuble, "Large molybdenum ingots by arc-casting," *Metal Progr.*, **67**, 87–90 (Apr. 1955).
10. "Handbook of Chemistry and Physics," 40th ed., Chemical Rubber Publishing Co., Cleveland, Ohio, 1958/59.
11. D. E. Gray, Ed., "American Institute of Physics Handbook," McGraw-Hill Book Co., Inc., New York, 1957.
12. O. Kubaschewski and E. L. Evans, 2nd ed., "Metallurgical Thermochemistry," John Wiley & Sons, Inc., New York, 1956.
13. D. R. Stull and G. C. Sinke, "Thermodynamic Properties of the Elements," *Advances in Chem.*, *Ser. 18*, American Chemical Society, Washington, D. C., 1956.
14. R. E. Honig, "Vapor pressure data for the more common elements," *RCA Rev.*, **18**, 195–204 (June 1957).
15. H. A. Jones, I. Langmuir and G. M. J. MacKay, "The rates of evaporation and the vapor pressures of tungsten, molybdenum, platinum, nickel, iron and copper and silver," *Phys. Rev.*, **30**, 201–214 (Aug. 1927).
16. Charles L. Mantell, Ed., "Engineering Materials Handbook," McGraw-Hill Book Co., Inc., New York, 1958.
17. J. W. Edwards, R. Speiser and H. L. Johnston, "High-temperature structure and thermal expansion of some metals as determined by x-ray diffraction data. I. Platinum, Tantalum, Niobium, and Molybdenum. *J. Appl. Phys.*, **22**, 424–428 (Apr. 1951).
18. C. Zwicker, "Physical properties of molybdenum at high temperatures," *Physica*, **7**, 71–74 (1927).
19. C. G. Fink, "Ductile tungsten and molybdenum," *Trans. Am. Electrochem. Soc.*, **17**, 229–234 (1910).
20. J. Engl and J. Katz, "The temperature dependence of the cone hardness of metals" (in German). *Z. Phys.*, **106**, 1–8 (June 1937); J. Engl and J. Folmer, *ibid.*, **98**, 702–708 (Feb. 1936).

21. B. Lustman, "Oxydation of molybdenum in air at 1100 to 1600°F," *Metal Progr.*, **57**, 629, 630, and 674 (May 1950).

22. A. G. Pincus, "Mechanism of ceramic-to-metal adherence; Adherence of molybdenum to alumina ceramics," *Ceram. Age*, **63**, 16–20, 30–32 (Mar. 1954).

23. R. Palme, "Tungsten and molybdenum in high-vacuum technique" (in German), *Glas u. Hochvakuum Technik*, **1**, No. 7, 134–139 (Dec. 1952).

24. P. D. Johnson, "Behavior of refractory oxides and metals, alone and in combination, in vacuo at high temperatures," *J. Am. Ceram. Soc.*, **33**, 168–171 (May 1950).

25. A. C. Zettlemoyer, J. J. Chessick and F. H. Healey, "Heterogeneity of surfaces, absorption of gases on metals, molybdenum and the thermodynamics of absorption," O.N.R. Tech. Rept. No. 4 (1 June 1951 to 31 May 1952). William H. Chandler Laboratory, Lehigh University, Bethlehem, Pa.

26. F. Gifford and E. A. Coomes, "Torsion-induced recrystallization of highly refractory filaments," ONR Tech. Rept. Univ. Notre Dame, June 4, 1956.

27. R. E. Maringer and A. D. Schwope, "On the effects of oxygen on molybdenum," *J. Metals, Trans. AIME*, **200**, 365–366 (Mar. 1954).

27a. P. E. Blackburn, M. Hoch, and H. L. Johnson, "The vaporization of molybdenum and tungsten oxides," *J. Phys. Chem.*, **62**, 769–773 (July 30, 1958).

28. E. A. Gulbransen and W. S. Wysong, "Thin oxide films on molybdenum," *Am. Inst. Mining and Met. Engrs.*, **14**, 1–17 (Sept. 1947).

29. F. C. Todd, J. E. Drennan and W. W. Kleinschmidt, "Solid-state purification of molybdenum by induction heating," Vacuum Metallurgy Symposium, (Electrochem. Soc.) Oct. 6/7, 1954, pp. 142–146.

30. E. A. Coomes, "Fundamental Study of Oxide Cathodes," Bu. Ships Contr. Nobsr-64045, Final Rept. (25 Apr. 1955) (AD 79621).

31. J. J. Ward, J. P. Ray and S. A. Herres, "Calculations for reactions of chromium, molybdenum, titanium, and tungsten with oxygen, nitrogen, hydrogen, carbon and sulfur." Project Rand (Contract No. W 33-038-ac 14105) July 19, 1948.

32. J. W. Pugh, "The tensile properties of molybdenum at elevated temperatures," *Trans. Am. Soc. Metals*, **47**, 984–1001 (1955).

33. R. W. Yancey, "Designing with molybdenum," Pt. I, *Fansteel Metallurgy* (July 1958); Pt. II, *ibid.* (Sept. 1958).

34. J. H. Bechtold, "Effects of temperature on flow and fracture characteristics of molybdenum," *J. Metals, Trans. Am. Inst. Mining, Metall. Engrs*, **197**, 1469–1475 (Nov. 1953).

35. *Fansteel Metallurgy*, Information Bulletin on the refractory metals published by Fansteel Metallurgical Corporation, North Chicago, Ill., Nov. 1955.

35a. M. Semchyshen and G. A. Timmous, "Preferred orientation of arc-cast molybdenum sheet," *Trans. Am. Inst. Mech. Engrs.*, **4**, 279–287 (Mar. 1950).

36. R. L. Bell and M. Hillier, "High melting point aluminosilicate glasses in microwave valves," *Services Electronics Research Lab. Tech. J.*, **4**, No. 1, 1–8 (Feb. 1954).

37. J. F. Duckworth, "Deep-drawing of molybdenum," *Machinery (London)*, **84**, 389–390 (1954).

38. J. M. White, "New concepts in deep drawing produce molybdenum anodes of higher reliability," *Tooling & Production* (June 1957).

38a. J. Chelius, "How to fabricate molybdenum," *Materials & Methods*, **32**, 45–48 (July 1950).

39. C. E. Swartz, "Present status of the art of molybdenum fabrication," *Metal Progr.* **58**, 181–184 (Aug. 1950).

40. N. L. Deuble, "Arc-cast molybdenum-fabrication of parts," *Metal Progr.* **67,** 101–105 (June 1955).

41. N. L. Deuble, "Arc-cast molybdenum ingot to bar, sheet, or wire," *Metal Progr.,* **67,** 89–92 (May 1955).

42. 'Old Dutch' in *Grits and Grinds,* **46,** pp. 12–13 (Apr. 1955), (Norton Company, Worcester 6, Mass.)

43. F. J. Norton and A. L. Marshall, "The degassing of metals," *Trans. Am. Inst. Mining Met. Engrs.,* **156,** 351–371 (1944).

44. F. C. Todd, J. E. Drennan and W. W. Kleinschmidt, "Solid-state purification of molybdenum by induction heating," pp. 142–146 Vacuum Metallurgy Symposium, Boston, Mass., Oct. 6–7, 1954, sponsored by the Electrochemical Society.

45. F. M. Penning and J. H. A. Moubis, "The sputtering phenomenon in a neon glow discharge with molybdenum cathode," *Philips Research Repts.* **1,** 119–128 (Jan. 1946).

46. W. E. Few and J. K. Manning, "Solubility of carbon and oxygen in molybdenum," *J. Metals,* **7,** 271–274 (Mar. 1952).

47. R. Speiser, J. W. Spretnak, W. E. Few and R. M. Parke, "Influence of carbon on the lattice parameter of molybdenum," *J. Metals,* **7,** 275–277 (Mar. 1952).

48. J. J. Harwood, "Protecting molybdenum at high temperature," *Materials & Methods,* **44,** 84–89 (Dec. 1956).

49. H. Rawson, "A note on oxidation resistant coatings on molybdenum and their use in glass seals for Hg-lamps," *J. Soc. Glass Technol.,* **39,** No. 189, 211T–214T (Aug. 1955).

50. J. H. O. Varley, "Radiation damage," *Nucleonics,* **13** (Sept. 1955).

51. C. A. Bruch, W. E. McHugh and R. W. Hockenbury, "Embrittlement of molybdenum by neutron radiation," *Trans. AIME, J. Metals,* **7,** 281–285 (Feb. 1955)

CHAPTER 11

TANTALUM AND NIOBIUM

TANTALUM

Introduction

As tantalum is very much more expensive than its two high-melting sister metals, tungsten and molybdenum, a word of warning is in order for the novice in the field not to order this material in quantity without having obtained proper authorization. Reasons of economy restrict the use of tantalum to power tubes and microwave tubes where the cost of a material is offset by some unique properties.

Tantalum is highly ductile, and can thus readily be worked into various shapes more easily than molybdenum; on the other hand, while molybdenum is available in very large sheets, tantalum sheets are limited in width to a maximum of 12 inches in thicknesses ranging from 10 to 40 mils, or less for heavier stock. Tantalum is also available in the form of tubing, either seamless or welded, so that almost any part can be made of tantalum if the need arises. Tantalum strips up to 6 inches wide can be obtained in thicknesses down to 0.5 mil with a ±0.1 mil tolerance.* Three-inch diameter tantalum ingots of very high purity, especially low in oxygen, nitrogen, and carbon content, can be rolled to 0.5-mil foil without intermediate annealing.†

One of the main advantages of tantalum over molybdenum is its lower vapor pressure at elevated temperatures and its ability to absorb oxygen and nitrogen when operating in the vicinity of 700°C and above, thus acting as an effective getter (see p. 591). For a number of years, medium-sized power tubes were made with tantalum anodes which were operating at a red heat; the availability of other, more effective, getter surfaces on molybdenum has mitigated against the widespread use of tantalum anodes in recent years.

The high corrosion resistance of tantalum has made it a valuable material in the chemical process field. In acid solutions, tantalum becomes immediately covered with a stable oxide film which is exceedingly thin and tenaciously bound to the base metal. The oxide film has unidirectional properties

---

* American Silver Company, Flushing, New York.
† National Research Corporation, 70 Memorial Drive, Cambridge 42, Massachusetts. (Rev. Sci. Instr., Vol. 29 (Sept. 1958), p. 814.

to the passage of electric current and thus forms the basis of the tantalum rectifier. Self-healing electrolytic condensers made from sintered tantalum powder also take advantage of this thin oxide film. Rectifiers and condensers consume by far the largest part of the tantalum tonnage.

Like tungsten and molybdenum, tantalum is made by the methods of powder metallurgy, but owing to the great affinity of tantalum for oxygen, nitrogen, and hydrogen it must be prepared in a vacuum. After being worked into the required shape at room temperature, annealing and re-crystallization must likewise be performed in a high vacuum; these complications in processing, coupled with the scarcity of high-grade ore, and the difficulty of its purification explain the high cost of tantalum.

The most important mineral source of tantalum and niobium is a ferrous niobate-tantalate, $Fe(NbTaO_3)_2$. When niobium predominates, the mineral is called niobite, and when tantalum predominates, tantalite. Australia, Brazil, the Belgian Congo, and Nigeria are the principal sources—a fact which makes tantalum a strategic material. Pure tantalum powder is obtained from the ore by several different reduction and refining processes[1] and then pressed into bars 24 or 30 in. long and up to 1 sq. in. in cross-section by cold-swaging. The bars are then held between water-cooled terminals in a vacuum furnace and heated to temperatures of 2600 to 2700°C by the passage of thousands of amperes. After this sintering treatment, the bar has attained about 90 per cent of the theoretical density of the pure metal in bulk, and is then subjected to rolling or forging operations at room temperature. A second high-vacuum sintering operation at close to the melting point of the metal leads to grain growth and liberation of remaining impurities and gases, thus resulting in a highly ductile ingot of high purity which has a bluish-white appearance like platinum. Ingots are rolled into sheet; rod and wire are fabricated by rolling and drawing, carbide and diamond dies are used for smaller wire sizes.

The physical characteristics of tantalum are tabulated in Table 11.1 and the chemical properties in Table 11.2. The references indicated under the various entries will serve as guides to the literature.

The rate of evaporation of tantalum as a function of temperature was determined by Langmuir and Malter[14] from weight measurements and expressed by the following relation

$$\log_{10} M = 7.86 - \frac{39,310}{T}$$

where M is the rate of evaporation in grams per square centimeter per second, and T is the temperature in degrees Kelvin. Figure 11.2 shows the corresponding graph, and Table 11.3 gives the values of M and P. The vapor

TABLE 11.1—PHYSICAL CHARACTERISTICS OF TANTALUM[2]

Atomic number: 73

Atomic weight: 180.95

Isotopes: 176, 177, 178, 179, 180, 181, 182, 183, 184, 185[3]

Density: 16.6 gm/cc (0.600 lbs/cu.in.)

    17.1 " (single crystal, calc.)

Melting point: 2996 ± 50°C

Boiling point: 5427°C[4]

Atomic valence: 5

Valence orbitals: $5d^3 6s^2$

Lattice type: B.C.C.

Lattice constant: 3.3026 ± 0.0003 Å

Atomic volume: 10.89 cc/gm atom

Atomic diameter: 2.94

Closest approach of atoms: 2.854 Å

Heat of fusion: 5,900 ± 700 cal/mole[5]

Heat of sublimation: 189.8 ± 7.0 cal/mole (25°C)[5]

Heat of combustion: 1380 cal/gm

Thermal-neutron-absorption cross-section: 20 barns

Specific heat (at 0°C): 0.036 cal/gm; 6.512 cal/gm atom

Vapor pressure:[4] $\log p = -41{,}600/T - \log T + 13.98$

10^{-8}	10^{-7}	10^{-6}	10^{-5}	10^{-4}	10^{-3}	10^{-2}	10^{-1}	1	Torr
2230	2360	2510	2670	2860	3080	3340	3645	4010	°K

Coefficient of linear thermal expansion:[6] (cm/cm/°C)

827	1227	1627	1827	2027	2227	°C
72.9	78.9	84.9	87.9	90.9	93.9	$\times 10^{-7}$

mean value[3]

  0° to 1000°C: 65×10^{-7}

  20 to 500°C: 66×10^{-7}

  27 to 1400°C: 73×10^{-7}

  27 to 2400°C: 78×10^{-7}

Thermal conductivity:[3]

Temp. °C:	20–100	1700	1900	2100
Cal/cm/°C/sec:	0.130	0.174	0.186	0.198

Electrical resistivity:[7]

Temp. (°C):	20[3]	927	1127	1327	1527	1727	1927	2127	2327	2527	2727	2927
Microhm-cm:	15.5	51.0	59.0	65.8	72.5	78.9	85.2	91.3	97.3	102.9	108.7	113.9

Temperature coefficient of electrical resistivity: 3.82×10^{-3}/°C   (0–100°C)

Total thermal emissivity:[8]

Temp. (°C):	1400	1500	2000
ϵ_t :	0.20	0.21	0.25

Spectral thermal emissivity:[8]

Temp. (°C):	900	1100	1800	2500;	20
$\epsilon_\lambda(\lambda = 0.66\mu)$:	0.459	0.442	0.416	0.392;	0.493 ($\lambda = 0.665\ \mu$)[9]

Total radiated power:[10]

Temp. (°C):	1330	1530	1730
Watts/cm²:	7.3	12.8	21.2

Surface yield of electrons:

Temp. (°K):	1273	1500	2000
ma/cm²:	1×10^{-5}	4.7×10^{-3}	19.5×10^{-3}

Thermal yield of electrons: 6 ma/w at 2200°K

Electron work function: 4.1 e.v.

Richardson constant $A_0 \epsilon^{-\alpha/k}$: 37 a/cm²/deg² ($A_0 = 40$ a/cm²/°K²)

Magnetic susceptibility: $+0.93 \times 10^{-6}$ (c.g.s.)

TABLE 11.1—*Continued*

Mechanical Properties:

		Tensile strength psi	Elongation p.c. (2 in.)	Hardness Rockwell
Sheet-annealed	0.010 in.	50,000	40	85 (E)
Sheet-worked	0.010 in.	110,000	1	95 (E)
Wire-annealed	0.002 in.	100,000	11	
Wire-worked	0.002 in.	180,000	1.5	
Plate-hardened	0.010 in.	145,000	18	103 (B)

Young's modulus of elasticity: 27×10^6 psi
Poissons's ratio: 0.36

pressure of tantalum at various temperatures, expressed in dynes/cm^2 and mm Hg, is derived from the relation

$$P = 1700M\,T^{1/2}$$

Electrical resistance, thermal emissivity, melting point, and rate of evaporation of tantalum were determined by Malter and Langmuir[7] in 1939 when these authors repeated earlier measurements of some of these quantities by Worthing[15, 16] and Utterback and Sanderman[17]. The values for specific resistance at a given power radiation were found to be about 4 per cent lower than those reported by Worthing. This discrepancy was ascribed to an advance in processing techniques making available a purer grade of tantalum; a similar change took place in the properties of tungsten between 1932 and 1934 as reported by Forsythe and Watson[18].

Some of the results from Malter and Langmuir's work on tantalum are here reproduced for convenience of reference. Figure 11.3 gives the true temperature ($T°K$) vs. brightness temperature $S(°K)$ at $\lambda = 0.665$ micron. Table 11.4 summarizes data on resistivity, emissivity, and thermal expansion for tantalum. The curve shown in Fig. 11.3 can be represented by the following equation:

$$T = 0.9919S + 37.14 \times 10^{-6}S^2 + 5.74 \times 10^{-9}S^3$$

The error at any point within the measured range is less than 0.5 percent. The spectral emissivity (0.665 micron) as a function of the true temperature T was determined from the curve of Figure 11.3 by means of the relation

$$\frac{1}{T} - \frac{1}{S} = \lambda_e \log_e \frac{(0.665 \text{ micron})}{0.434C_2}$$

C_2 is the Wien-Planck constant, which equals 1.433 centimeter degrees. A smooth curve was drawn through the values thus plotted and the re-

TABLE 11.2. CHEMICAL PROPERTIES OF TANTALUM

Electrochemical equivalent: 0.3749 mg/coul.
2.6675 coul./mg

A) *Reactions with gases and vapors:*

Air or oxygen at 20°C: practically none

Air or oxygen at 400°C: weak oxidation—blue film[10]

Air or oxygen at 600°C: weak oxidation—grey film[10]

Air of oxygen at >600°C: formation of Ta_2O_5—whitish;[10] M.P. 1470°C[11]

Water vapor at 700°C: rapid oxidation

Nitrogen: absorption below 600°C with ensuing embrittlement; nitride TaN formed in pure N_2 at 1100°C; nitrogen liberated at 2000°C in vacuo. TaN is an interstitial compound;[11] a substantial volume change accompanies its formation.[11a]

Hydrogen: absorption below 700°C with ensuing embrittlement; practically all absorbed hydrogen released in vacuo at 1300°C[12] (Fig. 11.1)

Carbon monoxide: absorption at 600°C

Carbon dioxide:

Hydrocarbons: partial carbide formation above 1200°C; complete carbonization at about 1400°C

Rare gases: none

Halogens: attack

B) *Reactions with liquids:*

Water: none

Mercury: none

H_2SO_4 or HCl, cold, dilute or conc.: practically none in absence of SO_3
    warm, dilute or conc.: practically none in absence of SO_3

HNO_3 or aqua regia ($1HNO_3 \cdot 2HCl$), cold, dilute or conc.: practically none; warm, dilute or conc.: formation of protective surface layer.

H_3PO_4 , 85 per cent, cold to 145°C: practically none
    100 per cent, above 200°C: attack

HF, cold or warm; dilute or conc.: attack with absorption of hydrogen

HF + HNO_3 , cold or warm; dilute or conc.: strong attack, rapid dissolution.

Na(OH) or K(OH), cold: slight attack
    warm: strong attack

H_2O_2 : practically none

C) *Reactions with solids:*

Carbon: partial carbide formation above 1200°C; complete at ∼1400°C

SO_3 : attack

D) *Oxides of Tantalum:*

Ta_2O_4 : Ta–tetroxide, dark grey powder

Ta_2O_5 : Ta–pentoxide, white or colorless rhombic crystals; decomposes at 1470°C;
    d = 8.74

E) *Cleaning solutions, etching and polishing:*

General cleaning: Saturated solution of $K_2Cr_2O_7$ in conc. H_2SO_4 at 110°C (keep solution red at all times) Saturated solution Cr_2O_3 in conc. H_2SO_4 preferred.

Metallurgical polishing on felt: use following mixture:[8]

levigated alumina:	35 gm
HF (60 per cent):	20 ml
$(NH_4)F$:	20 gm
distilled water:	1000 ml

TABLE 11.2.—*Continued*

Electrolytic polishing, or electroetching:[13]
  solution: H_2SO_4 (conc.): 90 ml
              HF (conc., 48 per cent): 10 ml; temp. 35 to 45°C
  cathode: graphite or platinum
  for polishing use 0.10 amp/cm² for 9 min.
  for etching use 0.02 amp/cm² for 10 min.
Etching reagents:[8] A) 20-per cent solution of NH_4F in water
  1) A above, used for 5 to 6 min. at 80°C: grain structure of matrix is developed
     but Ta_2S_5 is not affected.
  2) 10 ml of A + 10 ml HF (60 per cent), used at 50 to 60°C for 1 min. Develops
     grain structure without discoloring Ta_2S_5
  3) 10 ml of A + 20 ml H_2SO_4, used at 60°C for 1 to 2 min. Effects similar to
     No. 1
  4) 10 ml of A + 10 ml HNO_3, used at 60°C: Ta_2S_5 is blackened
  5) 20 ml of A + 10 ml H_2O_2, used boiling, colors Ta_2S_5 brown
  6) H_2O_4 (95%) + HNO_3 (70%) + HF (48%) in volume ratio 5:2:2.[11a]

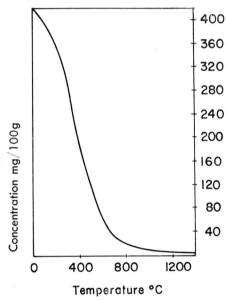

Figure 11.1. Tantalum-hydrogen isobar at one atmosphere. After Barrington.[12] (*Courtesy Services Electronics Research Laboratory.*)

sultant figures entered in the tabulation given in Table 11.4; the probable error of emissivity values is 0.1.

Electrical measurements were made on wires of diameter d_0, and the values $A' = A/d_0^{3/2}$, $V' = Vd_0^{1/2}/l_0$, $V'A'^{1/3} = VA^{1/3}/l_0$ determined. (A is the current in amps., V the measured difference of potential along the wire,

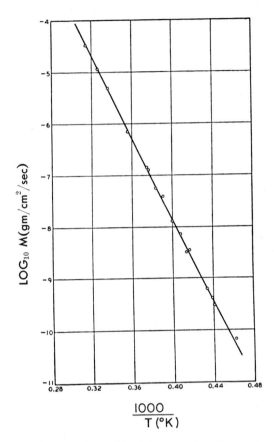

Figure 11.2. Rate of evaporation of tantalum as a function of temperature. After Langmuir and Malter.[14] (*Courtesy American Institute of Physics.*)

TABLE 11.3 RATE OF EVAPORATION M AND VAPOR PRESSURE P FOR TANTALUM
AT VARIOUS TEMPERATURES

(After Langmuir and Malter, Ref. 14)

T (°K)	M (g/cm² sec)	P	
		Dynes/cm²	mm Hg*
2,000	1.63×10^{-12}	1.27×10^{-7}	9.53×10^{-10}
2,200	9.78×10^{-11}	8.01×10^{-6}	6.01×10^{-9}
2,400	3.04×10^{-9}	2.58×10^{-4}	1.94×10^{-7}
2,600	5.54×10^{-8}	4.90×10^{-3}	3.68×10^{-6}
2,800	6.61×10^{-7}	6.07×10^{-2}	4.55×10^{-5}
3,000	5.79×10^{-6}	5.40×10^{-1}	4.05×10^{-4}
3,200	3.82×10^{-5}	3.77	2.83×10^{-3}
3,269 (M.P.)	6.80×10^{-5}	6.75	5.06×10^{-3}

* This column added by present author.

338

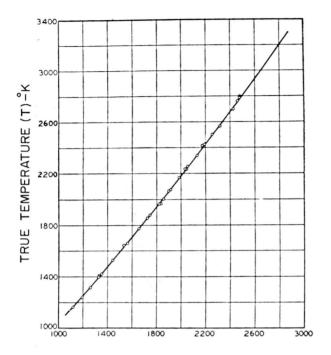

BRIGHTNESS TEMPERATURE (S at λ = 0.665 μ) − °K

Figure 11.3. True temperature T vs brightness temperature S for the effective wavelength λ = 0.665 microns. After Malter and Langmuir.[7] (*Courtesy American Institute of Physics.*)

d_0 the filament diameter in centimeters at room temperature, and l_0 the distance between the potential leads in centimeters at room temperature.) A', and V' thus become specific characteristics independent of filament diameter and have the same meaning as the corresponding quantities for tungsten shown in Table 11.8. The quantity $V \times A^{1/3}/l_0$ should be kept constant if the temperature of the filament is to remain constant while its diameter is being reduced by evaporation during prolonged operation at elevated temperature.*

The Mechanical Properties of Tantalum

Tantalum is twice as heavy as steel and, in the unannealed state, its strength is comparable to that of cold-rolled steel. The annealed metal may be compared with annealed steel. Fine wire and thin sheet have an

* This relation of constant $V^3 \times A$ for constant temperature was later questioned by Worrell.[19]

TABLE 11.4. DATA ON RESISTANCE, EMISSIVITY, AND THERMAL EXPANSION
OF TANTALUM.[7]

T is the true temperature; ρ is the resistivity corrected for thermal expansion; W is the total radiation intensity not corrected for thermal expansion and e_t is the power emissivity corrected for thermal expansion; M and L are the results of Malter and Langmuir; W are those of Worthing, and U and S those of Utterback and Sanderman. The spectral emissivity at 0.665 μ is indicated by $e_{0.665\mu}$. The thermal expansion given by Worthing is designated by l/l_0.

T (°K)	ρ Ohm·cm	W watts/cm²	e_t	A'	V'	$V'A'^{1/3}$	Brightness temperature			$e_{0.665\mu}$	l/l_0
							M and L	W	U and S		
1000	44.1 × 10⁻⁶	0.793	0.136	211	0.0118	0.0702	967	966		0.481	1.0047
1100	47.3	1.23	.144	254	.0152	.0963	1060			.476	1.0055
1200	51	1.84	.153	299	.0193	.1291	1152	1149		.469	1.0063
1300	54.8	2.73	.163	352	.0244	.1723	1242		1250	.462	1.0071
1400	59	3.95	.174	408	.0304	.2255	1332	1329	1337	.456	1.0079
1500	62.4	5.47	.184	469	.0368	.2855	1421			.449	1.0087
1600	65.8	7.36	.194	528	.0438	.3540	1508	1506	1508	.442	1.0095
1700	69.3	10.10	.205	602	.0527	.4450	1596			.437	1.0103
1800	72.5	13.28	.215	676	.0617	.5415	1682	1682	1678	.432	1.0111
1900	75.8	17.12	.223	751	.0716	.6508	1767			.426	1.0119
2000	78.9	21.63	.232	828	.0821	.7709	1852	1851	1843	.421	1.0127
2100	82	27.11	.240	910	.0936	.9071	1933		1926	.417	1.0135
2200	85.2	34.18	.247	1002	.1072	1.080	2018	2018		.413	1.0144
2300	88.3	42.23	.254	1095	.1212	1.250	2099			.409	1.0152
2400	91.3	51.27	.261	1189	.1357	1.437	2181	2181		.405	1.0161
2500	94.4	62.38	.269	1288	.1522	1.656	2261			.402	1.0170
2600	97.4	75.37	.276	1394	.1699	1.989	2341	2339		.400	1.0179
2700	100.2	89.89	.282	1502	.1880	2.153	2421			.397	1.0188
2800	102.9	105.5	.288	1606	.2064	2.417	2499	2495		.394	1.0197
2900	105.6	123	.293	1715	.2257	2.699	2575			.391	1.0206
3000	108.7	144.4	.298	1830	.2479	3.032	2652	2647		.388	1.0216
3100	111.4	167.4	.302	1948	.2700	3.367	2727			.386	1.0225
3200	113.9	194.2	.306	2075	.2940	3.749	2803			.384	1.0235
3269	115.5	214.5	.309	2164	.3110	4.025	2855			.383	1.0242

ultimate strength similar to that of steel. The brittle fracture strength of tantalum is higher than that of iron, molybdenum, or tungsten.[20]

The tensile strength of tantalum is increased only a small amount by working, i.e., 20 per cent, which explains the ease with which tantalum can be rolled to thin sheet and foil as thin as 0.4 mil. The absence of work-hardening makes deep drawing more difficult because tears are likely to occur. The hardness of tantalum can be increased by suitable heat treatment in vacuum at a temperature of about 1500°C. Rapid heating to a temperature not higher than 1600°C brings about a fine crystalline structure which is

TABLE 11.5. TIME-TEMPERATURE DATA FOR THE RECRYSTALLIZATION
OF 40-PERCENT COLD-ROLLED TANTALUM.*[21]

Annealing temp., °K	Annealing time, min.	State of tantalum
1520	110.00	Partial recrystallization
1520	140.0	Full recrystallization
1570	30.0	Partial recrystallization
1570	35.0	Full recrystallization
1620	12.0	Partial recrystallization
1620	14.0	Full recrystallization
1670	3.0	Partial recrystallization
1670	3.5	Full recrystallization

* Penultimate grain size 0.030 mm diameter.

correlated with maximum tensile strength at adequate workability; above 1600°C, a coarse crystalline structure results which has a lesser strength[10].

The time and temperature required for the recrystallization of cold-rolled tantalum were investigated by Wensch, Bruckart, and Deibler,[21] and their results are given in Table 11.5. By plotting the logarithm of time against the reciprocal of temperature, a straight-line relationship obtains as shown in Figure 11.4.

In the preceding chapter reference is made to the fact that the mechanical properties of metals with the body-centered-cubic crystal structure undergo marked changes at low temperatures, and some curves were shown which Bechtold had obtained for molybdenum. The same author investigated tantalum in this respect and found that this metal does not exhibit a transition from ductile to brittle fracture at temperatures as low as −195°C. Fully annealed and recrystallized test rods were subjected to a constant rate of elongation, and load-elongation curves plotted autographically. The proportional limit was used as the criterion for yielding and referred to as the yield strength; reduction in area determined from measurements after fracture was taken as the criterion of ductility.

"The load-percent-elongation curves in Figure 11.5 reveal the marked temperature dependence of the tensile properties of tantalum. The rapid increase in yield strength is readily evident from the curves of tests below room temperature. The percent elongation at fracture also varies significantly with temperature, being a maximum at about 25°C and decreasing at both higher and lower temperatures. The reduction in area at fracture, however, does not change greatly with temperature (Figure 11.3). The fractures at all temperatures were dull, fibrous, ductile types of failures.

"One of the more striking effects of test temperature is on the over-all shape of the load-elongation curves. The curves at −78°C and above are similar to those usually observed for annealed, polycrystalline body-centered cubic metals. Yielding is discontinuous, as revealed by upper and

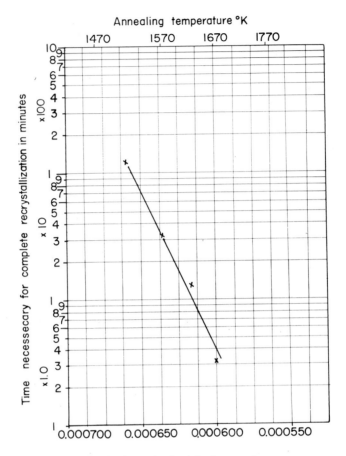

Figure 11.4. Time-temperature plot for the recrystallization of 40-percent cold-rolled tantalum. After Wensch, Bruckart, and Deibler.[21] (*Courtesy American Institute of Mining Metallurgical and Petroleum Engineers.*)

lower yield points at most temperatures, and a distinct yield-point elongation at all temperatures. The yield-point elongation increases with decreased test temperature. After the yield-point elongation, the load increases as the specimen elongates uniformly until a maximum, the ultimate tensile strength, is reached. Additional elongation occurs at decreasing load as the specimen necks down.

"Below −130°C, the pronounced upper and lower yield points again indicate that initial yielding is discontinuous. At the lower yield point stress, several per cent elongation occurs at essentially constant load and then the load decreases rapidly instead of increasing as it does at higher

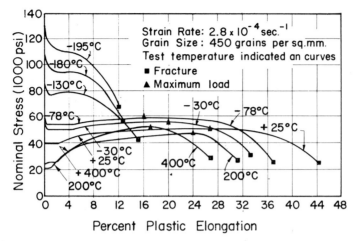

Figure 11.5. Nominal stress-percent elongation curves for annealed tantalum. After Bechtold.[20] (*Courtesy Pergamon Press, Inc.*)

temperatures. A load-elongation curve of this type indicates that there was no uniform elongation of the gage-length section of the specimen, and diameter measurements after test along the gage-length section revealed that all the deformation was concentrated in a relatively narrow necked-down region adjacent to the rupture. This type of stress-strain curve has not been observed in previous studies of molybdenum and tungsten. Although the percent elongation at fracture was considerably less than at higher temperatures, the reduction in area in the necked-down region was not significantly smaller than at high temperatures and the fractures at all temperatures were dull, fibrous ruptures. In iron, molybdenum and tungsten, bright, brittle fractures are always observed at low temperatures.

"The effects of temperature on the yield strength and ductility of tantalum and of several other metals are compared in Figures 11.6 and 11.7. The curves in Figure 11.6 show the marked temperature-dependence of the yield strength of body-centered-cubic metals and the relatively small effect of temperature on the yield strength of nickel, which is representative of face-centered-cubic metals. The yield strengths of iron, molybdenum and tungsten cannot be determined by the tensile tests below about −195°C, −75°C and 150°C respectively, since brittle fracture will occur before plastic yielding."[20]

Fabrication of Tantalum

Detailed instruction sheets on all aspects of the application of tantalum are available from the Fansteel Metallurgical Corporation* so that there

* North Chicago, Ill.

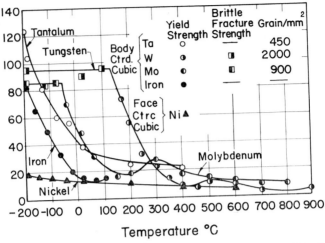

Figure 11.6. Effect of temperature on yield strength of tantalum. After Bechtold.[20] (*Courtesy Pergamon Press, Inc.*)

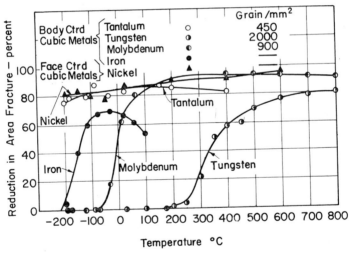

Figure 11.7. Effect of temperature on ductility of tantalum. After Bechtold.[20] (*Courtesy Pergamon Press, Inc.*)

is no need to repeat this information here; some data on joining, welding, and brazing of tantalum will be found in Chapter 12. It may be helpful, however, to emphasize the difficulties that may be encountered when tantalum is joined to metals with which it may form brittle alloys at elevated temperatures; this may lead to warpage and fracture. The same effect will

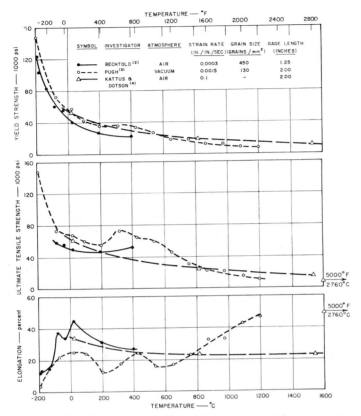

Figure 11.7(a). Tensile properties of tantalum over a wide temperature range. After Bechtold,[20] Pugh,[20a] and Kattus and Dotson.[20b] As presented by Tietz, Wilcox, and Wilson.[20c] (*By permission, The Department of the Navy, Bureau of Aeronautics.*)

ensue when tantalum members are operated in the vicinity of hot bodies, such as tungsten filaments, and gases are given off by the surrounding structures and absorbed by the tantalum member; this also may result in warpage and severe embrittlement.

A striking example of this kind of difficulty came to the author's attention several years ago. In the construction of a large power tube which was continuously exhausted, 15-in.-long tungsten strips about 0.10 in. wide and probably about 0.40 in. thick were used to form a ribbon beam of electrons; tantalum channels of U-shaped cross-section 0.200 in. wide, and 0.250 in. deep, made from 0.005-in. tantalum sheet were intended as reflectors behind these long strip filaments. In operation, the U-channels closed up and shortened to the tungsten strips as a result of continuous evolution of gases from massive metallic members that could not be properly outgassed. This difficulty was overcome by substituting molybdenum for tantalum and making the channel from several different sections rather than in one 15-in. piece.

The difficulties which may result from the alloying of tantalum with nickel were effectively demonstrated in a project at the same laboratory where resnatron filament baskets similar to the type shown in Figure 9.13 (p. 279) would fail where tantalum tabs were attached to a nickel ring. The tabs were folded around flat tungsten filaments at their free end and were intended to provide some measure of heat insulation owing to the low thermal conductivity of tantalum; substantial currents were passed through the junction. Figure 11.8 shows several photomicrographs of this joint

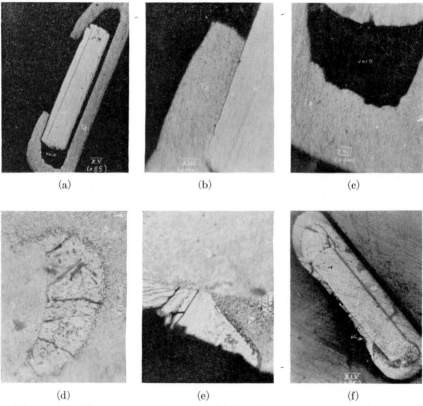

(a)   (b)   (c)

(d)   (e)   (f)

Figure 11.8. Alloy formation between nickel and tantalum. (a) Cross-section of tungsten ribbon (0.010″ × 0.050″) (×42) clamped and spot welded in a tantalum tab which in turn is spot welded to a nickel support ring (not shown). (×200.) (b and c) Enlarged detail of (a). (d) Void of (a) filled with nickel after operating assembly at 2400°C for 30 seconds. (e) Enlarged detail of (f) (where symbol Ni appears in (f)). (f) Same as (a) after operation at 2400°C for 30 seconds. Note: Temperature value approximate only. (*Courtesy Collins Radio Company.*)

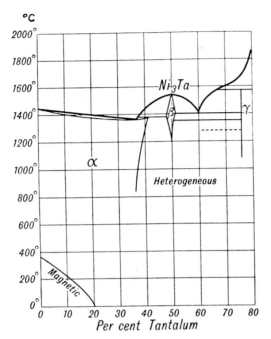

Figure 11.9. The constitution diagram of nickel-tantalum alloys. After Therkelson, Berlin, 1932. (*Courtesy Longmans Green and Company.*)[21a]

before and after operation. It is clearly evident how the voids between filament and tab were quickly filled by a lower-melting nickel-tantalum alloy. Figure 11.9 gives the nickel-tantalum phase diagram according to Therkelson[21a]. When the tantalum content is greater than 36 per cent, brittle intermetallic compounds are formed. Figure 11.10 shows the variation of hardness, tensile strength, Young's modulus, and electrical conductivity of nickel-tantalum alloys as a function of the tantalum content.

Outgassing of Tantalum

Tantalum has a high activity for various gases, especially in the temperature range 600 to 1,000°C where it acts as a getter when used for structural components of a vacuum tube. To take advantage of this property, it is of course necessary that the tantalum has been previously outgassed, and that the tube is designed to make possible the operation of the tantalum element at an elevated temperature. In order to drive out previously absorbed gases, it is necessary to raise the tantalum components to a temperature of at least 2000°C. For more critical applications, still higher outgassing temperatures are required.

Gebhardt and Preisendanz[22] recently investigated the solubility of oxy-

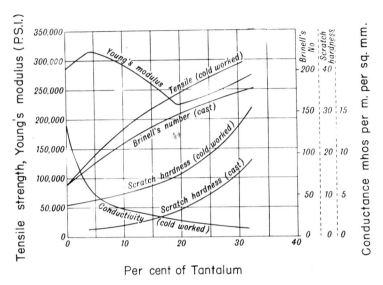

Figure 11.10. Hardness, tensile strength, and electrical conductivity of Ni-Ta alloys. After Therkelson.[21a] (*Courtesy Reinhold Publishing Corporation.*)

gen in tantalum and the changes of physical properties related to it. To establish clean conditions, these authors found it necessary to heat tantalum to a temperature ranging from 2600 to 2800°C in a vacuum of less than 5×10^{-6} Torr, and state specifically that at temperatures between 2200 and 2300°C complete degassing was not obtained, especially in regard to oxygen. After this careful degassing of the tantalum samples, which consisted of wires, rods or strips, they were exposed to oxygen atmospheres at various pressures and temperatures ranging from 750 to 1500°C. Figure 11.11 gives the results obtained.

It is important to note that the oxygen absorbed at these temperatures was not released when the temperature of the samples was lowered to room temperature. At low oxygen pressures, the surface of the samples retained its metallic appearance, whereas at higher oxygen pressures a very thin surface oxidation became apparent; this changed the emissivity of the surface, which was measured by means of a selenium photocell. The saturation limit for oxygen is 3.7 atomic percent at 1500°C, 2.9 atomic percent at 1200°C, 2.3 atomic percent at 1000°C and 1.4 atomic percent at 750°C. When these limits are exceeded, a surface oxidation becomes noticeable.

The absorption of oxygen has a marked effect on a number of physical properties of tantalum as found by various earlier investigations. The logarithmic decrement for damped oscillations at 1.4 cycles per second increases linearly with increase of oxygen content; the modulus of elasticity

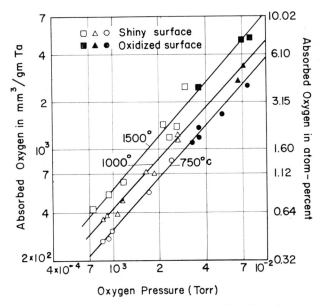

Figure 11.11. Sorption of oxygen by tantalum, as a function of pressure at various temperatures. After Gebhardt and Preisendanz.[22] (*Courtesy Dr. Riederer Verlag GMBH-Stuttgart.*)

likewise increases, and so do the hardness and the tensile strength. The specific magnetic susceptibility decreases linearly with increasing oxygen content; ductility and reduction of cross-section likewise decrease with increasing oxygen content. Another interesting effect of oxygen content of tantalum is the increasing solubility in 40 percent hydrofluoric acid, as shown in Figure 11.12.

The widely differing values for the hardness of tantalum which have been published from time to time no doubt can be ascribed to the different oxygen contents. Gebhardt and Preisendanz find that the hardness increases from about 40 kg/mm² for carefully outgassed material to a value of 630 kg/mm² at an oxygen content of 4.4 atomic percent (Figure 11.13). The pronounced discontinuity at 2.9 atomic percent oxygen content indicates the solubility limit for exposure at 1200°C. The electrical conductivity as a function of oxygen content shows a similar discontinuity at this point, according to the same authors.

When cold-worked tantalum is reheated *in vacuo*, a marked increase of hardness takes place at 1800°C, according to Greenwood and Myers.[23] The authors remark that hard tantalum becomes soft again if the heating is carried to 2400°C, followed by quick cooling, whereas slow cooling at the rate of 7°C per minute to 1100°C results in hard and brittle tantalum. The

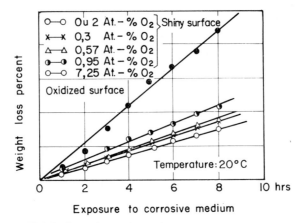

Figure 11.12. Weight loss of tantalum of different oxygen contents in 40 percent HF. After Gebhardt and Preisendanz.[22] (*Courtesy Dr. Riederer Verlag GMBH-Stuttgart.*)

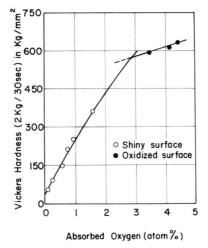

Figure 11.13. Vickers hardness of tantalum as a function of oxygen content. After Gebhardt and Preisendanz.[22] (*Courtesy Dr. Riederer Verlag GMBH-Stuttgart.*)

heating was carried out in a vacuum of the order of 1 to 10 microns by passing a current through the test sample. The authors express the view that some absorption of gases at these relatively low pressures is responsible for this strange behavior. Figure 11.14 gives the results of their measurements.

The tensile strength of tantalum can be increased to a value of 200,000 psi by heating sheets in air for prescribed times and temperatures followed

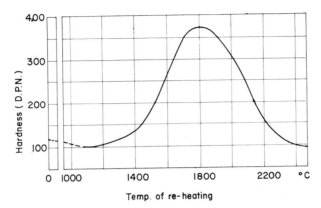

Figure 11.14. Annealing temperature and hardness of tantalum. After Greenwood and Myers.[23] (*Courtesy Macmillan & Co. Ltd., London.*)

by heating *in vacuo* at temperatures between 1150 and 1400°C. Bursting or pressure-indicating diaphrams are designed on the basis of this treatment.[24]

While the vapor pressure of tantalum is exceedingly low, even at elevated temperatures, that of the oxides of tantalum is much higher, and great care is thus required not only in properly cleaning tantalum parts before they are assembled but also in avoiding oxide contaminations in the remaining tube structure; such oxides may be decomposed at the high temperatures required for outgassing the tantalum itself. Tantalum oxides will be decomposed or volatilized at a level of 1800°C. Tantalum nitrides are decomposed at much higher temperatures than the oxides. If the full value of tantalum is to be realized in transmitting tubes containing tantalum electrodes, they should be heated to at least 2000°C for the purpose of proper outgassing, and preferably to 2600°C for a long time in an exceedingly good vacuum.

Alloys of Tantalum

An alloy of tantalum and tungsten is commercially available under the trade name "Tantaloy"; this material contains 7.5 per cent tungsten and is available in form of sheet and wire; it has the property of maintaining its elasticity at red heat and is thus useful for the fabrication of springs and tension members in vacuum tubes. Such parts can be made from annealed or unannealed alloy and can then be heat-treated to a point where the yield strength is equal to the tensile strength. Annealed "Tantaloy" wire, 0.010 in. diameter, has a tensile strength at room temperature of about 90,000 psi and a yield strength of about 85,500 psi. In the unannealed or cold-worked state, the tensile strength is about 250,000 psi and the yield strength about 245,000 psi.

The alloys of molybdenum and tantalum have been investigated by Geach and Summers-Smith.[25] The two metals crystallize in the same structure, (body-centered cubic), have similar electrochemical properties, and their atoms differ in size by less than 5 per cent; thus it is to be expected that they will form extensive solid solutions with each other. The alloys were produced by arc-casting in a purified argon atmosphere, or by powder metallurgical procedures; commercial applications have not become known.

Tantalum together with tungsten or molybdenum forms a thermocouple which is useful in the high-temperature range up to 3000°C for W-Ta, and up to 2600°C for Ta-Mo junctions. The Ta-W couple has a reasonably linear range from about 300 to 2000°C giving a thermal emf of 22.9 mV at 2000°C.[26, 27] Such couples must naturally be operated in a neutral atmosphere or vacuum, or they may be protected by a beryllium oxide ceramic tube (Chapter 8).

NIOBIUM

In the near future, this metal may well assume an important role in vacuum tube construction. Niobium is now available in form of sheet, bars, rod, tubing, wire, foil, powder, ingot, and can be readily fabricated and welded. In many respects its properties are similar to those of tantalum, but its density is about one-half that of tantalum and its neutron absorption cross-section is very much lower. The metal thus offers advantages for tubes to be used in critical environments where shock and vibration and radiation damage are likely causes of failure.

Saller, Stacy, and Porembka[29a] have reported on an "initial investigation of niobium and niobium-base alloys." Several papers on the production, purification, and fabrication of niobium were published in a special issue of the *Journal of the Institution of Metals* by O'Driscoll, Miller, and Williams.[38, 39] A symposium on the technology of niobium was held in Washington in May 1958, and the papers were recently published by Gonser and Sherwood.[29b] A substantial body of up-to-date literature on this metal is thus available.

The physical properties of niobium are given in Table 11.6. At room temperature, it has a high resistance to corrosion by liquids and gases, a property which makes it attractive to the chemical process industry and particularly to the designers of nuclear reactors on account of its superior resistance to corrosion from liquid sodium and sodium-potassium alloy at temperatures up to 660°C.[29, 30] However, its reactivity with oxygen, hydrogen, and nitrogen at elevated temperatures is a major difficulty associated with its use as a high-temperature material. Gulbransen and Andrew[36]

TABLE 11.6 PHYSICAL CHARACTERISTICS OF NIOBIUM[29]

Atomic number: 41

Atomic weight: 92.91

Atomic volume: 10.83 (cc/gr-atom)

Atomic diameter: 2.94

Isotopes: 90, 91, 92, 93, 94, 95, 96, 97, (98), 99

Density: 8.66 gm/cc[30] (0.313 lb/in.³)

Atomic valence: 5, 3

Valence orbitals: $4d^4 5s$

Lattice type: B.C.C.

Lattice constant (20°C):[30] 3.3004 ± 0.0003 A.U.

Closest approach of atoms:[28] 2.853 A.U.

Thermal-neutron-absorption cross-section: 1.1 ± 0.1 barns

Melting point: 2415 ± 15°C[31]   2468 ± 10°C[32]
         (4380 ± 30°F)   (4475 ± 18°F)
   Oxygen content causes a depression of the melting point; earlier values are probably lower for this reason.

Boiling point: 3300°C

Heat of combustion: 2379 cal/gm[31]

Heat of sublimation: 170.9 Kcal/gm-atom[31]

Heat of vaporization: 171.2 Kcal/gm-atom
                1.84 Kcal/gm

Specific heat (0°C): 6.012 cal/gm-atom
            0.065 cal/gm/°C

Thermal conductivity (20°C): 0.13 cal/cm²/cm/°C/sec

0	100	200	300	400	500	600	°C
0.125	0.13	0.135	0.140	0.145	0.151	0.156	[32, 33]

Coefficient of linear thermal expansion[33] (cm/cm/°C)

Temp. T:	300	400	500	600	700	800	900	1000	°C
Avg. 18° to T:	73.1	73.9	74.7	75.6	76.4	77.2	78.0	78.8	× 10⁻⁷
Inst. at T:	73.8	75.4	76.1	78.7	80.3	82.0	83.7	85.2	× 10⁻⁷

$$L = L_0(6.892 \times 10^{-6}T + 8.17 \times 10^{-10}T^2)$$
   (20°C): $\alpha = 71.0 \times 10^{-7}$ [28]
   (0–1000°C): $\alpha = 68.9 \times 10^{-7}$ [33]

Vapor pressure:[33b] $\log P_{atm} = (-40,169/T°_K) - 8.872$

2304		2358		2404		2463		2485	°K
2.6311 × 10⁻⁹	8.0977 × 10⁻⁹	1.6526 × 10⁻⁸	4.0512 × 10⁻⁸	5.8069 × 10⁻⁸	atm

Electrical resistivity microhm-cm[33]

0	100	200	300	400	500	600	°C
15.22	19.18	23.13	27.09	31.04	35.00	38.96	

Temperature coefficient of electrical resistivity
   0–600°C: 0.00396 microhm. cm/°C

Spectral thermal emissivity ($\lambda = 0.650$ micron): 0.37 ($T = 1730$°C)

Total radiation (Watts/cm²): 22(1880°C); 30(1980°C)[34]

Electron work function: 4.01 e.v.[31]

Richardson constant $A_0\epsilon^{-\alpha/k}$: 37 a/cm²/°K² ($A_0 = 40$)[35]

Magnetic susceptibility: +2.28 × 10⁻⁶ (c.g.s.)

Mechanical Properties[33, 33a] (see also Fig. 11.7a)

°C	Proportional limit 1000 psi	Tensile strength 1000 psi	Elongation (in 4 √area) %	Modulus of elasticity 10⁶ psi
20	24.2	39.4	49	12.4
200	14.6	33.6	48	10.9
300	14.1	34.7	38	8.0
400	14.6	33.2	28	7.5
500	15.2	35.6	35	6.4
550	10.5	32.3	24	4.7

TABLE 11.6—*Continued*

Typical values[29]	Tensile strength 1000 psi	Elongation in 2 in. %	Rockwell hardness R_E
Sheet annealed	48–59	30	80
Sheet worked	96–130	5	100

have recently extended their studies of this problem into ranges of higher temperatures (375–700°C) and have reevaluated earlier work by several investigators.

Niobium forms three oxides with limited regions of homogeneity, i.e., Nb_2O_5, NbO_2, and NbO. A transition in the rate of oxidation from the parabolic rate law to the linear rate law occurs at oxide film thicknesses of 50 to 67 $\mu gm/cm^2$ in the temperature range of 400 to 430°C. After the transition, the oxide is not adherent to the metal.

Like tantalum, niobium acts as a getter when operated at an elevated temperature (500°C) in a vacuum tube, either as a structural component or in the form of a getter flag.

An outgassing temperature of 2000°C has been reported.[29a] Oxygen, nitrogen, and hydrogen are rapidly absorbed.[38, 39]

Specific applications of niobium in the construction of vacuum tubes have been described by workers of the Bell Telephone Laboratories.[40, 41] It was stated by Pondy and McClure[40] that outgassing at 1650°C for 30 minutes rather than at 1250°C did not further improve the performance characteristics of their tube. The niobium parts (0.220-in.-dia. disks) were etched in 4M KOH, HF, and boiled in hydrogen peroxide to pass the atomizer test for clean surfaces. Niobium was found to maintain its shape better after forming, and not to sputter as much as molybdenum; its use in discharge tubes also resulted in more consistently low sustaining voltages, i.e., 98.7 ± 0.35 volts at 10 ma. Measured breakdown voltages were 146.3 ± 1.7 volts.[41]

REFERENCES

1. L. F. Yntema and A. L. Percy, "Tantalum and Columbium," Chapter 20, in "Rare Metals Handbook," C. A. Hampel, Ed., Reinhold Publishing Corp., New York, 1954.
2. Fansteel Metallurgical Corporation, "The Metal Tantalum," North Chicago, Ill., 1953.
3. American Institute of Physics Handbook, McGraw-Hill Book Co., Inc., New York, 1957.
4. R. E. Honig, "Vapor pressure data for the more common elements," *RCA Rev.*, **18**, 195–204 (June 1957).
5. O. Kubaschewski and E. L. Evans, "Metallurgical Thermochemistry," 2nd ed., John Wiley & Sons, Inc., New York, 1956.
6. J. W. Edwards, R. Speiser and H. L. Johnston, "High-temperature structure and thermal expansion of some metals as determined by x-ray diffraction data. I.

Platinum, Tantalum, Niobium, and Molybdenum." *J. Appl. Phys.*, **22**, 424–428 (Apr. 1951).

7. L. Malter and D. B. Langmuir, "Resistance, emissivities, and melting point of tantalum," *Phys. Rev.*, **55**, 743–747 (Apr. 15, 1939).

8. C. J. Smithells, "Metals Reference Book," New York, Interscience Publishers, Inc., 1955. (2 Vols.)

9. M. Davis and J. F. Duke, "An investigation into the possibility of fabricating rhenium metal," *Services Electronics Research Lab. Tech. J.*, **6**, 65–78 (Aug. 1956).

10. W. Espe and M. Knoll, "Werkstoffkunde der Hochvakuumtechnik," Berlin, Verlag Julius Springer, 1936.

11. R. E. Kirk and D. F. Othmer, "Encyclopedia of Chemical Technology," Vol. 13, Interscience Publishers, Inc., New York, 1954.

11a. R. Bakish, "Some observations on the effect of the interaction of tantalum with oxygen, nitrogen, and hydrogen," *J. Electrochem. Soc.*, **105**, 574–577 (Oct. 1958).

12. A. E. Barrington, "A high-temperature cantilever cathode for noise investigations of 8 mm CW magnetrons," *Services Electronics Research Lab. Tech. J.*, **5**, 74–79 (Aug. 1955).

13. G. W. Wensch, K. B. Bruckart and M. Connolly, "Electropolishing of tantalum," *Metal Progr.*, **61**, 81 (Mar. 1952).

14. D. B. Langmuir and L. Malter, "The rate of evaporation of tantalum," *Phys. Rev.*, **55**, 748–749 (Apr. 15, 1939).

15. A. G. Worthing, "Spectral emissivities of tantalum, platinum, nickel, and gold as a function of temperature and the melting point of tantalum," *Phys. Rev.*, **28**, 174–189 (July 1926).

16. A. G. Worthing, "Physical properties of well-seasoned molybdenum and tantalum as a function of temperature," *Phys. Rev.*, **28**, 190–201 (July 1926).

17. C. L. Utterback and L. A. Sanderman, "Some thermal properties of tantalum," *Phys. Rev.*, **39**, 1008–1011 (Mar. 15, 1932).

18. W. E. Forsythe and E. M. Watson, "Resistance and radiation of tungsten as a function of temperature," *J. Opt. Soc. Amer.*, **24**, 114–118 (Apr. 1934).

19. F. T. Worrell, "$V^3 \times A$ relation for vaporizing molybdenum," *Phys. Rev.* **6**, 520–524 (Apr. 1942).

20. J. H. Bechtold, "Tensile properties of annealed tantalum at low temperatures," *Acta Metallurgica*, **3**, 249–254 (May 1955).

20a. J. W. Pugh, "Temperature dependence of the tensile properties of tantalum," *ASM Trans.*, **48**, 677–688 (1956).

20b. J. R. Kattus and C. L. Dotson, "Tensile, Fracture, and Short-time Creep Properties of Aircraft Structural Materials at Very High Temperatures After Rapid Heating," Southern Research Inst. Rept. No. WADC-TR-55-391 (Dec. 1955).

20c. T. E. Tietz, B. A. Wilcox and J. W. Wilson, "Mechanical Properties and Oxidation Resistance of Certain Refractory Metals," Stanford Research Institute, Final Rept. Jan. 30, 1959; Contract No. NOas 58-366-d, Department of the Navy, Bureau of Aeronautics.

21. G. W. Wensch, K. B. Bruckart and R. H. Deibler, "Recrystallization of tantalum," *Trans. AIME, J. Metals*, **4**, 596 (June 1952).

21a. E. Therkelson, "The alloys of nickel with tantalum," *Metals and Alloys*, **4**, 105–108 (July 1933).

22. E. Gebhardt and H. Preisendanz, "On the solubility of oxygen in tantalum and

the ensuing changes of physical properties" (in German), *Z. Metallkunde*, **46**, 560–568 (Aug. 1955).

23. J. N. Greenwood and R. H. Myers, "Annealing temperature and hardness of tantalum," *Nature*, **160**, 675 (Nov. 1947).

24. R. W. Yancey, "Metallurgical characteristics of tantalum and their relationship to the fabrication of tantalum products," presented at Regional Conference on Reactive Metals, American Institute of Mining and Metallurgical Engineers, Buffalo, N. Y., March 20, 1956.

25. G. A. Geach and D. Summers-Smith, "The alloys of molybdenum and tantalum," *J. Inst. Metals*, **80**, 143–146 (1951).

26. H. A. Wilhelm, H. J. Svec, A. I. Snow and A. H. Danne, "High-temperature thermocouples," Ames Lab., June 29, 1948 (AECD-3275).

27. S. H. Morgan and W. E. Danforth, "Thermocouples of the refractory metals," *J. Appl. Phys.*, **21**, 112–113 (Feb. 1950).

28. Charles L. Mantell, Ed., "Engineering Materials Handbook," McGraw-Hill Book Co., Inc., New York, 1958.

29. R. O. Jaeger, Ed., *Fansteel Metallurgy*, Jan. 1958, pp. 2–3. "Columbium: an available engineering material with high-temperature strength, medium density, ductility, and other useful properties," Fansteel Metallurgical Corporation, North Chicago, Ill.

29a. H. A. Saller, J. T. Stacey and S. W. Porembka, "Initial investigation of niobium and niobium-base alloys," Battelle Memorial Institute, Report No. BMI-1003 (May 23, 1955); Contract No. W-7405-eng-92.

29b. B. W. Gonser and E. M. Sherwood, Eds., "Technology of Columbium (Niobium)," papers presented at the Symposium on Columbium (Niobium) of the Electrothermic and Metallurgy Division of the Electrochemical Society, May 15 and 16, 1958, Washington, D. C., John Wiley & Sons, Inc., 1958.

30. A. B. McIntosh, "The development of niobium," *J. Inst. Metals*, **85**, Pt. 8, 367–372 (Apr. 1957). Symposium on the Metallurgy of Niobium, London, May 1, 1957.

31. C. A. Hampel, Ed., "Rare Metals Handbook," Reinhold Publishing Corp., New York, 1954.

32. T. H. Schofield, "The melting point of niobium," *J. Inst. Metals*, **85**, Pt. 8, 372–374 (Apr. 1957).

33. C. R. Tottle, "The physical and mechanical properties of niobium," *J. Inst. Metals*, **85**, Pt. 8, 375–378 (Apr. 1957).

33a. G. L. Miller, "Columbium and its uses," *Materials & Methods*, **45**, 131–135 (May 1957).

33b. R. Speiser, P. E. Blackburn and H. L. Johnston, "Vapor pressure of niobium," *J. Electrochem. Soc.*, **106**, 52–53 (Jan. 1959).

34. W. Espe and M. Knoll, "Werkstoffkunde der Hochvakuumtechnik," Berlin, Verlag Julius Springer, 1936.

35. D. A. Wright, "A survey of present knowledge of thermionic emitters," *Proc. Inst. Elec. Engrs.*, **100**, Pt. 3 125–139 (May 1953).

36. E. A. Gulbransen and K. F. Andrew, "Oxidation of niobium between 375°C and 700°C," *J. Electrochem. Soc.*, **105**, 4–9 (Jan. 1958).

37. W. Espe, M. Knoll and M. P. Wilder, "Getter materials for electron tubes," *Electronics*, pp. 80–86 (Oct. 1950).

38. L. R. Williams, "The production and fabrication of massive niobium metal," *J. Inst. Metals*, **85**, Pt. 8, 385–392 (Apr. 1957).

39. W. G. O'Driscoll and G. L. Miller, "Purification of niobium by sintering," *J. Inst. Metals*, **85,** Pt. 8, 379–384 (Apr. 1957).

40. P. R. Pondy and B. T. McClure, "Processing niobium electrodes for use in gas discharge tubes," Report on 18th Annual Conference, Physical Electronics, March 20–22, 1958, Massachusetts Institute of Technology, Cambridge, Mass., p. 25.

41. A. D. White, "A subminiature metal-ceramic gas tube," Fourth National Conference on Tube Techniques, New York, Sept. 10–12, 1958. (Proceedings published by New York University Press, New York, 1959.)

CHAPTER 12

JOINING OF METALS BY BRAZING

Introduction

The various materials which have been described in the preceding chapters are interesting to the designer of electron devices only to the extent to which they can be used for the design of structures that perform a desired function. The joining of materials thus becomes an important subject. The present chapter will deal with the joining of metals, and the following two chapters will describe the joining of glass and ceramics to metals and to themselves, respectively.

Metals can be joined to each other in many different ways, and much ingenuity has been devoted to this subject[1-7]. In the present chapter, we will limit ourselves to the discussion of permanent joints which remain sound on exposure to temperatures of the order of 500°C and which can withstand adverse conditions of shock and vibration. As we are primarily concerned with vacuum tube structures, the joints must be vacuum-tight and must not contain components that would interfere with the quality of the vacuum. The fulfillment of these conditions eliminates soldered joints for internal components of vacuum tubes and limits the discussion to welded or brazed joints.

The American Welding Society defines the following terms:

"*Welding*, used by itself, is a generic term which describes a variety of metal-joining processes whereby a localized coalescence of metal is produced by heating to suitable temperatures, with or without the application of pressure, and with or without the use of filler metal. The filler metal, if used, either has a melting point approximately the same as the base metals or has a melting point below that of the base metals but above 800°F." (426.7°C)*

"*Braze Welding* is a method of welding whereby a groove, fillet, plug, or slot is made using a nonferrous filler metal, having a melting point below that of the base metals but above 800°F. The filler metal is not distributed in the joint by capillary attraction. ('Bronze Welding,' formerly used, is a misnomer for this term.)"

---

* It is unfortunate that the Fahrenheit scale of temperature is commonly used in engineering circles, and the centigrade scale among scientists; the fraternity of tube engineers generally prefers the centigrade scale, which is used throughout this text, except in direct quotations where the centigrade equivalent is added in parentheses.

"*Brazing:* a group of welding processes where in coalescence is produced by heating to suitable temperatures above 800°F and by using a nonferrous filler metal having a melting point below that of the base metals. The filler metal is distributed between the closely fitted surfaces of the joint by capillary attraction."

The term "brazing filler metal," or just "filler metal," is the name used to describe the nonferrous metal, or alloy, which is either placed between the abutting surfaces of the parent metals to be joined, or caused to flow into the interspace of the parent metals by capillary forces. The names "hard solder" and "silver solder" were formerly used to describe filler metals in distinction to the "soft solders." The American Welding Society and the American Society for Testing Materials have established a joint Tentative Specification for Brazing Filler Metals (AWS Specification A 5.8–52 T; ASTM: B 260–52 T) in which the composition of various filler metals is designated by a letter code in combination with the chemical symbols for the metal or alloy components; these codes appear in Table 12.1, where the filler metals commonly used in the construction of electron tubes are tabulated.

Many of the commercial brazing filler metals for ordinary applications contain zinc and cadmium; such alloys cannot be used for vacuum-tube joints on account of the excessively high vapor pressure of these metals. Filler metals containing phosphorus are an exception; while the vapor pressure of phosphorus is very high, the phosphorus primarily acts as a flux while making the joint at high temperature and does not cause any difficulty in high-vacuum applications. The present author has verified this fact repeatedly on critical tubes, and references from the literature seem to confirm this experience[8].

Brazing processes are usually classified, according to the particular technique used for supplying heat to the joint, as follows:

(1) Torch brazing
(2) Twin-carbon arc brazing
(3) Furnace brazing
(4) Induction brazing
(5) Resistance brazing
(6) Dip brazing
(7) Block brazing
(8) Flow brazing

Furnace brazing is usually performed in a reducing atmosphere, such as hydrogen, but it can also be done in a vacuum furnace, and one might thus distinguish between hydrogen brazing and vacuum brazing. Similarly, induction brazing is frequently done in a vacuum chamber, or a hydrogen-filled bell jar, so that these classifications are not mutually exclusive. In the present chapter we will concern ourselves exclusively with brazing operations that are performed either in a vacuum or in a reducing atmosphere, so that the application of brazing fluxes is not necessary. Details on the

TABLE 12.1 BRAZING FILLER METALS FOR ELECTRON TUBES*

No.	Liquid. Deg.C	Solid. Deg.C	Composition in Weight Percent[1]	Liquid. Deg.F	Solid. Deg.F	Notes	Alloy Designations and Suppliers[2]	Applications and Comments[3]
1	3180	3180	Rhenium	5756	5756		CBC; (GPD)	W
2	2996	2996	Tantalum	5425	5425	4B	FMC	W
3	2468	2468	Columbium (Niobium)	4474	4474	4B	FMC	Mo, W
4	2480	2480	Tungsten Carbide (W₂C)	4496	4496		CC	Mo, W, W₂C
5	2500	2500	Ruthenium	4532	4532		BPD; SCC; (GPD); (HH)	Mo, W
6	2450	2450	Iridium	4442	4442		BPD; SCC; (GPD); (HH)	Mo, W
7	2150	2120	Silicon–Molybdenum 10 90	3902	3848		TMC; VMC	
8	2080	2000	Dimolybdenumboride	3776	3632		BC	Mo, W
9	1990	1950	Iridium–Platinum 40 60	3614	3542		BPD; SCC; (GPD)	
10	1966	1966	Rhodium	3574	3574		BPD; SCC; (GPD); (HH)	Mo, W
11	1950	1935	Rhodium–Platinum 40 60	3542	3515		BPD; SCC; (GPD)	Mo, W
12	1900	1900	Ruthenium–Molybdenum 20 80	3452	3452		BPD; SCC	Mo, W
13	1852	1852	Zirconium	3366	3366	4B	CC; FMC	Mo, W
14	1769	1769	Platinum	3216	3216		APW; BPD; HH **Platinum VTG**; INCO; SCC; WGP; (GPD)	Mo; W
15	1695	1645	Gold–Palladium–Platinum 5 20 Bal.	3083	2993		HH **Premabraze 205 VTG**	Mo; W
16	1660	1660	Titanium	3320	3320		LFA et al	Ceramic seals
17	1552	1552	Palladium	2826	2826	4B	APW; BPD; HH **Palladium VTG**; INCO; WGP; (GPD)	Mo; W
18	1445	1445	Nickel–Iron 36 64	2651	2633		ASC **Ascovar 36**; DHC **Nilvar**; Inco **Invar**; SEP	(NAHg)
19	1453	1453	Nickel	2647	2647		DHC; INCO; WBD	Mo; W
20	1440	1427	Palladium–Gold 35 65	2624	2601		ASC **Ascobraze 65AC**; JMN; (HH); (GPD); (WGP)	
21	1410	1380	Palladium–Gold 25 75	2570	2516		HH **Premabraze 201 VTG**	Mo; W
22	1410	1210	Platinum–Gold 25 75	2570	2210		ASC **Ascovar 75AD**; JMN; (GPD); (HH); (WGP)	Mo; W
23	1330	1330	Molybdenum–Cobalt 37 63	2426	2426			Mo; W
24	1320	1320	Molybdenum–Nickel 46.5 53.5	2408	2408			Mo; W; Ni; (NM)
25	1320	1290	Palladium–Nickel 30 70	2408	2354		ASC **Ascobraze 70EC**; (BPD); (GPD); (HH)	SS
26	1305	1260	Palladium–Gold 13 87	2381	2300		HH **Premabraze 210 VTG**	Mo; W
27	1300	1230	Nickel–Copper 45 55	2372	2246		ASC **Ascobraze 55FE**; DHC **Advance**; WBD **Cupron**; Constantan, Eureka	Mo; W; (NM)
28	~1260	>1232	Chrome–Nickel–Palladium 10 36 Bal.	2300	>2250		HH **Premabraze 101**; (GPD)	
29	1250	1200	Platinum–Copper 40 60	2282	2192		ASC **Ascobraze 60FD**; WGP **Cuplat**; (GPD) (HH)	
30	1240	1190	Palladium–Gold 8 92	2264	2174		ASC **Ascobraze 92AC**; WGP **Paloro**; (GPD); (HH)	Mo; W; SS
31	1240	1170	Iron–Nickel–Copper 0.6 30 Bal.	2264	2138		ABC **Cupro Nickel 30%–702**; ASC **Ascobraze 70FE**	Mo; W; (NM); Watch for Zn
32	1238	1238	Nickel–Palladium 40 60	2260	2260		APW **APW 129**; BPD **Alloy No. 940**; (GPD); (HH)	SS; Inconel
33	1232	1149	Manganese–Palladium–Silver 3 33 Bal.	2250	2100		APW **APW 441**; BPD **Alloy No. 1170**; (GPD)	SS; Inconel
34	1220	1220	Cobalt–Palladium 35 65	2228	2228		ASC **Ascobraze 65CG**; WGP **Palco**; (GPD); (HH)	Mo; W; SS; Inconel
35	1205	1150	Nickel–Copper 25 75	2201	2102		ABC **Cupro Nickel 25%–705**; ASC **Ascobraze 75FE**; Coin Nickel	Mo; W; (NM)
36	1160	1070	Palladium–Silver 20 80	2120	1958		(GPD); (HH); (WGP)	
37	1160	995	Platinum–Silver 27 73	2120	1823		ASC **Ascobraze 73BD**; (GPD); (HH); (WGP)	Mo; W
38	1160	971	Carbon–Boron–Silicon–Iron– 0.45 max 2 2.5 2.5 Chromium–Nickel 10 Bal.	2120	1780	4A, B	APW; WCC **Nicrobraz 160**	SS; Inconel

*Copyright 1954 by WALTER H. KOHL, Electronics Consultant on Materials and Techniques, P.O. Box 426, Los Altos, Calif.
Revised 1959 for "MATERIALS and TECHNIQUES for ELECTRON TUBES," by W. H. Kohl, Reinhold Publishing Corporation, New York, N. Y.
Separately printed copies of this table are available as wall charts or file copies from the author.
Manufacturers of Brazing Materials have generously cooperated in the preparation of this table; their help is gratefully acknowledged. The data published in this table must, however, not be construed as committing the respective manufacturers in any way or form.

No.	Liquid. Deg. C	Solid. Deg. C	Composition in Weight Percent[1]	Liquid. Deg. F	Solid. Deg. F	Notes	Alloy Designations and Suppliers[2]	Applications and Comments[3]
39	1150	1100	Iron-Nickel-Copper 1.3 10 Bal.	2102	2012		Cupronickel 10%	(NM); Watch for Zn
40	1135	1080	Iron-Silicon-Chromium-Nickel 3 10 19 Bal.	2075	1975	4A, B, C	CM Alloy No. 60	SS; Inconel
41	1135	1080	Carbon-Silicon-Chromium-Nickel 0.15 max 10 19 Bal.	2075	1975		APW; WCC Nicrobraz 30	SS; Inconel
42	1121	1071	Manganese-Palladium-Silver 5 20 Bal.	2050	1960		APW APW 440; BPD Alloy No. 1795; (GPD)	SS; Inconel
43	1105	977	Carbon-Boron-Silicon-Iron 0.55 2.5 3.25 3.75 Chromium-Tungsten-Nickel 11.5 16 Bal.	2020	1790	4A, B	APW; WCC Nicrobraz 170	Mo; W; SS; Inconel
44	1105		Manganese-Nickel-Palladium-Copper 10 15 20 Bal.	2020			BPD Alloy No. 1804; (GPD)	
45	1094	971	Carbon-Boron-Silicon-Iron 0.15 max 3 3.5 3.5 Chromium-Nickel 11.5 Bal.	2000	1780	4A, B	APW; WCC WG Nicrobraz	SS; Inconel
46	1090		Manganese-Nickel-Palladium-Copper 15 20 30 Bal.	1994			BPD Alloy No. 1803; (GPD)	SS
47	1090	1080	Palladium-Copper 18 82	1994	1976		BPD Alloy No. 1800; (GPD); (HH)	
48	1083	1083	Copper	1981	1981	[B Cu]	ABC OFHC Copper-120; ASC Ascobraze OFHC; EWA EutecRod 184	Fe; Kovar; Monel
49	1083	1083	Nickel-Copper-Tungsten 3 35 Bal.	1981	1981		MWP Runnot C	Fe; Kovar; Monel; Contains W powder
50	1083	1083	Silicon-Copper 0.3 Bal.	1981	1981	Cu Base H (SAE)	ABC, RCB Silicon Copper-107; ASC Ascobraze 99FH	For Fe-Ni alloys
51	1077	971	Carbon-Boron-Silicon-Iron 0.15 max 3.5 4.5 4.5 Chromium-Nickel 13.5 Bal.	1970	1780	AMS 4776 4A, B	APW; WCC LC Nicrobraz	Inconel; SS
52	1075	965	Nickel-Gold 35 65	1967	1769	5	HH Premabraze 131 VTG; (GPD) (WGP)	
53	1070	1070	Tin-Platinum 29 71	1958	1958		ASC Ascobraze 70DJ; (GPD)	
54	1065	1002	Palladium-Silver 10 90	1950	1835	5	APW Alloy No. 431; ASC Ascobraze 90BC; HH Premabraze 901 VTG; (GPD); (WPG)	Mo; Ni; SS; W
55	1065	974	Chromium-Nickel-Gold 6 22 Bal.	1950	1785		APW Alloy No. 265; HH Premabraze 128; (WGP)	
56	1065	954	Boron-Silicon-Chromium 3 max 5 max 20 max Manganese-Nickel 30 max 60-85	1950	1750		SAC Solobraze NXI	SS
57	1063	1063	Gold	1945	1945		APW Alloy No. 200; ASC Ascobraze 99, 99A; HH Fine Gold VTG; WGP 24 Karat Gold; (GPD)	Diffusion seals; Cu; Mo
58	1060	1000	Silver-Copper 5 95	1940	1832	5	ASC Ascobraze 95FB; HH Braze 052 VTG; (GPD); (WGP)	Cu
59	1055	1055	Carbon-Boron-Chromium-Nickel 0.15 max 3.5 15 Bal.	1930	1930	4A, B	APW, WCC Nicrobraz 150	Inconel; SS
60	(1055)	1041	Boron-Silicon-Nickel 1.9 3.5 Bal.	(1930)	1905	7	CM Alloy No. 50; HH Handy Hi-Temp 93	Inconel; SS
61	1050		Manganese-Palladium-Silver 5 20 Bal.	1922			BPD No. 1168; (GPD)	
62	1050	1030	Nickel-Manganese 30 70	1922	1886		HH Handy Hi-Temp 30	SS
63	1038	1027	Carbon-Boron-Silicon-Nickel 0.15 max 3 4.5 Bal.	1900	1800	4A, B	APW; WCC Nicrobraz 130	Inconel; SS
64	1038	977	Carbon-Boron-Iron-Silicon 0.8 3.5 4.5 4.5 Chromium-Nickel 13.5 Bal.	1900	1790		APW; WCC Nicrobraz 120	Differs in mesh size from Standard
65	1038	971	Carbon-Boron-Iron-Silicon 0.60 3.85 4 4.5 Chromium-Nickel 16.5 Bal.	1900	1780	[B Ni Cr] AMS-4775 4A, B	CM No. 56; CSC Rexweld 64; EWA EutecBor 9; WCC Standard Nicrobraz	Inconel; SS
66	1035	1015	Gold-Copper 30 70	1895	1859	5	ACS Ascobraze 70FA; HH Premabraze 404 VTG; (GPD); (WGP)	Cu; Fe; Kovar, Ni
67	1032	1010	Carbon-Silicon-Manganese-Nickel 0.15 max 8 17 Bal.	1890	1850	4A, B, C	APW; WCC Nicrobraz 60	Inconel; SS
68	1030	975	Nickel-Gold-Copper 3 35 Bal.	1886	1787		HH Premabraze 129 VTG	Cu; Kovar; Mo; Monel; Ni; W
69	1025	970	Silicon-Copper 3 97	1877	1778		EWA EutecRod 182; RCB	Cu
70	1021	1005	Boron-Nickel-Cobalt-Manganese 1 16 16 Bal.	1870	1840		CM Alloy No. 62	SS

TABLE 12.1—Continued

No.	Liquid. Deg. C	Solid. Deg. C	Composition in Weight Percent[1]	Liquid. Deg. F	Solid. Deg. F	Notes	Alloy Designations and Suppliers[2]	Applications and Comments[3]
71	1020	1000	Gold–Copper 35　65	1868	1832	5, 8	APW Alloy No. 260; ASC Ascobraze 65FA; HH Premabraze 406 VTG; WGP Wesgo; (GPD)	Cu; Fe; Kovar; Ni
72	1025	990	Nickel–Gold–Copper 3　35　Bal.	1877	1814	5, 8	APW Alloy No. 243; ASC Ascobraze 62FAE; WGP Nicoro; (GPD)	Cu; Inconel; Kovar; Mo; Ni; Steel; W
73	1019	950	Manganese–Silicon–Copper 1.1　3.1　Bal.	1866	1742		ABC Everdur–1010	
74	1018	1018	Nickel–Manganese 40　60	1864	1864			SS
75	1015	990	Gold–Copper 37.5　62.5	1859	1814	[BCuAu-1] 5; 9 Karat red gold	APW Alloy No. 242; ASC Ascobraze 62FA; HH Premabraze 401 VTG; WGP; (GPD)	Cu; Fe; Kovar; Ni
76	1015	970	Indium–Gold–Copper 3　20　Bal.	1859	1778		ASC Ascobraze 77FAK; WGP Incuro 20	Cu; Kovar; Ni
77	1010	985	Gold–Copper 40　60	1850	1805	8	ASC Ascobraze 60FA; WGP Wesgo; (HH); (GPD)	Cu; Fe; Kovar; Ni
78	1010	970	Palladium–Silver 5　95	1850	1778		BPD Alloy No. 868; (HH)	
79	(1005)	996	Boron–Silicon–Chromium–Nickel–Iron 3.50　5　16　72.50　Bal.	(1840)	1825	7	HH Handy Hi-Temp 72	Inconel; SS
80	999	971	Carbon–Iron–Boron–Silicon 0.15 max 2.5　3　4.5 Chromium–Nickel 6.5　Bal.	1830	1780	AMS 4777 4A, B	APW; WCC LM Nicrobraz	Inconel; SS
81	(996)	979	Boron–Silicon–Chromium–Nickel–Iron 2.90　4.50　7.00　82　Bal.	(1825)	1795	7	CM Alloy No. 53; HH Handy Hi-Temp 82	SS
82	(993)	979	Boron–Silicon–Nickel–Iron 2.90　4.50　91.25'　Bal.	(1820)	1795	7	CM Alloy No. 52; HH Handy Hi-Temp 91	Cu; SS
83	993	979	Titanium–Boron–Silicon–Iron 0.75　3　4.5　Bal.	1820	1795		CM Alloy No. 59	
84	990	965	Copper–Gold 6　94	1814	1769		APW Alloy No. 259; ASC Ascobraze 94AF; (HH); (GPD); (WGP)	
85	985	664	Silver–Tin–Copper 7　8　Bal.	1805	1225	5	APW D-275; ASC Ascobraze 85FJB; GSR GB07; HH Braze 071 VTG; UWS Sil-7T; WEC Co-Silver 7T; (GPD)	
86	975	950	Copper–Gold 50　50	1787	1742	5, 8	APW Alloy No. 241; ASC Ascobraze 50AF; HH Premabraze 402 VTG; WGP Wesgo	Cu; Kovar; Ni
87	971	960	Manganese–Silver 15　85	1780	1760	[BAgMn]	APW Silvaloy 850; ASC Ascobraze 85BL; ARS Aircosil P; EWA EutecRod 1807; GSR GB No. 85; HH Braze 852; UWS Sil 85 M; WEC Co-Silver 85; (GPD)	Inconel; SS
88	963	924	Silver–Gold–Copper 2.8　41.7　Bal.	1765	1695	5	ASC Ascobraze 55FAB; HH Premabraze 031 VTG; (GPD)	Cu; Kovar
89	962		Nickel–Silver–Tungsten 3　35　Bal.		1764		MWP Runnot S	Contains W powder
90	961	961	Manganese–Silver 4　96	1762	1762		ASC Ascobraze 96BL; (HH); (GPD)	
91	960.5	960.5	Silver	1761	1761		APW; ASC Ascobraze 99.9B; HH Fine Silver VTG; WGP; (GPD)	Very ductile
92	950	950	Nickel–Gold 18　82	1742	1742	5 19.8 Karat White Gold	APW Alloy No. 255; ASC Ascobraze 82AE; HH Premabraze 130 VTG; WGP Nioro; (GPD)	Cu; Inconel; Kovar; Mo; Ni; W; SS
93	950	779	Silver–Copper 30　70	1742	1434		ASC Ascobraze 70FB; (GPD); (HH); (WGP)	
94	950		Palladium–Copper–Silver 10　22.5　Bal.	1742			BPD Alloy No. 1802; (GPD); (HH)	
95	950	901	Copper–Palladium–Silver 21　25　Bal.	1742	1654		BPD Alloy No. 1799; (GPD); (HH)	
96	942	942	Nickel–Titanium 28.5　71.5	1728	1728		LFA Ni-clad-Ti	Ceramic seals; (NM)
97	921	905	Silver–Copper–Gold 2.1　39.6　Bal.	1690	1660	5	ASC Ascobraze 59AFB; HH Premabraze 032 VTG; (GPD); (WGP)	Ferrous and nonferrous alloys
98	913	871	Copper–Cobalt–Phosphorus 5　7.5　11 Nickel–Iron 42　Bal.	1675	1600		CM Alloy No. 57	
99	910	900	Nickel–Copper–Gold 3.0　15.5　Bal.	1670	1652		ASC Ascobraze 82AFE; WGP Nicuro 80; HH Premabraze 409 VTG; (GPD)	Cu; Kovar; Mo; Ni; W; Steel
100	910	779	Silver–Copper 40　60	1670	1434	5	ASC Ascobraze 60FB; HH Braze 401 VTG; (GPD); (WGP); (German BTL)	Ferrous and nonferrous alloys

362

No.	Liquid. Deg. C	Solid. Deg. C	Composition in Weight Percent[1]	Liquid. Deg. F	Solid. Deg. F	Notes	Alloy Designations and Suppliers[2]	Applications and Comments[3]
101	900	860	Indium–Copper–Gold 3.0 37 Bal.	1652	1580		ASC **Ascobraze 60AFK**; WGP **Incuro 60**; (GPD)	Cu; Fe; Kovar; Ni
102	900	850	Palladium–Copper–Silver 15 20 Bal.	1652	1562		BPD **Alloy No. 1798**; (GPD); (HH)	
103	900	714	Phosphorus–Copper 5 95	1653	1317	[BCuP-1] CuBase B (SAE)	ARS, WEC **Phos Copper Strip**; BSR **Belmont BCuP-1**	Ag; Cu; Mo; W; Not for Fe or Ni alloys
104	898	879	Palladium–Copper–Silver 20 28 Bal.	1648	1614		BPD **Alloy No. 1801**; (GPD); (HH)	
105	896	885	Silver–Copper–Gold 5 20 Bal.	1645	1625	5	APW **Alloy No. 261**; ASC **Ascobraze 75AFB**; HH **Premabraze 050 VTG**; WGP **Silcoro 75**; (GPD)	
106	888	888	Carbon–Phosphorus–Chromium–Nickel 0.15 max 10 13 Bal.	1630	1630	4A, B, C	APW, WCC **Nicrobraz 50**	Inconel; SS
107	890	810	Copper–Silver 7.5 92.5	1634	1490	5	ASC **Ascobraze 92BF**; HH **Sterling Silver VTG**; (GPD); (WGP)	
108	890	780	Lithium–Copper–Silver 0.2 7.3 Bal.	1635	1435		APW, ARS **AE 100**; ASC **Ascobraze 92BFN**; HH **Lithobraze 925**; (GPD)	Inconel; SS; Extremely fluid
109	889	889	Copper–Gold 20 80	1632	1632	[BCuAu-2] 5; 19.2K red gold	APW **Alloy No. 238**; ASC **Ascobraze 80AF**/HH **Premabraze 403 VTG**; JMN **.800 Fine**; (GPD)	
110	885	779	Nickel–Copper–Silver 5 32.5 Bal.	1625	1435		APW **Silvaloy T 50**; (GPD); (HH)	Inconel; SS
111		800	Manganese–Silver–Copper 10 40 Bal.		1472		(GPD); (HH); (German Kusiman)	Ag; Fe; Steel
112	877	877	Carbon–Phosphorus–Nickel 0.15 max 11 Bal.	1610	1610	4A-D	APW, WCC **Nicrobraz 10**; INCO **Niphos** (German)	Cu; Fe; Inconel; Kovar; Mo; Ni; W; SS
113	875	779	Copper–Silver 50 50	1607	1434	5	ASC **Ascobraze 50BF**; HH **Braze 502 VTG**; (GPD); (WGP)	
114	870	779	Copper–Silver 10 90	1598	1434	5	ASC **Ascobraze 90BF**; HH **Coin Silver VTG**; (GPD); (WGP)	SS
115	852	824	Palladium–Copper–Silver 10 31.5 Bal.	1566	1515		BPD **Alloy No. 1797**; (GPD); (HH)	
116	849	752	Nickel–Manganese–Copper–Silver 2 5 28 Bal.	1560	1385		ASC **Ascobraze 65BF LE**; GSR **65 Mn**; HH **Braze 655**; (GPD)	Stellites, carbides, and re- fractory metals containing W
117	845	835	Silver–Copper–Gold 20 20 Bal.	1553	1535	5	ASC **Ascobraze 60AFB**; HH **Premabraze 408 VTG**; WGP **Silcoro 60**; (GPD)	Cu; Fe; Ni; Very short melting range
118	843	815	Copper–Silver–Gold 17.7 24 Bal.	1550	1500		ASC **Ascobraze 58ABF**; (HH); (WGP)	Cu; Fe; Ni
119	830	779	Nickel–Copper–Silver 2 21 Bal.	1525	1435		APW **Silvaloy T 52**; (GPD); (HH)	Inconel; SS
120	824	794	Copper–Silver–Gold 23.5 27.5 Bal.	1515	1460	12 Karat Gold	ASC **Ascobraze 49ABF**; (GPD); (HH); (WGP)	Cu; Fe; Ni
121	827	805	Copper–Silver–Gold 23.5 23.5 Bal.	1520	1480		JMN **No. 5087**; (GPD); (HH); (WGP)	Cu; Fe; Ni
122	821	794	Copper–Silver–Gold 20.5 29.5 Bal.	1510	1460	5	ASC **Ascobraze 50 ABF**; HH **Premabraze 202 VTG**; (GPD); (WGP)	Cu; Fe; Ni
123	815	641	Phosphorus–Silver–Copper 5 15 Bal.	1500	1185	[BCuP-5] 6	APW **Silvaloy 15**; ARS **Aircosil 15**; ASW **S-115**; EWA **EutecRod 1803**; GSR **15**; HH **Sil-Fos**; UWS **Phoson 15**; WEC **Phos Silver 15 M**	Not for Fe or Ni alloys. Wide melting range.
124	805	644	Silver–Phosphorus–Copper 5 6.25 Bal.	1480	1190	[BCuP-3] 6	APW **Silvaloy 5**; ARS **Aircosil 5**; ASC **Ascobraze FOS-5**; HH **Sil-Fos 5**; UWS **Phoson 6**; WEC **Phos-Silver 6M**	Ag; Cu; Mo; W; Not for Fe or Ni alloys
125	810	807	Palladium–Copper–Silver 5 26.6 Bal.	1490	1485		BPD **Alloy No. 1796**; (GPD); (HH)	
126	802	719	Nickel–Tin–Copper–Silver 2.5 6 28.5 Bal.	1475	1325	5	ASC **Ascobraze 63 BFJE**; HH **Braze 630 VTG**; (GPD)	Inconel; SS 430
127	795	780	Nickel–Copper–Silver 0.75 28.1 Bal.	1463	1436	5	ASC **Ascobraze 71BFE**; HH **Braze 720 VTG**; WGP **Nicusil 3**; (GPD)	Inconel; Mo; SS; W; Better wetting than Cu/Ag
128	788	640	Silver–Phosphorus–Copper 2 7 Bal.	1450	1185		ARS **Phos-Silver 2**; ASW **23**; GBS **02**	For nonferrous metals and alloys
129	780	660	Indium–Copper–Silver 10 27 Bal.	1436	1220	5, 8	ASC **Ascobraze 63 BFK**; HH **Premabraze 630 VTG**; WGP **Incusil 10**; (GPD)	
130	779	779	Copper–Silver (Eutectic) 28 72	1435	1435	[BAg-8]	APW **Silvaloy 301**; ARS **Aircosil M**; ASC **Ascobraze 72BF**; EWA **EutecRod 1806**; GPD **ML**; GSR **72**; HH **Braze BT VTG**; SC **Nu Braze**; UWS **Sil-72**; WEC **Co-Silver 72-28**; WGP **Cusil-Decarbonized**; (GPD)	Cu; Inconel; Kovar; SS
131	770	714	Phosphorus–Copper 7 93	1418	1317	[BCuP-2] 6	ASW **21**; ARS, WEC **Phos Copper Rod**; BSR **Belmont BCuP-2**; CLA **Lo-Melt Copper**; EWA **EutecRod 800**; UWS **Phoson 0**	Ag; Cu; Mo; W; Very free flowing; Not for Fe or Ni alloys

363

TABLE 12.1—Continued

No.	Liquid. Deg. C	Solid. Deg. C	Composition in Weight Percent[1]	Liquid. Deg. F	Solid. Deg. F	Notes	Alloy Designations and Suppliers[2]	Applications and Comments[3]
132	760	743	Tin–Copper–Silver 5 27 Bal.	1400	1370		ASC **Ascobraze 68 BFJ**; GPD **SI-1**; (HH)	
133	730	604	Manganese–Tin–Copper–Silver 3 7 32.7 Bal.	1345	1120		ASC **Ascobraze 57BFJL**; EWA **EutecRod 1602**; HH **Braze 580**; (GPD)	Chrome carbides
134	721	640	Silver–Phosphorus–Copper 5.5 7.25 Bal.	1330	1190	[BCuP-4] 6	ARS **Phos-Silver 6**; GSR **06**; WEC **Phos Silver**	Ag; Cu; Mo; W; Not for Fe or Ni alloys
135	718	602	Tin–Copper–Silver 10 30 Bal.	1325	1115	5	APW **Silvaloy 60**; ASC **Ascobraze 60BFJ**; GSR **160**; HH **Braze 603 VTG**; UWS **Sil-60T**; WEC **Co-Silver 60T**	
136	705	635	Indium–Copper–Silver 13 27 Bal.	1300	1175		ASC **Ascobraze 60BFK**; GSR **260**; (GPD); (HH)	
137	685	630	Indium–Copper–Silver 15 24 Bal.	1265	1166	5	ASC **Ascobraze 61BFK**; HH **Premabraze 615 VTG**; WGP **Incusil 15**; (GPD)	
138	485	473	Indium–Gold 20 80	905	883		ASC **Ascobraze 80AK**; ICA **19.2K**	Cu; Fe; Ni; Hard, brittle joints
193	425	425	Indium–Gold 25 75	797	797		ASC **Ascobraze 75AK**; ICA **18K**	Hard, brittle joints
140	232	232	Tin	450	450			Rarely used, poor wetting
141	230	166	Silver–Indium 10 90	446	331		ICA **Indalloy No. 3**	
142	157	157	Indium	315	315		ICA **Indalloy No. 4**	
143	117	117	Indium—Tin 50 50	225	225		ICA **Indalloy No. 1**	

NOTES

1—Alloy constituents are given in this sequence: the smallest additive first, others in increasing order, with the bulk constituent last, as balance.

2—Code letters signify suppliers and are alphabetically listed below. Names following code letters and in bold face are registered trademarks of the supplier. Code letters in parentheses signify that the alloy is not a stock item but can be custom-made. Omission of a supplier does not imply that the quality of his products is inferior.

3—The chemical symbols for metals (Mo = molybdenum, W = tungsten, W₂C = tungsten carbide, Ni = nickel, Fe = iron, Cu = copper, Ag = silver) and the names of alloys, or abbreviations (SS = stainless steel), suggest parent metals which may be joined by the filler metal in question. (NM) = nonmagnetic; (NAHg) = not attacked by mercury.

4—Brazing operations for electron devices must be performed in inert or reducing atmospheres, or in vacuum: a-Pure dry hydrogen or inert gases, b-Vacuum, c-Dissociated ammonia (−60°F dew point or better), d-Exothermic; rich, unpurified 6:1 air to gas ratio, or purified and dried.

5—Handy & Harman alloys marked "VTG" are produced as "Vacuum Tube Grade" with specially controlled, low impurity content, if so ordered. Items

not marked VTG are not available from HH at this controlled level but as commercial alloys only. It might be well to emphasize Vacuum Tube Application when ordering alloys from other suppliers and to watch impurity content in all cases.

6—The liquidus temperatures of the Ag-Cu-P alloys Numbers 123 and 124 are 1480–1500°F; their working temperatures are near 1300°F.

7—The temperatures listed as liquidus temperatures for B-Si alloys No.'s 60, 81, and 82 are working temperatures rather than liquidus temperatures.

8—Alloys #68 and #72 are a duplication, and different values are given for liquidus and solidus. Entry #68 presents data recently released by Handy & Harman, while #72 is close to values published by Western Gold & Platinum Company. Similarly, the HH values for alloys #71,75,77,86,129 are higher than those given by WGP who believe on the basis of their own extensive tests, substantiated by others, that their data are correct. The author of this chart does not intend to discriminate against these claims. Similar discrepancies may exist in other cases. Double entries contained in the original manuscript were eliminated to avoid confusion.

SUPPLIERS

ARS Air Reduction Sales Company
150 East 42nd Street
New York 17, N. Y.

ASW All-State Welding Alloys Company, Inc.
249 55 Ferris Avenue
White Plains, N. Y.

ABC American Brass Company
414 Meadow Street
Waterbury 20, Conn.

APW American Platinum & Silver Division
Engelhard Industries, Inc.
231 New Jersey Railroad Avenue
Newark 5, N. J.

ASC American Silver Company, Inc.
36-07 Prince Street
Flushing 54, N. Y.

BPD Baker Platinum Division
Engelhard Industries, Inc.
113 Astor Street
Newark 5, N. J.

BSR Belmont Smelting & Refining Works, Inc.
330 Belmont Avenue
Brooklyn 7, N. Y.

BC The Borolite Corporation
Box 337
Niagara Falls, N. Y.

CLA Canadian Liquid Air Company Limited
1111 Beaver Hall Hill
Montreal, P. Q.

CC The Carborundum Company
P. O. Box 337
Niagara Falls, N. Y.

CBC Chase Brass & Copper Company
236 Grand Street
Waterbury 20, Conn.

CM Coast Metals, Inc.
199 Rednick Avenue
Little Ferry, N. J.

CSC Crucible Steel Company of America
Oliver Bldg., Mellon Square
Pittsburgh 22, Pa.

DHC Driver-Harris Company
201 Middlesex Street
Harrison, N. J.

EWA Eutectic Welding Alloys Corporation
40 40 172nd St.
Flushing 58, N. Y.

FMC Fansteel Metallurgical Corporation
2200 Sheridan Road
North Chicago, Ill.

FMC Foote Mineral Company
18 W. Chelten Avenue
Philadelphia 44, Pa.

GPD General Plate Division
Metals and Controls Division
Texas Instruments Incorporated
34 Forest Street
Attleboro, Mass.

GSR Goldsmith Bros. Smelting & Refining Co.
1300 W. 59th Street
Chicago 36, Ill.

HH Handy & Harman
82 Fulton Street
New York 38, N. Y.

ICA The Indium Corporation of America
1676 Lincoln Avenue
Utica 4, N. Y.

INCO The International Nickel Co., Inc.
67 Wall Street
New York 5, N. Y.

JMC Johnson, Matthey & Company, Inc.
608 5th Avenue
New York, N. Y.

LFA Little Falls Alloys, Inc.
189 Caldwell Ave.
Paterson 1, N. J.

MWP Metallwerk Plansee
Reutte, Tirol
Austria

JMN J. M. Ney Company
P. O. Box 990
Hartford 1, Conn.

RCB Revere Copper and Brass Incorporated
230 Park Avenue
New York 17, N. Y.

SCC Sigmund Cohn Corporation
121 S. Columbus Avenue
Mt. Vernon, N. Y.

SAC Solar Aircraft Company
2200 Pacific Highway
San Diego 12, Calif.

SEP Sylvania Electric Products, Inc.
Chemical and Metallurgical Division
Towanda, Pa.

TMC Temescal Metallurgical Corporation
1201 S. 47th Street
Richmond, Calif.

UWS United Wire & Supply Corporation
Providence 1, R. I.

VMC Vacuum Metals Corporation
Div. of Crucible Steel Co. of America
P. O. Box 977
Syracuse 1, N. Y.

WCC Wall Colmonoy Corporation
19345 John R Street
Detroit 3, Mich.

WGP Western Gold & Platinum Company
525 Harbor Boulevard
Belmont, Calif.

WEC Westinghouse Electric Corporation
P. O. Box 868
Pittsburgh 30, Pa.

WBD Wilbur B. Driver Company
1875 McCarter Highway
Newark 4, N. J.

other brazing techniques just listed above will be found in the "Brazing Manual" or other literature sources.[3-7]

In addition to the conventional heating methods, listed above, heating by electron bombardment has recently been practiced for fusion welding[9, 9a] and vacuum melting of refractory metals. Kohl suggested use of this method of heating for the brazing of large components as early as 1952. Electron bombardment heating must necessarily be performed in a high vacuum, requires an electron gun and associated focusing system, a high-voltage source, and means of passing the workpiece under the focused beam, unless a ring source of electrons is used for a circular braze mounted coplanar with the source. The investment required in special equipment is thus quite formidable. Shielding from X-rays must also be considered, but in special cases this method offers advantages in flexibility, speed, and resulting quality of the braze that could not readily be obtained by more conventional means of heating.

Brazing Metallurgy

In order to get a clear understanding of the mechanism of brazing, it is essential to have some knowledge of physical metallurgy and the principles which govern the formation of alloys. Just as some liquids, as for example water and alcohol, will enter into solution with each other in all proportions, and others, such as ether and water, will not do so if certain limits are exceeded, but will separate into two visibly discernible layers because they have only a limited solubility in each other, so will various metals enter into solution with each other in the molten state and form a solid solution on cooling, or do this only partially because their mutual solid solubility is limited.

In the case of binary alloys, this behavior is best illustrated by constitutional diagrams, which are also called phase diagrams; for alloys containing three or more components, a graphical representation becomes a little more involved but is still possible for ternary systems.

Figure 12.1a shows the constitutional diagram for a binary alloy consisting of components A and B, which are completely soluble in each other in all proportions. The ordinate of this diagram represents temperature, and the abscissa gives the relative composition of the alloy in weight percent. At point A, only one component is present, and at point B only the other, so that the temperatures T_A and T_B represent the melting points of the two pure components. If an increasing amount of B is added to molten A, the melting point of A is raised in this particular example, and the liquidus line, L, for the alloy is traced until it reaches the melting point of the pure component B at T_B. The area above the liquidus line represents the liquid phase of the various alloy compositions. On lowering the temperature from

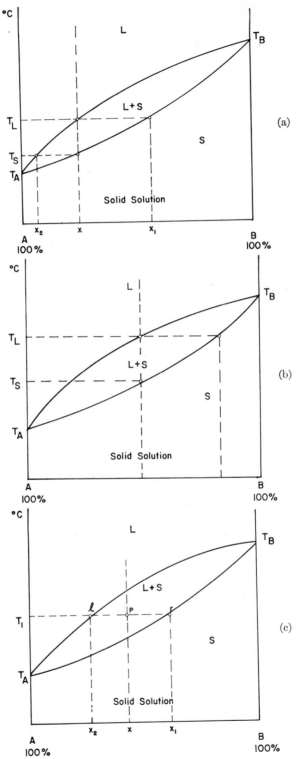

Figure 12.1 a–c. The constitutional diagram of a binary alloy system. (See text for explanation.)

the liquid state, an alloy of a given composition does not freeze until the temperature indicated by the solidus line, S, is reached.

A melting range is thus indicated for any alloy composition by the vertical distance between the liquidus and solidus lines in Figure 12.1. All alloy compositions are solid in the area below the solidus line. An alloy of given composition can be represented by a vertical line; such an "isopleth" is indicated in Figure 12.1 by a dotted line at composition X, which represents 50 per cent A and 50 per cent B. It is then apparent that the first solid crystallites will appear at temperature T_L when the temperature of the liquid melt is gradually lowered, and that very little of the liquid phase remains when the temperature T_s has been reached. Below this temperature T_s, all the melt has solidified into a solid solution of A plus B. During the transition of the area enclosed by the liquidus and solidus lines, both liquid and solid phases are present, and the composition of this mixture of phases is determined by the intersection of the horizontal temperature line with the liquidus and solidus, respectively.

Figure 12.1b illustrates the conditions where the original composition X of the melt is 25 per cent B and 75 per cent A. On lowering the temperature from the molten state, crystallites of the composition X_1 appear when the temperature T_L has been reached, and at temperature T_s, solid-phase crystals of composition X are in equilibrium with a small amount of remaining liquid phase which has the composition X_2, as determined by the intersection of the horizontal T_s with the liquidus line.

Figure 12.1c illustrates how the relative composition of the liquid and solid phases can be determined by means of the "lever rule." At a temperature T_1, the liquid phase of an original composition X of the alloy has the composition X_2, and the solid phase has the composition X_1. The relative amounts of liquid and solid at temperature T_1 can be expressed by the relation $L/S = pr/pl$.

Figure 12.2 illustrates a condition where the melting point or freezing point of metal A is lowered on addition of metal B rather than raised, as was the case in Figure 12.1. Likewise, the melting or freezing point of metal B is lowered on addition of metal A. Another peculiarity of this diagram is the fact that the liquidus and solidus lines have a point E in common where the alloy has a uniquely defined melting point X at temperature T_E and composition F. At this composition and temperature the liquid phase and the solid phase are in equilibrium and the alloy behaves like a pure metal (congruent melting). Between the temperatures T_E and T_1, the two alloy components A and B are again soluble in each other in all proportions. Below temperature T_1, the solubility is restricted by the area CGD.

On lowering the temperature of an alloy of the original composition F from the molten state, solidification will occur at temperature T_E, and the

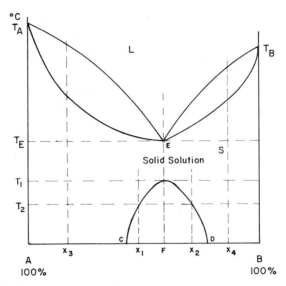

Figure 12.2. The constitutional diagram of a binary alloy system showing congruent melting at E and limited solid solubility below temperature T_1.

composition of the solid solution remain unchanged until temperature T_1 is reached. Below T_1, say at T_2, two separate solid phases appear which have the composition X_1 and X_2, and their relative proportions are again determined by the lever rule. An alloy composition outside the area of limited solid solubility will not encounter the separation into two solid phases on cooling. Compositions X_3 or X_4, on cooling from the molten state, will pass through a mushy range between liquidus and solidus and then form a single solid solution. Alloys with compositions given by points falling within the interval C-D in Figure 12.2, such as X_1 and X_2, will exist as a single solid solution only between T_E and the temperatures delineated by curve CGD. Below this boundary, these alloys separate into a mixture of two solid solutions.

When the area of limited solid solubility becomes larger and larger, a constitutional diagram like that shown in Figure 12.3a results, which represents a simple eutectic system. At composition F, the liquid and solid phases are in equilibrium, and an alloy of this composition will have a sharply defined melting point. The areas denoted by α and β are called terminal solid solutions and represent single phases. At room temperature T_0, C per cent of metal B can be dissolved in metal A as a solid solution, either substitutionally or interstitially. With increasing temperature, increasing amounts of metal B can be dissolved in metal A until temperature T_E is reached, above which the solid solubility of B in A decreases. Similarly, a small

amount of metal A is soluble in metal B at room temperature, and this
amount again increases with temperature up to T_E and then decreases with
further increase in temperature. When a melt of eutectic composition F
is slowly cooled from the molten state to temperature T_E, the liquid phase

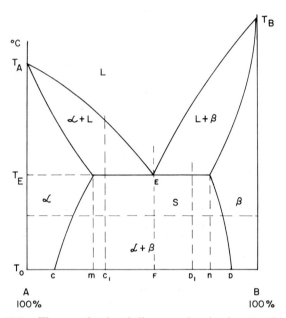

Figure 12.3a. The constitutional diagram of a simple eutectic system.

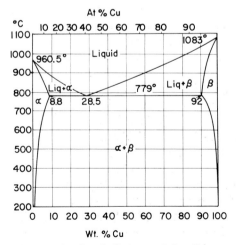

Figure 12.3b. The constitutional diagram of the silver-copper system.

of composition F will be in equilibrium with the solid solution α of composition m and solid solution β of composition n.

Constitutional diagrams for most of the common alloys have been compiled in the literature.[10-12] Examples for specific brazing alloys will appear on the following pages. It is of course an intriguing problem to determine what factors influence the behavior of given alloys and make them perform according to one diagram or another. Certain guiding principles have been established, and the electronic theory of the solid state has made great progress in recent years in its efforts to explain the mechanism of alloy formation.

The size of the atoms of component A and component B is an important factor, which determines whether the two metals will form a complete solid solution in each other such as represented by Figure 12.1. Solid solutions are generally formed between metals that have atoms of similar size and which crystallize in the same crystal system, such as silver and gold, or copper and nickel. When the relative size of the atoms differs by more than 15 per cent, limited solid solubility sets in, such as shown in Figure 12.2, and eutectic alloys are formed when the size factor is still more unfavorable. Other factors, such as electron affinity and the number of valence electrons per atom, play an important role. The reader is referred to texts on physical metallurgy and solid state physics for more detailed information.[13-16]

It should be emphasized that constitutional diagrams are equilibrium diagrams; this term imposes the condition that sufficient time is allowed at any temperature to permit establishment of complete equilibrium between the various phases present in the system. At the eutectic point E in Figure 12.3a, for example, liquid phase of composition F is in equilibrium with the α and β solid solutions, as explained above. On cooling below temperature T_E, the liquid phase solidifies and must have time to change its original composition F to that of the terminal solid solutions. If temperature changes take place too rapidly in a practical process, deviations from the idealized phase diagram will take place, and advantage is taken of this fact in processes such as precipitation-hardening.

The point just made should not be taken to mean that brazing operations must be carried out very slowly; just the opposite is true. Brazing operations should in general be performed quickly after the joint assembly has reached a uniform temperature which is high enough to insure melting of the filler metal. Figure 12.3b gives the phase diagram for a silver-copper binary alloy which forms a eutectic according to the diagram shown in Figure 12.3a.

If two pieces of copper are to be brazed with a eutectic composition of silver and copper which melts at 779°C, one will generally raise the temperature of the assembly about 50°C above the liquidus point, i.e., to 830°C. At this temperature, liquid and solid phases of the terminal solid solution are in equilibrium, and there is also a tendency of copper to dissolve in the silver of the filler metal and silver from the filler metal to dissolve in the copper of the joint. Both these effects tend to shift the isopleth to the copper-rich side of the diagram so that the liquidus temperature is raised if these effects are allowed to take place. This erosion of the joint area is minimized by performing the braze quickly and staying at the brazing temperature not longer than necessary. Apart from the time factor, the relative amounts of filler metal and parent metal present at the joint will have a determining effect on the extent to which erosion can take place. Very thin members can be seriously damaged by erosion, especially when an excessive amount of filler metal is used.

The increase of the liquidus temperature by enrichment of the filler metal with parent metal, to which reference was made above, can at times be used to advantage when a second braze is to be made with the same filler metal after the first braze has been completed. It is then necessary, however, that the second braze be made faster than the first, so that the liquidus temperature in the second braze cannot rise as much as in the first.[16a]

Figure 12.4 gives the phase diagram for the copper-gold system; this looks very similar to the one shown in Figure 12.2 but the area of limited solid solubility is further complicated by the appearance of intermetallic compounds Cu_3Au and $CuAu$ when the alloy contains from 37 to 88 per cent gold. These compounds are brittle and should therefore be avoided when ductility of the joint is important. The formation of intermetallic compounds can be circumvented by quenching from 500°C to room temperature so that sufficient time is not available for these compounds to form. A copper-gold brazing alloy should thus not contain more than 37 per cent gold. If larger amounts of gold are present in the alloy, the formation of intermetallic compounds can be avoided by quenching from 500°C to room temperature so that not sufficient time is available for these compounds to form. In vacuum-tube practice, such a procedure would be very awkward in most cases, and it is thus better to avoid alloys which have a tendency to form brittle compounds. In any case, it is most advisable to have a good look at the phase diagram not only for the alloy composition chosen for the filler metal, but also for the possible reaction that may take place between a pure filler metal and the parent metal from which the joint is made.

Another important consideration in selecting materials for a brazed joint is the content of gas and impurities. Filler metals should not only be carefully cleaned before use, but also outgassed by separately firing them in vacuum. It is obvious that gas released during the brazing operation may cause porosity of the joint. For the same reason, filler metals should have as low a carbon content as possible because traces of oxides would be reduced by it, leading to the formation of carbon monoxide or carbon dioxide.

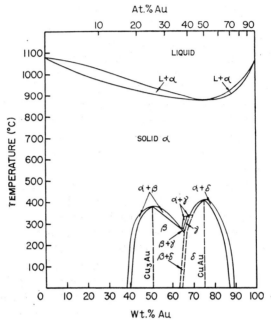

Figure 12.4. The constitutional diagram of the copper-gold system showing the formation of intermetallic compounds.

When a brazed joint is rapidly cooled to room temperature, the filler metal may become supersaturated in the α and β terminal solid solution on account of the decrease of solubility with decreasing temperature. Similar effects may take place in the parent metal if this is an alloy in which phase transformations take place. An ageing treatment may be necessary after the completion of the braze in order to reestablish the desired structure.

The strength of brazed joints is of particular interest when structural members are joined in this manner and exposed to mechanical stresses in service, either by having to support substantial loads, or by being exposed to shock and vibration. It is probably safe to say that brazed joints used in the construction of tubes are rarely exposed to static stresses that approach the yield stress; but vibration and shock may well endanger the soundness of a joint unless some consideration is given to the stress limit that can safely be tolerated. When tubes are expected to operate at elevated temperatures, normal stress limits decrease rapidly for many materials. It is generally desirable to design a joint in such a way that it is in compression rather than tension. Strength tests are usually performed in tension. Shear strengths are materially lower than tensile strengths, and fatigue strength is generally proportional to the tensile strength.

The strength of a joint depends on many factors,[17] and, unless one refers to an ideal joint, it is misleading to compare results obtained under different conditions of test. The tensile strength of the completely sound joint will be approximately equal to the cast strength of the brazing filler metal, irrespective of the joint clearance. The joint clearance usually will have definite bearing on the soundness of the joint achieved, however, and thus will indirectly affect its strength.[6] The smoother and more perfect the surfaces, the smaller is the joint thickness at which the peak strength is reached.

When materials are joined which are softer than the filler metal, tension failure usually occurs outside the joint; but for a joint consisting of materials which are harder than the filler metal, failure occurs within the joint at loads greatly in excess of the strength of the brazing alloy itself. For soft materials, the thickness of the joint is relatively less important, but for strong materials it is a major factor. Copper-brazed mild steel and medium carbon steels are an exception in this respect and give greatest strengths with moderate interference fits. When a butt joint is made between two steel rods with the aid of silver as a filler metal, and axial tension is applied, the silver will tend to yield shortly after the load is applied. In order to be able to yield, the silver would have to suffer a lateral plastic deformation and reduce its cross section; the adjacent steel will prevent it from doing so and constrain the silver, with the result that shear stresses are built up at each steel-silver interface. These shear stresses act in planes normal to the axis of the specimen under test and induce tensile stresses within the silver and compression stresses within the steel.[18]

Figure 12.5 illustrates the interplay of forces at the joint in diagrammatic form.[19] The net effect of this state of stress is to raise the yield, and hence the ultimate strength of the brazing alloy in the joint to a value considerably above that of the bulk brazing alloy. It is apparent that, other things equal, the strengthening effect on the brazing alloy produced by the restriction imposed by the adjacent base metal is more pronounced the smaller the joint thickness.

Moffatt and Wulff[20] have recently demonstrated that the ultimate tensile strength of butt joints of mild steel rods brazed with pure silver is a linear function of the thickness-to-diameter ratio rather than only of the thickness of the filler metal for constant specimen diameter. (Figure 12.6)

When the joint clearance is made too small, on the other hand, and the surfaces are not perfectly smooth, the filler metal may find it difficult to fill the joint completely on account of the presence of "capillary dams." The maximum strength obtained on butt joints of steel with silver alloys for a joint clearance of 1.5 mil is frequently explained in this manner. Other tests performed in different laboratories disclose that the ultimate tensile

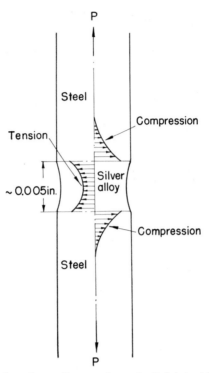

Figure 12.5. Interface force diagram for a butt joint. After Udin, Funk, and Wulff.[19] (*Courtesy John Wiley & Sons, Inc.*)

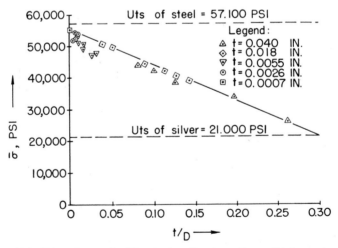

Figure 12.6. Dependence of ultimate tensile strength on thickness-to-diameter ratio for butt joints of mild steel rods brazed with pure silver. After Moffatt and Wulff.[20] (*Courtesy American Institute of Mining, Metallurgical, and Petroleum Engineers, Inc.*)

374

TABLE 12.2. MECHANICAL PROPERTIES OF SOME FILLER METALS*

Metal or Alloy	Annealing Temperature °C	Yield Strength (1% offset) psi	Tensile Strength psi
60 Ag, 30 Cu, 10 Sn	563	51,000	71,900
65 Ag, 28 Cu, 5 Mn, 2 Ni	724	39,500	53,900
72 Ag, 28 Cu	752	33,600	45,600
85 Cu, 8 Sn, 7 Ag	635	29,100	62,400
99 Ag, 1 Zr	927	16,200	21,600
85 Ag, 15 Mn	924	12,700	40,000
Cu (OFHC)	1038	5,575	33,000
Ag	927	4,330	22,500

* After Bender.[21]

strength of the bulk silver alloy can be realized in a joint between steel rods for clearances ranging from 0 to 20 mils.

Mechanical properties of some filler metals used in the construction of electron tubes have been described by Bender;[21] Table 12.2 gives his results.

Different filler metals show a varying affinity for various parent metals and thus display a different degree of "wetting." The distance which filler metals can be counted on to travel within a given joint is also affected by their wetting ability. This subject has been treated in some detail by Funk and Udin,[22] who give the following equation for the distance x which a given filler metal of viscosity μ and surface tension γ will travel in a horizontal joint of clearance D during time t:

$$x = \sqrt{\gamma t D/3\mu}.$$

It is evident from this equation that the distance over which the filler metal flows in a horizontal joint depends on the physical properties of the brazing alloy, plate separation, and the time allowed above liquidus temperature. In order to fill a given joint in a minimum of time, the filler metal should thus be as fluid as possible (low viscosity) and have as high a surface tension as possible. The ratio γ/μ increases quite rapidly with temperature.

The vertical distance which a filler metal is able to travel in a capillary joint is given by the following equation:

$$y_{max} = 2\gamma/\rho g D$$

where ρ is the density of the liquid and g is the gravitational constant. While the horizontal distance traveled is theoretically not limited and will increase in time indefinitely as long as there is an adequate supply of filler metal available, the vertical distance has an upper limit determined by the balance between driving capillary force and the weight of the liquid column.

Milner[23] discusses this subject very thoroughly and his article is highly recommended to the reader.

Brazing Techniques and Joint Design

The remarks made in the preceding paragraph will make it apparent that the design of a joint and the techniques chosen to realize it deserve a good deal of thought. Much has been written on the subject, which cannot be covered in detail here. The reader is referred to the "Brazing Manual"[5] and the Handy and Harman "Technical Bulletins on Silver Alloy Brazing".[18] Other manufacturers of brazing alloys also have issued very attractive bulletins from time to time which cover the fundamentals of brazing.[23-25]

Before embarking on the design of a joint, the designer should not only know what equipment is available to him, but also be familiar with the characteristics of this equipment. The following questions arise:

(1) What is the power output of available spot welders and induction heating units?

(2) How many furnaces are available, what type are they, what is their maximum temperature, and what is the maximum size of the workpiece they can handle?

(3) How much time does it take each furnace to get up to temperature and how uniform is the temperature within the heat zone?

(4) What atmosphere is being used in the furnace, and what dew point can be maintained?

(5) Are there provisions for separate preheat and cooling chambers, or must the work rise and fall in temperature with the furnace? Is it possible to use two furnaces in tandem so that the workpiece can quickly be passed from one furnace at a lower temperature into a second furnace which has been preheated to a higher temperature?

(6) Finally, and probably most important, is good housekeeping being enforced so that furnaces intended for electronic components cannot be contaminated by zinc, cadmium, and other high-vapor-pressure materials which are constituents of filler metals used for conventional brazing jobs?

After these questions have been answered, suitable parent metals and filler metals can be chosen, and the method of feeding the filler metal to the joint established. Figure 12.7 illustrates some of the conventional joints.

It is strongly recommended to try out the chosen design in a test braze so that optimum time-temperature cycles can be determined, and unforeseen difficulties do not ruin a costly final assembly.

When brazing thin members to heavier structures, it is desirable, if not essential, to feed the filler metal from a location within the heavier part to the thin member by capillary forces rather than placing it in close prox-

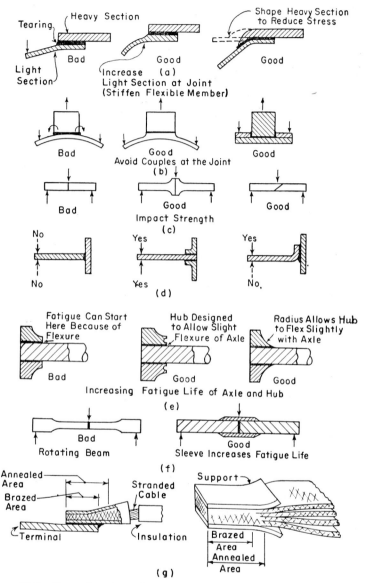

Figure 12.7a. Examples of good and bad designs of brazed joints. Reproduced from Brazing Manual.[5] (*Courtesy Reinhold Publishing Corporation.*)

imity to the thin member; this is necessary to avoid erosion by prolonged exposure of the thin member to the filler metal.[25a] (See also Figure 14.12). As illustrated in Figure 12.8, it thus becomes necessary at times to enlarge the structure and machine off part of it after the braze has been completed.

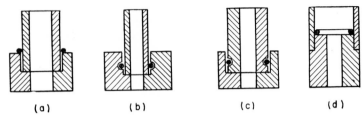

Figure 12.7b. Examples of different placements of a filler metal wire preform. Methods a) and d) do not require machining of the parts but may entail some running of the filler metal on the surface of the lower part. Staking of the rings may be necessary to prevent their springing out of contact with the outer or inner wall of the upper cylinder, respectively. Methods b) and c) locate the rings securely and ensure their being consumed in the joint; b) is a more expensive machining job than c). Reproduced from Brazing Manual.[5] (*Courtesy Reinhold Publishing Corporation.*)

The filler metal is usually located at the joint to be made in the form of rings, washers, disks, or foil, or applied in paste form with provision to prevent the alloy from "running off" before entering the joint. Sometimes the parent metal may be electroplated with the filler metal when it is difficult to place the filler metal in any other way, or when very close control over the amount of filler metal used is required. Metal salt solutions, such as platinum chloride, silver chloride, and others may be used for very delicate parts which do not withstand much heating, or for repairing microscopic leaks after an assembly has been made and found to be defective, and a rerun is not possible in the furnace. The salt, or salt solutions, may be reduced by local application of heat by means of a torch, if necessary.

In attempting to realize a desired joint clearance, of which examples are given below, the relative thermal expansion of the joint members must be considered so that the desired joint clearance exists at the brazing temperature.[25b] If the joint components materially differ in mass and thus have different thermal capacities, they will not reach the same temperature at the same time, and the clearance at brazing temperature calculated on the basis of thermal expansion alone will not hold unless this factor is taken into account. It may become necessary to soak the assembly at a lower temperature for a longer time to insure equalization of temperature in the assembly, and then proceed rapidly to the brazing temperature by transferring the work to a preheated furnace for a short time and remove the work into the cooling zone thereafter. Recourse has been taken at times to the construction of special brazing retorts which can be water-quenched after the braze has been completed, to avoid effects of erosion at the joint interface or oxidation.[26]

Very short times at brazing temperatures and very small joint clearances are required when parent metal and filler metal have a tendency to form brittle intermetallic compounds by diffusion; the strength of a joint would be materially lowered if such effects were allowed to take place.

Intergranular corrosion of the parent metal in the presence of strain may also weaken the structure and, in the extreme, produce cracks that cause

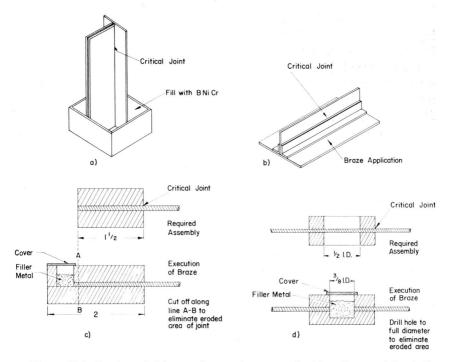

Figure 12.8. Brazing of thin members to heavy stock. After Rose and Lewis.[25a] (*Courtesy American Welding Society.*)

(a) Brazing of stainless steel members by allowing molten filler metal to rise by capillarity to a height of 8 in. above level of liquid. The immersed part and about 2 in. of the joint above the liquid level is eroded and unfit for use; the upper part of the joint is of high quality. BNiCr is used for filler metal, brazing is done at 1205°C (2200°F). A porcelain crucible may be used for the container.

(b) A T-joint between a 0.010-in. thick partition and a 0.050-in. thick wall, using 0.015-in. thick flanges. By placing the BNiCr filler metal on the outside of the flanges, as shown, excessive erosion of the thin member is avoided.

(c) A sandwich joint between a 0.032-in. thick sheet and 0.250-in. thick bars. BNiCr filler metal powder is placed in a channel on excess stock which is machined off after the braze is completed, thus removing the eroded part of the joint. Gap width: 0.003 in. The cover provided over the groove prevents premature heating of the filler metal.

(d) Brazing two 0.250-in. thick washers onto 0.032-in. thick AISI Type 410 steel sheet. The hole in the upper disk and the matching well in the lower disk are drilled undersize and enlarged after completion of the braze.

gas leakage. The mechanical strains that must be present before stress-corrosion cracking occurs may be locked in the material if it has not been properly annealed, or they may be produced by stresses resulting from improperly designed fixtures. Stress-corrosion cracking can be induced by the filler metal itself, or by gases present in the furnace atmosphere[27] as impurities in the form of sulfur and nitrogen compounds; sulfur or lead-bearing lubricating oils used for machining the parts, or sulfur-containing paper in which the parts may be wrapped for storage after machining can be sources of such injurious effects and must be carefully avoided. The great stress put on rigorous cleaning of all components and the need for clean fixtures and tools used during assembly as well as clean conditions for the furnace itself are thus brought into focus.

The brazing of electronic components is often achieved most conveniently by means of induction heating in a bell jar that is either filled with hydrogen or forming gas, or evacuated. The induction coils can be mounted either within the bell jar or outside, provided that enough power is available to achieve close coupling of the electromagnetic energy to the work piece. Heating the workpiece by convection in the presence of an atmosphere, or by radiation alone in an evacuated bell jar from specially constructed ovens that surround the work, is another practical approach.[27a] In all types of brazing, it is desirable to mount a flag made from the filler metal close to the joint so that the temperature of fusion can be observed.

It is frequently desirable to concentrate the heat within the joint area without overheating adjacent parts; this can readily be achieved by eddy-current concentrators which have been described in the literature and of which some examples are given in Figure 12.9.[28, 29]

Very short heating times can be achieved by pulse techniques where the power is concentrated in the joint area for a matter of seconds, or less, so that critical components in close proximity of the joint, such as a glass seal, will not have time to heat up sufficiently to become damaged.[30]

Examples of typical metal combinations and filler metals commonly used for such joints will be given in the following paragraphs. An extensive tabulation of metal combinations and possible filler metals has been published by Espe.[31] It should be borne in mind, however, that special circumstances may preclude direct application of any of the examples to a given structure.

It will always be most desirable that the chosen filler metal should wet the parent metal to a high degree and therefore flow readily in the joint. As pointed out above, this condition calls for a high surface tension and a low viscosity of the filler metal at brazing temperature; but it also seems desirable that the molten filler metal should be able to dissolve a small amount of the metal on which it flows without increasing its liquidus tem-

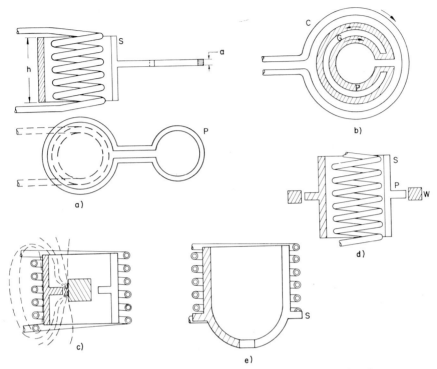

Figure 12.9. Different types of Eddy-current concentrators. The flux concentrators shown under c–e are derived from a single-turn transformer and act as such. By visualizing the right-hand extension of the single turn at a) flipped to the inside at b) with the exciting coil put outside and filling in the gap where opposite currents flow, the form at c) results with its solid internal platform. The platform may be arranged externally as at d), or extended downward as at e). After Babat and Losinsky[28] and Kohl.[29]

perature very much, when its composition has been altered by the addition of the metal which it has dissolved. The excellent wetting properties of copper when used as a filler metal for joining steel parts is an example of this mechanism. Molten copper will dissolve up to 2.8 per cent iron and thereby increase its liquidus temperature by only 11°C. The surface layer of this iron-enriched copper thus remains liquid and is quickly saturated with iron, thus permitting the pure molten copper to flow onto adjacent joint surfaces and there repeat the process just described. Molten silver, on the other hand, wets pure nickel but flows on it very poorly.

An inspection of the appropriate constitutional diagram will disclose that silver dissolves a very small amount of nickel, but in the process of doing so raises its liquidus temperature by several hundred degrees. The liquid silver alloy film in contact with pure nickel will thus immediately freeze and form a barrier to the further spreading of pure silver. A silver-copper alloy such as the commonly used eutectic composition, on the other hand, will wet nickel and flow on it very well. Copper and nickel form continuous solid solutions in each other in all proportions, and the addition of copper to nickel lowers the liquidus temperature of nickel slightly when a small enrichment of nickel with copper occurs. When the filler metal has a very large tendency to alloy with the base metal and lowers its liquidus temperature in the process, as is the case for silver on copper, the silver will penetrate into the copper part rather than flow on the surface. These examples may suffice to illustrate that good flow properties of the filler metal are observed when it has a small solubility in the parent metal and the alloy thus formed has a liquidus temperature which differs from that of the pure filler metal by only a small amount.[32]

1. **Copper-to-copper.** For this combination, the silver-copper eutectic is ordinarily very suitable; its liquidus point of 780°C is sufficiently far removed from the melting point of copper (1083°C) to allow a wide margin in temperature. The remark made earlier in the chapter on erosion of joints should be clearly kept in mind. For step-brazing of copper assemblies, a wide variety of alloys is available as shown in Table 12.1. Silver-copper-gold alloys or nickel-gold alloys will serve for brazes at the higher temperatures, and some of the copper-tin-silver alloys or copper-indium-silver may be used at lower temperatures.

Gold diffusion seals between copper members can be achieved at 450°C by placing a gold washer, or wire ring, between flat surfaces of well-annealed OFHC copper and clamping the assembly during the heat treatment which usually calls for a period of two hours; a vacuum-tight joint thus results by virtue of diffusion of gold into the copper, and the clamp can be removed after completion of the joint. An alloy containing 37.5 per cent gold and 62.5 per cent copper can be used as a gasket for diffusion seals under the same conditions of heat treatment, as described by Nelson.[33-35]

Joint clearances for copper or copper-base-alloy members may range from 1.5 to 10 mils for silver-base alloy filler metals, from 2 to 12 mils for silver-copper-phosphorus filler metals, and from 3 to 15 mils for copper-phosphorus filler metals.[6]

2. **Copper-to-nickel.** Joints between these two materials may be made with silver-copper eutectic, gold-copper, or gold-copper-nickel alloys. A nickel-bearing gold alloy which has a lower solubility for copper and nickel, and therefore better flow characteristics, is to be preferred to a straight gold-copper alloy when good penetration into a long joint interface is desired.

3. **Copper-to-steel.** It is frequently desirable to copper-plate the steel and sinter this coat in hydrogen at about 1000°C for 30 minutes; brazing

can then be achieved with any of the filler metals mentioned above for copper joints. Gold diffusion joints can also be made on copper-plated steel.* Phosphorus-containing filler metals cannot be used on iron or ferrous alloys because brittle compounds are formed.

4. **Copper-to-Kovar.** Some precaution is necessary when using silver or silver-bearing filler metals for this combination, because "Kovar" as well as stainless steels is subject to stress corrosion cracking. By copper-plating the "Kovar," as described above, this danger can be materially reduced. Gold, copper, nickel, and gold-nickel alloys flow better on "Kovar" than do the binary copper-gold alloys. The reason for this behavior is not fully understood, but it has been suggested that the solubility of oxygen and nickel oxide in molten nickel may enhance the flow properties of nickel-bearing filler metals.[32]

5. **Nickel-to-nickel.** These joints can be made with silver-copper eutectic alloy or the gold-copper and gold-copper-nickel alloys; pure copper can also be used. Recommended joint clearances range between 0.5 and 6 mils for silver-alloy brazing of nickel parts and from a light press fit to 2 mils maximum clearance in the case of brazing with copper. Copper alloys very readily with nickel and raises its liquidus temperature in the process of doing so. Copper will thus not flow as far in a joint between nickel members as it does when used for steel assemblies.

Nickel and nickel alloys are subject to corrosion cracking at elevated temperatures in the presence of sulfur and lead. Oil, grease, paint, marking pencils, drawing or cutting lubricants, and some papers contain enough sulfur or lead to cause embrittlement of nickel and nickel alloys; careful cleaning procedures are thus in order. Like "Kovar" and other high-alloy steels, nickel and nickel alloys also show stress corrosion cracking in the presence of molten silver, as pointed out above. The design of the joint must thus be such that stresses are avoided. Silver-brazing should be done only on annealed material, and stresses should not be reintroduced by poorly designed fixtures, steep thermal gradients in heavy parts caused by very rapid heating, or poorly chosen companion materials for nickel, where disregard of thermal expansion differences may introduce stresses at the joint during the brazing operation.

The strength of silver-brazed nickel joints decreases rapidly when the temperature during operation exceeds 150°C, and cannot be relied on above 260°C; copper-brazed nickel joints will lose their strength rapidly by oxidation of the filler metal above 500°C. Several nickel-base alloys are available which can be used as filler metals for high-nickel alloys and stainless steels for high-temperature service where such joints will maintain adequate strength and have good oxidation resistance up to 1100°C. These filler

---

* Gold diffusion joints are also possible between "Kovar" and nickel.[35a]

metals are generally applied in the form of powders or pastes because the ductility of these alloys is low and they cannot be drawn into wires; they contain nickel, chrome, boron, and silicon in varying amounts as shown in Table 12.1. Nickel vanes have been brazed onto a nickel base plate for a thyratron cathode by using molybdenum powder which forms a eutectic of Mo and Ni at about 1315°C.[43c]

6. **Stainless Steel Joints.**[25a, 36-43] Apart from the nickel-chromium-boron and nickel-chromium-silicon alloys just mentioned, an 82 gold-18 nickel alloy which can be obtained in the form of wire and sheet is most suited to the brazing of stainless steels. Chang[43] has investigated these heat-resisting brazing filler materials in some detail. Careful study of this report is recommended to any reader particularly interested in the intricacies of brazing, because many of the observations made in the present chapter are elucidated by Chang in a most searching manner. The following highlights are taken from his paper.

Table 12.3 describes the filler metal used by Chang and Table 12.4 gives the chemical composition of the base metals which were brazed with the filler metals in the form of rectangular butt-type specimens, ½ x 2 x 3 in. in over-all dimensions; the filler metal was placed in a small cavity at the center of the rectangular joint. Provisions were made to produce joint clearances of 0, 2, 4, and 6 mils during the various tests. Brazing was performed in a hydrogen furnace by placing the test assemblies in a low-carbon steel box provided with gas entrance and exit ports, and the dew point was held at −62.2°C (−80°F). A brazing temperature of 1204°C (2200°F) was chosen for Ni-Cr-B alloy number 1 and the Ni-Cr-Si alloy, and 1093°C (2000°F) for Ni-Cr-B alloy number 2. In the case of the Au-18 percent Ni

TABLE 12.3. DESCRIPTION OF BRAZING FILLER MATERIALS USED BY CHANG[43]

Filler material	Nominal composition, %	Approximate liquidus, °F	Applied form
Ni-Cr-B Alloy No. 1	15 Cr, 4 Si, 3.5 B, 1.0 C, 4.0 Fe, Bal. Ni.	1925	−325 mesh powder
Ni-Cr-B Alloy No. 2	7 Cr, 4.5 Si, 3 B, 3 Fe, Bal. Ni	1825	−250 mesh powder
Ni-Cr-Si Alloy	19 Cr, 10 Si, 5.0 Fe, Bal. Ni.	2035	−200 mesh powder
Au-18% Ni Alloy	82 Au, 18 Ni	1742	$\frac{1}{32}$-in wire

TABLE 12.4. COMPOSITION OF BASE MATERIALS USED BY CHANG[43]

Base material	Nominal composition, %
N-155	0.15 C, 20 Ni, 20 Cr, 20 Co, 3 Mo, 2.5 W, 1 Cb + Ta, 0.15 Al, Bal. Fe
AISI 347	0.08 C, 2.0 Mn, 0.75 Si, 10 Ni, 18 Cr, 0.8 Cb + Ta, Bal. Fe
AISI 405	0.09 C, 0.5 Mn, 0.5 Si, 12 Cr, 0.5 Ni, 0.2 Al, Bal. Fe

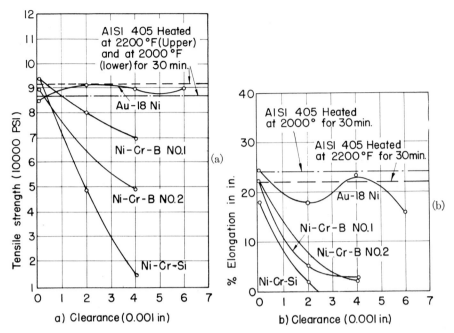

Figure 12.10a,b. Tensile strength and percent elongation of brazed AISI 405 joints. After Chang.[43] (*Courtesy American Welding Society.*)

alloy, a temperature range of 1037 to 1093°C (1900 to 2000°F) was used. The brazing time was fixed at 30 minutes for all the filler materials except the gold-nickel alloy, for which a brazing time of 10 minutes was chosen. The mechanical properties of the joint were measured at room temperature after completion of the braze, and metallographic sections were also made in order to obtain microphotographs of the joint.

The results obtained from these measurements indicate that the tensile properties of the joints made with the first three types of filler metal listed in Table 12.3 are markedly dependent on joint clearance whereas this is not the case for the gold-nickel filler metal. Figure 12.10 illustrates this statement for N-155 joints, showing how both tensile strength and percent elongation drop rapidly when joint clearance takes on values greater than zero for the first three of the listed filler metals while joints made with gold-nickel alloys are not affected in this manner. The reason for this behavior is the formation of brittle phases in the joint when complex filler metals are used in combination with complex parent metals. The alloying elements boron, silicon, or carbon in the first three filler metals tend to diffuse from the joint into the base material and the extent of diffusion will be governed by the volume and geometry of the space between the joined surfaces.

At "zero" clearance, the diffusion distance is so short and the amount of the B, Si, or C in the joint so small that sufficient diffusion takes place during the brazing time to change the complex filler metal into essentially a solid solution of Cr in Ni. On the other hand, when the intended clearance was 2 mils or more, the diffusion distance was lengthened and the amount of B, Si, or C initially present in the joint was too large for the brittle phases to disappear completely during the cycle. If a filler material neither contains brittle phases nor forms such phases with the base material, the tensile properties of the resulting joint will not be appreciably affected by joint clearance, as demonstrated by the joints made with gold-18 nickel alloy which showed excellent strength and ductility over a clearance range from 0 to 6 mils.

The gold-nickel alloy is of course much more expensive, and its rather low melting point in comparison to that of the other filler metals tested limits service temperature of the joint; it also presents difficulties in certain heat treatments of the brazed part because the heat-treating temperatures must necessarily lie below the melting range of the brazed joint. On the other hand, gold-nickel alloy filler metal does not show the effect of liquation which is pronounced in the other three filler metals tested in the series of experiments just described.

In order to evaluate the erosion of stainless steel Type 304 by various brazing alloys, a number of tests were performed by Handy and Harman[18] and described in their Technical Bulletin No. T-11. Very severe test conditions were imposed in order to obtain significant results. Type 304 stainless steel cylinders, $\frac{3}{8}$ in. round and $\frac{3}{4}$ in. long were made into small crucibles by drilling a $\frac{1}{8}$-in.-dia. hole to a length of $\frac{5}{8}$ in. and filling these holes with filler metals in the form of powder or chips. The loaded specimens were then heated in an atmosphere of hydrogen at a dew point of $-62.2°C$ and soaked at a temperature of 1121°C (2050°F) for a period of one hour. Metallographic sections were then taken and the joint penetration by the filler metal measured under the microscope. Table 12.5 summarizes the results; the last column gives the combined effect of solution of the parent metal in the filler metal and penetration of the filler metal into the base metal. While a joint will in practice never be exposed to the brazing temperature for a period of one hour, as was the case in these tests, one should nevertheless exercise caution when brazing thin members of stainless steel[25a] where some penetration is indicated in the table. Huschke and Hoppin III[42] have reported on the relative advantages and disadvantages of brazing jet engine material with NiCrSi and NiSiB filler metals in extremely pure hydrogen or vacuum and evaluate the different methods for joint preparation and application of the powders to super alloys containing titanium and aluminum.

7. Tungsten and Molybdenum Joints. In brazing the refractory

TABLE 12.5. JOINT CORROSION OF STAINLESS STEEL TYPE
304 BY VARIOUS FILLER METALS*

Filler Metal Composition (%)	Combined solution and penetration
Fine silver	None
99.5 Ag-0.5 Li	None
85 Ag-15 Mn	None
84.5 Ag-15 Mn-0.5 Li	None
72 Ag-28 Cu	<0.001 inch
72 Ag-27.5 Cu-0.5 Li	<0.001
68 Mn-32 Ni	0.003
72 Au-22 Ni-6 Cr	0.003
Pure copper	0.004
91.25 Ni-4.50 Si-2.90 B-Bal. Fe	0.0135
22.00 Ni-4.50 Si-2.90 B-7.00 Cr-Bal. Fe	0.014
56.0 Ni-24.0 Pd-10 Cr-10 Si	0.0065

* Handy & Harman Technical Bulletin No. T-11 (Dec. 1956).

metals to themselves or to each other, the temperature encountered in operation will to a large extent determine the choice of the filler metals used. Whether the joint should have some ductility during its use, is another important consideration. It is very difficult to avoid embrittlement of the joint by oxide inclusion during the brazing operation even after all possible precautions have been taken to ensure clean conditions. Severe conditions of vibration and shock will thus naturally endanger such joints.

Sound joints between tungsten and molybdenum can be made by brazing in a hydrogen atmosphere with copper or copper-silver eutectic as a filler metal. Spot welds between tungsten and molybdenum are commonly made by inserting a thin foil of nickel or platinum; brazing can similarly be achieved by using nickel or platinum as a filler metal when operating temperatures exceed the melting points of copper or copper-silver eutectic; numerous alloys are listed in Table 12.1 from which a selection can be made which suits particular conditions. Espersen[43b] reports using finely divided nickel oxide powder for brazing porous tungsten to molybdenum in L and in impregnated Philips cathodes (see Chapter 15). A satisfactory joint is achieved by firing in hydrogen at 1400°C when the oxide reduces to nickel which melts and forms alloys with molybdenum and tungsten having lower vapor pressures than pure nickel. Molybdenum disks have been brazed to 0.031 in.-thick copper cups with Au/Ni eutectic in high-power thyratrons.[43c]

Thoriated tungsten wire has been brazed to molybdenum with tungsten carbide. Rhodium wire is a suitable brazing filler metal for tungsten, according to J. F. Gittins,* and can also be used for molybdenum. Ruthenium

* Services Electronics Research Laboratory, Baldock, Hertfordshire, England; Ann Arbor IRE Tube Conference, June 1950.

powder or mixtures of ruthenium and molybdenum powders give sound joints for high-temperature operation, according to Jasionis and Cline.[44] A mixture of 80 Mo/20 Ru powder suspended in a nitrocellulose lacquer was painted to the joint surface and presintered in hydrogen at 1150°C, and the final braze made at 2100°C in forming gas by induction heating.

The possibilities of arc-welding in an atmosphere of hydrogen, helium, or argon should not be overlooked.[45]

8. **Titanium Joints.** The great affinity of titanium for oxygen, hydrogen and nitrogen (see Chapter 16) makes it necessary that brazing operations involving this metal be carried out in a very pure, neutral atmosphere, such as argon, or in a vacuum of the order of 10^{-5} Torr, or less. To ensure these conditions, it is generally advisable to place some Ti sponge or fine clean swarf in the furnace so that traces of water vapor are absorbed by this "getter" rather than cause contamination and discoloration of the components.

"Filler alloys of silver can be used where brazing cycles are short. With longer brazing cycles, however, marked alloying occurs and the resulting joints are usually brittle. For large components there is not much possibility of speeding up the brazing cycle, and considerable effort has been directed towards the development of alternative filler materials. In this connection the use of eutectiferous alloys of titanium of suitable composition has proved of value in certain applications, while another approach involves the use of nickel or copper as the brazing foil, which alloys with the titanium to form the bond. With nickel or copper fillers some eutectic is formed, but by suitable choice of brazing cycles it is possible to free the joint from this by promoting diffusion into the titanium components. In these circumstances extremely high joint strengths can be obtained, but ductility is low. Joints made using titanium alloys, nickel, or copper as fillers are more suitable for use at elevated temperatures than those produced with silver or aluminum alloys.

"The use of filler metals favoured for other materials might also be possible if the brazing operation could be carried out sufficiently quickly to prevent harmful alloying effects. Indeed, some of the results obtained from silver solders in induction brazing experiments indicate quite significant changes in joint properties with variation of the brazing cycle. In general, joints made with a long brazing cycle are stronger but less ductile than those made with a short brazing cycle.

"Resistance brazing also offers attractions for certain types of work, and joints of high strength have been obtained with a variety of brazing alloy shims, including silver, silver solder, aluminium and aluminium alloys.

Flux dip brazing is another method in which high working speeds are possible, but so far experience with this method is limited."[46]*

Long and Ruppender[47] found it almost impossible to furnace braze titanium with silver-base alloys because the time cycle required to prevent formation of brittle intermetallic compounds by diffusion would be shorter than commercially practical. By substituting Ti/Ni alloys for silver-base alloys and lowering their flow point by proper additives, they succeeded in keeping the brazing temperature below 1070°C and brazing periods within 30 minutes. Of some 15 different alloy compositions that seemed to give promising results, the one most fully tested had the following analysis: Ti: 28; Ni: 52; Cu: 15; Co: 5. A gap clearance of 2 mils was used, and compressive and tensile shear strengths in excess of 40,000 psi were obtained.

Lynch, Feinstein, and Huggins[47a] have recently discussed brazing by the diffusion-controlled formation of a liquid intermediate phase and applied this technique to the joining of titanium parts. A nickel shim, 0.010 in. thick, is placed in the joint, as practiced previously by Beggs for ceramic-to titanium joints (see Chapter 14). The authors show how a joint can be made at lower temperatures than given by the melting point of the interspersed metal, if the components of the joint form a liquid phase at such lower temperature.

9. Beryllium Joints. Beryllium is extensively used for x-ray tube windows which are generally brazed in vacuum by induction heating to a retaining ring made from Monel. Brazing in a pure hydrogen atmosphere is also possible, but calls for more extensive precautions in the preparation of the beryllium surface; electroplating the joint areas with silver or copper prior to brazing with either copper, silver, or copper-silver eutectic is frequently practiced. Good vacuum-brazed joints have been made without electroplating the beryllium when inserting thin zirconium or titanium washers between the beryllium and the brazing metal washers. Sometimes titanium and zirconium, to the extent of 5 to 15 per cent, are added to the brazing material itself.[48]

"No applications of beryllium should be planned without a full appreciation of the toxicity of this metal and its compounds. A Materials Advisory Board Panel on the Toxicity of Beryllium, headed by Professor Harold Hodge of the University of Rochester, has recently prepared a report on this subject, from which the following remarks are abstracted.

"In contrast to former beliefs, no reasonable doubt now remains that small amounts inhaled have produced an acute disease (pneumonitis) and/or a chronic disease (granulomatosis), the latter having a high mor-

---

* Quotation by permission of Imperial Chemical Industries, Ltd., Metals Division, Birmingham, England.

tality rate. Contact with certain beryllium compounds can produce a dermatitis which may be serious with respect to lost time, but which can be combatted with suitable protective clothing or skin creams.

"Protection against beryllium poisoning is largely a matter of controlling the dust evolved in the operations on the metal. As a target figure for the average allowable concentration of beryllium in the air, 2 micrograms per cubic meter may tentatively be acceptable. This does not constitute a guarantee that no chronic illness will develop; there are cases in which a lag time as long as 16 years intervened between exposure and symptoms.

"To keep air-borne beryllium at the required low level, the following principles are suggested:

(1) Manual handling should be reduced to an absolute minimum.

(2) Every implement which has been in contact with beryllium should be regarded as contaminated, and therefore, a potential dust source.

(3) Every process step should be examined critically to determine whether by arrangement or substitution it can be made less dusty.

(4) Essentially every process step must be provided with some degree of ventilation. The only effective method of control is to contain and remove the dust at its source."[49]

Ultrasonic Welding[50-52]

During the past several years, a new method of metal joining has been developed under the sponsorship of the Bureau of Aeronautics principally at Aeroprojects, Inc. The parts to be joined are held in alignment under mechanical pressure between support members which have the appearance of electrodes used in a spot welder. To one of the rods, ultrasonic energy is fed from a transducer which imparts a vibratory motion to the rod in contact with the joint. The vibrational energy delivered to the weld zone produces a sliding motion on a microscopic scale and thus a temperature rise owing to friction which produces a plastic flow of the metal and results in an intimate bond between the two components in contact with each other. The joints thus produced are mechanically sound. A wide variety of similar and dissimilar metals can be joined to each other; these include copper, steel, platinum, molybdenum, Inconel, tungsten, and tantalum. The technique has been applied, so far, mostly to sheet stock limited in thickness up to 0.090 in. in the case of "Alclad" aluminum, and thinner stock for other metals. The time for which the ultrasonic energy is applied to the joint must be carefully controlled and rarely exceeds three seconds. Examples are quoted in the literature according to which 1.5-mil tungsten wire has been welded across two 25-mil copper posts and, in another case, a bond has been made between two 3-mil sheets of nickel- and gold-plated "Kovar."

The technique is still under development but commercial units are available from several sources.* The ultrasonic transducers range in power from 300 to 6000 watts. While this method of joining does not properly fall into the category of brazing in so far as no external heat is applied, and no filler metal is fed to the joint area, it is nevertheless mentioned in this chapter because it promises to be of considerable interest to the electronics industry.

REFERENCES

1. J. Soled, "Fasteners Handbook," Reinhold Publishing Corp., New York, 1957.
2. V. H. Laughner and A. D. Hargan, "Handbook of Fastening and Joining of Metal Parts," McGraw-Hill Book Co., Inc., New York, 1956.
3. "Welding Handbook," American Welding Society, New York, 1950.
4. "Metals Handbook," American Society for Metals, Cleveland, Ohio, 1948.
5. "Brazing Manual," prepared by the Committee on Brazing and Soldering of the American Welding Society; Reinhold Publishing Corp., New York, 1955.
6. H. R. Brooker and E. V. Beatson, "Industrial Brazing," Iliffe & Sons, Ltd., London, 1953.
7. W. Espe, "Welding in Vacuum Techniques" (in German), *Vakuum-Technik*, **6**, 91–101 (Aug. 1957); 123–129 (Sept. 1957). Extensively illustrated review of the many different welding techniques including arc-welding, spot-welding, cold-welding, etc.; 51 references.
8. H. V. Neher and S. Prakash, "Metal system for chemical reactions and for studying properties of gases in liquids," *Rev. Sci. Instr.* **28**, 267–270 (Apr. 1957).
9. W. L. Wyman, "High-vacuum electron-beam fusion welding," *Welding J.*, **37**, 49s–53s (Feb. 1958).
9a. J. A. Stohr, "Vacuum brazing of metals" (in French), *Le Vide*, **13**, No. 75, 163–171 (May/June 1958).
10. F. N. Rhines, "Phase Diagrams in Metallurgy," McGraw-Hill Book Co., Inc., New York, 1956.
11. C. J. Smithells, "Metals Reference Book," Interscience Publishers, Inc., New York, 1955, and Butterworth's Scientific Publications, (Vol. 1) London, 1955.
12. W. Hume-Rothery, J. W. Christian and W. B. Pearson, "Metallurgical Equilibrium Diagrams," The Institute of Physics, London, 1952.
13. W. Hume-Rothery, "Atomic Theory for Students of Metallurgy," The Institute of Metals, London, 1948.
14. W. Hume-Rothery, "The Structure of Metals and Alloys," The Institute of Metals, London, 1947.
15. G. E. Doan, "The Principles of Physical Metallurgy," 3rd ed., McGraw-Hill Book Co., Inc., New York, 1953.
16. J. E. Goldman, "The Science of Engineering Materials," John Wiley & Sons, Inc., New York, 1957.
16a. G. D. Cremer and R. S. Mueller, "One temperature for successive brazes," *Product Eng.*, **29**, No. 50, 84–86 (Dec. 8, 1958).
17. N. Bredzs, "Investigation of factors determining the tensile strength of brazed joints," *Welding J.*, **33**, 545s–563s (Nov. 1954).

---

* Gulton Industries, Inc., Metuchen, N. J.; Aeroprojects, Inc., Westchester, Pa. through the Sonobond Corporation; Westinghouse Electric Corporation.

18. Handy & Harman Technical Bull. No. T3 (1951), revised 1957. Handy & Harman, New York, N. Y.

19. H. Udin, E. R. Funk and John Wulff, "Welding for Engineers," John Wiley & Sons, Inc., New York, 1954.

20. W. G. Moffatt and J. Wulff, "Strength of silver brazed joints in mild steel," *J. Metals, Trans. Am. Inst. Met. Engrs.*, **209**, 442–445 (Apr. 1957).

21. H. Bender, "New developments in metal-ceramic seals," *Sylvania Technologist*, **8**, 22–26. (Jan. 1955).

22. E. R. Funk and H. Udin, "Brazing hydromechanics," *Welding J.*, **31**, 310s–316s (June 1952).

23. D. R. Milner, "A survey of the scientific principles relating to wetting and spreading," *British Welding J.*, **5**, 90–105 (March 1958).

24. General Plate Division, Metals & Controls Division, Texas Instruments Incorporated, Attleboro, Mass.

25. Western Gold and Platinum Company, 525 Harbor Boulevard, Belmont, California.

25a. A. S. Rose and W. N. Lewis, "High-temperature alloy brazing of thin materials for jet engines," *Welding J.*, **34**, 30–39 (Jan. 1955).

25b. D. C. Herrschaft, "Predicting gap change reduces trial runs in brazing dissimilar metal joints," *Welding J.*, **38**, 232–235 (Mar. 1959).

26. R. A. Wallace and W. R. Vanderveer, "Brazing vacuum-tight joints with high-nickel alloys," Materials & Methods, **36**, 117–118 (Dec. 1952).

27. A. G. Hotchkiss and H. M. Webber, "Protective Atmospheres," John Wiley & Sons, Inc., New York, 1953.

27a. F. Bernhard and H. Bumm, "Brazing in vacuum" (in German), *Vakuum-Technik*, **7**, No. 7, 152–158 (Oct. 1958).

28. G. Babat and M. Losinsky, "Concentrator of eddy-currents for zonal heating of steel parts," *J. Appl. Phys.*, **11**, 816–823 (Dec. 1940).

29. W. H. Kohl, "Flux concentrators for induction heating," Electronics Research Laboratory, Stanford University, Technical Data Bulletin, Feb. 24, 1954 (unpublished).

30. J. L. Reinartz, "Industrial brazing by pulse techniques," *Electronics*, **23**, 78–80 (Jan. 1950).

31. W. Espe, "Welded and brazed joints of metallic components in high-vacuum technique" (in German), *Vakuum-Technik*, **4**, 51–64 (Aug. 1955). (69 references.)

32. W. L. Hack, "Brazing of high-vacuum system components." A paper presented at Stanford University on Feb. 17, 1954 before the IRE Professional Group On Electron Devices (not published, but distributed in mimeographed form by Western Gold and Platinum Company, Belmont, California).

33. R. B. Nelson, "A gold-copper alloy solder," General Electric Co., OEM sr-931 (1944); U. S. Patent 242,467 (Aug. 26, 1947).

34. J. B. Fisk, H. D. Hagstrum and P. L. Hartman, "The magnetron as a generator of centimeter waves," *Bell System Tech. J.*, **25**, (Apr. 1946).

35. R. R. Law, W. B. Whalley and R. P. Stone, "Developmental television transmitter for 500–900 megacycles," *RCA Rev.*, **9**, 643–652 (Dec. 1948). (Copper-plated Kovar parts are joined by gold diffusion.)

35a. J. H. Carmichael and E. A. Trendelenburg, "Ion-induced reemission of noble gases from a nickel surface," *J. Appl. Phys.*, **29**, 1570–1577 (Nov. 1958).

36. "Brazing and soldering nickel and high-nickel alloys," Tech. Bull. T-34, The International Nickel Company, Inc., New York, (Aug. 1957).

37. G. H. Sistair, J. J. Halbig and L. H. Grenell, "Silver-brazing alloy for corrosion-resistant joints in stainless steels," *Welding J.*, **33**, 137–143 (Feb. 1954).

38. R. C. Grassi, I. Cornet and R. S. Berger, "Investigating the strength of copper-brazed joints," *Mech. Eng.*, **78**, 630–632 (July 1956).

39. R. L. Peaslee and W. M. Boan, "Design properties of brazed joints for high-temperature applications," *Welding J.*, **31**, 651–662 (Aug. 1952).

40. W. Feduska, "The nature of high-temperature brazing alloy-base metal interface reactions," *Welding J.*, **37**, 62s–73s (Feb. 1958).

41. A. S. Rose and W. N. Lewis, "High-temperature alloy brazing of thin materials for jet engines," *Welding J.*, **34**, 30–39 (Jan. 1955).

42. E. G. Huschke, Jr. and G. S. Hoppin III, "High-temperature vacuum brazing of jet-engine materials," *Welding J.*, **37**, 233s–240s (May 1958).

43. W. H. Chang, "Basic characteristics of some heat-resisting brazing filler materials," *Welding J.*, **35**, 431s–443s (Sept. 1956).

43a. "Further evaluation of Ni-Cr-B and Au-18 Ni brazing alloys," *Welding J.*, **37**, 535s–542s (Dec. 1958).

43b. G. A. Espersen, "Dispenser cathode magnetrons," *IRE Trans.*, **ED-6**, 115–118 (Jan. 1959).

43c. S. Goldberg and D. F. Riley, "Research and Development Program on 12 MW Ceramic Hydrogen Thyratron," Edgerton, Germeshausen & Grier, Final Rept. (June 1958); Contr. No. DA 36-039-sc-73161.

44. J. P. Jasionis and J. E. Cline, "Brazing molybdenum and tungsten cathode part with ruthenium," *IRE Trans. Electron Devices*, **ED-3**, 162 (July 1956).

44a. L. C. Herman, "The brazing of tungsten and molybdenum above 1900°C," Fourth National Conference on Tube Techniques, September 10–12, 1958, New York. Proceedings of the Conference published by New York University Press, New York, N. Y., 1959.

44b. R. E. Monroe, "Brazing of molybdenum," Chapter 8 in "The Metal Molybdenum," Proceedings of a Symposium sponsored by The Office of Naval Research, held in Detroit, Michigan, September 18–19, 1956; Published by American Society For Metals, Cleveland, Ohio, 1958; (192–198).

45. T. Perry, H. S. Spacil and J. Wulff, "Effect of oxygen on welding and brazing molybdenum," *Welding J.*, **33**, pp. 442s–448s (Sept. 1954).

46. "Wrought Titanium," Fourth Ed., pp. 49–50. Imperial Chemical Industries, Ltd., March 1958.

47. R. A. Long and R. R. Ruppender, "High-temperature alloy fusion brazing for titanium and titanium alloys," *Welding J.*, **33**, 1087–1090 (Nov. 1954).

47a. J. F. Lynch, L. Feinstein and R. A. Huggins, "Brazing by the diffusion-controlled formation of a liquid phase," *Welding J.*, **38**, 85s–89s (Feb. 1959).

47b. E. J. Clark, "Vacuum diffusion joining of titanium," *Welding J.*, **38**, 251s–258s (June 1959).

48. M. J. Zunick and J. E. Illingworth, "How to braze beryllium," *Materials & Methods*, **39**, 95–97 (Mar. 1954).

49. J. R. Lane, "Beryllium, its problems and possibilities," *J. Metals*, **10**, 738–742 (Nov. 1958).

50. J. N. Antonevich and R. E. Monroe, "Ultrasonics and welding," *Battelle Tech. Rev.*, **8**, 9–13 (Mar. 1959).

51. J. B. Jones, "Ultrasonic welding—a new technique grows," *Metal Progr.*, **73**, 68–72 (Apr. 1958).

52. J. B. Jones and F. R. Meyer, "Ultrasonic welding of structural aluminum alloys," *Welding J.*, **37**, 81s–92s (Mar. 1958).

CHAPTER 13

GLASS-TO-METAL SEALING

Introduction

The reason for the widespread use of glass for tube envelopes has been explained in Chapter 1. In order to make electrical connections to the internal electrodes of the tube, it becomes necessary to seal metallic leads into the glass so that they become an integral part of it. These seals between glass and metal must be vacuum-tight and remain so under the fluctuations of temperature encountered during processing of the tube on the pump and during its operational life. The various types of glass-to-metal seals now being used for this purpose and the techniques by which they are made will be described in this chapter. The treatment of this subject must of necessity be very condensed; the exhaustive monograph on glass-to-metal seals by Partridge[1] is available for a more detailed study of the subject.

The manipulation of glass by itself is a skill which must be mastered before any seals to metal can be made, and the reader is again referred to competent books and articles on this subject.[2-4] The commercial production of glass-to-metal seals is highly mechanized and thus does not require a knowledge of bench-working of glass in the blow torch. The experimenter in the laboratory, however, should be familiar with this technique.

The formation of a strong bond between glass and metal is due, in general, to the presence of an oxide layer which is formed on the metal just before the seal is made; this layer partly diffuses into molten glass when it is brought into physical contact with the oxidized metal under slight pressure. A bridge, which is firmly anchored at each end by atomic forces, is thus formed between the metal and the glass. If this bridge has too wide a span, i.e., if the oxide layer is too thick, it will collapse in the middle in spite of the firm foundations at its ends. Careful control of temperature and time is thus important in order to obtain an oxide layer of the right thickness and texture (see also p. 455).

The color of the finished seal usually is a good indication of its quality. For most metals, overoxidized seals have a dark color and underoxidized seals appear too light in color. With some experience, it is possible to judge the quality of the seal by its color within reasonably close limits. Metals which oxidize readily must be protected from over-oxidation during preparation of the seal. The nature of the oxide depends, to a large extent, on the composition of the metal and glass and the presence of impurities and

394

admixtures. The presence of carbon dioxide, water vapor, and sulfur compounds in the gas flame, if used, also have an effect.

The expansion coefficients of the oxide layers differ markedly in some cases from those of the base metal; for this reason, it is advisable not to let the metal cool after the oxide has been formed until the glass has been laid down on the oxide and the seal assembly will cool as a unit. Partridge has made a number of observations on the structure of oxides on different metals and has reviewed the various mechanisms which have been proposed from time to time for the formation of a bond. Other investigations of this subject of bonding are given in references 5–9.

Classification of Seals

The classification of seals can be undertaken from several different viewpoints. Glass-to-metal seals can be made by different techniques and thus be classified accordingly as

> flame seals
> induction seals
> seals made by high-frequency resistance welding
> pressure diffusion seals
> powder glass seals
> frit seals
> silver chloride seals

The geometry of the metal parts leads to the following classification:

> bead seals
> tubular seals
> disk seals
> ribbon seals
> feather-edge seals

Depending on whether the metal surrounds the glass, or vice versa, one speaks of "outside seals" and "inside seals" according to a terminology introduced by Monack.[10]

A broad classification of seals into the two categories of "matched seals" and "unmatched seals" refers to the attempt of having seal partners of equal thermal expansion coefficients in the first group and the absence of such agreement in the second group. Coaxial pressure seals (Druckglaseinschmelzungen) are an example of the second class.

Finally, the type of metal or alloy used for the metallic component and the type of glass can be used for the description of the seal, so that one speaks of soft-glass seals and hard-glass seals to metal, or "quartz"-to-metal seals,* as the case may be, and, in specific cases, of Dumet seals,

* See footnote p. 20.

iron alloy seals, "Kovar" seals, tungsten seals, molybdenum seals, platinum seals, copper seals, and so on. These different types of seals will be discussed in more detail later in the chapter; but first some general observations will be made that govern all seals between metal and glass.

Stresses in Seals

When two bars of the same kind of metal are joined by cold-welding, or brazed with a very thin film of pure metal at the interface by methods described in the preceding chapter, the assembly will expand on heating in a uniform manner, without any tendency to warp. No stresses will arise in the interface as long as the heating is carried out uniformly by placing the part in an oven where the temperature is constant, or rises uniformly, so that the heat penetrates the assembled bar at a constant rate from all sides.

If two strips of different metals with different thermal expansion coefficients are joined, and the temperature of the resulting bimetallic strip is raised, one component tends to become longer than the other. As the interface of the two strips must remain common to both metals, a curvature of the biform results because the higher-expansion metal is free to grow in length in the layers at its surface and less so at layers closer to the interface. A considerable force acts on the interface at elevated temperature, and permanent deformation will result if the elastic limit of shear is exceeded. If it is not exceeded, the curved biform will return to its original shape when the temperature has fallen to its initial value. Such bimetallic strips are widely used for temperature compensation or translation of motion by the application of heat in thermostats. One may similarly visualize two coaxial cylinders of dissimilar metals being brazed together at their common cylindrical interface. Assuming a tight fit to begin with, and assigning the larger expansion coefficient to the outer cylinder, considerable radial tension will be exerted on the interface during heating.

These examples serve to illustrate the problems that arise in joining metals to glass. Ideally, one would wish glass and metal in a seal to have identical values of thermal expansion over the entire range of temperatures to which the seal is exposed during sealing, annealing, and operation (matched seals). Unfortunately, this ideal situation cannot be realized in practice. Pure metals expand at a uniform rate so that their specific thermal expansion is a constant which, for practical considerations, is independent of temperature as long as no phase changes take place. Glasses, on the other hand, grow in length at an increasing rate when they are heated because their specific thermal expansion usually increases with temperature, as shown in Figure 13.1.

The expansion coefficient of glasses depends on the composition and the

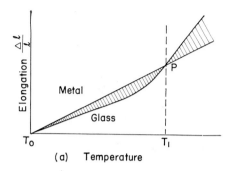

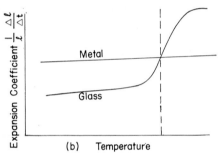

Figure 13.1. Thermal expansion characteristics for metals and glasses (schematic); (a) elongation vs temperature, (b) expansion coefficient vs temperature.

thermal history of the glass. In the lower range of temperatures, up to the vicinity of the annealing point, the expansion coefficients of glasses are fairly constant, but at higher temperatures they rise rapidly. For this reason, expansion coefficients of glasses given in reference tables are referred to this lower temperature range, usually from 0 to 300°C (see Appendix Table A3). Referring to Figure 13.1a, it is evident that the joint between the two materials will be free of strain at temperature T_1 where both have increased in length by the same amount, and the expansion curves cross at point P. During further heating above T_1, and cooling below T_1, strains will be introduced which are proportional to the differential expansion shown by the shaded area between the two curves. If point P should lie within the annealing range for the glass, as is often the case, and the strains introduced during cooling do not exceed the breaking strength of the glass in question, a sound joint will result at room temperature T_0. These conditions are not always attainable in practice so that compromises become necessary.

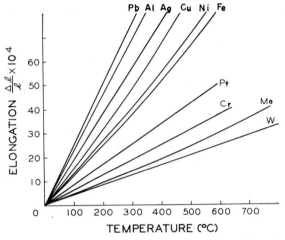

Figure 13.2. Thermal expansion of various metals as a function of temperature.

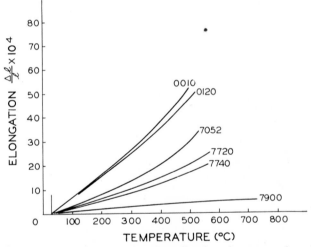

Figure 13.3. Thermal expansion of various Corning glasses as a function of temperature. (*Courtesy Corning Glass Works.*)

Figure 13.2 shows the thermal expansion of various metals as a function of temperature, and Figure 13.3 the corresponding curves for various Corning glasses. It is apparent that the curves for metals are nearly straight lines while those for glasses show a marked curvature. Later illustrations, such as Figure 13.17 (p. 434), give superimposed elongation for metal and glass of a given joint corresponding to Figure 13.1a.

Rather than plotting elongation curves in this manner, it is at times convenient to show the difference between metal and glass expansion such as shown by the shaded area in Figure 13.1a as a function of temperature. Figure 13.21 (pp. 439) is an example of this method of portraying the expansion differences. As these expansion differences between metal and glass usually result in strains, either tension or compression, plots of strain vs temperature can be obtained when these strains have been separately measured or calculated. Engel[10a] reports on measurements made with the high-temperature polarimeter (see p. 53) and discusses the significance of different traces obtained with rising and falling temperature (hysteresis). This effect is related to the "fictive temperature" of a glass, introduced by Tool and described in Chapter 1.

The stresses encountered in cylindrical configurations of glass and metal combinations are of three kinds, i.e., axial (longitudinal), radial, and circumferential (tangential); each of these may assume the form of compression or tension, as the case may be. The manner in which these stresses arise is illustrated in Figure 13.4a–g. Assuming that two slabs of glass and metal are of equal length at a high temperature (a), it is obvious that they will both be smaller in length by different amounts if they are allowed to contract freely while cooling to room temperature. If the two slabs are joined while hot, so that they become an integral unit, and then allowed to cool, the tendency of the metal to contract by a greater amount than the glass will be counteracted in part by the glass which "likes" to remain longer than the metal (b). To some extent, however, the glass will have to follow the metal; it is thus compressed into a shorter length than it would have assumed if it had been free to contract in a natural way by itself. The glass is thus in compression while the metal is in axial tension when the seal has cooled to room temperature. If the thermal expansion coefficient of the glass had been larger than that of the metal, the reverse conditions would apply.

The radial strains which arise in a cylindrical seal are illustrated in Figure 13.4d–f, again for a case where the metal has the higher expansion and the two parts are in contact when hot, but sealing is prevented by some artificial means. The central metal rod is thus free to shrink away from the surrounding glass cylinder, and a gap will form. If the two parts are actually sealed at a high temperature, the same argument as given above for the two slabs applies so that the glass cylinder and the central metal rod will be in radial tension (f). Similarly, a circumferential stress exists as indicated in Figure 13.4(g), because the metal tries to pull the glass into a smaller compass, so that a tangential compression resides in the glass, and tangenital tension in the metal, by induction.

Table 13.1 tabulates the different kinds of stresses that arise in cylindrical seals for glasses and metals of different expansion coefficients.[1] The intensity

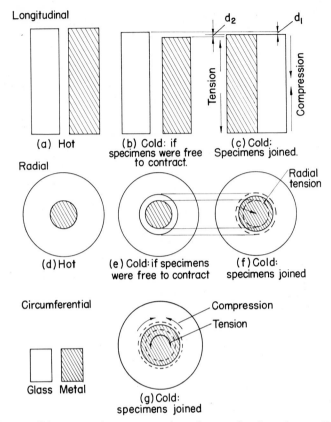

Figure 13.4. Diagrammatic representation of stress in glass due to differential contraction of glass and metal; expansion of metal higher than that of glass. After Partridge.[1] (*Courtesy The Society of Glass Technology, Sheffield, England.*)

TABLE 13.1. DEPENDENCE OF STRESS CHARACTER IN BEAD SEALS ON RELATIVE THERMAL EXPANSION OF METAL AND GLASS[1]

Relative thermal expansion	Stresses at glass/metal boundary		
	P_z(axial)	P_ϕ(tangential)	P_r(radial)
$\alpha_M > \alpha_G$	C	C	T
$\alpha_M < \alpha_G$	T	T	C

α_M = expansion coefficient of metal
α_G = expansion coefficient of glass
C = compression
T = tension

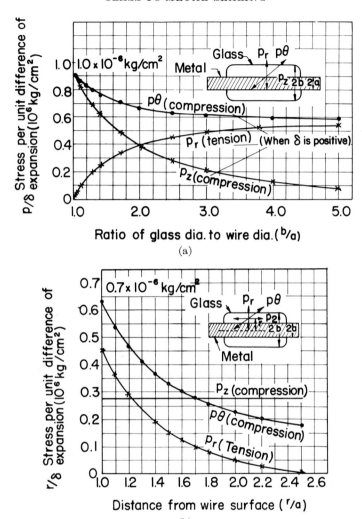

Figure 13.5. Types of stresses in glass bead seals. After Hull and Burger.[11] (*Courtesy American Institute of Physics.*)

of the stresses actually depends not only on the kind of metal and glass used, but also on the geometry of the seal assembly. Hull, Burger, and Poritsky[11, 12] have made an analysis of the stress conditions in cylindrical seals, and Figure 13.5(a,b) gives a graphical representation of the stresses at the surface of the metal as a function of the relative diameters of glass and metal and the distribution of the stresses within the glass for increasing distances away from the wire surface.

It is apparent from Figure 13.5(b) that the longitudinal strain is independent of the distance from the surface of the wire for a given configuration and drops off rapidly for seals in which the diameter of the metal rod is an ever-smaller fraction of the diameter of the surrounding glass bead. It is also apparent that the circumferential strain can be very much larger than the longitudinal strain. The fact that the observation of the strain pattern in the polariscope when viewing a bead seal at right angles to the axis is only an indication of the longitudinal strain must thus be clearly kept in mind. When it is said that a seal is in compression or tension, reference is made to the longitudinal or axial stress unless other types of stresses are clearly mentioned.

The amount of strain that remains in a seal at room temperature can be estimated from a knowledge of the expansion curves of the particular types of glass and metal used for the seal (Figure 13.6). It should be mentioned here that, for the case of glass, contraction rather than elongation is actually measured because it gives the more reliable data that are not affected by the thermal history of the glass, or remaining strains. As the seal between metal and glass is actually made at high temperature, it is also more logical to consider the events that occur during cooling. When the glass is molten and has contacted the metal, it is in a viscous state and will not sustain any strains. After the glass has been attached to the metal, it is allowed to cool; it will thus pass through the annealing range where stresses can still be released by viscous flow provided that the rate of cooling is slow (1°C per minute). When the glass has reached a temperature about 20°C below the annealing point, it can be considered as rigid, and this

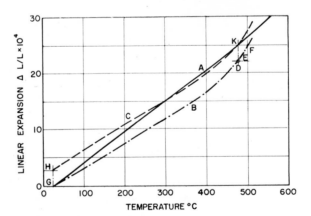

Figure 13.6. Differential free contraction of glass and metal after being sealed together, as determined from their expansion curves. *By permission from "Glass Engineering Handbook" by E. B. Shand.*[13] *Copyright 1958, McGraw-Hill Book Co., Inc., New York (2nd ed.).*

temperature is called the setting point. From then on, the different contraction rates of metal and glass come into play.

By shifting the expansion curve of the glass (B) parallel to itself so that the setting point E coincides with point K on the expansion curve for metal, the distance DK will reappear as distance GH at room temperature and indicate the magnitude of the stress. Obviously, glass and metal are in intimate physical contact at room temperature just as they are at the setting point. The shifted contraction curve K-H for glass indicates that the glass would have "liked" to be longer than the metal at room temperature and is thus in compression. The tangential stresses encountered in annealed cylindrical joints between common glasses and between glasses and metals can be calculated according to a simplified formula given by Lillie[14] and Rawson,[15] i.e.,

$$S = \bar{E}D/2 \tag{13.1}$$

where S = tangential stress

$\bar{E}$ = the average of the values of Young's Modulus for the two glasses in the same units, e.g. kg/mm^2

D = the differential contraction $\Delta l/l$ between the two materials at the lower setting point, if two glasses are joined, or at the setting point of the glass, if glass and metal are joined.

While a minimum value of stress will result when the two glasses have the same elastic moduli, it can be shown that the two moduli can differ greatly from each other without introducing much change in the resulting stress value. The accuracy is thus impaired only slightly by introducing the average $\bar{E} = 7000$ kg/mm^2 for glasses commonly used for seals. Table 13.2 gives the tangential stresses encountered in glass-to-glass and glass-to-metal seals according to Lillie's formula. Stresses from 0.5 to 1.5 kg/mm^2 can be tolerated in tubular butt seals of glasses, depending on size and perfection of fusing. The lower figure is safe under quite unfavorable conditions.* The physical characteristics of metals and alloys used for glass-to-metal seals are given in Table 13.3; various glasses recommended for matched seals are also listed.

The expansion differentials in parts per million at the setting point of glass, in the case of a glass-to-metal seal, or at the setting point of the softer glass, in the case of a glass-to-glass seal, are a useful guide in appraising the practicality of a seal combination. Table 13.4 gives these differentials for commonly used combinations of Corning glasses and metals, according to Hagy. The setting point has been arbitrarily defined as the temperature midway between the annealing and strain points. A number with a dash

* For "Standard Method for Measuring Residual Stress in Cylindrical Metal-to-Glass Seals" see ASTM Standard F 218 – 50.

TABLE 13.2. STRESSES IN GLASS-TO-GLASS AND GLASS-TO-METAL SEALS (kg/mm²)*

	7050	7052	7070	7040	3320	7720	7740	7750	Tungsten	Kovar
7050	0	−0.9	+1.7	−0.7	+1.8	+1.9	+3.1	−0.1	+2.1	−1.9
7052	+0.9	0	+2.7	−0.3	+2.4	+2.7	+	+0.7	+	0
7070	−1.7	−2.7	0	−2.5	+0.2	+0.2	+1.4	−2.0	−1.2	−
7040	+0.7	+0.3	+2.5	0	+2.4	+2.6	+	+0.5	+3.2	+0.4
3320	−1.8	−2.4	−0.2	−2.4	0	−0.5	+1.6	−1.6	−0.7	−
7720	−1.9	−2.7	−0.2	−2.6	+0.5	0	+1.9	−1.9	−0.1	−
7740	−3.1	−	−1.4	−	−1.6	−1.9	0	−2.7	−3.5	−
7750	+0.1	−0.7	+2.0	−0.5	+1.6	+1.9	+2.7	0	+1.5	−1.4
Tungsten	−2.1	−	+1.2	−3.2	+0.7	+0.1	+3.5	−1.5	0	
Kovar	+1.9	0	+	−0.4	+	+	+	+1.4		0

This table represents the approximate amounts of stress that can be expected with more or less normal treatment in seals of common sizes and types, and with both materials having nominal properties. Since the stress depends on geometry and on the annealing treatment, the table can be taken only as a guide to the expected final condition. In addition, the experimental error in determining the expansion curves, and inferring the stress, is equivalent to about ±0.2 kg/mm²; accordingly, stress values of this order represent a very close match.

Values less than 1 kg/mm² indicate a satisfactory match. If the value is 1–2 kg/mm², greater care must be taken in producing a good bond, and the danger of breakage increases with the size of the article. Stresses up to 3 kg/mm² can be tolerated under ideal conditions if the seal is not expected to have to withstand subsequent minor abrasion. Values in excess of 3 indicate an undesirable condition and are generally omitted from the table, being indicated by an algebraic sign to show direction of stress; the positive sign means that the material in the left-hand column contracts more on cooling and vice versa.

* After H. R. Lillie, Corning Glass Works, Corning, N. Y. By permission from MIT Tube Laboratory Manual, 2nd ed. (1956); Massachusetts Institute of Technology, Research Laboratory of Electronics, Cambridge, Mass.

above it indicates that the material listed in that row has a lower effective expansion than the material listed in that column. Values in excess of 1000 ppm are indicated by a large plus or minus sign (±). Metal-to-metal combinations are indicated by a large X.

As a general rule, any differential smaller than 100 ppm can be interpreted to indicate a very good sealing condition. Good seals can be made between materials with differentials ranging from 100 to 500 ppm, but at the higher end of this range the risk of failure is of course greater, and more care should be exercised in making the seal. Materials with differentials from 500 to 1000 ppm can be used for progressively smaller and thinner seals.

"Caution should be observed in any attempt to predict residual stress in a seal from the differentials given in these tables, since in any particular seal the setting is a function of

(a) The geometry of the seal

(b) The cooling rate used in the annealing of the seal. (The cooling rate used in the determination of the expansion curves was one degree per minute.)

(c) The difference in the annealing ranges in the case of a glass-to-glass seal. A seal made between glasses having similar annealing ranges will, in general, have a lower setting point than that assumed in the tables." (H. E. Hagy)

Looking at a few examples in Table 13.4, it is of interest to note that 7720 glass is a better match to tungsten than glass type 3320, the "canary glass," which so many glass blowers still prefer. Chemical "Pyrex" type 7740 is not suited for tungsten sealing unless one deals with fine wire.

In concluding these remarks on stresses in glass-to-metal seals, it should be emphasized that only the simpler concepts have been introduced in this discussion. It is, for example, a simplification of the physical phenomena which actually take place to say that viscous flow ceases at the setting point. Actually, a certain amount of viscous flow takes place during cooling at temperatures below the setting point, and the amount of this fractional equalization of stress may not be the same in all directions. The amount of strain remaining in a seal at room temperature is thus usually less than indicated by the contraction curves, but markedly depends on the geometry of the seal and the rate of cooling. A faster rate of cooling introduces stress at a higher temperature but causes viscous flow to persist to a lower temperature. For the more detailed theory of these effects the reader is referred to references 16–22.

Another complication appears when glass-to-metal seals are baked for prolonged periods of time for purposes of outgassing the tube envelope. Such outgassing treatment may take place initially in dry air at elevated temperature (see page 69) and is always followed by an oven-bake on the pump where the temperature is limited by the deformation of the glass under atmospheric pressure, unless an auxiliary vacuum jacket is built around the tube to prevent such deformation and make higher bake-out temperatures possible (see also p. 427). 450°C is thus a maximum temperature at which common commercial glass envelopes can be baked on the pump, 425°C being a more practical and safe value.

It has been known for some time that the density of glass increases in the transformation range on rapid heating (Fig. 1.1) but the influence of heat treatment on stresses in glass-to-metal seals at temperatures more than 50°C below the strain point of the glass has not been investigated very widely. Turnbull[22a] has studied this effect for thin glass coatings on AISI 430 alloy, and Oldfield,[22b] more recently, has reported on the effect of prolonged heating on Kovar seals.

An increase in density of the glass results in contraction which is counter-

TABLE 13.3. PHYSICAL CHARACTERISTICS OF METALS AND ALLOYS FOR GLASS-TO-METAL SEALS

Metal or Alloy	Typical Percent Composition	Thermal Expansion Coefficient $\Delta l/l/\Delta t$ cm/cm/°C × 10⁷	Thermal Conductivity cal/cm²/cm/ sec/°C	Electrical Resistivity ohm. cm × 10⁶	Other Data	Sealing Glasses		
						Hard	Soft	Code Numbers
A) *Pure Metals:* Copper (OFHC)	Cu + Ag: 99.92/99.96	168 (25–100) 178 (25–300) 182 (0–500)	0.918 (18) 1.043 (100–197) 0.969 (100–268)	1.724 (20)		H	S S	Almost any glass for Houskeeper seals GEC: CSG3 for matched seal with copper. Glass expansion coeff. 149.5 ± 1.5 (20–350°C) 152.5 ± 1.5 (20–400°C) 176.0 ± 2.0 (20–480°C) CGW: 7295
Molybdenum		49 (25–100) 55 (25–500)	0.32 (0)	5.78 (27)		H		CGW: 7510, 7052, 7040, 8830, 7742, 7050, 7750, 7060, 7055, 1720, 1723, 7331, 7720 KGC: 51-26 BTH: C37, C46, C11, C14; GEC: H26X, HH P & T: Kodial
Rhenium		67 (20–500)	0.111 (0–100)	21.1 (20) 52.6 (500)		H		GEC: HH, H26X
Titanium (A-40)	Si: 0.10 max.; Fe: 0.25 max.; Mn: 0.15 max.; N: 0.05 max. C: 0.10 max.; Bal.: Ti	94 (20–400) 101 (20–800)	0.036				S	BTH: C77, C78
Tungsten		46 (0–500) 47 (27–1000) 52 (27–1750) 58 (27–2400)	0.476 (17) 0.249 (1600) 0.272 (2000) 0.294 (2400) 0.313 (2800)	5.5 (20)		H		CGW: 7720, 7780, 3320, 7741, 7070, 7750, 7331, 5420, 7252, 7251, 7760, 7991, 7050 KGC: K-772 BTH: C9, C14 GEC: W1
Zirconium		54 (20–200) 61 (20–400) 71 (20–700)	0.0505 (25) 0.0488 (100) 0.0469 (200)	41.0 (0)		H		BTH: C40

Material	Composition				Magnetic	S	References
Platinum		92 (0-300) 96 (0-500) 102 (0-1000)	0.1664 (18) 0.1733 (100)	9.83 (0)		S	CGW: 0280, 0041, 7570, 7560, 0120, 0080, 0050, 8870, 0281, 0010 Ch: PWD, PWL KGC: R-5, R-6 BTH: C12, C19, C94 GEC: L15
Iron	C: 0.004, Fe: 99.996	122 (18-100) 129 (18-200) 134 (18-300) 138 (18-400) 142 (18-500) 145 (18-600) 146 (18-700) 146 (18-800)	0.18 (20)	9.71 (20)	Magnetic	S	CGW: 7290, 1990, 1991 KGC: R3 BTH: C41, C76 GEC: ISG20 $\alpha = 117 \pm 1.5$ (20-350°C) 130 ± 2.0 (200-Tg) ISG30 $\alpha = 125 \pm 1.5$ (20-350°C) 139 ± 2.0 (200-Tg) NSG2 $\alpha = 127 \pm 1.5$ (20-350°C) 147 ± 2.0 (200-Tg)
Nickel		133 (25-100) 155 (25-600)	0.198 (100) 0.148 (500)	6.844 (20) 37.2 (600)	Magnetic	S	GEC: NSG2 $\alpha = 127 \pm 1.5 \times 10^{-7}/°C$ (20-350°C) $136 \pm 1.5 \times 10^{-7}/°C$ (20-450°C) $147 \pm 2.0 \times 10^{-7}/°C$ (20-500°C)
B) *Alloys:* Cold-rolled steel (SAE-1010)	Mn: 0.30/0.50; C: 0.08/0.13; S: 0.050 max.; P: 0.040; Bal.: Fe	126 (25-100) 135 (25-300) 142 (25-500) 143 (0-500)	0.144 (25-500) 0.121 (25-300) 0.098 (25-500)	12.0	Magnetic	S	CGW: 1990, 1991, 0110 GEC: ISG20, ISG30 BTH: C41, C76
Nickel-Iron	Superior #42: Ni + Co + Cu: 40.25/41.75; C: 0.10 max.; Mn: 1.00 max.; Si: 0.15/0.35; Bal.: Fe Driver Harris 142; Carpenter 42 Allegheny AL42: similar Nilo 42 (Br.)* Nilo 40 (Br.)*	48 (20-100) 53 (20-400) 130 (20-1000)	0.038 0.025 0.026	66.5 72 66	Magnetic	S	CGW: 0010, 0120, 0080, 8160 Ch: PWD, PWL
	Superior #52: Ni + Co + Cu: 50.0/51.0; C: 0.08 max.; Mn: 0.60 max.; P: 0.02 max.; S: 0.01 max.; Si: 0.20/0.35; Bal.: Fe.	93 (20-100) 95 (20-500) 130 (20-1000)	0.04	43.2	Magnetic	S	GEC: L1

407

TABLE 13.3—*Continued*

Metal or Alloy	Typical Percent Composition	Thermal Expansion Coefficient $\Delta I/I/\Delta t$ cm/cm/°C $\times 10^7$	Thermal Conductivity cal/cm²/cm/sec/°C	Electrical Resistivity ohm. cm $\times 10^6$	Other Data	Sealing Glasses Hard	Sealing Glasses Soft	Code Numbers
Driver Harris 52: Similar Driver Harris 146 (Ni: 46.0) Niron 46 (WBD) Niron 52 (WBD) Allegheny AL 4750 (Ni: 57/50) Carpenter 49 (Ni: 49) Vacovit 540 (Ger.)* (Ni: 54.) Nilo 50 (Br.)*		80 (25–425) 98 (20–500) 97 (20–530)	0.037 0.037 0.032	45.7 50. 48.	Magnetic		S	CGW: 0010, 0120, 0080, 7570, 8160, 9010 KG: R-5, R-6, KG-12, KG-1 Ch: PWD, PWL BTH: C12, C19, C94 GEC: L1.
Dumet:	Core: Ni:42; Bal.: Fe Sheath: Cu (25 p.c. of total wt.) Nilo 42 (Br.)*	92 (radial) 65 (axial)	0.4	4.6	Magnetic		S	
Chrome-Iron (AISI-430)	Superior #430: Cr: 16.00/18.00; Mn: 1.00 max.; Si: 0.75 max.: Ni: 0.50 max.: Bal.: Fe Superior #430 Ti	115 (0–500)	0.057		Magnetic		S S	CGW: 9019 GEC: X8
(AISI-430 Ti)	Cr: 16.00/18.00; Mn: 1.00 max.; Si: 1.00 max.; S: 0.03 max.; Ti: 5 × C min: Bal. Fe	61 (20–500)	0.057				S	
AISI-446 (ASC alloy 446)	Cr: 25.00/30.00; Mn: 1.5 max.; C: 0.20 max.; P: 0.03 max.; S: 0.03 max.; Si: 0.75 max.; N_2: 0.10/0.25; Bal.: Fe	105 (25–300)	0.06					CGW: 9019
Sealmet 1		98 (20–300)	0.059	63			S	CGW: 0050, 0080, 0240, 9012, 9010 KGC: R6, K-51 GEC: X8 Ch: PWD BTH: C31 Osram M $\alpha = 96 \times 10^{-7}$/°C (20–300°C)
Carpenter 27 Dilver O (Fr.)* Novar B (Ger.)*	Cr: 28.00; Mn: 0.60; Ni: 0.50 max.; Si: 0.40; C: 0.15 max.; Bal.: Fe Nb: 0.5/1.0; Cr: 19; Ni: 0.25; Mn: 0.25	105 (20–500) 108 (21–482) 106 (20–300)	0.054	63				
Allegheny Telemet	Cr: 16/23; Mn: 2. max.; C: 0.25 max.; S: 0.03 max.; P: 0.040 max.; Si: 1.0 max.; Bal.: Fe	104 (20–300) 110 (20–500)	0.057	60				GEC: X4/3

408

Ni-Cr-Fe

Alloy	Composition						Company codes / references
Sylvania 4	Superior: Ni: 41.50/42.50; Cr: 5.40/5.90; Al: 0.15 max.; C: 0.07 max.; Mn: 0.15/0.25; P: 0.025 max.; Si: 0.15/0.30; Bal.: Fe	85 (25–300)	0.032		Magnetic	S	CGW: 8870, 0080, 0014, 0120, 0010, 8160, 0050, 9010, 7570, 0014 GEC: L1 BTH: C12 KGC: KG12 Ch: PWD, PWL
Sealmet 4	Similar		0.029	94		S	
Driver Harris 14	Ni: 42; Cr: 6; Bal.: Fe		—				
Carpenter 426	Ni: 42.50; Cr: 5.75; Mn: 0.50; Si: 0.25; C: 0.10 max.; Bal.: Fe	98 (20–565)	0.032	95			
Nilo 475 (Br.)*	Ni: 47; Cr: 5; Bal.: Fe			82–88			
Vacovit 426 (Ger.)*	Ni: 42; Cr: 6; Bal.: Fe						
Vacovit 511 (Ger.)*	Ni: 51; Cr: 1; Bal.: Fe						
Vacovit 501 (Ger.)*	Ni: 49; Cr: 1; Bal.: Fe						

Ni-Co-Fe

Alloy	Composition						Company codes / references
Kovar	Ni: 29.0; Co: 17.0; Mn: 0.50; Si: 0.20 max.; C: 0.06 max.; Bal.: Fe	57.1–62.1 (30–500)	0.0395	49	Magnetic	H	CGW: 7052, 8800, 7520, 7040, 7055, 7750, 7050, 7510, 7340, 7060, 8830, 1720, 1723 KGC: K-650, K-704, K-705, EN-1 BTH: C40 GEC: FCN, SBN 475, SBN 124 (especially for humid conditions)
Therlo (DH)* Rodar (WBD)* Sealvac-A(VMC)* Nilo K (Br.)* Dilver P (Fr.)* Vacon (Ger.)*	Ni: 29.0; Co: 17.0; Bal.: Fe	50–60 (30–500)		44–50			
Fernico II	Ni: 31; Co: 15; Bal.: Fe				Magnetic	H	GE: 7060 GEC: FCN BTH: C40

Ni-Co-Cr-Fe

Alloy	Composition						Company codes / references
Fernichrome	Ni: 30; Co: 25; Cr: 8; Bal.: Fe				Magnetic	H	CGW: 0050, 0080 KGC: R6 Ch: PWD

Company Codes

BTH—British-Thomson-Houston Co. (Br.)
CGW—Corning Glass Works
Ch—Chance Brothers Limited (Br.)
CSC—Carpenter Steel Company
DH—Driver Harris Company
GE—General Electric Company (U.S.A.)
GEC—General Electric Company Ltd. (Br.)
KGC—Kimble Glass Company
P&T—Plowden and Thompson (Br.)
VMC—Vacuum Metals Corp.
WBD—Wilbur B. Driver Company

Br.—British
Fr.—French
Ger.—German

F.I.20 for X8, "Pyrista Steel" for X4/3, "Staybrite" F.D.P. for CSG3
Firth-Vickers Stainless Steels Limited, Sheffield 9, England
"Teloseal"—The Telegraph Construction & Maintenance Co. Ltd.
"Nilo"—Henry Wiggin & Company Limited, Birmingham 16, England
"Dilver"—Aciéries d'Imphy, Imphy (Nièvre), France
"Novar"—Stahlwerk Hagen, Germany
"Vacovit"—Vakuumschmelze AG, Hanau/Main, Germany

TABLE 13.4(a). EXPANSION DIFFERENTIAL TABLE. LOW EXPANSION RANGE.*

METAL	GLASS CODE NO.	LAB NO.	7070 707DG	7740 726MX	7760 720GO	7720 702P	7251 720WH	5420 542P	7780 GT-70	7741 726YM	7252 726XP	3320 371BN	7750 705R	1720 172AJ	7331 108PN	7052 705FN	7050 705AJ	7742 726ABE	7040 705BA	7510 750AI	8830 866LC	7055 710HY	8800 G80	7520 750AJ	7340 733B	7530 805F
	7070	707DG	0	400	245	55	175	195	35	210	50	50	565	195	155	480	325	585	700	525	625	760	970		610	
	7740	726MX	400	0	230	305	265	330	475	345	135	460	780	560	375	880	240	985	890	480	760		970	830		
	7760	720GO	245	230	0	345	235	505	20	5	105	185	670	375	380	725	560	780	890	835	900	995	925			
	7720	702P	55	305	345	0	300	10	305	275	35	135	540	50	60	540	240	460	730	535	690	715	925			
TUNGSTEN	7251	720WH	175	505	235	300	0	335	105	15	105	215	210	230	440	300	590	750	455	480	495	630				
	5420	542P	195	330	505	10	335	0	255	85	35	145	645	260	95	525	595	720	660	580	855	955	525	560	280	585
	7780	GT-70	35	475	20	305	105	255	0	275	85	115	500	205	190	455	265	525	835	580	855	595	920		280	585
	7741	726YM	210	345	5	275	15	85	275	0	110	230	595	190	460	685	265	645	660	490	880					
	7252	726XP	50	135	105	35	105	35	85	110	0	240	555	0	260	675	675	810	840	850	850	990				
	3320	371BN	50	460	185	105	215	145	115	230	240	0	445	205	190	525	370	555	685	650	715	820				
	7750	705R	565	780	670	540	645	600	500	595	555	445	0	260	430	40	95	175	130	80	105	275	525			
	1720	172AJ	195	560	375	50	210	125	220	315	0	205	190	0	190	285	530	210	440	455	475	605		280		
	7331	108PN	155	770	380	410	335	95	460	95	260	190	430	190	0	320	190	230	485	450	505	610	900	900		295
	7052	705FN	480	895	760	230	875	825	785	785	675	525	40	285	320	0	260	50	80	145	110	65	300	300	610	825
	7050	705AJ	325	880	540	300	720	670	455	685	655	370	370	320	190	260	0	155	205	50	135	160	495	495	345	805
	7742	726ABE	585	560	240	590	595	525	265	675	810	95	555	190	325	0	155	0	105	275	335	435	700	700	
MOLYBDENUM	7040	705BA	700	890	730	455	875	835	660	840	805	555	175	230	50	110	105	105	0	125	80	200	840	320	630	855
	7510	750AI	525	835	535	480	835	785	480	850	835	685	130	485	80	205	315	50	50	0	65	30	320	405	725	980
	8830	866LC	625	900	690	495	855	855	580	880	850	650	80	450	145	275	335	45	125	115	0	175	405	325	640	870
KOVAR	7055	710HY	760	995	715	630	955	595	720	595	715	200	505	610	110	335	715	80	65	0	145	0	10	345	575
	8800	G80	970	865		720	990	920	990	920	200	155	65	900	5	275	715	60	330	175	5	140	0	240	240	805
	7520	750AJ	970	925	925	920	525	605	300	435	160	495	105	200	325	405	325	240	0	0	560	585
	7340	733B	610					525	300	525	840	700	630	725	640	345	240	0	0	280	585
	7530	805F					830	610	805	855	980	870	805	585	280	295	0

* After H. E. Hagy. (Courtesy Corning Glass Works, Research and Development Division, 1956)

410

TABLE 13.4(b). EXPANSION DIFFERENTIAL TABLE. HIGH EXPANSION RANGE.*

METAL	GLASS CODE NO.	LAB NO.	7340	7530	7550	0280	PLAT	7570	0041	7560	0281	28%Cr	9010	0014	SYLV	0120	8870	0050	8160	0081	0010	0080	430Ti	9012	8871	7290	IRON
	7340	733B	0	295	870		830	940	930																		
	7530	805F	295	0	565	845	680	785			580	685															
	7550	805G	870	565	0	260	230	580	400	330	440																
	0280	128G		845	260	0	65	400	95	255	310																
PLATINUM			830	680	230	65	0	100	270	265	200	350			150	65	10	80	35	85	20	35	485			890	
	7570	750GL	940	785	580	400	100	0	0	220	135	565			355	390	390	315	435	15	120	415	330			955	
	0041	G-4D	930	585	400	95	270	0	0	0	130	510			710	310	430	400	15	385	230	80	700	955	425	690	930
	7560	750AL		580	330	255	265	220	0	0	0	450			605	340	355	325	510	470	495	465	740				
	0281	128AQ		685	440	310	200	135	130	0	0	0			480	395	285	335	225	260	90	350	680	955	425	690	
28% Cr. STEEL							350	565	510	450	0	0	715		185						195		255	300	320	885	
	9010	856DO		895	730	420	25	440	560	480	185		0	0	120	70	10	25	340	270	485	340	535	190	855	690	950
	0014	G-14		840	665	360	50	340	490	410	250	120	0	0	0	10	95	125	265	195	120	635					
SYLVANIA NO. 4							150	355	710	605		65	30	0	0	40	30	60	365	50	230	575					
	0120	G-12		710	550	240	65	390	310	340		70	20	40	0	0	80	90	175	100	115	500	575		320		
	8870	858V		740	590	275	10	390	430	355	285	10	20	40	80	0	0	220	190	160	440	465		855	690	
	0050	G-5		735	570	255	80	315	400	325	335	100	60	30	0	80	0	0	125	190	120	485	635		425	
	8160	814KW		830	670	360	435	15	510	430	225	25	125	0	290	0	125	0	0	290	230	380	500				
	0081	124HD		895	660	465	85	385	260	270	365	60	220	290	255	190	0	290	0	0	90	495	825				
	0010	G-1		785	630	320	415	470	395	20	115	50	100	190	10	255	0	195	10	470	855	690					
	0080	G-8		960	730	510	35	80	465	350	215	270	195	280	115	160	120	230	90	195	0	430	755	745			
430Ti. STEEL							485	700	740	680	340	420	500	440	485	380	495	410	430	145	0		190	925		950
	9012	174PA		890	330	955	955	300	535	635	575	575	465	635	500	825	470	755	145	0	320	855	885	
	8871	1891A		825	540	990	920	335	710	745	770	700	770	720	800	710	745	320	0	425	855	690	885	855	0	85	445
	7290	167GL																						85	0	690	445
IRON	1990	1891Y																						140	445	140	0

411

* After H. E. Hagy. (Courtesy Corning Glass Works, Research and Development Division, 1956)

acted by the bond to the metal so that tension stresses arise in the glass. For the case of Kovar seals, Oldfield has shown that, in the temperature range from 300 to 450°C, a stabilization of the alloy results in a volume increase which further contributes to tension stresses in the glass-metal interface. After only six hours at 400°C, a change of stress of approximately 40 kg/cm² can occur and after 17 days the total change in stress is about 200 kg/cm². Fracture of the seals may result when the geometric factors are unfavorable (see Table 13.2). The cause of the instability of the iron-nickel-cobalt alloy in the temperature range 300–450°C appears to be dependent upon the transformation in the alloy of the austenitic iron phase to the ferritic iron phase, the latter having the larger expansion (see Chapter 5).*

Houskeeper Seals

At a time when glass-to-metal seals were restricted to wire and ribbon seals, W. G. Houskeeper,[23] introduced a very ingenious technique which made possible, for the first time, the production of large tubular seals and disk seals and thus the construction of large water-cooled power tubes for the broadcasting industry, which was in its early stages at that time.† High-purity copper (OFHC) is used in these seals. Cooper is readily worked into any desired shape even in large sizes, whereas the other sealing metals available at that time, such as molybdenum and tungsten, could be used only in wire and rod form. A glance at Figure 13.2 will reveal that copper has an extremely high expansion coefficient, i.e., $165 \times 10^{-7}/°C$, so that a matched seal to any of the known glasses was impossible. On the other hand, copper has a very low yield point (Table 6.6.).

By providing the end of a copper tube with a taper, or "feather-edge," and sealing the glass to the thin edge of the taper, the flexibility of the feather-edge will permit sufficient movement to equalize any difference in contraction between the glass and the metal after the seal has been made. Similarly, when glass is sealed to both sides of a thin copper disk, such difference in contraction will be taken up by plastic flow of the copper under the radial strains present. Houskeeper seals can thus be made to any kind of glass, either soft or hard. This possibility immediately suggests transition members from soft-glass systems to a hard-glass tube, or *vice versa*, by using a copper tube with a feather-edge on each end and sealing the respective glasses on each side. It is not practical, however, to seal a soft glass to

* The author is indebted to Dr. L. F. Oldfield for providing an abstract of his paper before it became available in printed form.

† In the German literature, copper-to-glass seals are called "Kruh seals" after the German originator of feather edge seals, O. Kruh, who filed his disclosure in 1917 (DRP 424,133 (1926)).

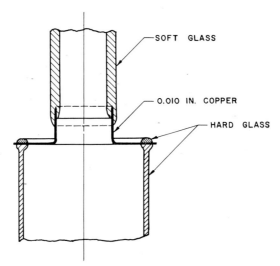

Figure 13.7. Copper flange transition seal from soft glass to hard glass.

one side of a copper disk and a hard glass in juxtaposition on the other side, because the copper in the disk would then be in a difficult position to please both partners at the same time. A flange can be used, however, as shown in Figure 13.7; the author took advantage of this configuration many years ago.

The techniques used for making Houskeeper seals of the feather-edge type have been described in several texts.[1, 10, 24] One generally speaks of inside seals or outside seals, depending on whether the metal is on the inside of the glass cylinder or on the outside, and there may also be inside-outside seals as illustrated in Figure 13.8. Such seals may be produced in the manner illustrated in Figure 13.9.

On an inside-outside feather-edge seal, the glass on the inside generally covers the taper twice as far as it does on the outside. The physical dimensions of the feather-edge itself are quite critical; the thickness at the edge should be from 1 to 2 mils, and a taper of about 5 degrees should extend back from the edge until the wall is about 40 mils thick. These dimensions will depend a great deal on the diameter of the tube and must be chosen so as to form a practical compromise between strength and elastic yield. Outside tapers may be rolled or machined against a steel arbor, and the excess material cut off with a sharp steel roller. Inside tapers may be ground, but they are less common. Table 13.5 gives the typical dimensions of different commercial Houskeeper seals after Düsing.[25] It will be noticed that the angle of the taper can be changed to larger values as the distance from the edge increases in order to avoid an excessive length

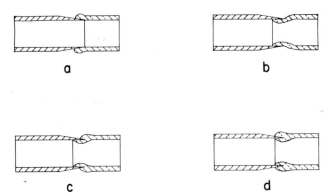

Figure 13.8. Various tubular Houskeeper seals. (a) Inside seal; (b)Outside seal; (c) Inside-outside seal; (d) Push-in or edge seal.

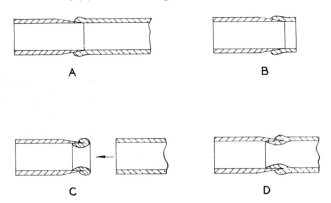

Figure 13.9a. Schematic outline of the production of an inside-outside tubula Houskeeper seal by prebeading of the feather edge.

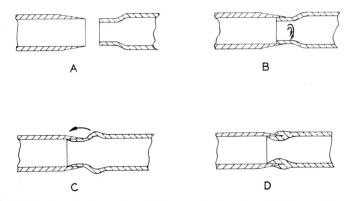

Figure 13.9b. Schematic outline of the production of an inside-outside tubular Houskeeper seal by a combination of centrifuging and spading.

TABLE 13.5. TYPICAL DIMENSIONS OF COMMERCIAL HOUSKEEPER SEALS*

Diameter of the copper ring (mm)	Thickness of the taper— 1 mm distance from the edge (mm)	Taper of the feather edge (mm/mm)	Width of glass coating (mm)
10	0.08 ± 0.01	0.04 ± 0.01	2.5 + 0.5
11–50	0.08 ± 0.01	0.04 ± 0.01	3.0 + 0.5
51–100	0.12 ± 0.01	0.04 ± 0.01	3.5 + 0.5
101–125	0.14 ± 0.01	0.06 ± 0.01	4.5 + 0.5

* After Düsing.[25] Courtesy Telefunken A. G.

of the tapered section; 0.375 in. is about the shortest length within which one can accommodate a Houskeeper seal. Short seals are especially desirable in high-frequency tubes to minimize induction losses. It is also important to avoid electrical field concentrations at the copper edge, and guard rings are therefore an indispensable requirement whenever such seals are used in the presence of high voltages.[25]

The surface of the copper at the feather-edge should be highly polished, and it must of course be oxidized before the glass is attached to it; this is usually done by heating the thicker portions of the copper tube with the torch when the seal is made on the glass lathe, to prevent burning the thin part of the feather-edge. The amount of oxidation is also critical, as explained above. Some workers prefer to borate the copper by heating the metal to a bright red heat and then immersing it immediately in a concentrated solution of sodium borate; this is a sensitive test for the surface condition of the copper; any impurities or contaminations will show up as dark spots. A properly treated part will have a uniformly deep red to purple sheen of cuprous oxide. McCarthy[26] has described the details of cleaning and borating copper for such seals.

In oxidizing copper disks, the author[27] has found it convenient to utilize induction heating in an atmosphere of carbon dioxide or nitrogen; he has also found it advisable to have the copper disks hydrogen-fired after chemical cleaning and to use the disks for sealing fairly soon after this treatment, preferably on the same day. The strength of such seals has been materially improved by chrome plating by a procedure described by Davis.[28]

Feather-edge seals are necessarily weak in critical environments where mechanical shock and vibration and corrosive atmospheres are encountered. For this reason, many power tubes are now made with Kovar seals which will be discussed later in this chapter. Many of the vacuum condensers are still made with feather-edge Houskeeper seals. Disk seals are widely used in microwave tubes of the lighthouse type, and most of the TR/ATR tubes employ disk seals; these are made on the production line by induction heating, and it may be in order to insert a section on this subject.

Induction Seals

Conventional flame-sealing is performed by applying the heat from an air-gas or oxygen-hydrogen flame to the glass and metal either by manipulating a hand torch or the fires of a glass lathe. Induction-sealing by radio-frequency heating (r.f.-sealing) produces heat in the metal part by creation of eddy currents (E.C.-heating) when a copper coil carrying alternating current of high frequency is placed around the seal assembly which is vertically supported in a suitable fixture. If the metal has been previously oxidized, the glass part may be in physical contact with the metal part at the beginning of the heating cycle; but if oxidation of the metal and sealing is performed in the same cycle, the fixture must provide for some slight vertical movement so that the glass contacts the metal after the latter has been oxidized. Heat is then transferred from the hot metal to the glass, which will soften at the seal area and flow under gravity on the metal unless a slight mechanical pressure is applied. This method lends itself particularly well to the fabrication of disk seals. Figure 13.10 gives a schematic outline of the procedure, which can of course be applied to multiple as well as to single-disk seals. An array of thirteen apertured disks for an external-circuit travelling-wave tube made at the Stanford Electronics Laboratories is shown in Figure 13.11.

While the principle of induction-sealing was suggested by Houskeeper, this technique was not applied on a large scale to the production of various types of microwave tubes until the beginning of World War II when workers in England and the author in Canada developed the details of this procedure.[29-33]

In making multiple-disk seals, it is advisable to use a flux concentrator in conjunction with the induction coil so that the major part of the electromagnetic field is concentrated in the plane of the disk. The concentrator assembly can then be moved up or down along the stack, and any one double-sided seal be made without excessively heating the previously made seal. Such "eddy current concentrators," "focus inductors," or "applicators" have been described in the literature and also in a Technical Data Bulletin by Kohl.[34-40] Concentrators may take on various physical shapes, as shown in Figure 12.9; they are useful not only for induction-sealing but for induction-heating in general, for the purpose of brazing without overheating adjacent parts, or for flashing of getters.

Induction heating has also been used for sealing glass components by interposing thin copper rings as, for instance, in the case of sealing a stem to a glass bulb;[23, 27, 41] a method of sealing polished glass members by silverplating their surface and heating the interface by induction heating has been described by Bleuze and Dussaussoy.[42]

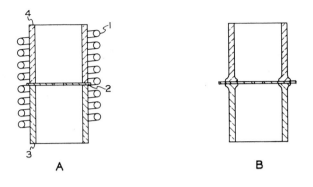

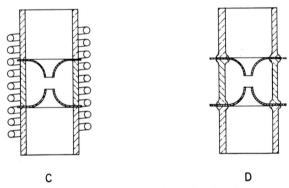

Figure 13.10. Disk seals by induction heating.

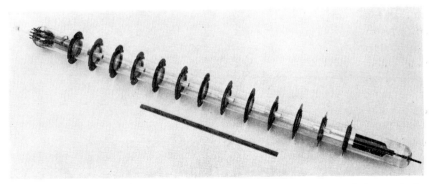

Figure 13.11. 13-disk multiple seal. (*Courtesy Stanford Electronics Laboratories.*)

Sometimes flame-sealing and induction-sealing are combined.[33] When a short glass ring is sealed to the metal disk by induction, thus laying down an annular bead, the main glass member can then be sealed to this glass bead on reheating the metal disk. This procedure permits closer control over the oxidation of the metal in a controlled-atmosphere chamber.

Induction-sealing has many advantages over conventional flame-sealing because the process can be mechanized to a high degree and thus be performed by unskilled labor. Apart from this economic factor, better control can be exercised over the time-temperature cycle, and the uniformity of the product thus be greatly improved. If the metal part has been pre-oxidized, the seals can be made in a neutral atmosphere, thus preventing the oxidation of other metal parts which may be present. After completion of the seal, the metal outside the seal area can be deoxidized by bubbling the gas for the sealing chamber through methyl alcohol for a few seconds.

Robinson *et al.*[43] have described an interesting technique for the introduction of multiple leads into a glass tube by means of the copper disk seal technique. As illustrated in Figure 13.12, radial slots (0.75 mm wide $\times$ 5 mm long) are punched into a copper disk and then swaged with a suitable tool so that the edges of the slots take on a 20-degree taper. During this operation, the width of the slots is reduced to less than 0.5 mm. After the glass tubes are sealed to the copper in the usual manner, the copper disk is cut along the periphery determined by the end of the slots showing on the outside, so that separate sections result which can be utilized as current leads.

Brief reference was made above to the possibility of sealing glass to glass by induction heating when the end faces of the glass surfaces have been metallized. Glass can be heated in any one of several ways, or by a combination of them. The conventional flame heating imparts heat to the surface, and adjacent areas then become hot by conduction. When the glass members to be joined are relatively thick, the surface temperature may have to be raised to such a degree that the glass surface boils and loses volatile components. Uniform heating throughout the body of the glass can be achieved by dielectric heating, in which the glass is placed between the plates of a condenser activated by a high-frequency alternating field in the mega-cycle range. On the other hand, if the glass is preheated to a temperature where it becomes sufficiently conductive, a surrounding induction coil will cause eddy currents that will heat the glass body as if it were metallic.

Another technique, known as electric welding of glass and chiefly developed at Corning Glass Works,[44-49] permits joining heavy-wall glass members, or punching smooth holes, by causing conduction currents to flow through the glass in confined regions. The area to be worked is preheated by sharp oxy-hydrogen flames which are connected to a source of

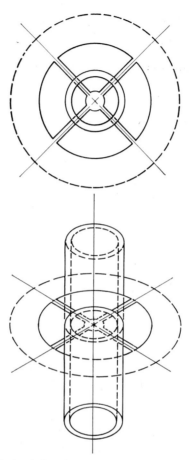

Figure 13.12. Multiple leads by disk seal. After Robinson *et al.*[43] (British Patent 627,289)

high-frequency current. When the glass is hot enough to be conductive, the two opposing torches are switched into the electrical circuit formed by the conducting flames and the conducting glass. For tubular joints, the glass members may be caused to rotate by supporting them in the chucks of a lathe. Special r-f generators are required, which compensate for the wide range of impedance encountered during sealing and produce square-wave currents that seem to be most suited for this technique. The process has found extensive commercial application.

The use of flames for preheating the glass can be circumvented altogether by passing a spark discharge between two electrodes along the surface of the glass in the region where heating is required. When the resistance of the glass becomes lower than that of the air gap along the surface, the discharge path will move into the body of the glass and effect uniform heating.[44] This technique has more recently been applied to the encapsulation of transistors as described by Whitney.[49a]

Sealing to Pure Metals

Platinum seals were used as early as 1821 by Davy, and they served in Edison's incandescent lamp in 1879, in the early x-ray tubes, and later in electron tubes and lamps until more economical substitutes were developed. The thermal expansion coefficient of platinum is $90.0 \times 10^{-7}/°C$, a value which lies close to that of the soft glasses for which the expansion coefficient ranges from 89 to $91 \times 10^{-7}/°C$. A special technique for sealing platinum to chemical Pyrex brand glass Code 7740 was described by Wichers and Saylor[50] and also by Kraus.[51] While ordinary lead seals to soft glass employ platinum in the form of wire, seals to hard glass, as described by these authors, utilized platinum tubing to minimize the strains that would ordinarily develop between hard glass and platinum. Such seals stood up satisfactorily if the outside diameter of the platinum tube was at least twelve times its own wall thickness; in the particular case described, the platinum tubes were 2 mm in diameter and had a wall thickness from 0.075 to 0.15 mm. Such tubular seals take advantage of the principles embodied in Houskeeper seals and require that the metal have a sufficiently low yield point—a condition which is well satisfied by copper and platinum.* In the next chapter, seals of molybdenum tubing sealed through ceramics will be described.

Copper seals were, until quite recently, possible only in the form of Houskeeper seals, as described earlier in this chapter. In 1958, both the General Electric Company, Ltd., at Wembley and Corning Glass Works at Corning, New York, announced the availability of high-expansion glasses which match copper and are supplied in the form of rod, powder, or sintered beads. The G.E.C. glass bears the code "C.S.G.3 Copper Sealing Glass," and the Corning glass is known under the designation "7295 Copper Sealing Multiform Glass." Table 13.6 gives some of the characteristics of these glasses.

According to Oldfield,[51a] the main application of C.S.G.3 glass is the hermetic sealing of electronic components, such as crystal diodes, where the use of copper conductors as lead wires, instead of the nickel-iron or iron-nickel-cobalt alloy leads sealed to conventional glasses previously employed, has permitted higher power ratings to be obtained without harmful heat dissipation within the sealed units. This glass may also be

---

* Rawson[52] has pointed out that the equation given by Wichers and Saylor for the radial stresses at the metal-to-glass interface in a seal of this type is not correct.

TABLE 13.6. CHARACTERISTICS OF COPPER-SEALING GLASSES

	C.S.G.3	7295
Thermal expansion/°C	176×10^{-7} (20–480)	154×10^{-7} (25–300)
Working point (°C)		655
Softening point (°C)	570	465
Annealing point (°C)	430	366
Strain point (°C)		344
Density (g/cc)	2.78	2.56
Log resistivity	11.1 (100°C)	6.78 (250°C)
Log resistivity (350°C)	5.2	5.01
Durability in water	like X8	0.05 (like 0080)

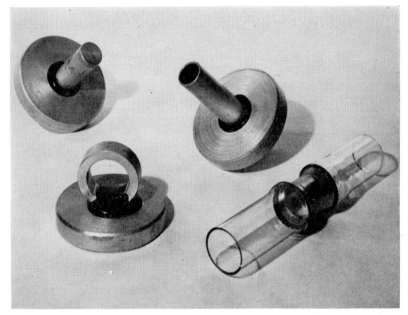

Figure 13.12(a). Three seals to bulk copper made with CSG3 glass confronted with a conventional feather edge seal (M 1765) at lower right. (*Courtesy The General Electric Company, Ltd., Wembley.*)

sealed to high-expansion stainless steel, so that combination seals of copper and steel may be made when it is preferable to use copper for the conductor while employing steel for the housing, where good mechanical strength is required (Fig. 13.12a).

Nickel seals also have not been known until recently when a nickel-sealing glass was announced by G.E.C. under the code NSG2 (February 1958). It is a high-expansion glass that may also be used for alloy steels with similar expansion characteristics. Electrical insulation, durability, and

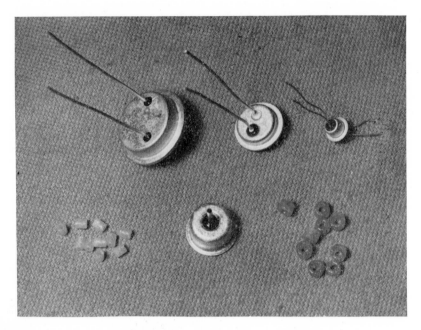

Figure 13.12(b). Upper row: Three electron devices encapsulated by copper shells to which leads are sealed with CSG3 glass. Lower row: Nickel-to-glass seal with NSG3 glass at center, sintered beads of CSG3 glass at either side. Enlargement: 2X (*Courtesy The General Electric Company, Ltd., Wembley.*)

working properties are said to be good. The rapid annealing range is from 500–450°C and the preferred upper annealing temperature for the rapid annealing of small glass-to-metal seals is 490°C (Figure 13.12b).

"Seals made with an oxide-free interface between the glass and metal are very weak. Oxide seals which show a 'gherkin' green color owing to a tenacious layer of nickelous oxide are strong and vacuum-tight. Prior to the preparation of the seals, the nickel should be cleaned in a cold nitric-sulfuric acid mixture consisting of 900 ml distilled water, 750 ml sulfuric acid, 1000 ml concentrated nitric acid, and 50 gm sodium chloride, until the metal gases freely. All traces must then be removed with water. After rough drying, the nickel is cooked in wet hydrogen at 1050°C for about 30 minutes. Preoxidation of the nickel is carried out by heating it in a reducing hydrogen flame to approximately 1000°C for a few seconds followed by cooling in air to about 650°C. The preferred oxide is formed during cooling. The sealing of the glass to the prepared nickel is then carried out with an oxidizing flame at a working range from 650–750°C. To avoid embrittlement of the nickel, sulfur-containing flames should not be used."*

Iron seals, like those previously mentioned, require high-expansion glasses of which several are listed in Table 13.3. Pure iron is rarely used for electron tube seals, but the various steels fall into the same category and find application in a variety of electronic devices which are hermetically sealed for exclusion of atmospheric moisture.

"With pure iron and with those alloys which are easily oxidized during glassing, it is recommended that the metal components should be chromium, copper, or nickel-plated before sealing. Alternatively, a nickel 'dip' made by dipping a clean, grease-free component into a hot nickel ammonium sulfate aqueous solution may be used. It is often beneficial to decarburize the surface of irons and steels before glassing to avoid seals having bubbles at the metal-glass interface. This may be carried out by heating the component in wet hydrogen at approximately 1000 to 1050°C for a short period; 30 minutes is usually satisfactory before treatment with nickel, copper, or chromium.

"Glass-to-metal seals in which much iron oxide is present at the interface due to over-oxidation are usually porous, and must not be used when hermetic seals are needed. The chromium, copper, and nickel-treated seals are hermetic; the chromium-treated seal makes an unusually strong glass-to-metal bond.

"An alternative technique is to use preoxidized seals to a predetermined and controlled amount of oxidation and to effect glassing in an inert atmosphere."*

Seals comprising iron, low-carbon steel, and stainless steel are commonly used for terminals, instrument housings with high-voltage feed-throughs, and enclosure of crystal diodes, wherever a "hermetic seal" is required to exclude the harmful effects of the atmosphere, or maintain a protective filler gas within the enclosure. In the manufacture of ignitrons, thyratrons, and high-power, gas-filled rectifiers, where the housing often is made of steel, the need for suitable seals to insulate the electrodes is evident.

Instead of trying to match the expansion coefficients of the seal components, such as the metal housing (1), the current lead (2), and the insulating glass button (3), in the case of a straight feed-through (Figure 13.13a), compression seals are frequently used. The steel ring (1), which may be part of the housing, is chosen of sufficient thickness ($\sim$3 mm, or more)

* Quoted text material on copper, nickel, and iron seals has been extracted from the respective bulletins on sealing glasses issued by the Research Laboratories of the General Electric Company Limited, Wembley, Middlesex, England (1957/1958), with the Laboratory's kind permission.

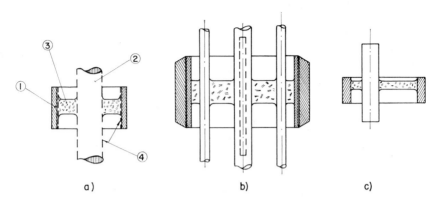

Figure 13.13. Examples of glass compression seals. (a) simple rod seal, (b) multiple rod seal, (c) excentric rod seal. After Adam[52b] and additional data submitted to the present author. (*Courtesy Lancashire Dynamo Nevelin Ltd., England.*)

that no plastic deformation occurs in the temperature range encountered during operation of the device, and the glass (3), which has a lower thermal expansion coefficient than the outer ring, is thus kept in compression at all times. This condition must be fulfilled regardless of whether the central conductor is matched to the glass, or made of the same material as the surrounding pressure ring. In the latter case, $(\alpha_1 = \alpha_2 > \alpha_3)$, the tension which would result at the interface between rod and glass button on cooling must be compensated by an additional compression increment calling for added thickness of the ring.

Multiple-lead headers, (Figure 13.13b), or eccentric leads (Figure 13.13c), can be made on this principle. The design principles of such compression seals have been given by Adam[52a] and Adam, Espe, and Schwarz-Bergkampf.[52b] While the fabrication of such seals follows more or less conventional techniques, it has been pointed out by Fischer[52c] that oxidation of the metal surfaces is not a necessary prerequisite for the attainment of vacuum-tight pressure seals, which thus can be made in a neutral or reducing atmosphere.* In practice, oxide seals are usually made. Pressure seals are mechanically rugged, withstand temperature-cycling, as long as the entire seal is heated or cooled in such a way that the temperature is kept higher at the center than on the outside ring—a condition which naturally results in the operation of feed-throughs. It has not been possible, so far, to stand off voltages in excess of 5000 v because, regardless of size, the electrolytic decomposition of the glass at the inner conductor sets an upper limit.

Tungsten seals readily to special hard glass as indicated in Table 13.3,

* Personal communication from Dr. H. Adam.

and wide use is made of this material for lead seals in power tubes. The methods of production for such lead seals are straightforward and involve chemical cleaning, oxidation and beading, after which another chemical cleaning operation must follow to remove the oxide layer outside of the glass bead. The main seal is then made between the beading glass and the glass stem. A number of pitfalls exist, however, which make tungsten seals most unreliable unless special precautions are taken. The difficulties are twofold. The tungsten rod or wire may be of an inferior quality and may contain cracks and fissures that lead to gas leakage after the seal has been made. Microscopic inspection of tungsten rod and bend tests on wires may be used to discover such defects.[53] In general, such faulty wire will be discarded, but there may be cases, especially in the laboratory, where the wire must be salvaged for economic reasons, or where the inspection methods are not trusted, and a second line of defense is needed rather than taking the risk of having a very expensive tube fail on account of a leaky seal.

Reimann[56] has described a method by which cracks and fissures in tungsten rod or wire can be filled with copper. After cleaning the tungsten chemically, preferably by immersing the barely red-hot tungsten in a solution of sodium nitrite several times in succession, the rod is copper-plated in a bath consisting of 160 gm copper sulfate, 28 gm sulfuric acid and one liter of water using a current density from 25 to 35 ma/cm^2. After rinsing thoroughly in distilled water, the plated wire is hydrogen-fired at 1130°C for 10 to 15 minutes. This treatment will permit the copper to flow into the cracks and also leave a firmly adhering film of copper on the surface of the rod, which is then built up to a thickness of about one mil by further plating, and again sintered by hydrogen-firing. The copper is then borated and ready for beading with a suitable sealing glass. As the presence of copper increases the radial expansion of the rod, a glass of slightly higher expansivity has to be chosen than would be the case in the absence of copper.

The other cause of leaky seals is the chemical instability of the oxide layer between metal and glass in the presence of water vapor at elevated temperatures, such as may be encountered in tropical climates. There is no way of detecting such potentially leaky seals, as tubes made with them will test vacuum-tight on a leak-detector and have a reasonable shelf life in ordinary climates. These so-called "water leakers" caused a great deal of difficulty during World War II, and the author well recalls being involved in such epidemics. No solution to this problem was known at that time. Both drawn tungsten wire and swaged tungsten rod give the same effects which, in extreme cases, can be detected by immersing the tubes for a few hours in water; but slower leakers will take several days' immersion to show the effect.[57]

Partridge[1] remarks that "tungstic oxide WO_3 often reacts with soda in the glass to form the well-known tungsten bronzes which are complex sodium tungstates of the type Na_xWO_3, where x does not exceed unity. The color varies with the proportion of soda present, and this may be responsible for the characteristic color of tungsten-glass seals. This tungsten bronze is soluble in hot water so that seals in which it is present are likely to leak when exposed to hot, humid conditions. The presence of sodium tungstate can be avoided by using an alkali-free glass." Trébuchon and Kieffer[20] also refer to the adverse effects of humid atmospheres on the quality of seals in general. It has been suggested by these authors that flame-polishing of the glass surfaces near the seal is a means of overcoming water leakage effects. Davis[58] has described a technique which improves the strength of seals made from many different metals and alloys, and particularly refers to the complete elimination of water leakage on tungsten seals when plating the surface of the tungsten rod or wire with nickel to a thickness of 2.5 microns and then with chromium, also to a thickness of 2.5 microns. The double-plated surface is then subjected to a diffusion treatment in dry hydrogen at 1200°C for about five minutes. Some embrittlement of pure tungsten occurs during the diffusion treatment at 1200°C owing to recrystallization. This embrittlement may be avoided by using thoriated tungsten or silicated tungsten; the former is better for maintaining ductility. Taylor and Fincke[58a] have also reported work on this problem.

Molybdenum seals to matching glasses have not been too common in the tube industry until the past few years, and, even now, they are used only on special tubes and not in mass production. The widespread use of very thin molybdenum members in fused silica-to-metal seals will be described in a later section (page 461). The availability of aluminosilicate glasses which seal to molybdenum and have a softening point between 900 and 1000°C has made the use of molybdenum seals interesting to the designer of microwave tubes because improved performance of the tube can be obtained as a result of the more thorough outgassing treatment near 700°C to which these glasses can be subjected. Bell and Hillier[59, 60] have described the techniques by which these seals are being made, and the following remarks are taken from their papers.

"Molybdenum begins to oxidize at 200°C, and at 400°C readily forms the trioxide, which is volatile at around 800°C. Thus, large seals to molybdenum cannot be made in air. Nitrogen also is an unsuitable atmosphere, since it dissolves in molybdenum, slowly at 600°C and very rapidly at 1200°C. The resulting compound is brittle and useless for further work. These difficulties can be overcome by making the seal in an inert atmosphere, e.g., one of the rare gases. Dry-cylinder argon was used to make the seal by heating the components by means of eddy-current heating in a gas-tight bell jar.

"The metal is prepared for sealing by furnacing in wet hydrogen at 900°C, and deplating the edge to be glassed. It is then oxidized at 580°C for five minutes in air or oxygen.

"In sealing, the temperature of the metal is raised gradually. At 800°C, the trioxide evaporates or is reduced to the dioxide, a thin layer of which remains. At 1000°C, the glass is plastic and at 1200°C it wets the metal satisfactorily in about three minutes. Prolonged heating decomposes the glass and/or dissolves off the oxide layer. The rest of the metal is now covered with the dioxide, which is practically impossible to remove chemically. The seal can however be annealed in cracked ammonia by cooling slowly from 780°C for glass Type C37,* at the same time reducing most of the exposed oxide to the metal. The outside of the seal is unaffected. Some strain remains in the glass after annealing because of the difference in expansion coefficients between glass and metal.

"Molybdenum wires can be beaded in air, since the glass tends to protect the wire from overoxidation. If the wires subsequently suffer prolonged heating at 1200°C in air, however, as is necessary to make a glass pinch, they must be plated with a two and one-half mil thick protective layer of chromium, which is diffusion-bonded to the molybdenum by furnacing at 1200°C in dry hydrogen for five minutes. Even so, some molybdenum diffuses to the surface during sealing, oxidizes and evaporates, and the pinch must be cleaned afterwards to obtain high insulation. In pinch making the glass should be heated slowly in the oxidizing tip of a bushy oxygen-air-gas flame to avoid decomposition."[59]

At a bake-out temperature of 700°C, molybdenum and other metals are noticeably pervious to most gases, especially hydrogen and nitrogen, and it is thus desirable to provide a protective vacuum of the order of 10^{-5} Torr during the bake-out process. This requirement is a severe limitation to the practical application of these high-temperature glasses on a larger scale, but is nevertheless worth while.

A number of aluminosilicate glasses for molybdenum sealing have become available from different manufacturers since the end of World War II and are undergoing gradual refinement. For a time, the British glasses of this type seemed to have advantages over comparable glasses available in U.S.A., so that various laboratories went to the trouble of importing them. Table 13.7 lists some of the properties of these glasses, their compositions, and code numbers. The great emphasis on high-temperature tubes, be it for operation in high ambient temperatures, or to make better tubes

---

* Manufactured by British Thomson-Houston Co. (see Table 13.3).

TABLE 13.7. PROPERTIES OF ALUMINOSILICATE GLASSES*

	Code					
	C37	C46	H26X	1710/1720	1723	EE-2
Manufacturer(1)	B.T.H.	B.T.H.	G.E.C.	Corning Glass Works		Kimble
Thermal expansion coefficient, × 10⁻⁷ °C	42.5(50-400)	43(50-400)	46(50-400)	42(0-300)	48.(0-300)	42.(0-300)
Working point, °C	1200	—	1100	—	—	1210
Flow point, °C	—	—	—	—	910	—
Softening point, °C	—	—	—	—	—	—
Annealing point, °C	775	790	726	715	709	755
Dielectric constant at 25°C	4.2(35kMc)	5.9(1Mc)	4.1(35kMc)	6.3(1Mc)	6.4(1Mc); 6.19(8.5kMc)	6.25(1Mc)
Power factor (%)	0.9(35kMc)	0.19(25°C-1Mc)	0.08(1Mc); 1.2(35kMc)	0.37(25°C-1Mc)	0.15(25°C-1Mc); 0.5(350°C-1Mc); 2.0(500°C-1Mc); 0.69(25°C-8.5kMc)	0.2(25°C-1Mc)
Dielectric loss factor, %	—	—	—	—	—	1.2
Log resistivity	12(300°C)	11.9(300°C)	16.6(100°C); 11.6(300°C); 9.0(500°C)	11.4(250°C); 9.4(350°C)	14.1(250°C); 11.7(350°C)	11.5(350°C)
Index of refraction	—	—	1.535	—	—	1.55
Specific gravity	2.55	2.62	2.30	2.53	2.63	2.58
Stress - optical coeff. mμ/cm/Kg/cm²	—	—	—	—	—	2.8
Sealing metal	←————————————— Molybdenum —————————————→					

NOTES

(1) Manufacturers: B.T.H.—British Thomson-Houston Co., Ltd., Rugby, England
G.E.C.—The General Electric Company, Ltd., Wembley, England
Corning Glass Works, Corning, N.Y.
Kimble Glass Company (Owens-Illinois), Toledo 1, Ohio

* For the composition of some of the glasses listed above see Table 1.2.

for normal operation by baking them at high temperatures on the pump, has greatly stimulated interest in these glasses, especially for microwave tubes where they compete with ceramics as an envelope material.

In order to minimize the objectionable "boiling" of the glass on the one hand, and excessive oxidation of molybdenum, to which the glass is frequently sealed, some precautions are necessary in making such seals.

"A simple, effective method for preventing reboil during flame working of certain glasses has been developed by Corning Glass Works Research Laboratory. The procedure consists of bubbling the gas through solutions, which results in material being carried into the flame.

"1. *Methyl Borate*. A 5 % solution of boric acid in methyl alcohol is used. The gas for the burner is bubbled through this solution. This is particularly effective in preventing reboil of Code 8161 glass and partially effective in the case of Codes 1710, 1720, and 1723.

Note that the boron causes the flame to have a green color.

"2. *Ethyl Orthosilicate*. Use of this compound is effective for 1710, 1720, and 1723. If all the gas to the burner is bubbled through this fluid, too much material is carried into the flame. The optimum quantity can be added by dividing the gas flow and bubbling only part of it through the fluid. In work in the Laboratory, satisfactory results were obtained when 0.15 liters per minute of treated gas and 1.1 liters per minute untreated gas were mixed and delivered to the burner. This corresponds to 1.7 milligram of silica (6 mg. of the ethyl orthosilicate) per liter of gas." (Communication from Corning Glass Works)

Molybdenum can be protected against oxidation by forming a coating of molybdenum disilicide or chromium oxide according to methods described by Stanworth[60a] and Rawson.[60b] This can be achieved by placing the molybdenum part in a stream of hydrogen saturated with silicon tetrachloride at 1000–1200°C, or by packing the metal in silicon powder in a molybdenum boat and exposing it for 30 min. at about 1000°C to a mixture of H + HCl, according to Rawson.[60b] He reports that wires coated in this manner and made into bead seals withstood exposure to air at 1400°C for several hours. "Chromising" was achieved in a similar manner at 1100°C for 60 min. when the wires were packed in a mixture of chrome and alumina powder, the latter being added to prevent sintering of the chrome powder into a solid mass which would prevent easy removal of the wires from the boat.

In the manufacture of mercury-arc power rectifiers of the grid-controlled type, borosilicate glasses ("Kodial"*) are used on a commercial scale,

---

* Kodial is the trade name for a borosilicate glass manufactured by Plowden and Thompson, Limited, Worcester, England. The chemical composition of this glass is very similar to entry number 21 in Table 1.2 (page 24).

according to Adam.* Seals of molybdenum rods, ranging in diameter from 2–10 mm, are made in a more or less conventional way in the open atmosphere, like tungsten rod seals, where a close-fitting glass tube protects the molybdenum against excessive oxidation. This bead is then provided with a rim by wrapping "Kodial" around it, and the assembly sealed into a "Kodial" glass envelope. The working temperature during sealing ranges from 1100–1150°C, and the interface of a satisfactory seal has a matt-brown, but not dark-brown, color. The presence of milky streaks, or spots, on a dark-brown background indicates excessive oxidation and inclusion of molybdenum trioxide fumes; such seals are culled out. In making seals with rods larger than 5 mm dia., it was found advantageous to anneal the rods in hydrogen or vacuo at about 1000°C before glassing. The operating temperature of such rod seals, up to the largest diameters, is given as 200°C.

Cup or ring seals, ranging from 40–70 mm in dia., with a wall thickness from 1.2–1.5 mm and 26–31 mm depth, are being made, according to Adam, by the following method. Again, no protective atmosphere is used, but excessive oxidation prevented by exclusion of air. Figure 13.14 shows the arrangement by which a ring bead (1) is attached to the chamfered periphery of the molybdenum cup (2). The glass ring is formed from a rod 4–5 mm dia. and ground flat on one side. The cup has been preoxidized. The ring is placed on a groove in the graphite block (3), an iron weight (4) put on the cup, and the assembly enclosed by a suitably shaped graphite cup (5). The seal is then made by induction-heating in a carefully controlled temperature-time cycle. After cooling to about 400°C, the graphite parts can be removed, and the seal left to cool in air. No further annealing is necessary before attaching the beaded cup to a glass tube by conventional methods on a glass lathe. The finished seal is then annealed at 530°C.

Such seals resist temperature shock, as evident from the method suggested for the removal of remaining oxides from the inner surface of the cup. A few lumps of sodium nitrate are placed in the cup, which is then heated over a small flame to cause the crystals to melt at about 400°C. The liquid $NaNO_2$ can then be swirled around to cover the inner surface of the cup and clean it by chemical action. After cooling, the nitrite is dissolved in hot water, and subsequent rinses in distilled water and acetone complete the cleaning operation in the usual manner.

It is worth noting that many of the aluminosilicate glasses can also readily be sealed to "Kovar." The techniques outlined above have been successfully applied to the construction of travelling-wave tubes both at the Stanford Electronics Laboratories and at the Sylvania Microwave

* Personal communication from Dr. H. Adam of Lancashire Dynamo Nevelin Ltd., Hurst Green, Oxted, Surrey, England, to whom the author is indebted for furnishing a detailed description (in German) of the methods used in making such seals.[60c]

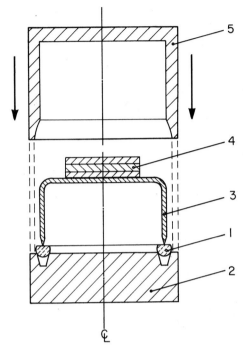

Figure 13.14. Method for the production of cup or ring seals between alumino-silicate glass and molybdenum. After H. Adam. (*Courtesy Lancashire Dynamo Nevelin Ltd., England.*)

Component Laboratories where the present author initiated their use. The special techniques for the deep-drawing of molybdenum were described by Duckworth and referred to in Chapter 10.

Titanium and zirconium seals have been described in the literature and have found application in the laboratory in special cases where more conventional seals could not be used. Corak and Wexler[61] describe a tubular zirconium seal to Corning type 7052 glass where the zirconium tube was 1 in. OD × 1/32 in. wall for use at liquid helium temperatures. Reference is made to E. A. Gulbransen of the Westinghouse Research Laboratories and D. M. Wroughton of the Westinghouse Atomic Power Division as having first demonstrated the usefulness of zirconium-to-glass seals at elevated temperatures. Taylor[62] described a flux for glass-to-tantalum or zirconium seals to Corning type glasses 7052, 7720, and 7740. Rawson and Denton[63] have tested the sealing properties of titanium and zirconium. Bead seals (6-mm dia. on 1-mm dia. wire) to various BTH* glasses were

* The British Thomson-Houston Company, Limited, Rugby, England.

TABLE 13.8. COMPARATIVE STRENGTH TESTS ON GLASS-TO-METAL SEALS[63]

Sealing combination	No. seals tested	Mean breaking load (lb.)	Coefficient of variation
Zirconium—C.40 glass	8	96.4	6.4
Titanium—C.77 glass	9	109.0	1.3
Titanium—C.78 glass	6	109.6	1.0
Nilo K—C.40 glass	5	85.0	4.8
Nilo 475—C.12 glass	6	69.3	6.5

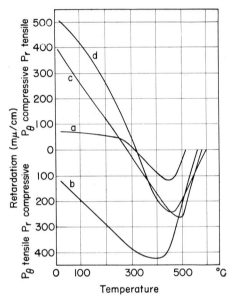

Figure 13.15. Retardation-temperature curves for bead seals of a) C40-zirconium (b/a = 7.6); b) C77-titanium (b/a = 7.5); c) C78-titanium (b/a = 7.9); d) C9-tungsten (b/a = 6.2); After Rawson and Denton.[63] (*Courtesy Institute of Physics, London.*)

subjected to a shearing force, and the breaking load in pounds observed, as shown in Table 13.8, where comparative values for "Kovar" (Nilo K) and nickel-chrome-iron alloys (Nilo 475) are also shown (see page 409). Figure 13.15 gives the stress retardation curves measured in a polariscope where the light beam was passing axially through the section of the bead near the interface between metal and glass, so that the retardation measured was proportional to the sum of the hoop stress T_0 and the radial stress T_r. Titanium and zirconium wires from different sources show markedly different behavior, and their expansion characteristic is altered by heating the rods for five minutes in air at 1100°C, a treatment which

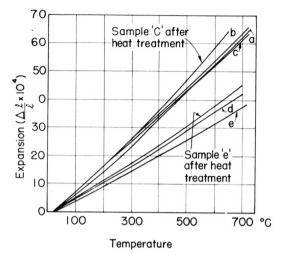

Figure 13.16. Thermal expansion curves of various samples of titanium and zirconium; a–c: Ti; d–e: Zr. After Rawson and Denton.[63] (*Courtesy Institute of Physics, London.*)

closely simulates the conditions encountered during the actual seal fabrication (Figure 13.16).

Satisfactory vacuum-tight seals made with zirconium and titanium wire were obtained with no special treatment of the wire prior to sealing other than rubbing it with fine emery paper to remove the drawing marks and then heating for a few seconds in the flame. Such seals are of interest where resistance to chemical attack or lack of ferromagnetism are required.

Iron alloy seals. Many of the various pure metals discussed in the preceding sections have found extensive commercial applications, but none of them is particularly suited for the economic mass production of soft-glass seals, either on account of excessive cost of the metal, as in the case of titanium and zirconium seals, or on account of high fabrication cost and mechanical weakness, as is the case of Houskeeper seals of the feather-edge type. The need for wires, rods, and tubes that can readily be sealed to soft glasses was satisfied by the development of a number of iron alloys which will be discussed in the following sections. Nickel-iron, chrome-iron, nickel-chrome-iron alloys seal to soft glasses, while a special nickel-cobalt-iron alloy is widely used for sealing to hard glasses. These alloys have expansion characteristics which closely match those of the glasses with which they are used, and they can be used in bulk without the need for feather edges. The alloys mentioned can be economically produced in quantity while maintaining the necessary close control over their composition; they form in general a well-adhering oxide, and they have such electrical conductivity as to make them useful as current leads without overheating. In high-frequency tubes, however, it becomes necessary to reduce the resistivity of the alloy by applying a surface coating of a pure, highly conducting metal such as gold, silver, copper, or chrome.

It has been suggested by Wroughton and Gregory[64] that the poor electrical conductivity of nickel iron alloys for soft-glass seals could be improved by making wires and sheet, from which cups could be formed, from a mixture of copper and molybdenum by powder-metallurgical techniques and thus arrive at metallic members which have expansion coefficients ranging from 88×10^{-7} to $111 \times 10^{-7}/°C$—a range which would satisfy seals to soft glasses. While this is an interesting approach, no doubt useful in special cases, the fabrication is necessarily costly, and commercial seals have not been made by this technique.

In distinction to pure metals, iron alloys have a nonlinear expansion characteristic. Like glasses, these alloys thus have an inflection point, or range, where the rate of elongation with temperature begins to increase, as shown in Figure 13.17 for a number of nickel alloys. To avoid excessive stresses, it is desirable that the inflection range of the alloy and that of the glass to which it is sealed should coincide. A close approximation to this condition is illustrated in Figure 13.18 where the photoelastic stress pattern of the seal is also shown. The temperature at which the inflection of the alloy expansion characteristic occurs depends on the magnetic properties of the material and lies near the Curie point where ferromagnetism is lost.

In addition to the proper location of this magnetic inflection, it is necessary that the temperature at which the iron component of the alloy under-

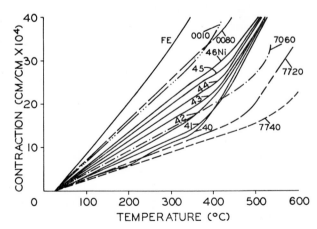

Figure 13.17. Thermal expansion curves for Fe-Ni alloys and some Corning glasses. After Hull, Burger and Navias.[90] (*Courtesy American Institute of Physics.*)

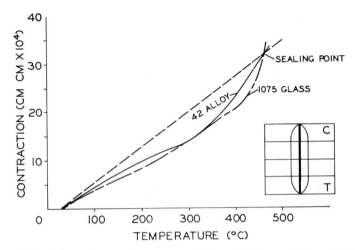

Figure 13.18. Thermal expansion curves of Type 42 alloy and Type 1075 glass; insert: photoelastic stress pattern of a single wire bead seal; the absence of stress in the seal is demonstrated by the straightness of the interference lines crossing it. After Hull, Burger, and Navias.[90] (*Courtesy American Institute of Physics.*)

goes an allotropic transformation from the α-phase to the γ-phase (Ar$_3$ point) lies outside the range of temperatures to which the glass seal is exposed during fabrication and operation of the completed tube, i.e., $-50°C$ to $600°C$, approximately. If this condition is not satisfied, the expansion curve is not reversible and will follow a different course on heating than on cooling. Figure 13.19 illustrates this behavior for a nickel-cobalt-iron alloy ("Kovar") according to Scott.[89] To ensure that the alloy is in the γ-state, it is advisable to subject the parts prior to sealing to an annealing treatment, which well exceeds the Ar$_3$ point, followed by slow cooling.

Nickel-iron alloy seals. The use of Ni-Fe alloys for seals with soft glasses was suggested as early as 1897 by Guillaume.[65] Fink [66] and Eldred[67] introduced an alloy wire in 1911 which became known under the name "Dumet"; this replaced platinum for lead seals used up to that time in lamps and experimental tubes. "Dumet" wire, used in all soft-glass receiving tubes up to the present time, consists of a 42-percent nickel-iron alloy coated with a thin film of copper; it is made by fusing or welding an alloy core into a copper tube with an intermediate sheath of brass. This billet is swaged and then drawn into wire which is passed through a solution of sodium borate. The final thickness of copper is about 0.5 mil, depending on the diameter of the wire, and the copper surface represents about 25 per cent of the total weight of the wire. "Dumet" wire seals are practical up to 40-mil diameter, but are rarely used above 20 mils in the tube industry for seals with Corning glasses types 0010, 0080, and 0120. A

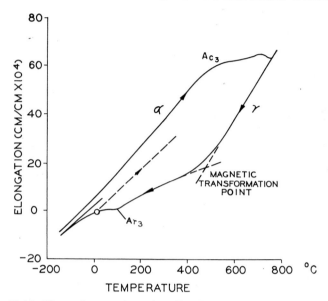

Figure 13.19. Thermal expansion of an Fe-Ni-Co alloy not suitable for sealing purposes; the Ar₃ transformation point lies above room temperature. After Scott.[89] (*Courtesy American Institute for Mining, Metallurgical, and Petroleum Engineers, Inc.*)

32-mil diameter wire will pass currents as high as 20 amperes. The sandwich structure of the wire results in quite unusual expansion characteristics. The longitudinal expansion coefficient of the wire is $65 \times 10^{-7}/°C$, and the radial expansion coefficient is $92 \times 10^{-7}/°C$.[11] The large stresses which would ordinarily be present in "Dumet" seals are taken up by the thin copper sheath, in accordance with the principle applied later by Houskeeper. "Dumet" seals are usually not fully annealed so that the glass is left in longitudinal compression.[68]

Figure 13.20 gives a graph of the mean expansion coefficient (0–100°C) for different weight-percentage compositions of nickel-iron alloys, as well as a curve for the corresponding thermal conductivities.[69] It will be apparent from a study of Table 13.3 that the range of commercially available sealing alloys of this type contains from 42 to 50 per cent nickel.

"42 alloy" is used in the electronic industry for receiving and transmitting-type tubes, x-ray tubes, cathode ray tubes, mercury arc rectifiers, and ignitrons. Sealed instruments and radio components, hermetic seals, sealed headlights for motor cars, and sealed refrigeration units, are other examples. Hard-glass seals with "42 alloy" can be made by using a feather edge of about 4 mil thickness, according to the technique described by Houskeeper for copper seals.

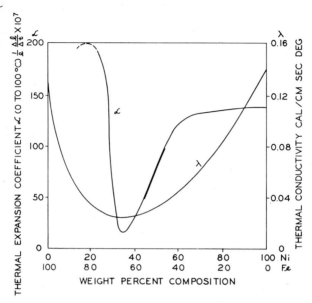

Figure 13.20. Thermal expansion coefficient α (0–100°C) and thermal conductivity λ for Fe-Ni alloys. After Espe and Knoll.[69] (*Courtesy Julius Springer-Verlag, Berlin.*)

Nickel-iron alloys should preferably be heated to 950°C in hydrogen to obtain a clean surface prior to sealing; this treatment also removes the effects of cold work without causing excessive grain growth. Kingston,[70] in his extensive investigation of Ni-Fe alloys for the development of pin seals for "Loctal" tubes, found that pure Ni-Fe alloys are not suited for this purpose because their oxide does not adhere well to the metal, but is rich in nickel next to the surface of the metal and tends to be loose and scaly. Hull, Burger, and Navias[90] were not troubled with this difficulty when using their particular "42 alloy," which had additions of magnanese, silicon, and carbon, and was sealed to a specially developed glass (G. E. Type 1075) that had the following percent composition:

SiO_2	34
B_2O_3	28
PbO	29
Al_2O_3	7
Na_2O	2

There was a tendency, however, for lead oxide to be reduced, and for lead to appear at the interface between metal and glass. By prebeading the metal with a lead-free glass, such as Corning type 7060, or by coating the alloy with copper or platinum which do not reduce lead oxide, this difficulty was overcome. Small additions of one or more of the elements Cr,

Co, Mn, Si, Al, or B had been suggested by Scott[71] as beneficial for the production of a more fusible oxide coating on nickel-iron alloys for soft-glass seals.

Foley, Alvord, and Easley[72] have described the details of a method for depositing a layer of silver on 42 Ni-Fe alloy for glass-to-metal seals, using lead-free borosilicate glass, to prevent scaling during the annealing process of cast bushings. To develop a surface which would participate in the glass-to-metal seal and be resistant to the diffusion of oxygen, it was necessary to cover the silver plate with a thin coating of indium.

More recently, Düsing[73] has reported on a systematic study to find an economically feasible sealing metal with a suitably improved surface to reduce r-f losses encountered in microwave tubes. After investigating all the various metals and alloys here under discussion, he chose a 54 Ni/46 Fe alloy ("Vacovit" 540) as the best compromise and thus was led to accept soft-glass envelopes made of a 30% lead glass (Type M). Strain measurements disclosed that disk seals made with this combination show radial compression strains between room temperature and 180°C and radial tension above this temperature. Of 628 disk seals tested, none showed cracks. To improve the surface conductivity of the 54 Ni/46 Fe alloy disk (20 to 40 mils thick), they were first plated with gold to a thickness of 5 to 6 microns and then with silver of 15 micron thickness. The power output of tubes type 2C39 and 2C40 made with such seals was improved by 35 per cent, i.e., an increase from 11 watts to 15 watts.

Several observations made by Düsing in his paper should be of interest to the reader of this book and are given here; others will be mentioned later in this chapter in the appropriate sections. Silver coatings on the 54/46 Ni/Fe disks were not satisfactory by themselves* because they either caused gas leakage between base metal and silver, or poor adhesion between silver and glass. Silver is notoriously permeable to oxygen at elevated temperature (a 0.2-mm thick silver layer will pass 3.6×10^{-2} cc oxygen per square centimeter per hour at 625°C when a pressure difference of 1 atm is maintained[75]) so that oxidation of the base metal cannot be avoided at the glass sealing temperature, and peeling of the silver coating results. When seals were made in a nitrogen atmosphere, this difficulty was avoided, but the mechanical bond between silver and glass turned out to be poor. By applying an intermediate layer of gold, a barrier to oxygen penetration to the base metal was provided, but enrichment of the silver layer with oxygen from the atmosphere during sealing made for a tight bond with the glass.

The base metal was decarburized by firing in wet hydrogen at 900°C.

---

* Contrary to the reports on this subject by Freedman.[74]

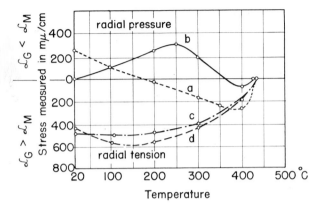

Figure 13.21. Strain vs temperature curves for disk seals made with 30 per cent lead glass (German Type M) to the following alloys: (a) 54Ni-46Fe (b) 42Ni-52Fe-6Cr (c) 51Ni-48Fe-1Cr (d) 49Ni-50Fe-1Cr. After Düsing.[73] (*Courtesy Telefunken A.G.*)

While this treatment effectively removes carbon from the surface layer, it also causes a barely visible oxidation which must subsequently be removed by an additional light etching treatment. If this precaution is not taken, pores or blisters result on subsequent heat treatment of the plated surface, or later in service.

Figure 13.21 gives the strains measured for the various alloys considered by Düsing.[73] Radial compression of the glass exists when the thermal expansion of the metal is greater than that of the glass and vice versa. The 42 Ni/52 Fe/6 Cr alloy (b) thus shows the most favorable characteristic, but was rejected because it cannot be electroplated very easily. In addition, Düsing states that chrome alloys always show surface cracks on formed parts which must be removed by finish grinding. Alloys (c) and (d) are not acceptable because they show radial tension over the whole range of temperature. Alloy (a), the one chosen by Düsing, represents a fair compromise, particularly since it has no strain at the operating temperature of the tube, which is stated to be 180°C. Silver-plated plain iron in combination with an iron sealing glass[76] was rejected as a possible choice for the microwave tubes under consideration because the high alkali content of the sealing glass makes for lower chemical stability in humid atmospheres, and its heat shock resistance is lower than that of lead glass by virtue of the higher thermal expansion (Table 13.3).

The permissible bake-out temperature of iron-sealing glasses (Corning Types 1990, 1991) is also lower by as much as 70°C. The reader may wonder why a hard glass was not chosen in combination with "Kovar." To obtain a seal of high electrical conductivity, gold plating seems to be the only practical surface coating. On account of the high rate of diffusion of gold into Fe-Ni-Co alloys at the sealing temperature, the initial thickness of the gold layer must be high (25 to 30 microns) if there is to be any gold left in the glass-metal interfa   after sealing; this approach therefore is not economically feasible.

Chrome-iron alloy s   s. These alloys fall into the category of stainless steels, as they contain more than 10 per cent chromium; they began to be used as sealing materials in conjunction with soft glasses, particularly in Europe, about 1930. Their properties were investigated by Bain[77] and Hidnert[78]. Several patents on chrome-iron sealing methods were issued to the Philips Company in Holland from 1927 to 1934. The chromium content ranged from 20 to 30 per cent, and small amounts of silicon, manganese, and carbon were usually present. Twenty-eight percent chrome-iron will retain without change its predominantly α-ferritic crystal structure when heated to 1200°C and higher, and consequently will suffer no change of its thermal expansion coefficient. Alloys with a chrome content lower than 26 per cent, on the other hand, change to the austenitic structure on heating and retain it partly on cooling. This results in an increase of the thermal expansion over a temperature range where the glass has already set and cannot yield, thus causing the seal to fracture. This objectionable transformation to the austenitic phase can be suppressed by the addition of varying amounts of aluminum, niobium, molybdenum, titanium, vanadium, tungsten, and tantalum. AISI 430 Ti is an example of 17 % chrome iron thus stabilized with titanium which is present to at least five times the carbon content in order to tie up this free carbon as TiC. It is the presence of carbon (as well as nitrogen and nickel) which brings about the transformation of α-iron to γ-iron above 800°C.

During World War II, substantial quantities of a British high-frequency pentode, Type VR 91 (Philips Type EF 50), were produced in the United States and Canada; this program familiarized tube workers on this continent with the properties of chrome-iron alloys that were used in this particular tube for pin seals with a special glass, Corning Type 0240. Kingston[70] had studied this material for the same application in "Loctal" tubes. With the onset of large-scale production of television tubes with metal cones after World War II, chrome-iron alloys found extensive application, and many improvements were made in the techniques of producing large-area seals.[79-83]

Two specifications were issued by ASTM covering the use of chromium-iron alloy for sealing to glass;[84, 85] they concern two grades of chromium-iron alloys, one containing 28 per cent chromium and the other 17 per cent chromium. Their chemical percent compositions are given as follows:

Carbon, max.	0.25
Manganese, max.	2.00
Phosphorus, max.	0.040
Sulfur, max.	̇.030
Silicon, max.	)0
Chromium,	̣3 to 30
Chromium,	16 to 23

The procedure recommended for the determination of thermal expansion characteristics of these alloys is as follows:

"The alloy shall be heated in air to 1200° ± 10°C and held for 15 minutes at temperature, at the end of which time it shall be cooled continuously to a temperature of 530° ± 10°C within a maximum period of eight minutes. Upon further cooling from 530° ± 10°C to 30° ± 5°C, there shall be no evidence of transformation as manifested by an abrupt discontinuity in the cooling curve. In the latter range the coefficient of thermal contraction shall not exceed 11.7 × 10⁻⁶ in./in./deg. C. (11.4 × 10⁻⁶ for the 28 per cent alloy). If x is the length at 530° ± 10°C in inches per inch and y is the length at 30° ± 5°C, then the coefficient of contraction, c, shall be calculated as follows:

$$c = \frac{x - y}{y(T_x - T_y)} \quad *$$

where T_x = temperature at which x was measured
T_y = temperature at which y was measured

Upon still further cooling from 30° ± 5°C to −40°C the cooling curve shall be free of evidence of transformation as indicated by abrupt changes."

The 17-percent chrome alloy has greater ductility than the 28-percent alloy and it is thus more suited to spinning of sheet in the production of cones; it also is less costly than the 28-percent chrome alloy, and its corrosion resistance and resistance to thermal shock are superior. The slightly higher thermal expansion of the 17-percent alloy which varies between 111 × 10⁻⁷ and 113 × 10⁻⁷ in./in./deg. C in the range from 30° to 500°C is still entirely acceptable for sealing to a high grade of soda-lime window glass as long as the metal surrounds the glass. Typical compositions of three modified alloys which are commercially available are given in Table 13.9. These high-chrome alloys are available under the tradenames "Sealmet 1," "Carpenter 27," "AL Telemet," "Dilver O," and "Novar B," as indicated in Table 13.3. The standard designations in the United States are AISI 446, AISI 430, and AISI 430 Ti.

---

* Formula given here is a revised version suggested by R. H. Dalton.

TABLE 13.9. TYPICAL CHROME-IRON ALLOY COMPOSITIONS

	A (%)	B (%)	C (%)
Chromium	18.5	17.1	18.1
Carbon	0.08	0.06	0.08
Manganese	0.49	0.42	0.51
Phosphorus	0.02	0.02	0.02
Sulfur	0.01	0.006	0.008
Nickel	0.20	0.34	
Titanium	0.62	0.68	0.35
Aluminum	0.11		
Silicon	0.29	0.84	
Molybdenum			0.9

High-chrome alloys form a very firmly adhering green oxide layer when heated to 950°C in wet hydrogen prior to sealing. Acid-pickling by immersion in 20 percent hydrochloric acid for about two minutes also brings about oxidation. The electrical resistivity of this alloy is rather high, and spot-welding is very difficult without first sandblasting the surface to remove the outside layer. Silver-plating overcomes this difficulty, and glassing operations can be carried out in the ordinary manner on silver-plated chrome iron.[72] Plain chrome iron cannot be brazed to copper in a hydrogen atmosphere unless precautions are taken to remove the last traces of oxygen from hydrogen gas. Brazing to nickel is less difficult.

Commercial production of faceplate seals for color television tubes (RCA Type 21 GXP 22) utilizes the technique of applying a coating of powdered glass (enamel frit) to the sealing land of the cylindrical top cap made of AISI Type 430 (modified) stainless steel according to Rose[97].

"The metal top-cap is prepared for sealing by alundum blasting the sealing land and adjacent side wall to present a uniformly roughened and cleaned surface. Following this, an enamel frit application is made by spraying a coating approximately 0.007 in. thick in the bisque. The frit is confined to the sealing land and a narrow area below and serves as an intermediate layer between the Type 430 alloy and the glass faceplate. The glazing operation, in which the enamel is fired, is performed by placing the fritted top-cap on a rotating turntable and heating by oxy-gas fires until the sealing land reaches a temperature of approximately 1100°C. At this point, the enamel wets out as the top-cap is removed from the fire. A glazing is performed as a separate operation to maintain close control over the surface defects and enamel thickness, which is held to 0.003 in. to 0.005 in."

The faceplate, consisting of Pittsburgh Plate Glass Company Teleglas No. 3720, is then placed on the enameled sealing land of the top-cap and sealed to the enameled surface by the application of fires, while being held in controlled space relationship to the sealing land by means of three positioning pins that can be raised when the rim of the faceplate has been softened in order to produce the proper seal contour. Many interesting details of this operation as well as the analysis of the resulting strains are described by Rose.

For a very detailed review article on all the various aspects of chrome iron for glass-to-metal seals, process techniques, mechanical properties, and examples of applications, the reader is referred to an article by Espe.[86]

Nickel-chrome-iron alloy seals. The sealing alloys discussed in the preceding sections were found to be unsuited for the economical mass production of multiple-pin headers for receiving tubes when this type of structure was under development (about 1940). Neither the 42-percent nickel-iron alloy nor a 28-percent chrome-iron alloy could be readily sealed to Corning Type 0010 glass without the introduction of dangerous strain patterns. A fairly close match in expansion exists between 0010 glass and the 48 to 60 percent nickel-iron alloys but, as mentioned above, the objectionable properties of their oxides resulted in leaky seals. Although Corning Type 0240 glass had been successfully used with chrome alloy pins and 024 envelopes, as mentioned above, it was not acceptable for the production of headers for regular receiving tubes because the electrical resistivity of this glass is much lower than that of the proven 0010 or 0120 glass. It furthermore does not match Corning Type 0080 glass which is generally used for the production of receiving tube bulbs. Kingston[70] thus extended his search for a more suitable pin alloy that would satisfy all the required conditions, which he enumerates as follows:

(1) "The expansivity of the glass and metal must match closely over a given temperature range.

(2) "It should be possible to obtain a layer of oxide on the surface of the metal which will adhere tightly throughout all processing involved in the forming of the glass-to-metal seal.

(3) "This oxide coating must be of such a nature and thick enough to prevent the formation of iron oxide or other loosely adhering oxide on the surface of the metal during subsequent processing.

(4) "This oxide coating should dissolve (wet) mutually with the glass.

(5) "It is desirable that the oxide formed on the metal have a sufficiently low electrical resistance to weld easily to other metals such as nickel and iron by electric spot welding.

(6) "It is essential that the alloy for the glass-to-metal seal be a reversible one insofar as elongation is concerned and that no thermal critical point (allotropic transformations) occur in any temperature region to which the finished article might be subjected.

(7) "The alloy should be comparatively low in cost and should have a

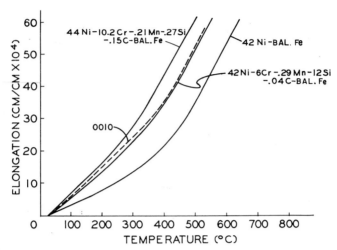

Figure 13.22. Thermal expansion curves for Ni-Fe and Ni-Cr-Fe alloys and Corning Glass 0010. After Kingston.[70] (*Courtesy Allegheny Ludlum Steel Corp.*)

composition relatively easy to melt and capable of close reproduction in commercial quantities.

(8) "The alloy must have physical characteristics which allow normal hot and cold working without forming cracks, seams, or other mechanical defects. Also, it should be capable of being processed to obtain different degrees of hardness or ductility."

These conditions were satisfied by an alloy which became known as "Sylvania No. 4" alloy, or "Sealmet 4," and other designations listed in Table 13.3. The composition of this alloy is nickel 42%, chrome 6%, carbon 0.52%, balance iron. The addition of chromium to the "42 alloy" raises its expansion curve as shown in Figure 13.22 and thus brings it very closely in coincidence with that for 0010 glass. Figure 13.23 shows the corresponding expansion curves for the seal partners Sylvania No. 4 and 0120 glass on the one hand, and 28 chrome-iron and 0240 glass on the other. Sylvania No. 4 alloy has a reversible expansion over the range of −75 to 1000°C and forms a well-adhering protective layer of chromic oxide (Cr_2O_3) at the surface. This surface oxide must be produced prior to seal making by firing the alloy in a hydrogen atmosphere enriched with water vapor at a temperature ranging from 1050 to 1250°C.[1]

Stanworth[87] has further improved the composition of the alloy described by Kingston in order to get a still better match to lead glasses. The following illustrations are taken from his work in order to give a further example of the portrayal of expansion characteristics of metals and glasses by plotting the differential expansion. Figure 13.24 indicates that the stress

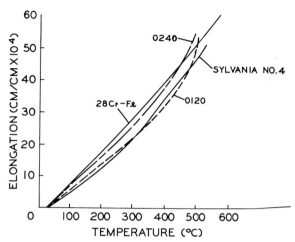

Figure 13.23. Thermal expansion curves for 28% Cr-Fe and Sylvania No. 4 alloy. Also shown are the corresponding curves for Corning Glasses 0240 and 0120 which match these alloys. After Monack.[10] (*Courtesy The Gage Publishing Company.*)

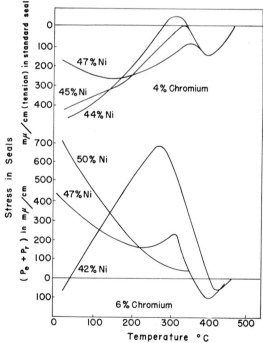

Figure 13.24. Stress-temperature curves obtained with alloys containing 4% and 6% Cr, respectively. The 42Ni-6Cr alloy was available in wire form only; the results for the lower three curves are thus given for the sum of the circumferential and radial stresses in bead seals. After Stanworth.[87] (*Courtesy Institute of Physics, London.*)

445

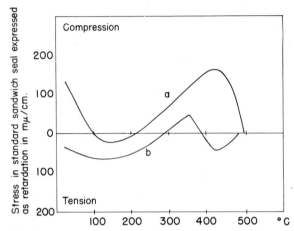

Figure 13.25. Stress-temperature curves for a) Type C40 borosilicate glass to Kovar-type alloy; b) Type C12 lead glass to 47Ni-5Cr-Fe alloy. (For glass types C40 and C12 see Table A3.) After Stanworth.[87] (*Courtesy Institute of Physics, London.*)

in a 42 Ni-6 Cr-Fe seal, cooling from the annealing temperature, increases to a peak at about 300°C before decreasing to a very low value at room temperature. In an attempt to find an alloy composition which would have at least as good a match to lead glass as "Kovar" has to borosilicate glass, Stanworth arrived at the alloy 47 Ni-5 Cr. Figure 13.25 gives the stress-temperature curves for these two metal-to-glass seals. It is evident that a very good match to lead glass is obtained with the new alloy composition. The interface of the seals made with this new alloy shows an olive-green color, and adhesion of the glass to the metal is very satisfactory.

Figure 13.26 shows the effect on the stress-temperature curves when varying amounts of chromium are added to a 47-percent nickel alloy, and Figure 13.27 gives the results for the corresponding additions of chromium to a 49-percent nickel alloy.

"It will be noted that the stress developing below about 470°C in all cases passes through a minimum, then through a maximum, and then, in some cases, through a second minimum. The more pronounced minimum and maximum stresses at about 400°C and 275–375°C are caused respectively by the transformation in the glass contraction curve and the inflection in the metal contraction curve at its Curie temperature. This is shown diagrammatically for a particular case in Fig. 13.28. The higher rate of contraction of the glass between H and G gives tension in the glass of the sandwich seal at temperatures immediately below about 470°C because the contraction of the glass is in this region greater than that of the alloy.

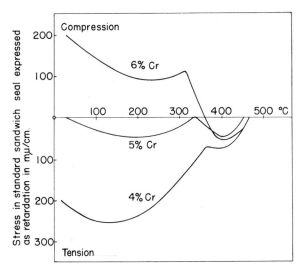

Figure 13.26. Effect of chromium on 47% Ni alloy. After Stanworth.[87] (*Courtesy Institute of Physics, London.*)

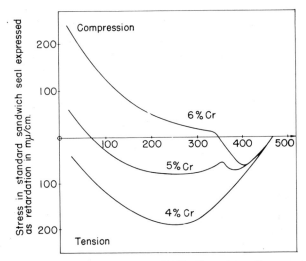

Figure 13.27. Effect of chromium on 49% Ni alloy. After Stanworth.[87] (*Courtesy Institute of Physics, London.*)

Below G the contraction of the glass decreases, and the stress, therefore, goes through a minimum, to become zero at F, but then passes through a maximum at E, and becomes increasingly more tensile in the region EC, because, once again, the glass is contracting at a greater rate than the

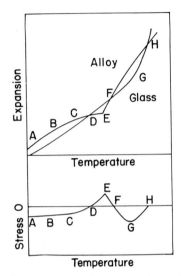

Figure 13.28. Relation between expansion properties and the stress-temperature curve. After Stanworth.[87] (*Courtesy Institute of Physics, London.*)

metal. Below C the metal contraction increases so that the increasing tensile nature of the stresses in the glass is arrested; the stresses throughout the whole range down to room temperature remain low."

Davis[88] has described a method by which the strength of seals made with the various iron alloys can be materially improved, and failures due to gas leakage completely eliminated. The technique consists in plating the alloy pins to a thickness of 2.5 microns with nickel and then plating onto the nickel an additional layer of chromium 2.5 microns thick. The parts are then given a diffusion treatment in dry hydrogen at 1000°C for a few minutes and then oxidized in air for a few seconds by passing a current through the wire; short pieces of lead glass were then fused to the pins.

Nickel-cobalt-iron alloy seals. The need for an alloy that would seal to hard glasses without requiring a feather edge and which, at the same time, would lend itself to the fabrication of geometrical shapes such as cylinders, sheet, and tubing was satisfied by the basic investigations carried out by Scott,[89] Hull, Burger, and Navias,[90] who developed the Ni-Co-Fe alloys known under the trade names "Kovar" and "Fernico." Since the original patents have expired, these alloys are now available from different sources under a variety of trade names which are listed in Table 13.3. In England, the corresponding alloy is known as "Nilo K," in France as "Dilver P," and in Germany as "Vacon." These alloys contain from 17 to 18 per cent cobalt, from 28 to 29 per cent nickel, the balance being iron; they are ductile and free from embrittlement under all conditions of

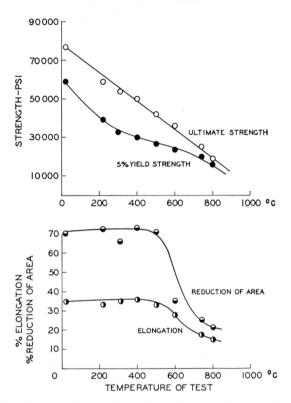

Figure 13.29. Plot of ultimate strength, yield strength, reduction of area, and elongation vs temperature of test for "Kovar." After Theilacker.[92] (*Courtesy West-inghouse Electric Corporation.*)

ordinary use including heating and annealing in air, hydrogen, or rare gases, and can be soldered, brazed, and welded.*

Graphs of ultimate strength, yield strength, reduction of area and elongation vs temperature of test are given for "Kovar" in Figure 13.29, according to Theilacker.[92] The thermal expansion of "Kovar" in comparison with that of copper, nickel, stainless steel, and SAE 1020 is plotted in Figure 13.30; the expansion of two "Kovar"-sealing glasses is given in Figure 13.31. It is evident that "Kovar" matches Corning glasses Types 7052 and 7040 exceedingly well over the whole range of temperatures encountered in operation and seal making.

Figure 13.32 shows expansion curves for "Fernico" and Corning glass Type 7060; an insert shows the stress pattern for a wire-bead seal of 7.5 mm-dia. glass on a 2.5 mm-dia. "Fernico" wire. The lines in the stress pattern are straight within one hundredth of the distance between two

* Physical characteristics of Kovar are listed in Table A5 in the Appendix.

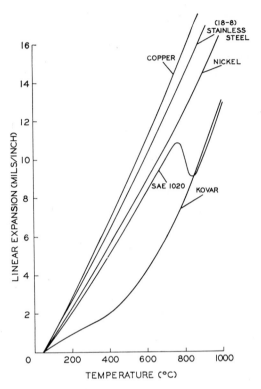

Figure 13.30. Thermal expansion curve of "Kovar," copper, 18–8 stainless steel, nickel, and SAE 1020. After Theilacker.[92] (*Courtesy Westinghouse Electric Corporation.*)

adjacent fringes; this indicates that the remaining stress after cooling at the rate of one degree per minute is less than 0.02 kg/mm².

To appraise the expansion match between glass and sealing alloy at the sealing temperature, Hull, Burger, and Navias defined a "sealing point" as the temperature given by the intersection of a straight line with a slope 15 per cent greater than the average expansion coefficient between 0 and 300°C of the glass with the actual expansion curve of the glass, and thus arrived at a temperature which closely coincides with the temperature used for sealing borosilicate glasses.

The metallurgical problems involved in the selection of a stable three-phase alloy, such as "Kovar," have been extensively treated in the literature.[91-94] The low expansion rate of hard glasses of the borosilicate type, observed in the lower range of temperatures, as well as the much higher expansion rate beyond the inflection point, must be matched by such an alloy as closely as possible. In addition, it is important that the expansion curve be followed by the alloy in a reversible manner for increasing and decreasing temperatures over the whole range of temperatures encountered during sealing and in service, without discontinuities such as those characteristic of pure iron and iron-nickel alloys at the transformation from the

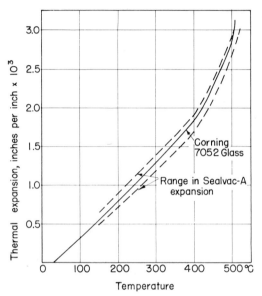

Figure 13.31. Thermal expansion curves for "Sealvac A" and Corning glass Type 7052. (*Courtesy Vacuum Metals Corporation.*)

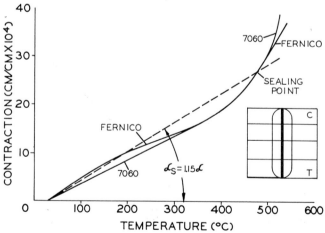

Figure 13.32. Thermal contraction of Fernico and Corning glass 7060. The insert shows the stress pattern of a test seal between these materials. After Hull, Burger, and Navias.[90] (*Courtesy American Institute of Physics.*)

γ-phase to the α-phase on cooling (Ar$_3$ point) which were illustrated in Figure 13.19 and described on p. 181. For a constant cobalt content, this $\gamma \rightarrow \alpha$ transformation is increasingly shifted to lower temperatures with increasing nickel content and comes to lie at $-130°$C for 28.5 per cent nickel in the alloy (Figure 13.33). Figure 13.34 shows the expansion curve for "Kovar" over an extended temperature range, after Theilacker.[92]

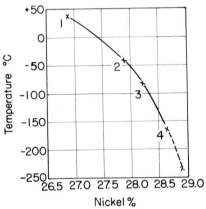

Figure 13.33. Dependence of γ-α transformation temperature in Fe-Ni-Co alloys on nickel content. After Herrmann and Thomas.[93] (*Courtesy Dr. Riederer Verlag GMBH-Stuttgart.*)

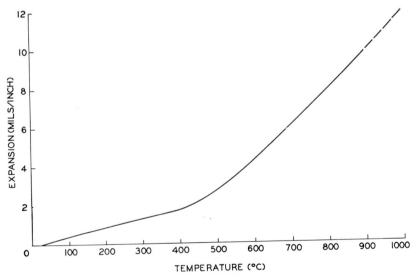

Figure 13.34. Thermal expansion of "Kovar." After Theilacker.[92] (*Courtesy Westinghouse Electric Corporation.*)

Cold-working of "Kovar"-type alloys enhances the $\gamma \rightarrow \alpha$ transformation; formed parts must thus be annealed above 700°C to restore the γ-phase. The α-phase has a much lower electrical resistivity than the γ-phase, and this fact can be used to follow the transformation by electrical measurements.

Processing of "Kovar" Parts. "Kovar" parts are available in a wide range of standard sizes from commercial suppliers so that maching operations are generally confined to cutting the part off to the length required. Spinning is not recommended since there is danger of fracturing the metal. Prior to seal-making, the machined parts must be carefully polished in the area where the seal is to be made, and edges should be free from burrs. After degreasing and chemical cleaning, the part must be annealed and decarburized by firing in wet hydrogen at near 1000°C for about 30 minutes,* and the glass-sealing operation should follow this treatment within a few hours. A well-adhering oxide is produced on "Kovar" by heating it to a temperature above 650°C in a slightly oxidizing atmosphere, and the glass is applied to the oxidized surface in its plastic state by the application of slight pressure. Details of the techniques used for sealing glass to "Kovar" have been described in Bulletin 145 issued by Stupakoff Ceramic and Manufacturing Company† who formerly were the sole fabricators and distributors of "Kovar," which is produced by the Westinghouse Electric Corporation.

"During the glass-to-metal sealing process, alloys of the nickel-iron-cobalt type (Nilo K, Kovar) become heavily oxidised and it is necessary to remove this oxide before further processing, such as electroplating, can take place. The removal of this oxide without appreciable attack on the underlying metal is not easy. Several methods have been put forward but the following process has been found to be most reliable and effective.

"The glass-to-metal seal, freed of any grease, is immersed in Solution 1 until, on inspection, the metal is seen to be free of oxide. The time may vary from 10–60 minutes depending on the thickness of the oxide. A rinse in chromic acid solution will remove any smut remaining. Loss measurements on unoxidized Nilo K in Solution 1 at 75°C disclose a loss from the surface of 0.0004 in. per hour.

"The addition of nitric acid to Solution 1 gives an etchant for oxide-free Nilo K which produces a bright finish. This etchant (Solution 2) has found use as cleaning pickle for nickel-iron-cobalt alloy prior to glass sealing and an etchant for nickel components where an etched surface is required. The optimum temperature is 60°C and the reaction is fairly vigorous. At

---

* Obviously, one cannot use graphite boats to support the Kovar parts in the furnace!

† Now: Refractories Division, Carborundum Co., Latrobe, Pa.

this temperature, 0.001 in. of alloy is lost from the surface per minute. A 10–30 second dip is usually adequate to produce a clean, bright finish; again, the smut can be removed by a chromic acid dip."*

Solution 1	Ferric ammonium sulfate	50 gm
	Sulfuric acid 1.84	125 ml
	Hydrochloric acid 1.16	150 ml
	Water to make	1 liter
	Temperature	60–80°C
Chromic acid	Chromium trioxide	100 gm
	Sulfuric acid 1.84	30 ml
	Water to make	1 liter
Solution 2	Ferric ammonium sulfate	50 gm
	Sulfuric acid 1.84	30 ml
	Hydrochloric acid 1.16	150 ml
	Nitric acid 1.42	150 ml
	Water to make	1 liter

When "Kovar" is oxidized on the glass lathe, the attainment of the optimum thickness of the oxide layer is left to the judgment of the operator. This variable can be eliminated by oxidizing the part in a furnace where temperature and time of exposure are carefully controlled. The oxide layer can then be protected from adverse effects of the atmosphere by spraying onto it a layer of powdered glass to which the main seal can then be made at any convenient time after storage. Figure 13.35 gives the results of measurements on controlled oxidation carried out by Pask,[95] according to which excellent adherence of the glass to "Kovar" is obtained with a weight gain of about 0.0003 to 0.0007 gram per sq. cm regardless of the temperature of oxidation, which could be 800°C for 17 minutes, 900°C for 3 minutes, 1000°C for 1 minute, or 1100°C for one-quarter minute. The area marked in the figure by a V-shaped dotted curve indicates conditions under which the greatest tendency for oxide flaking exists.

The application of the powdered glass is described by Pask as follows:

"Grinding of glass in any form to pass through a 200-mesh sieve constitutes the first step in the preparation of the glass for use in the powder-glassing method of making seals. A porcelain-ball mill is used to avoid contamination by iron. The composition of the ground glass is the same as normally used for sealing to a given metal; for instance, Corning 7052 or 7040 for 'Kovar.'

"The powdered glass is suspended in a suitable liquid, such as water or alcohol. With alcohol, which has been used most extensively at Westinghouse, a few drops of $LiNO_3$ solution in NH_4OH keep the glass particles

---

* According to Rain.[94a] Reproduced with the kind permission of the Services Electronics Research Laboratory, Baldock, Herts, England.

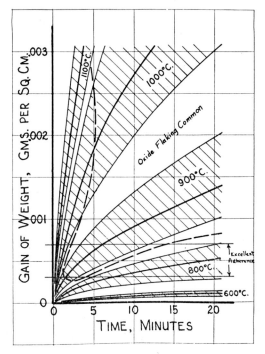

Figure 13.35. Oxidation of "Kovar." Time-rate curves are shown. Area inside V-shaped dotted curve indicates conditions under which greatest tendency for oxide flaking exists. After Pask.[95] (*Courtesy The Institute of Radio Engineers.*)

from settling out into a hard mass, thus enabling the suspension to be easily dispersed after standing. The best ratio of liquid to solid is determined by careful experimentation.

"The powdered-glass suspension is then applied to the oxidized 'Kovar' surface by spraying. The pressure of the spray is controlled by the viscosity of the suspension and the shape of the piece. Pressures ranging from 10 to 40 pounds have been employed.

"If the powdered glass is to be applied by dipping or slushing, the suspension is adjusted to the proper viscosity and mobility to obtain the necessary thickness of coating. In either case the glass is restricted to the desired areas by proper masking prior to application, or by brushing afterwards.

"The dried powdered-glass coating is then fused in an electrically heated oven. 7052 and 7040 glasses produce a smooth coating by firing at 1000°C for 6 minutes. The powdered glass can also be fused by fires or by induction heating of the metal. 'Kovar'-glass seals are fired in air since the rate of oxidation of the 'Kovar' is slow in relation to the rate of fusion of the glass.

For seals with copper, however, if oxidation during fusion is undesirable, the firing would have to be carried out in a neutral atmosphere, since the rate of oxidation of the metal is faster than the rate of fusion of the glass. The fired pieces are removed from the heat and allowed to cool in air without any annealing. These powder-glassed parts are now ready for tube assembly and can be stored indefinitely.

"The thickness of the fused-glass coating is not critical, but has ranged mostly from 4 to 6 mils. The thinner coatings are generally preferred since there is less tendency for pulling away from edges. Considerable amounts of bubbles, seen with low-power magnification, are present. However, these can be ignored, since no detrimental effects have been noticed because of their presence.

"Afterwards, the sealing of the tube or bulb to the powder-glassed parts becomes simply a glass-to-glass seal. Nothing is gained in temperature, since just as much heat and 'working' are necessary to make the glass-to-glass seal. The advantage lies in the fact that the seals are now protected and extended heating will not affect them allowing the operator to work on the seals without any time limitations, which is very important in some cases."

Edwards and Garoff[96] report on the application of powdered glass by using one part of 200-mesh Corning Type 7052 glass to 3 parts ethyl alcohol by volume as follows:

"Spraying the powdered glass takes some practice if an even coating of the desired thickness is to be obtained. A small DeVilbiss gun under 20 lbs pressure of tank nitrogen, with the work 8 to 12 inches from the gun gives the most satisfactory results. The first coat is light and wet and permitted to dry only partially before the next coat is added. The 7052 powdered glass should be used as soon as possible after it is ball-milled and sized, in order to minimize the moisture absorbed by the glass. The mixture must be stirred after every minute of spraying to maintain a uniform density of the sprayed material. Methyl alcohol was found to be a very poor substitute for ethyl alcohol as a carrier for the powdered glass. However, Sylvania has reported favorably on the use of 'Isco Algin No. 117'* as a binder."

The relatively high electrical resistivity of "Kovar" leads to circuit losses and excessive heating of the glass at the joint, particularly in high-frequency applications. In order to minimize this effect, "Kovar" is frequently plated with gold, silver, or chrome. Turnbull[98] describes a method where "Kovar" parts are plated first with copper and then with a layer of chromium and fired in a dry-hydrogen atmosphere; the parts are then oxidized by firing in moist hydrogen, and sealing conditions were generally found to be less critical for the plated metal than for unplated "Kovar." An example

* Obtained from Innis Speiden and Co., 121 Liberty St., New York 6, N. Y.

is given where the thickness of the copper plating was 0.0013 in. and that of chromium plating 0.00005 in.

"Because copper has a higher thermal expansion coefficient than Kovar, the copper plating in a high-conductivity seal is subjected to strain as a result of temperature changes. The effect of the strain is relatively small in directions parallel to the plated layer. The increase in thermal expansion coefficient for sheet 'Kovar' caused by 12 percent copper cladding on either side, measured in a parallel direction, was found to be 3×10^{-7} parts per degree C, which represents a 6 percent change in the thermal expansion coefficient of 'Kovar.' It is possible therefore that glass strains can be kept low in seals to copper-plated or copper-clad 'Kovar,' particularly since the stress necessary to deform the copper layer comes principally from the Kovar, the material with the highest value of Young's modulus, rather than from the glass.

"In the direction perpendicular to the copper layer, however, the change in thermal expansion coefficient is larger. Table 13.10 shows transverse thermal expansion coefficients for 'Kovar' plated with various thicknesses of copper. When these values were calculated, it was assumed that stresses in the copper are continuously relieved; if the copper layer supports stress, smaller values than those given are obtained. The effect of copper on transverse thermal expansion coefficient of 'Kovar' is an important consideration in the design of high conductivity seals."

Table 13.11 gives average values of seal heating in terms of the r-f current at 120 megacycles required to produce a rise in seal temperature of 40°C. These values of current correspond to constant power input to the seal; the currents squared give the relative conductivity of the seals.

"The r-f current required to raise the temperature of these high-conductivity seals by 40°C is approximately 23 to 25 amperes per inch of seal circumference at 120 megacycles. The average value required to produce a

TABLE 13.10. COMPUTED TRANSVERSE THERMAL-EXPANSION COEFFICIENT FOR COPPER-PLATED KOVAR.*

Relative amount of copper[†]	Expansion coefficient (parts per degree centigrade)	
	Sheet	Wire
0.00	50×10^{-7}	50×10^{-7}
0.01	53.3×10^{-7}	53.3×10^{-7}
0.02	56.5×10^{-7}	56.4×10^{-7}
0.05	65.7×10^{-7}	65.3×10^{-7}
0.10	80.0×10^{-7}	78.7×10^{-7}
0.15	93.1×10^{-7}	90.2×10^{-7}

* After Turnbull.[98]

† Thickness of plating/thickness of kovar (flat sheet). Thickness of plating/radius of kovar wire (wire).

Table 13.11. R-F Heating of Seals Made to Plated and Unplated Kovar.*

Plating thickness (inches)			Current for 40°C rise in seal temperature (ampers per inch)
Copper	Chromium	Gold	
0.002	0.00002	None	24.5
0.002	0.00015	None	21.1
0.0015	None	None	24.3
0.0012	0.0001	None	26.1
0.0008	0.0001	None	22.9
0.0004	0.0001	None	17.1
None	0.0001	0.002	24.9
	No Plating		4.3

* After Turnbull.[98]

similar temperature rise in unplated 'Kovar' seals is only 4.3 amperes per inch. The plated 'Kovar' seals have a current carrying capacity more than five times that of unplated 'Kovar' at 120 megacycles, and a conductivity more than 25 times that of 'Kovar'."[98]

The copper-chrome-plated "Kovar" seals described by Turnbull apparently have not found widespread commercial application.[73]

Düsing[25] remarks on the use of plated "Kovar" seals as follows:

"As the commonly used "Kovar" sealing glasses have a relatively high softening point, it requires some care to preserve the conductive coating during the glassing operations. In order to avoid the attack of the film by gas flames, such seals will generally be performed by induction heating. Copper and gold are more suited than silver for the protection of Kovar. A gold film 30 microns thick will give good results after some experimentation. It is not advisable to use much thinner gold films, say 5 microns thick, as such thin gold films rapidly diffuse into the Kovar and partly into the glass during the sealing operation and thus lose their effectiveness. In order to prevent gassing of the gold films, which are applied by electrolysis, the gold-plated "Kovar" parts are annealed for 2 to 3 minutes at 950°C. Figure 13.36 illustrates the current-carrying capacity of three unplated and three gold-plated "Kovar" butt seals at a frequency of 100 megacycles per second. A "Kovar" washer was gold-plated to a thickness of 30 microns, and a glass tube butt-sealed on each side. Silver-plated brass rods were introduced on each end of the tubes and screwed together but separated from the "Kovar" washer by a disc made from Calit.* High-frequency currents up to 90 amperes were passed through the central conductors and currents of the same magnitude were thus induced in the gold-plated ring. It was possible by this arrangement to produce strong high-frequency currents in the 'Kovar' ring without carrying the heat thus created away by

* "Calit" is a steatite ceramic produced by Hermsdorf-Schönberg Isolatoren Gesellschaft, Hermsdorf, Thuringia, Germany.

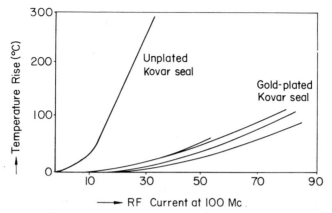

Figure 13.36. Effect of gold plating on the current-carrying capacity of "Kovar seals." After Düsing.[25] (*Courtesy Telefunken A.G.*)

the presence of metallic contacts. Unplated seals cracked when 30, 35, and 36.5 amperes were passed through them, respectively, whereas the plated seals could be operated at up to 90 amperes without cracking. The increase in temperature was only 60 to 100°C. The different behavior shown by the gold-plated seals can be explained by the varying thickness of the gold plating." (See also p. 438).

Silver chloride seals. A rather specialized technique for the sealing of metals to soft and hard glasses takes advantage of the unusual properties of silver chloride which is a plastic material but nevertheless has the properties of metals; it behaves as an elastic material at low stress levels at low temperature and becomes ductile as the stress is raised. Silver chloride is transparent in the visible and infrared range of the spectrum and therefore is used for infrared cells and optical instruments. The transmission in the visible range is about 60 per cent, but for radiation of wave lengths of from 1 to 20 microns, transmission is uniformly 80 per cent, and can be further increased to 93 per cent by special nonreflecting films applied to the surface of the silver chloride.[99]

Being a cubic crystal, silver chloride is optically isotropic in the unstressed state; when stressed, it becomes doubly refracting so that its state of stress can be analyzed with the aid of polarized light.

Fused silver chloride will wet glass and precious metals without being itself adversely affected; ordinary metals react with AgCl and cause its rapid decomposition by a simple replacement reaction. Actinic radiation of a wave length shorter than 4550 A.U. will cause discoloration of AgCl, but protective coatings are available which prevent this effect.[99, 100] Silver chloride is insoluble in hot or cold water and common acids; it is soluble in NH_4OH, $Na_2S_2O_3$, and KCN. Being a soft, wax-like substance with a Mohs hardness of 1 and a melting point at 457.5°C, silver chloride must be protected against abrasion and cannot be exposed to excessively high temperature; its machinability is similar to that of aluminum.

Means have been developed to produce a uniform and pure material which can be cast, extruded, rolled, and drawn into a variety of shapes. For optical purposes, plates, curved windows, cones, crescent-shaped windows, lenses, prisms can readily be formed by impact flow pressing. For cold-pressing of such objects, pressures of approximately 15,000 psi are required. It is also essential that the crystal blank used in the pressing operation approximate somewhat the final shape desired. Special shapes such as rods and tubes can be extruded by corresponding pressures. Lap welds of sheet are readily made by pressing the overlapped seam between platens of a hydraulic press at a temperature from 180 to 200°C. Flame-welding of joints, or joining sheets to glass, noble metals, or silver-plated base metals can be carried out with the usual gas-air or gas-oxygen mixture. Silver sulfide is used as the protective coating to protect the silver chloride against effects of weathering and that of actinic radiation. Selenium and antimony trisulfide have also been used for this purpose and may be produced by chemical reduction, or by evaporation at reduced pressure. Antimony trisulfide has been found most satisfactory by Hyman and Billings,[99] who evaporated this material unto silver chloride at a pressure

TABLE 13.12. PHYSICAL CHARACTERISTICS OF SILVER CHLORIDE (CERARGYRITE)

Molecular weight: 143.34
Crystal lattice: F.C.C.
Recrystallization temperature: 160°C.
Density: 5.56
Hardness: 1 (Mohs' scale)
Melting point: 457.5°C
Boiling point: 1431.3°C
Latent heat of fusion: 3155 cal/mole
Heat capacity: $9.60/9.29 \times 10^{-3}T$ cal/°K/mole
Thermal conductivity: 27.1 at 52°C cal/cm²/cm/sec/°C
                      25.6 at 64°C
Coefficient of thermal expansion: 310×10^{-7} at 20°C
Electrical conductivity: 10^{-8} mhos/cm at 20°C
Tensile strength: 2500 psi at 25°C for 0.070 in.-thick sheet
                 1500 psi at 93°C
Young's modulus: 4.4×10^6 psi
Poisson's ratio: 0.41
Ultimate strength: 1970 psi (annealed)
                  6050 psi (cold rolled)
Compressibility: 0.0838 at 20°C (up to 50,000 kg/cm²)
Solubility: Cold water at 10°C: 0.000089 g/100 ml
           Hot water at 100°C: 0.0021   ''

of 10^{-4} Torr. Radiation below 470 millimicrons is completely absorbed by the surface of Sb_2S_3 and hence no photochemically active light can penetrate to the silver chloride layer.

As the data on silver chloride are widely scattered in the literature, a compilation of the physical characteristics of silver chloride is given in Table 13.12, and available references are listed.[99-109]

Fused-silica-to-metal seals. The successful realization of permanent gas-tight joints between silica and refractory metals that can withstand the necessary very high working temperatures has been a challenge to the glass worker for a long time. Partridge[1] gives a description of the various methods which have been devised, and the patent literature is replete with information on this subject.[110-115] The approach generally taken consists of sealing very thin molybdenum disks into the silica and attaching these disks to current-carrying tungsten rods as shown in Figure 13.37 after Nelson *et al.*[114] Many variations of this general theme are possible.

Another approach to the problem of providing current leads into fused silica vessels, such as high-pressure mercury discharge tubes, consists in sealing fairly large-diameter tungsten rod to silica by means of a single in-

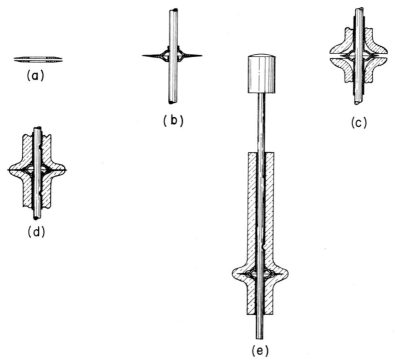

Figure 13.37. Quartz-to-metal seal. After Nelson *et al.*[114]

termediate glass. Martin[116] describes this technique as follows: "A tungsten wire is sealed by means of a single intermediate glass directly through the envelope. In this case the tungsten wire is prebeaded with a glass which may have a somewhat higher expansion than the quartz envelope. It may also have a somewhat lower viscosity. The tungsten wire is heated so intensely that the tungsten oxide volatizes as fast as it is formed, thus yielding a shiny metallic interface. Beading glass is applied as a thread of glass to the rotating lead. A small sealing lathe is used for this operation. The bead is carefully shaped so as to be very thin at the ends with a thicker portion in the center. Very high stresses occur in such a bead, however, it is only the radial stress which is a tension stress. Since the radial stress must be zero at the outer surface the stress is limited at the ends of the bead by the small thickness of the glass. The surfaces are all fire-polished and, probably of great importance, the interface between the tungsten and the glass is very smooth. The bond between the virgin tungsten surface and the glass appears to be very strong. With flaws largely eliminated and with careful control of the glass shape, it is thus possible to work with an expansion mismatch many times greater than can be tolerated in the conventional beaded-wire seal. In sealing to Code 7900 glass, it is customary to fuse a short length of the beading glass to the end of the 7900 tube into which is sealed the beaded lead. A number of glasses have been used for beading, the most used being Code 7230. The beading glass must be quite free of dissolved gas. Vacuum-melting of the glass is sometimes resorted to."

Partridge[1] also describes this technique and emphasizes the importance of laying down a thin sheath of alkali-free sealing glass, about 0.25 mm thick, on which a bead is then formed as suggested in Figure 13.38. Great care should be taken in producing a smooth, rounded transition from button to silica tube which has also been built up with sealing glass to join the button as shown. General Electric Co. glass Code ⚹2023 is used by some workers to extend the silica tube, and Code ⚹1404 glass for beading the tungsten. A "Vycor" (Corning Code 7900) tube can also be extended by sealing on successive rings of higher-expansion glasses, thus forming a graded seal to which tungsten, or "Kovar," can be sealed by conventional methods. Such seals take on considerable length and are not favored for this reason. Corning Glass Works supplies two types of graded seals which are made by different methods and overcome the objection to excessive length; these are the multiform graded seal and the impregnated type.

"In the multiform graded seal a tubular section is built up of rings of powdered-glass mixtures. While several glasses may be used in the powdered-glass mixtures that make up the rings, it is not necessary to have a different glass for each ring. The glass powders are 'granulated', using a binder to give the moulded tubular section sufficient 'green' strength. After a preliminary firing in a furnace to burn out the binder and consoli-date the soft end, the grade is completed by fusion in an oxygen-gas burner of special design. The grade is either extended to match tungsten and Code 7720, or a bit farther, to match 'Kovar' and Code 7052. Beyond this it would be more practical to make two grades and seal them together. Chief volume in a graded seal of this type has been a unit ⅝ in. diameter for use in sterilamps. A graded seal 1⅞ in. diameter was developed for use in a cooking lamp but is not being currently used.

"To make an impregnated type graded seal, 'Vycor' brand glass in the porous state is dipped into a solution containing alkali-borates. When such an impregnated section is dried and fired, a higher-expansion and softer glass is obtained. Above the solution level some of the solution is carried upward by capillary action. This creates the grade which is considerably shorter than that obtained in other type graded seals and results in a tube in which the properties vary continuously from one expansion to the other. It is possible to make an impregnated seal which matches tungsten or Code 7720 at the soft end. Actually the soft end is usually brought to a

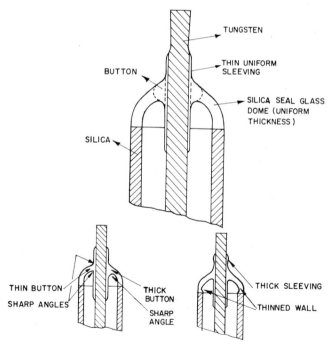

Figure 13.38. Quartz-to-metal seal. After Partridge.[1] (*Courtesy The Society of Glass Technology, Sheffield, England.*)

point where Code 7720 can be joined but with some expansion mismatch. The Code 7900-Code 7740 grades listed in our standard laboratory ware catalog are of the impregnated type. Greatest volume to date has been in a ⅝-in. diameter seal for the range lamp."[116]

REFERENCES

1. J. H. Partridge, "Glass-to-metal Seals, "The Society of Glass Technology, "Elmfield," Sheffield, England, 1949.
2. W. E. Barr and V. J. Anhorn, "Scientific and Industrial Glass Blowing and Laboratory Techniques," Instrument Publishing Company, Pittsburg, 1949.
3. A. J. B. Robertson, D. J. Fabian, A. J. Crocker and J. Dewing, "Laboratory Glass-Working for Scientists," Academic Press, Inc., New York, 1957.
4. J. A. Frost, "Glassblowing," *Laboratory Practice*, **5**, 134–138 (Apr. 1956).
4a. E. L. Wheeler, "Scientific Glass Blowing," Interscience Publishers, Inc., New York, 1958.
5. R. C. Dartnell, H. V. Fairbanks and W. A. Toehler, "Investigation of the adherence of glass to metals and alloys," *J. Am. Ceram. Soc.*, **34**, 357–360 (Nov. 1951).
6. A. Dietzel, "Reactions and bonding between glass and metal on melting" (in German), *Glastech. Ber.*, **24**, 263–268 (Nov. 1951).
7. V. F. Zackay, D. W. Mitchell, S. P. Mitoff and J. A. Pask, "Fundamentals of glass-to-metal bonding: I, Wettability of some Group-I and Group-VII metals by sodium-silicate glass," *J. Am. Ceram. Soc.*, **36**, 84–89 (Mar. 1953).
7a. R. M. Fulrath, S. P. Mitoff and J. A. Pask, "Fundamentals of glass-to-metal bonding: III, Temperature and pressure dependence of wettability of metals by glass," *J. Am. Ceram. Soc.*, **40**, 269–274 (1957).
7b. M. L. Volpe, R. M. Fulrath and J. A. Pask, "Fundamentals of glass-to-metal bonding: IV, Wettability of gold and platinum by molten sodium disilicate," *J. Am. Ceram. Soc.*, **42**, 102–106 (Feb. 1959).
8. W. Weiss, "Wetting properties and mechanical strength of glass-to-metal seals" (in German), *Glastech. Ber.*, **29**, 386–392 (Oct. 1956).
9. H. E. Hagy and H. N. Ritland, "Viscous flow in glass-to-metal seals," *J. Am. Ceram. Soc.*, **40**, 58–62 (Feb. 1957).
10. A. J. Monack, "Glass-to-metal seals in electronic components and applications," *Elec. Mfg.*; **39**, 96–101, 162, 164, 166, 168, 170, 172, 174, 176, 178, 180 (Feb. 1947).
10a. F. Engel, "On the hysteresis of polarimeter curves" (in German), *Glastech. Ber.*, **31**, 133–137 (Apr. 1958).
11. A. W. Hull and E. E. Burger, "Glass-to-metal seals," *Physics*, **5**, 384–405 (Dec. 1934).
12. H. Poritsky, "Analysis of thermal stresses in sealed cylinders and the effect of viscous flow during anneal," *Physics*, **5**, 406–411 (Dec. 1934).
13. E. B. Shand, "Glass Engineering Handbook," 2nd ed., McGraw-Hill Book Co., Inc., New York, N. Y. 1958.
14. H. R. Lillie, "Viscosity-time-temperature relations in glass at annealing temperatures," *J. Am. Ceram. Soc.*, **16**, 619–631 (Dec. 1933).
15. H. Rawson, "A theory of stresses in glass butt seals," *Brit. J. Appl. Phys.*, **2**, 151–156 (June 1951).
16. H. E. Hagy and H. N. Ritland, "Viscous flow in glass-to-metal seals," *J. Am. Ceram. Soc.*, **40**, 58–62 (Feb. 1957).

17. F. W. Martin, "Stresses in glass-metal seals: 1. the cylindrical seal," *J. Am. Ceram. Soc.*, **33**, 224–229 (July 1950).

18. G. D. Redston and J. E. Stanworth, "Glass-to-metal seals," *J. Soc. Glass Technol.*, **29**, 48–76 T ((132) 1945).

19. G. D. Redston and J. E. Stanworth, "The effect of various treatments on the stresses in glass-to-metal seals," *J. Sci. Instr.*, **25**, 138–140 (Apr. 1948).

20. G. Trébuchon and J. Kieffer, "The physical aspect of glass-to-metal seals in the electron tube industry" (in French) *Ann. radioélec.*, **5**, 125–149 (Apr. 1950); 243–258 (July 1950); 407–418 (Oct. 1950).

21. J. T. Littleton, "The effect of temperature treatment on glass-to-metal seals," *J. Am. Ceram. Soc.*, **18**, 239–245 (Aug. 1935).

22. W. J. Scott, "Glass-to-metal seal design," *J. Sci. Instr.*, **23**, 193–202 (Sept. 1946).

22a. J. C. Turnbull, "Tension stresses in glass coatings and in glass-metal seals in the annealing range," *J. Amer. Ceram. Soc.*, **41**, 372–376 (Sept. 1958).

22b. L. F. Oldfield, "The effects of heat treatments on the thermal expansions of some borosilicate glasses and iron-nickel-cobalt alloys and their significance in the behaviour of glass to metal seals," *Glastech. Ber.* **32K**, V/16-V/25 (1959).

23. W. G. Houskeeper, "The art of sealing base metals through glass," *J. Am. Inst. Elec. Engrs.*, **42**, 870–876 (June 1923); U. S. Patent 1,294,466 (Feb. 18, 1919); 1,560,690 (Nov. 10, 1925).

24. A. J. Monack, "Theory and practice of glass-metal seals," *Glass Ind.*, **27**, 389, 446, 502, and 556 (Nov. 1946).

25. W. Düsing, "Glass-to-kovar seals for high-vacuum tubes" (in German), *Telefunken Zeitung*, **26**, 111–120 (Mar. 1953).

26. H. J. McCarthy, "Glass-to-metal seal," U. S. Patent 2,422,628 (June 17, 1947).

27. W. H. Kohl, "A hollow-cathode projection tube as a laboratory experiment in tube techniques," Report of 16th Annual Conference on Physical Electronics, pp. 111–115 (Mar. 1956).

28. M. Davis, "Glass-to-metal seals of strong adherence," Services Electronic Research Lab. Tech. J., **4**, 1–11 (Feb. 1954).

29. V. L. Ronci, "Improvements relating to glass-to-metal seals," Brit. Patent 474,706 (Nov. 5, 1937).

30. W. H. Kohl, "Development of induction sealing for reflex klystrons and T.R. tubes," carried out at Rogers Electronic Tubes, Ltd., Toronto, Canada without knowledge of the work done previously in England. (Report to U. S. and British War Production Agencies, 1941).

31. E. E. Spitzer, "Induction heating in electron-tube manufacture," *Proc. IRE*, **34**, 110W–115W (Mar. 1946).

32. D. L. Holloway, "The manufacture of a reflex klystron," *J. Brit. IRE*, **8**, 97–109 (May/June 1948).

33. R. R. Machlett and G. W. Steen, "Method for making metal-glass seals," U. S. Patent 2,462,205 (Feb. 22, 1949). Also: Machlett Laboratories, Inc., Springdale, Conn., Machlett Cathode Press, **3**, pp. 5–7 (Summer 1946).

34. G. Babat and M. Losinsky, "Concentrator of eddy currents for zonal heating of steel parts," *J. Appl. Phys.*, **11**, 816–823 (Dec. 1940).

35. P. L. Spencer, "Method of forming seals," U. S. Patent 2,386,820 (Oct. 16, 1945).

36. F. Violet, A. Danzin and A. Commin, "Glass in the electron tube industry" (in French), *Ann. radioélec.*, **2**, 24–77 (Jan. 1947).

37. E. F. Northrup, "Principles of induction heating with high-frequency currents," *Trans. Electrochem. Soc.*, **35**, 69–159 (1919).

38. L. Hartshorn, "Radio Frequency Heating," pp. 78, 79, George Allen and Unwin Ltd., London, (1949).

39. J. L. Reinartz, "Industrial brazing by pulse techniques," *Electronics*, **23**, 78–80 (Jan. 1950).

40. W. H. Kohl, "Flux concentrators for induction heating," Technical Data Bulletin (Feb. 1954) Electronics Research Laboratory, Stanford University, Stanford, California (unpublished).

41. A. P. Haase and C. E. Horton, "Sealing techniques for miniature tubes," *Ceramic Age*, **66**, 16–18 (Nov. 1955).

42. J. Bleuze and P. Dussaussoy, "Sealing techniques by optical polishing" (in French), *Verres et réfractaires*, **6**, 347–355 (June 1952). Also: *Le Vide*, **7**, 1182–1190 (May 1952).

42a. M. P. Wilder, "A quasi-optical seal for vacuum tubes," Proceedings of The Fourth National Conference on Tube Techniques, Sept. 10–12, 1958, Cambridge, Mass., pp. 30–33.

43. N. W. Robinson, J. F. Spilling and C. S. Wright, Brit. Patent 627,289 (Aug. 5, 1949).

44. E. M. Guyer, "Electronic welding of glass," *Electronics*, **18**, 92–96 (June 1945).

45. E. M. Guyer, "H. F. glass working," *Electronic Ind.*, **5**, 65–67 (Dec. 1946).

46. E. M. Guyer, "Electric welding of glass," *Elec. Eng.*, **67**, 446–447 (May 1948).

47. U. S. Patent 2,306,054 (Dec. 22, 1942) E. M. Guyer-Corning, "Glass heating and working."

48. U. S. Patent 2,389,360 (Nov. 20, 1945) E. M. Guyer, J. T. Littleton and M. R. Shaw, Jr., "Double glazed window and method of manufacture."

49. U. S. Patent 2,394,051 (Feb. 5, 1946) E. M. Guyer and M. R. Shaw, Jr., "Method and apparatus for electric glass working."

49a. R. G. Whitney, "A glass transistor enclosure," *Semiconductor Products*, **2**, 32–33 (Jan. 1959).

50. E. Wichers and C. P. Saylor, "Sealing platinum to pyrex glass," *Rev. Sci. Inst.*, **10**, 245–250 (Sept. 1939).

51. C. A. Kraus, U. S. Patent 1,093,997 (April 21, 1914).

51a. L. F. Oldfield, "Sealing Glass to Metal," The Times Review of Industry, Sept. 1958; The Times Publishing Company, Limited, London, E.C.4., England.

52. H. Rawson, "The theory of stresses in two-component glass-to-metal tube seals," *J. Sci. Instr.*, **26**, 25–27 (Jan. 1949).

52a. H. Adam, "The theoretical foundations of glass compression seals and their practical consequences" (in German), *Feinwerktechnik*, **56**, 29–40 (Feb. 1952). Also *Trans. Soc. Glass Technol.*, **38**, 285–296 (1954).

52b. H. Adam, W. Espe and E. Schwarz-Bergkampf, "Glass compression seals—theory, fabrication, and technical applications" (in German), *Glas-u. Hochvakuum-Technik*, **1**, 123–134 (Dec. 1952).

52c. W. Fischer, "Sealing techniques and investigation of underlying physical principles" (in German), Thesis, University Mainz, 1954 (unpublished).

53. A.S.T.M. Specification F204–50, "Test for Surface Flaws in Tungsten Seal Rod and Wire."

54. A.S.T.M. Specification F113–41, "Bend Testing of Wire for Radio Tubes and Incandescent Lamps."

55. D. W. White, "A mechanical test for detecting longitudinal fissures in fine wire," *Metal Progr.*, **54**, 837–841 (Dec. 1948).

56. A. L. Reimann, "Coppered tungsten seals through hard glass," *J. Sci. Instr.*, **23,** 121–124 (June 1946).
57. A. L. Chilcot, "Leakage of water through tungsten seals," *Electronic Eng.*, **17,** 693 (Sept. 1945).
58. M. Davis, "Glass-to-metal seals of strong adherence," *Services Electronics Research Lab. Tech. J.*, **4,** 1–11 (Feb. 1954).
58a. G. C. Fincke, Jr. and G. W. Taylor, "A method of improving the glass-to-metal seal resistance to high-humidity deterioration in electron tubes," Proceedings Fourth National Conference on Tube Techniques, New York, N. Y., September 10–12, 1958 (Published by New York University Press).
59. R. L. Bell and M. Hillier, "High-melting point aluminosilicate glasses in microwave valves," *Services Electronics Research Lab. Tech. J.*, **4,** 1–9 (Feb. 1954). Also "An 8-mm Klystron Power Oscillator," *Proc. IRE*, **44,** 1155–1159 (Sept. 1956).
60. M. Hillier and R. L. Bell, "Aluminosilicates and the high-temperature processing of microwave tubes," *Brit. J. Appl. Phys.*, **9,** 94–97 (Mar. 1958).
60a. J. E. Stanworth, H. Rawson and Mary Knowles, "Surface treatment of molybdenum and tungsten for glass sealing," U. S. Patent 2,836,935 (June 3, 1958).
60b. H. Rawson, "A note on oxidation-resistant coatings on molybdenum and their use in glass seals for mercury lamps," *J. Soc. Glass Technol.*, **39,** 211T–214T (Aug. 1955).
60c. H. Adam, "Vacuum-tight molybdenum-to-glass seals" (in German), *Vakuum-Technik*; **8,** 59–62 (Apr. 1959).
61. W. C. Corak and A. Wexler, "Metal-to-glass seals for sub-λ point helium apparatus," *Rev. Sci. Instr.*, **24,** 994–995 (Oct. 1953).
62. R. L. Taylor, "Flux for glass-to-tantalum or zirconium seals," U. S. Patent 2,399,770 (May 7, 1946).
63. H. Rawson and E. P. Denton, "The glass sealing properties of titanium and zirconium," *Brit. J. Appl. Phys.*, **5,** 352–353 (Oct. 1954).
64. D. M. Wroughton and E. D. Gregory, "Metal mixture for sealing to glass," U. S. Patent 2,699,015 (Jan. 11, 1955).
65. C. E. Guillaume, "On the expansion of nickel-steels" (in French), *C. R. Acad. Sci., Paris*, **124,** 176–179 (1897).
66. C. G. Fink, "Copper-sheathed sealing wire," U. S. Patent 1,498,908 (June 24, 1924).
67. B. E. Eldred, "Copper-sheathed wire for glass seals," U. S. Patent 1,140,134/135/136 (May 18, 1915).
68. E. M. Guyer, "Electrical glass," *Proc. IRE*, **32,** 743–750 (Dec. 1944).
69. W. Espe and M. Knoll, "Werkstoffkunde der Hochvakuumtechnik," Julius Springer, Berlin, 1936.
70. W. E. Kingston, "Hygrade Sylvania's low-expansion alloy for glass-to-metal seals," *Technical Horizons*, **3,** 1–12 (1942), published by Allegheny Ludlum Steel Corp., Pittsburgh, Pa. "Low-expansion alloys for glass-to-metal seals," *Trans. Am. Soc. Metals*, **30,** 47–67 (Mar. 1942).
71. H. Scott, U. S. Patent, 2,065,404 (Dec. 22, 1936).
72. R. T. Foley, R. D. Alvord and J. K. Easley, "The electrodeposition of silver on an iron-nickel alloy for a glass-to-metal seal arrangement," *J. Electrochem. Soc.*, **99,** 349–353 (Sept. 1952).
73. W. Düsing, "Seal metals with precious metal coatings for microwave tubes" (in German), *Telefunken-Zeitung*, **30,** 264–269 (Dec. 1957). See also *Glastech. Ber.*, **31,** 137–142 (Apr. 1958).

74. N. S. Freedman, "Silver-plating facilitates bonding glass to steel," *Steel*, **121**, 92–94 (Aug. 25, 1947).

75. F. M. Johnson and P. Larose, "The diffusion of oxygen through silver," *J. Am. Chem. Soc.*, **49**, 312–326 (Feb. 1927).

76. A. J. Monack, "Method of sealing glass to iron," U. S. Patent 2,345,278 (Mar. 28, 1944).

77. E. C. Bain, "The nature of the alloys of iron and chromium," *Trans. Am. Soc. Steel Treating*, **9**, 9–32 (1926).

78. P. Hidnert, "Thermal expansion of heat-resisting alloys: Ni-Cr, Fe-Cr, and Ni-Cr-Fe alloys," *J. Research Bur. Standards*, **7**, 1031–1066, (RP388) (Dec. 1931).

79. H. P. Steier, J. Kelar, C. T. Lattimer and R. D. Faulkner, "Development of a large metal kinescope for television," *RCA Rev.*, **10**, 43–58 (Mar. 1949).

80. H. P. Steier and R. D. Faulkner, "High-speed production of metal kinescopes," *Electronics*, **49**, 81–83 (May 1949).

81. A. S. Rose and J. C. Turnbull, "The evaluation of chromium-iron alloys for metal kinescope cones," *RCA Rev.*, **10**, 593–599 (Dec. 1949).

82. A. S. Rose, "Stainless steel for television," *Metal Progr.*, **57**, 761–764 (June 1950).

83. A. S. Rose, "Structural aspects of metal-glass color television bulbs," *Am. Ceram. Soc. Bull.*, **35**, 97–104 (Mar. 1956).

84. ASTM Standard Specification for 28-percent chromium-iron alloy for sealing to glass: S257–53.

85. ASTM Standard Specification for 17-percent chromium-iron alloy for sealing to glass: S256–53.

86. W. Espe, "Ferritic chrome iron for vacuum-tight glass-to-metal seals" (in German), *Vakuum-Technik*, **4**, 82–100 (Sept. 1955).

87. J. E. Stanworth, "A nickel-chromium-iron alloy for sealing to glass," *J. Sci. Instr.*, **27**, 282–284 (Oct. 1950).

88. M. Davis, "Glass-to-metal seals of strong adherence," *Services Electronics Research Lab. Tech. J.* **4**, 1–10 (Feb. 1954).

89. H. Scott, "Expansion properties of low-expansion iron-nickel-cobalt alloys," *Trans. Am. Inst. Mining Met. Engrs.*, **89**, 506–537 (1930). Also "Recent developments in metals sealing into glass," *J. Franklin Inst.*, **220**, 733–753 (Dec. 1935).

90. A. W. Hull, E. E. Burger and L. Navias, "Glass-to-metal seals II," *J. Appl. Phys.*, **12**, 698–707 (Sept. 1941).

91. G. D. Redston, "Iron-nickel-cobalt alloy for sealing to glass," *J. Sci. Instr.*, **23**, 53–57 (Mar. 1946).

92. J. S. Theilacker, "Elevated temperature properties of Kovar," Special Alloy Memo No. 24, Westinghouse Electric Corp., Metallurigcal Development Section, Materials Engineering Dept. (Nov. 7, 1947).

92a. "Sealing glass to Kovar," Bull. 145, Stupakoff Ceramic and Manufacturing Co., Latrobe, Pa. (1945) (now Carborundum Co., Refractories Division, Latrobe, Pa.

93. H. Herrmann and H. Thomas, "Iron-nickel-cobalt alloys for glass-to-metal seals" (in German), *Z. Metallkunde*, **48**, 582–587 (Nov. 1957).

94. K. H. Mairs, "Fe-Ni-Co alloys for glass-to-metal seals," *J. Metals*, **40**, 460–464 (May 1952).

94a. N. Rain, "A note on the chemical cleaning of oxidised nickel-iron-cobalt alloys for glass-to-metal seals," *Services Electronics Research Lab. Tech. J.*, **9**, 119 (May 1959).

95. J. A. Pask, "New techniques in glass-to-metal sealing," *Proc. IRE*, **36**, 286–289 (Feb. 1948).

96. E. V. Edwards and K. Garoff, "Fabrication of a high-power resonant waveguide window," *Rev. Sci. Instr.*, **21**, 787–789 (Sept. 1950).

97. A. S. Rose, "Structural aspects of metal-glass color television bulbs," *Am. Ceram. Soc. Bull.*, **35**, 97–104 (Mar. 1956).

98. J. C. Turnbull, "A high-conductivity glass-to-metal seal," *RCA Rev.*, **13**, 291–299 (Sept. 1952).

99. H. Hyman, Jr. and B. H. Billings, "High-transmission windows for radiation of 3 to 14 microns wave length," *J. Opt. Soc. Amer.*, **37**, 113–118 (Feb. 1947).

100. J. E. Goodman and J. G. Sutherland, "Elasto-plastic stress-optical effect in silver chloride single crystals," *J. Appl. Phys.* **24**, 577–584 (May 1953).

101. R. D. Moeller, F. W. Schonfeld, C. R. Tipton, Jr. and J. T. Weber, "A metallurgical investigation of silver chloride," *Trans. Am. Soc. Metals*, **43**, 39–69 (1951).

102. P. Fugassi and D. S. McKinney, "The preparation of silver chloride films," *Rev. Sci. Instr.*, **13**, 335–337 (Aug. 1942).

103. Wm. Zimmerman III, "The preparation of high-purity silver chloride and silver bromide," NRL Report No. 3879 (Oct. 24, 1941).

104. V. Caglioti, "The structure of cold-worked silver chloride and its recrystallization," *Atti accad. Lincei*, **18**, 570–574 (1933).

105. J. R. Haynes, "Technique for obtaining increased range and mobility of free electrons in silver chloride," *Rev. Sci. Instr.*, **19**, 51 (Jan. 1948).

106. A. W. Stepanow, "The plastic properties of silver chloride and sodium chloride single crystals" (in German) *Phys. Z. Sowjetunion*, **8**, No. 1, 25–40 (1935).

107. R. M. Fuoss, "Silver chloride windows for infrared cells," *Rev. Sci. Instr.*, **16**, 154–155 (June 1945).

108. B. M. Axilrod and J. J. Lamb, "Tensile properties of rolled silver chloride," *J. Appl. Phys.*, **19**, 213–216 (Feb. 1948).

109. F. W. Schonfeld, C. R. Tipton, Jr., J. T. Weber and R. D. Moeller, "The microscopy of silver chloride," *Mikroskopie*, **16**, 201–212 (1951).

109a. E. Jeltsch, "Conductivity measurements on silver chloride crystals" (in German), *Z. Phys.*, **154**, No. 5, 601–612 (1959).

110. E. B. Power and E. H. Nelson, "Method of Making Quartz-to-Metal Seals," U. S. Patent 2,659,965 (Aug. 30, 1948); (General Electric Company).

111. J. N. Aldington, "Quartz-Metal Seals to Withstand High Pressure and Carry Large Current," Brit. Patent 623,650 (May 20, 1949); (Siemens Electric Lamp and Supplies, Ltd.).

112. A. Greiner, "Quartz-to-Metal Seal," U. S. Patent 2,504,521/22 (Apr. 18, 1950); (General Electric Company).

113. L. R. Peters, "Quartz-to-Metal Seal," U. S. Patent 2,664,180 (Dec. 29, 1953); (General Electric Company).

114. E. H. Nelson, H. Weald, and E. B. Power, "Quartz-to-Metal Seal," U. S. Patent 2,699,847 (Jan. 18, 1955); (General Electric Company).

115. E. H. Nelson, H. Weald, and J. Whittemore, "Quartz-to-Metal Seal," U. S. Patent 2,760,310 (Aug. 28, 1956); (General Electric Company).

116. F. W. Martin, "Methods of introducing conducting leads into Vycor vessels," Corning Glass Works Application Note, June 15, 1954.

CHAPTER 14

CERAMIC-TO-METAL SEALING

Introduction

In the introductory chapter of this book, reference is made to the increasing use of ceramics for tube envelopes in order to overcome the disadvantages of glass in critical applications. Ceramic materials are mechanically stronger; they lend themselves to automatic assembly of the tube structures, withstand much higher temperatures and greater heat shock than glass, their dielectric properties are better, and they do not suffer any noticeable change in characteristics when exposed to nuclear radiation. Tubes made with ceramic envelopes can thus be outgassed on the pump at very much higher temperatures than is possible for glass envelopes, and this leads to a considerable improvement in the quality of the tubes in terms of longer life, greater emission densities obtainable from oxide cathodes, and lower noise factors in microwave tubes.

The use of ceramic envelope structures has very few disadvantages. As all conventional ceramics are opaque, one cannot of course look inside the tube to see whether the filament is lit, or whether some parts of the internal structure are misaligned. In cases where radiation must enter or leave the tube in order for it to function, one must provide windows of material which is transparent to this radiation. Photoelectric cells have so far not been made with ceramic envelopes, but x-ray tubes are commercially available with ceramic envelopes and beryllium windows. Heat will not be as readily dissipated through a ceramic envelope as through glass, and ceramic tubes will thus run a little hotter; but this depends to a large extent on the type of structure used, because metal members naturally form part of the tube structure and extend to the outside, thus providing a conductive path for the heat created inside the tube.

For the time being, ceramic receiving-type tubes are more costly than their glass counterparts, so that their use is restricted to critical applications. The increased ruggedness of ceramic envelope tubes at times leads the user to believe that they can be mistreated mechanically and electrically beyond all reason, thus forfeiting their intrinsic merit. It should also be mentioned that it is more difficult to detect flaws in ceramics, and impossible to be forewarned against the presence of locked-in stresses; in glass, these are readily detected by means of the polariscope.

When deciding on the use of ceramic structures for tubes that have previously been made with glass, it becomes necessary to learn a number of new techniques and to revise design procedures in order to take full advantage of the benefits that accrue from the use of ceramics. The higher temperatures to which ceramic tubes can be exposed in many cases preclude the use of a number of materials which would be acceptable for lower-temperature operation. The increased mechanical strength of ceramics enables the tube to withstand much higher levels of mechanical shock, and the internal structure must thus be designed to withstand without harmful effects high levels of acceleration and vibration. A very good appraisal of the advantages and disadvantages of ceramic tubes has been given by Gallet.[1]

The design of small ceramic tubes usually follows the principle of a "stacked assembly" in which the active electrodes are necessarily made of metal and insulated from each other by ceramic spacers. The external shape of the tube may be cylindrical or tetragonal, and the stacking principle may be applied to the whole tube structure, or only to the internal elements. One thus arrives at two distinct design approaches which, for the purposes of further discussion, may be designated Type A and Type B.

In design A, the insulating spacers take on the form of rings or wafers which at the same time constitute the tube envelope when they are joined with the interspaced metal members (Figure 14.1). In design B, the stacked assembly of electrodes and spacers is a separate unit which is then suitably supported on a multi-pin ceramic header to which a ceramic or metal dome is brazed which encloses the stacked structure (Figure 14.2). In both cases,

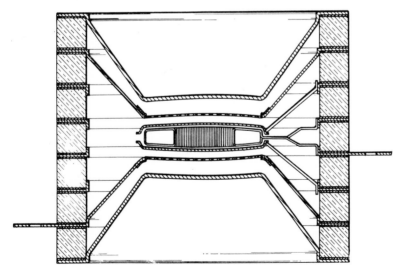

Figure 14.1(a). Stacked ceramic receiving tube—Design A; Double triode CD16-(6SN7). (*Courtesy Eitel McCullough, Inc.*)

Figure 14.1(b). Ceramic power tetrode 4CX300A, using Design A approach, Maximum plate dissipation 300 watts at 500 MC. Maximum operating temperature 250°C. (*Courtesy Eitel McCullough, Inc.*)

it becomes necessary to make a vacuum-tight joint between the metal and ceramic members. The methods used for this purpose are the subject of the present chapter. Many of the concepts described in Chapter 13 will be useful in this discussion. The matching of expansion coefficients between ceramic and metal will be important in the construction of matched seals, and flexible seals, similar in principle to Houskeeper seals, will make differences of expansion less critical. The mechanism by which the bond is formed will again be an important subject, as it was in the construction of glass-to-metal seals. Before going into details, a brief review will be given of the historical development of ceramic tubes and sealing techniques.

History of Ceramic Tube Development

Efforts toward the realization of ceramic tube structures date back to 1934 when Siemens and Halske, Telefunken, and the Allgemeine Elektrizitäts Gesellschaft (AEG) in Germany independently began to develop

Figure 14.1(c). New ceramic receiving tubes under development by General Electric Company, using Design A approach:

    Z-2537 cathode-type UHF diode
    Z-2696 print board version of 7077 UHF triode
    7077   UHF triode used in Pioneer IV (this tube is in production)
    Z-2692 cold-cathode voltage reference diode
    Z-2689 cathode-type low-current diode
    Z-2693 high-mu triode (gm = 25,000 μmhos)
    Z-2664 high-gain triode
    Z-2353 high-mu triode for AF or RF
    Z-2352 med.-mu triode for AF or RF
    Z-2536 power rectifier
    Z-2354 power output triode
    Z-2727 power output pentode

(*Courtesy Receiving Tube Department, General Electric Company.*)

ceramic sealing techniques. These early experiments utilized special low-loss steatites which had been developed for the electrical industry in the late 1920's. By 1936–37, Telefunken had developed special ceramics for sealing purposes which were suitable for brazing cylindrical surfaces by means of compression seals. By 1940–41, internal seals became possible and led to a series of microwave tubes manufactured under the code num-

Figure 14.1(d). G.E. Type 7077. (Registered Type Number; first ceramic receiving tube in regular production (1959)). (*Courtesy Receiving Tube Department, General Electric Company.*)

bers LD 6–9, LD 11–12, LD-14, LD-11, LS-500, LS-1000. Disk seals were realized in 1943–44 by means of thin-film metal interfaces which avoided objectionable shear stresses; this technique was applied in tube type LD-10, which was produced in relatively large quantities in Germany during World War II.[2-5]

After that, the application and further development of the German ceramic tube technique was taken up in the United States under the spon-

Figure 14.2(a). Stacked ceramic receiving tube—Design B; Double triode SN-1724F(6J6). (*Courtesy Sylvania Electric Products Inc.*)

sorship of several government agencies; it may thus be said that the ceramic tube effort in this country has now extended over a period of ten years and that experience in the field has accumulated over the last twenty years. The pressing need for more reliable tubes for civilian and military application was clearly demonstrated in a number of survey reports which became available early in 1952.[6, 7]

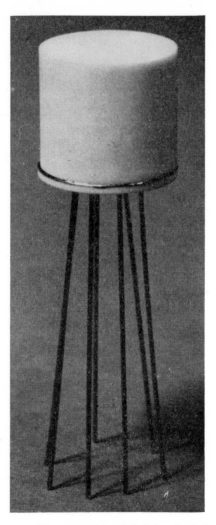

Figure 14.2(b). Same as Fig. 14.2a, but with flying leads instead of pin connections.

SN–216C   SN–2358C   SN–1724H   SN–1809C

Figure 14.2(c). Internally stacked ceramic receiving tubes (Design B) under development by Sylvania Electric Products Inc.
SN–2146C beam power amplifier (6AQ5)
SN–2358C med. mu dual triode (6111)
SN–1724H med. mu dual triode (6J6)
SN–1809C R.F. pentode (6AK5)

It was realized at that time that efforts to improve existing tube structures by more elaborate processing, by more carefully designed mechanical structures to suppress harmful effects of vibration and shock, and by substitution of harder glasses for the commonly used soda-lime glass envelopes, could only be stop-gap measures in view of the still more exacting operating requirements that loomed ahead. A more radical approach to the problem was required if substantial advances were to be made. A number of study contracts were issued by the Armed Services to tube producers in the United States with the purpose of critically analyzing the techniques used in Germany and adapt them where possible to future programs.[8, 9]

The development of a ceramic version of the disk-seal UHF tube Type 3039 by General Electric Co., Eitel McCullough, Inc., and Machlett Laboratories, Inc. was an outcome of these early efforts to produce ceramic envelope tubes. By 1952, major development contracts for the automatic production of receiving-type ceramic envelope tubes had been let, principally to Eitel McCullough, Inc. of San Bruno, California and Sylvania Electric Products Inc.

The General Electric Research Laboratories at Schenectady were actively pursuing the development of a low-noise triode (L29) under a Bureau of

Ships contract since 1947 and, in a partly company-sponsored effort, were led to the titanium ceramic structure embodied in tube types L54, L55, and 6BY4 of more recent origin. Since 1952, the Minneapolis-Honeywell Research Center at Hopkins, Minnesota, has carried on a company-sponsored effort aimed at the development of ceramic tubes for their own needs which was terminated in 1956 after small quantities of two prototypes of Type 6SN7 had been successfully produced.[10, 11] These various projects have now advanced, in varying degrees, to the stage where sample lots of tubes are available, or pilot production is under way. Ceramic receiving tubes should soon be available for general commercial use.

In addition to the production of receiving-type tubes, ceramic versions of special tube types such as high-power transmitting tubes, microwave triodes and tetrodes, klystrons, magnetrons, traveling-wave tubes, backward-wave oscillators, TR and ATR tubes, thyratrons, and x-ray tubes are now being made in regular production by a number of companies (Figure 14.3 a–h).

Early in 1956, the Electronic Components Laboratory, Wright Air Development Center (WADC) of the U. S. Air Force assigned a contract to Stanford Research Institute of Menlo Park, California with the object of surveying the then existing state of the art for making ceramic tubes of all kinds that can withstand an ambient temperature equivalent to 500°C and generally operate without harm in critical environments where high levels of shock and vibration and nuclear radiation prevail.[12, 13]

A special *ad hoc* Committee was formed by the Advisory Group on Electron Tubes (AGET) in May 1957 to review for the Armed Services the status of the various government-sponsored ceramic tube programs and make recommendations to the Joint Services for future policy.[14]*

The development of ceramic sealing techniques has been reviewed by a number of authors; the reader is referred to references 15-19a.

Bond Formation and Sealing Techniques

In discussing the joining of metals in Chapter 12, the simplest procedure from a phenomenological point of view was to push the two surfaces against each other and let the surface forces do the permanent coupling once the molecules of adjacent metals had been brought into sufficiently close con-

---

* The present author was actively engaged as a consultant on both surveys. Parts of the manuscript for the present book were used in both reports; at the same time, these activities afforded a rare opportunity to gain first-hand information on the latest developments in this field which are described in the present chapter. The author gratefully acknowledges this opportunity.

Figure 14.3(a). Ceramic envelope VHF power tetrode ML-7007; power output 10KW at 220MC. (*Courtesy Machlett Laboratories, Inc.*)

tact. Cold-welding is done in this manner, and the well-known technique of pinching off copper tubulations on power tubes was quoted as an example.

The frictional adhesion of metal to glass, fused silica, and ceramic surfaces has been observed by several workers.[20-22] Vacuum-tight seals between optically polished surfaces of fused-silica cylinders have been described by Danzin and Destois,[23] and this principle has been applied to commercial production of receiving tubes in France by Bleuze and Dussausoy[24] and recently adapted in this country by Wilder.[24a]

At the Large Power Tube Development Section of the Electron Tube Division of the Radio Corporation of America at Lancaster, Pa., commercial

Figure 14.3(b). Ceramic-metal envelope hydrogen thyratron Type 1802; peak output power 30MW. (*Courtesy Edgerton, Germeshausen & Grier, Inc.*)

Figure 14.3(c). Components of EG&G Type 1802; from left to right: alumina ceramic cylinder 3 in. dia. × 3¼ in. high; copper grid cup and grid baffle (in front); cathode assembly; copper anode cup with molybdenum face; ceramic backing ring. After Goldberg.[46] (*Courtesy Edgerton, Germeshausen & Grier, Inc.*)

479

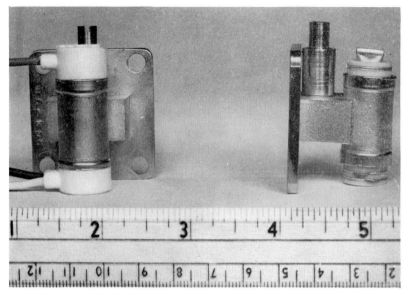

Figure 14.3(d). Type 1K20 Reflex Klystron available for X-band and K-band operation; with encapsulation (left) and without (right). Power output 75 mw; a fixed-tuned inner cavity is closely coupled to a secondary cavity outside the vacuum through a ceramic window. Tuning over a minimum range of 700MC is accomplished by a capacitive slug which is visible in the picture at the right. (*Courtesy Eitel McCullough, Inc.*)

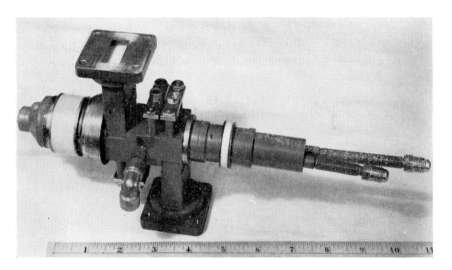

Figure 14.3(e). Type VA 806 X-band Klystron; power output 2KW (CW). (*Courtesy Varian Associates.*)

Figure 14.3(f). Type VA-842 Klystron; average power output 75KW, peak power output 1.25MW. Pulse duration 2 milliseconds, tunable frequency range 400-450MC, stable R.F. power gain 40db. (*Courtesy Varian Associates.*)

use is made of this phenomenon of cold welding by interdiffusion in the construction of large power tubes with ceramic envelopes. High-alumina ceramic cylinders,* as large as 20 inches in diameter, are ground to a blunt

* Frenchtown Porcelain Company, body number 4462 (Almanox) has been used exclusively in the past for this purpose.

Figure 14.3(g). Type X626 Klystron; average power output 75KW, peak power output 1.25MW, pulse duration 2 milliseconds, tunable frequency range 400-450MC, gain 30db (approx.); length 9 feet 8¾ in., diameter 18 in., circuitry is shown at right. (*Courtesy Eitel McCullough, Inc.*)

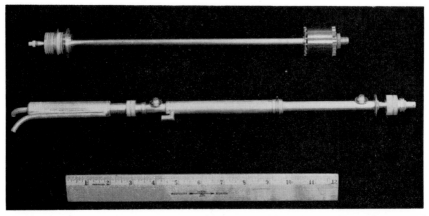

Figure 14.3(h). Ceramic-metal travelling-wave tubes Types X686 (above) and X620 (below) frequency coverage 4-7KMC (for both), output power 1W and 100W, respectively. Type X620 is liquid-cooled. (*Courtesy Eitel McCullough, Inc.*)

bevel at the end and a copper-plated tool-steel cylinder of smaller I.D. than the O.D. of the ceramic cylinder is pushed onto the latter under considerable pressure to effect a seal at room temperature which afterwards can be exposed to a temperature as high as 550°C and heat cycled many times.[13, 14, 24a,b,c] These seals have become known as "Crunch Seals," or "Ram Seals," and, apart from the cylindrical geometry just described, coaxial, inside-outside planar seals are also being made.

The formation of a tight bond is further promoted by making such pressure seals at elevated temperature. This approach was first taken by Tank,[25, 26] who produced vacuum-tight seals by pressing together metals and ceramics at a pressure of several thousand pounds per square inch and heating to temperatures ranging as high as 1000°C, depending on the particular combination of metals and ceramics involved. These seals are generally made either in a neutral atmosphere, or under vacuum. This technique was further investigated under sponsorship of the U. S. Air Force at the Electrical Engineering Research Laboratory, Engineering Experimental Station, Univ. of Ill. (Contract No. AF18(600)-23). These apparently simple techniques have so far been found to be practical only for relatively large components which can withstand the required pressure.

A modified diffusion seal has been developed by workers at Eitel-McCullough, Inc. at San Bruno, California and is finding practical application in ceramic envelope receiving tubes.[14] Ceramic rings, metallized by more or less conventional methods, are subjected to pressure at moderate temperature, and reliable diffusion seals are effected in this manner.

The earliest efforts in Germany to realize ceramic seals took the obvious approach of joining ceramics by means of a lower-melting ceramic, i.e., glass, or by the interposition of thin metal films. Espe and Knoll[27] give several examples of these earlier techniques. It goes without saying that bonding materials, if separately introduced and if they maintain their identity in the finished seal, should be temperature-resistant up to the maximum temperature to which the seal is exposed during processing of the tube, or during its operational life. It is possible, however, that ceramic glazes and glass frits, which by themselves have a lower softening point, may be used in such thin layers that they become incorporated into the ceramic-metal lattice structure and then permit operation at substantially higher temperature than indicated by their bulk softening temperatures. Litton[28] has followed this line of reasoning in the construction of magnetron windows.

Apart from such thin-film glaze joints, the value of sealing ceramics to their metal frames with glass should not be overlooked. The proper choice of glass and frame composition permits fabrication in hydrogen and thus eliminates the need for chemical cleaning which exists when glass seals are made in air or forming gas; this is a distinct advantage, particularly in the case of complex assemblies. The use of a high-temperature glass will permit subsequent heating of the joint up to 700°C or more (see page 426).*

The soldering of ceramics and metal with glass, as practiced by the earliest workers in the field, was soon largely replaced by other techniques but soldering with alloys of tin, lead, and indium according to the techniques described by Bondley[29] is practiced even today for commercial tubes intended for low-temperature applications. As many of these alloys have a great ductility, they will flow under stress after the seal has been made and thus allow the joining of parts that have widely different expansion coefficients.

The sealing methods most widely used today are refinements of techniques developed in Germany prior to World War II by Pulfrich and Vatter, who were working, respectively, at Telefunken, and Siemens and Halske A.G., and to which companies many of the basic patents have been assigned. While one of these now generally practiced processes is known under the name "Telefunken Process," Vatter[30] has pointed out that his work at Siemens preceded the work of Pulfrich at Telefunken and incorporated the concepts of active-alloy seals and automatic production of tubes. To do justice to both inventors, one should thus speak of a Siemens-Telefunken process.

As originally practiced by the German workers, the Sintered Metal Powder Process, as we shall call it, requires several steps to produce a

---

* Personal communication from B. Winters of the Research and Development Section of Sperry Electronic Tube Division, Gainesville, Florida.

brazed joint between ceramic and metal. First, finely divided powders of tungsten, tantalum, molybdenum, rhenium, or iron in a suitable suspension of nitrocellulose lacquer are applied singly or in combination by brushing or spraying on the clean and smooth ceramic surface. This metal powder coating is then sintered to the ceramic by firing in a hydrogen atmosphere at temperatures ranging from 1300 to 1500°C, depending on the ceramic composition and that of the powder coating. After this sintering operation at elevated temperature, a thin film of copper or nickel is applied by means of electroplating, or the reduction of oxide powders in a hydrogen atmosphere at a temperature of about 1000°C. The metallized ceramic is then ready to be joined to the metal part by conventional methods of brazing in a controlled-atmosphere furnace.

The addition of manganese oxide, titanium oxide, barium oxide, or calcium oxide, either to the ceramic body or the metal powder mixture applied to its surface, was variously suggested by the German workers as a means for improving the adhesion of the metal powder coating and the strength of the resulting seal. Vatter[30] remarks, however, that such addition agents are liable to produce slow leakers after weeks, or months, because the filler metal does not completely penetrate the pores of the metallized layer when such addition agents are used without proper caution. The metallized ceramic part is assembled with the metal components with which a joint is to be made, and a ring of brazing filler metal is placed near the interface, or, in the form of a thin washer, between the ceramic and the metals parts. There are thus three firing operations required in the practice of the Telefunken process.

Another technique, which competes with the sintered metal powder process, is the *"active alloy process."* It had been noted a good many years ago that titanium and zirconium have a great affinity for glass and ceramics and leave indelible marks on these bodies when the metals are rubbed against them at room temperature. Belser[22] has studied these effects in some detail, as mentioned above. At elevated temperatures, these reactions between titanium and zirconium and the ceramic crystal lattice take place more vigorously; in addition, when other metals are present at the interface with which titanium forms solid solutions, an intimate bond is established between the ceramic body and the metal member with which the ceramic was put into intimate contact during assembly. It does not matter very much whether the titanium or zirconium is made available at the interface by reducing their hydrides, or whether the metal powders are painted onto the ceramic surface and placed in contact with a suitable brazing filler metal and the main parent metal to which the joint is to be made. The various approaches to realize the final objectives have been given different names and were developed at different times by different workers, but they may all be classified under the general category of "active-alloy seals." The titanium hydride technique was initiated by Kelly[31] and first described by Bondley;[29] Pearsall[32] extended the method to the use of zirconium hydride. The formation of titanium-nickel alloy at the interface between a forsterite ceramic and a titanium metal member, which frequently serves as the tube envelope, has been described by Beggs[33] of the General Electric Company Research Laboratory at Schenectady.

One of the main advantages of the active-metal process is that it requires only one firing operation in a high vacuum of the order of 10^{-5} Torr, or in a protective atmosphere of helium, argon, or dry hydrogen. For this reason, active-alloy seals are preferred by some workers and are practiced on a commercial scale.

For the sake of completeness, another method for the joining of metals and ceramics should be mentioned which is interesting, but so far has not found commercial application. Knecht[34] of the U. S. Air Force Electronic Components Laboratory at Wright Field followed the reasoning that underlies the production of graded seals between hard glass and soft glass by the stepwise interposition of glasses of gradually decreasing expansion coefficients. It was suggested that layers of metal powder were to be gradually enriched with ceramic powder until layers of pure ceramic were reached which would in effect produce a graded seal from metal to ceramic when such layers are pressed together. Original experiments to realize this idea were carried out at Wright Field, and a contract was later issued to American Lava Corporation at Chattanooga, Tennessee[35] (AF 33(600)-27329); the final report was issued in Dec. 1956. The difficulties that had to be overcome were rather formidable, but about twenty-eight successful seals were produced after over ninety different metals, alloys, and metal-oxide mixtures were investigated in combination with approximately thirty ceramic formulations. The most successful ceramic-metal system consisted of an 85 percent alumina ceramic and a 30 percent spinel metallized with a tungsten-copper-nickel alloy mixed with 25 per cent chromium.

Still another approach to the problem of joining ceramics to metals has been taken by workers at the Electron Tube Laboratory of the Stanford University Electronics Research Laboratory. Hare, Keller, and Meneses[35a] have recently described electroformed seals which are made by stacking up premetallized and copper-plated ceramic cylinders in accurate alignment under slight pressure with disk electrodes inserted between the abutting cylinder surfaces. The assembled stack is then placed in a copper-plating bath for several days to build up the required thickness of copper at the joint. Excess copper is then machined off; a minimum thickness of 8 mils

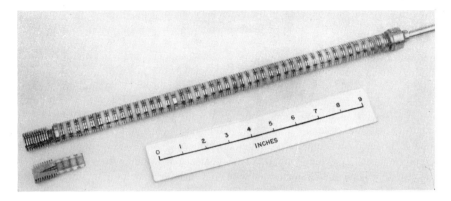

Figure 14.4. Stacked assembly of 44 copper disks sealed to intermediate ceramic rings by electroforming. After Hare, Keller, and Meneses.[35a] (*Courtesy Stanford Electron Devices Laboratory.*)

deposited copper is required to insure a vacuum-tight joint. Such seals withstand temperature cycling up to 850°C; the main advantage is the circumvention of a high-temperature braze. Figure 14.4 gives an example of a stack comprising 44 joints.

The various sealing methods discussed in this introduction can now be classified under the following headings:

(1) pressed diffusion seals

(2) solder seals

(3) sintered metal powder seals

(4) active-alloy seals

(5) graded-powder seals

(6) electroformed seals

The mechanism by which a bond is formed in any seal is not as yet fully understood, but much work has been done in this field.[36-38] The bond mechanism may well be different for the different types of sealing processes enumerated above; in a general way, it may be said that it depends on a critical interaction of physical and chemical forces in the very thin interface. It will be of interest to note some of the critical factors emphasized by Pulfrich[38, 39, 40] as having an important bearing on the formation of a satisfactory bond in seals made by the sintered-metal-powder process.

Glassy phases should be avoided in the seal interface; the metal should have a high melting point, i.e., 200°C or more above the temperature at which the powder coating is sintered. The ceramic should have a eutectic bond which melts at 300°C, or more, below the deformation temperature of the ceramic as a whole and 200°C below the metallizing temperature. The brazing filler metal should melt below the melting point of the ceramic's lowest-melting eutectic. Neither the filler metal nor any alloys formed between it and the metal component should alloy with the metallizing metal. It was found to be advantageous to use a filler metal which flows plastically under tensile stress before the tensile strength of the ceramic is exceeded.

At the seal, the metal wall should be thin. The hydrogen used as a furnace atmosphere should contain about 0.25 per cent oxygen to form a trace of molybdenum trioxide. At the temperature of sintering the metallizing coating, the molybdenum particles are wetted by the liquid formed by the eutectic constituent in the surface of the ceramic. During cooling, it is desirable that this eutectic recrystallize completely to a uniform crystal structure free from residual glass so that the molybdenum particles are locked within the crystals rather than within a glass flux.

The Sintered Metal Powder Process

In 1950, Nolte and Spurck[41] of the General Electric Company Power Tube Department introduced a modification of the Telefunken process by adding a substantial amount of manganese powder to the molybdenum powder. In this manner, it was possible to metallize forsterite bodies at as low a temperature as 1250°C. The composition of the metallizing coating was given by Nolte and Spurck as follows:

  160 g molybdenum powder (200 mesh)
   40 g manganese powder (150 mesh)
  100 cc pyroxyline binder (Du Pont 5511)
   50 cc amyl acetate
   50 cc acetone

"A mixture of these ingredients is ball-milled for 24 hours, and sufficient amylacetate-acetone (1:1 by volume) solution should then be added to the ball-milled mixture to give a viscosity reading of 22 seconds with a Zahn viscosimeter. The resultant metal suspension should be suitable for brushing or spraying, and is applied to the ceramic in a thickness of one to two mils."

This mixture has been the basis for the commercial application of the Sintered Metal Powder Process, or, as it is also called, the "Moly-Manganese Process." Nevertheless, many modifications have been made by various workers, and it is almost safe to say that no two commercial establishments will use exactly the same procedure. It may even be said that a process which has been successfully practiced in one plant may not be successful for some time when taken over by another plant unless the same ceramics, the same metals, the same metallizing composition, and the same equipment are used; one might also add, that unless the same people perform the operation, because the human element naturally enters into an industrial process and must be taken into account. An experienced operator will be able to judge when the viscosity of the metallizing suspension is such as to give optimum results, for example, and there seem to be no instruments available as yet to measure this factor in a reliable manner. Considerable effort will thus be necessary to transfer a successful process from the laboratory to the pilot plant or production line.

Many of the intricacies entering into the proper fabrication of ceramic-to-metal seals have been well described by Chick and Speck[42] of the Bell Telephone Laboratories, who used a suspension of iron and molybdenum powders in the proportion 1 to 50, i.e., 0.8 g of iron fine, 40.0 g of molybdenum fine, and 10 g of amyl acetate solution of nitrocellulose in 150 ml of lacquer thinner. An example of a suitable lacquer thinner is given as follows:

Aromatic naphtha: 60 to 66 per cent (by volume)
Ethyl or butyl alcohol: 6 per cent
Ethyl acetate, 85 to 88 percent grade: 18 per cent
Normal butyl acetate, 83 to 92 percent grade: 16 per cent

While other suspensions may be employed, it is worth noting that the composition of the lacquer and its concentration are of considerable importance in order to obtain a uniform coating of the right thickness on the ceramic part. Chick and Speck mention in their patent dislosure that the insulator was sprayed to a thickness of from 0.6 to 0.8 mil and that this thickness had to be measured to ascertain whether there were any portions of the coating either above or below this range of thickness; if there were, these insulators were discarded. This extreme accuracy in both the smoothness of the coating and its thickness was important, and for the particular granular size particles employed these limits could not be varied by any substantial amount. The coated ceramics were fired in an atmosphere of wet forming gas consisting of 72 per cent nitrogen and 28 per cent hydrogen, for 20 minutes at a temperature of from 10 to 15°C below the initial maturing temperature of the steatite which they used; this requirement resulted in a firing cycle of from 1245 to 1250°C for about 20 minutes. Variations of less than 10°C had a damaging effect.

The influence of the particle size of the powder used in preparing the metallizing suspension has been found to be most critical by some workers and not so critical by others, largely depending on the type of process used. Bender[43] has investigated at some length the bonding of molybdenum and nickel powders to zircon and found a considerable improvement when the average particle size was kept below 2 microns. Particles of this degree of fineness are difficult to obtain commercially and were thus produced in the laboratory by reduction of molybdenum oxide powders in hydrogen. An average size of about 1 micron was found to be satisfactory for seals made by the Sintered Metal Powder Process. The molybdenum oxide powder was ballmilled for ten hours and then placed in a thin layer on a nickel boat and fired at 550°C in very dry hydrogen for a period of 56 hours and then at 700°C for 24 hours.

In order to avoid oxidation of the powder on removal from the furnace, powdered dry ice was inserted into the cooling region of the furnace and sprinkled onto the material in the boat. The boat was then taken from the cooling zone and placed in a large box with a layer of powdered dry ice on the bottom. While the boat containing the powder was in the large box, the material was removed from the boat to a container, or weighed out into the container in given amounts, mixed with a suitable lacquer in which the powder was ballmilled to break up clumps that may form in the process of mixing, and then the suspension was applied to the ceramic by dipping, painting, or spraying. The viscosity of the suspension should be equivalent to 1300 centipoises and the mixture be stirred between the dipping or spraying operations.

The periodic reports issued by the various companies and institutions working under government contracts contain much detailed information on process techniques. These reports are available through the Armed Services Technical Information Agency (ASTIA)* to other companies or institutions working under government contracts who have established a need-to-know and filed the necessary papers with the contracting officer. When a project has been completed by any one company or institution, a final report is issued which contains the latest findings. The currently issued intermediate reports often give an interesting portrayal of the trials and tribulations that had to be faced before a satisfactory solution of the problem was found, and they may serve as an encouragement to those engaged in the solving of similar problems in related fields.

It also happens quite often that the really pertinent information is left out of the reports, since process development is frequently carried out with the support of company funds to avoid the need of making such information available to competitors. Nevertheless, with these reservations in mind, much can be gained by taking the time to read these reports. A few examples will be given in the following of the compositions of metallizing suspensions that have been used by Eitel McCullough, Inc. in their work under

---

* 346 Broadway, New York 13, New York, or regional offices throughout the country.

Contract AF33 (600)-17125. Report No. 7 (February 8, 1954 to May 7, 1954) gives the composition of metallizing solution No. 5A as follows:

176 g molybdenum powder (400 mesh)
44 g manganese (MD* 301)
55 ml acetone
25 ml methyl ethyl ketone
50 ml "Cellosolve"†
45 ml nitrocellulose lacquer (600–1000 seconds)

This solution is ballmilled for approximately 100 hours. The tensile strengths of ceramic-to-metal seals made with it were found to be 8,500 psi under the best processing conditions when tested on a Tinius-Olsen tensile strength test machine. Metallizing composition No. 10A is described in Report No. 9 (August 8, 1954–November 7, 1954) as follows:

176 g molybdenum powder (200 mesh)
44 g manganese powder (200 mesh)
 9 g Titanium hydride
45 ml nitrocellulose lacquer (600–1000 seconds)
25 ml methyl ethyl ketone
50 ml "Cellosolve" (ethyl ether)
55 ml acetone

This solution was ball-milled for about 100 hours.

Owing to the friendly relations which exist between the San Francisco Bay Area electronic industry and Stanford University, the W. W. Hansen Laboratories have had early access to some of the Eimac metallizing techniques for the Moly-Manganese Process. High-power klystrons are in continuous pilot production at Stanford for the operation of the 200-foot linear accelerator, and a ceramic construction is used for these tubes. Very satisfactory results have been obtained up to the present time with coating composition No. 5A for metallizing high-alumina ceramics of the type AI-200 made by Coors Porcelain Company, Golden, Colorado. Firing for sintering purposes is carried out at a temperature of 1525°C, as read by an optical pyrometer without correction. The coating is generally applied and fired twice in succession and then plated with nickel so that the total thickness of the metallizing coating is of the order of 1 mil. Copper-silver eutectic brazing filler metal is used to make the joints to the copper components.

When metallizing a high-alumina body such as AL300, produced by Western Gold and Platinum Company, Belmont, California, the following

---

* Metals Disintegrating Company, Inc., Elizabeth, N. J.
† Carbide Carbon Chemical Company.

coating composition (Mix No. 2A) is used at the W. W. Hansen Laboratories:

200 g molybdenum powder (400 mesh)
40 g manganese powder (400 mesh)
10 g hydrogen-reduced iron powder
2 g silica in the form of silicic acid (fine powder)
2 g calcium oxide (200 mesh or finer)
50 ml nitrocellulose lacquer (600–1000 seconds)
55 ml acetone
30 ml methyl ethyl ketone
50 ml "Cellosolve"

The nitrocellulose lacquer is prepared by mixing the following ingredients in the order shown:

400 g nitrocellulose
1650 ml toluene
750 ml ethyl alcohol, or methyl ketone
600 ml ethyl acetate

This mixture is ball-milled for 100 hours.

It is apparent from these few examples that many variations in the composition of the metallizing mixture are possible. The various companies active in this field have developed their own techniques after painful experimentation over a prolonged period of time, and are sometimes hesitant to change over to basically different procedures simply because so much time and effort has been invested in establishing the techniques which they use.

Burnside[18] of the Radio Corporation of America has described the use of tungsten-iron powder mixtures for metallizing ceramics. Molybdenum oxide in place of metallic molybdenum powder has been evaluated by Navias[16] and Pincus;[38] the oxide melts at 795°C and interacts with the ceramic while being reduced to molybdenum by the hydrogen atmosphere at 1350°C. Burnside refers to a preferable particle size range of from 1 to 4 microns and claims that a rigid schedule of processing is not required to produce successful seals; he finds that considerable variations in metal powder composition, firing rate, temperature, and atmosphere can be tolerated. The powder mixture, suspended in a suitable lacquer, is applied in a thickness of from 1 to 2 mils and, in the case of forsterite and zircon bodies, the coated ceramics were fired between 1340 and 1360°C, while high-alumina bodies required higher temperatures.

As suggested in the original disclosure by Pulfrich and his co-workers, other additives have been found beneficial for the quality of the resulting seals. Metallizing coating compositions containing titanium hydride or titanium, calcium oxide, and silicon oxide have been used by various workers as indicated by the composition of the metallizing paint given above for body AL300 which was described by LaForge[44] and designated as "activated" molybdenum-manganese composition.

LaForge states that the activated mixtures are desirable for ceramic bodies containing 95–97 per cent aluminum oxide and necessary for compositions having 98 per cent alumina content or more. The Raytheon Manufacturing Company is using a molybdenum-titanium composition on their high-alumina body R95 which contains 95 per cent alumina. In all these cases, the sintered powder coating is given a nickel flash of a thickness ranging from 0.25 to 0.5 mil.

Ron F. Keller, formerly of the Stanford Electronics Laboratories, has recently developed a metallizing mixture which is giving more reliable results and stronger joints between copper disks and high-alumina ceramics than any of the previously mentioned compositions. The composition of this particular activated molybdenum-manganese-iron coating mixture is as follows:

```
200 g molybdenum powder (400 mesh)
 40 g manganese powder (400 mesh)
 10 g hydrogen-reduced iron powder
  8 g alumina powder (AL300) 90 mesh
  2 g silica powder
  8 g titanium hydride powder
 40 ml nitrocellulose lacquer (600–1000 sec)
 30 ml methyl ethyl ketone
 40 ml "Cellosolve"
 20 ml toluene
160 ml acetone
```

This mixture is ball-milled for 96 hours. After painting or spraying the resulting mixture on the ceramic surface, unusually good adherence is observed; the film is not readily damaged by mishandling. Firing in wet or tank hydrogen at 1500°C for about 30 min, or at 1250°C for 45 min., and plating with nickel as usual (0.2 to 0.3 mil) gives good seals on any of the high-alumina bodies with 10-mil OFHC copper disks by brazing with nickel-copper-gold or silver-copper eutectic filler metals. The heat shock resistance is excellent and the mechaincal strength superior (1500 psi). Joints to "Kovar" or molybdenum have also been made successfully, but the heat shock resistance is not as good as that of copper disk seals. Figure 14.5 shows a multiple disk seal of 41 copper disks brazed by induction heating; all seals were vacuum-tight when tested on a helium leak detector.

Active-alloy Seals

As mentioned in the introduction, the term "active-alloy seals" covers a number of processes which take advantage of the great affinity of titanium and zirconium for oxygen and their ability to enter into solid solutions with a number of metals and suboxides. If we recall that titanium oxide and zirconium oxide are highly refractory ceramics, and that ceramics in general

Figure 14.5. Stacked assembly of 41 copper disks sealed to intermediate ceramic rings with SEL mix No. 101. (*Courtesy Stanford Electron Devices Laboratory.*)

are constituted of a number of different oxides, it becomes plausible that titanium and zirconium will, under favorable conditions, reduce some of these ceramic oxides and combine with the released oxygen as long as active gases are not present in the atmosphere in which the seal is being made.

All that is necessary, then, to make these desired reactions occur is to put titanium or zirconium in contact with two abutting ceramic surfaces that are to be joined, or, as the case may be, in contact with a ceramic part and a metal part between which a seal is to be made. As the exclusion of oxygen from the surrounding atmosphere is one of the most important conditions, active-alloy seals must be made either in a high vacuum, or in an atmosphere of very pure hydrogen, argon, or helium. Hydrogen of a high degree of purity can be obtained by dissociation of a heap of TiH_2 placed in the furnace with the parts to be joined in such a position that the hydride decomposes at the time the braze is being made.

The purity of the active metals themselves and that of the gases used as a protective atmosphere is of critical importance. Precautions must also be taken that undesirable gases such as oxygen, carbon monoxide, or carbon dioxide are not released from components which are part of the tube structure. Careful outgassing of all metal parts is thus necessary prior to assembly. If the brazing operation is performed *in vacuo* at such temperatures that an oxide-coated cathode is undergoing decomposition of the carbonates, sufficient quantities of CO_2 can be released from large cathodes that titanium carbide is formed rather than the desirable compounds necessary for establishing a satisfactory seal.[46]

The active titanium, or zirconium, is frequently applied in the form of its hydride which is made into a paint by mixing the powder with a nitro-cellulose lacquer and applying it to the ceramic in a thin, uniform layer, either by brushing or spraying. This operation requires considerable skill on the part of the operator. When the assembled parts are then heated to a temperature of about 900°C, the hydride dissociates* and leaves a residue of pure titanium on the ceramic, which then readily alloys with the metal placed next to it and also enters into a chemical reaction with the ceramic constituents, forming a tight bond.

Instead of painting the ceramic surface with titanium hydride, a thin washer of titanium metal can be interposed between the two ceramic parts, or between the ceramic and the metal part. For such a procedure to be successful, the abutting surfaces must be flat to a very high degree of accuracy and, the melting point of titanium being 1710°C, a rather high temperature would be necessary to effect a seal. By placing another lower-melting metal in contact with the titanium and using one with which titanium readily alloys, the seal can be produced at a much lower temperature. Silver, copper, nickel, tin, and lead are used for this purpose.

A convenient form of supplying the titanium and the brazing alloy to the joint area is the placement of a ring of titanium-cored BT† which consists of a sheath of silver-copper eutectic around a core of titanium. This cored wire is available with 3, 5, 8, and 12 per cent titanium by weight and has a diameter of 10 mils for the first three and 15 mils for the 12-percent core. The titanium is effectively protected from contamination by the atmosphere during handling and alloys with the silver-copper eutectic when heated to 950°C. The cored wire can, of course, be flattened into washers when necessary, or foils of eutectic silver-copper alloy about 10 mils thick can be sandwiched with foils of pure titanium, 2 to 4 mils thick, and placed between the ceramic and metal parts which are to be joined. It is recommended that a pressure of the order of 0.1 kg/cm² be applied to the assembly.[47]

The titanium-silver-copper alloy is very hard and brittle, and its usefulness as a sealing material is limited to those applications where the thermal expansion coefficients of metal and ceramic are relatively closely matched and where the seal is subjected to compressional stress only. In such cases, successful seals can be made either to forsterite, zircon, or alumina ceramics; when tension stresses are encountered, active-alloy seals can be made only to high alumina bodies which have sufficient strength in tension to resist fracture that would be caused by these stresses during cooling in the other ceramic bodies.

Titanium-silver-copper alloys have a high degree of fluidity and tend to spread beyond the joint area unless proper precautions are taken; this tendency is most pronounced for the alloys of higher titanium content. The supplier, therefore, recommends the use of 8- and 12-percent cored wire for metal-ceramic joining and the 3- and 5-percent cored wire for all-

---

* TiH₂ breaks down in the range of 550 to 580°C.

† Supplied by Handy and Harman, 82 Fulton Street, New York 7, New York.

ceramic assemblies. Sometimes it is beneficial to provide grooves or undercuts in which the cored wire is placed. The relatively high vapor pressure of silver has also caused a great number of difficulties in the manufacture of ceramic receiving tubes of the stacked type on account of conductive deposits on the ceramic parts, which lead to insulation difficulties and objectionably high interelectrode capacities. For this reason, the use of silver alloys is generally frowned upon, and titanium-nickel alloys have taken their place. Nickel-clad titanium wire is available from Little Falls Alloys, Inc.*

A ceramic can also be metallized by painting it with a powder paste mixture of 75 per cent copper dust and 25 per cent TiH_2, firing it at about 925°C in a vacuum, and then building up the metal film by electroplating. This metallized ceramic can then be brazed to the desired assembly in hydrogen at a lower temperature with a filler metal that satisfies this requirement.†

The art of ceramic sealing has received a great impetus from the increasing need for more reliable tubes for critical applications, especially in the military field. It was this objective which led the workers at the General Electric Company Research Laboratory in Schenectady to develop tubes which are made from stacked-up parts of ceramic and titanium metal with thin wafers of nickel foil interposed between the ceramic and metal parts so that, on heating, an alloy is formed between nickel and titanium which readily wets the ceramic and forms a vacuum-tight joint. Figure 14.6 shows the constitution diagram for nickel-titanium alloys. An inspection of Figure 14.6 will disclose that 11 per cent nickel will reduce the melting point of titanium from approximately 1700 to 955°C. Three eutectic points are present: 955, 1100, and 1285°C at 30, 66, and 84 per cent nickel. Successful seals have been made in the range of temperatures from 955 to 1300°C by using nickel parts with titanium shims, and from 955 to 1100°C by using titanium parts with nickel shims. Quoting from a paper by Beggs:[33]

"A wide variety of materials can be sealed in this manner. Table 14.1 shows a tabulation of a few of the materials that have been sealed and the temperatures at which the reactive alloys are formed. Also listed for each combination is the maximum temperature at which an enclosure can be sealed without formation of visible or conducting films. This is the temperature at which the most volatile component has a vapor pressure of 10^{-6} mm of Hg. Prolonged heating would require this maximum temperature to be somewhat lower, and rapid heating might permit it to be somewhat higher.

* 189 Caldwell Ave. Paterson 1, N. J.
† Personal communication from B. Winters of the Research and Development Section of Sperry Electronic Tube Division, Gainesville, Florida.

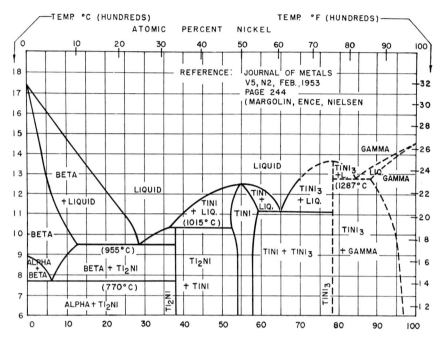

Figure 14.6. Titanium-nickel constitution diagram. After Taylor and Floyd (see Beggs[33]). (*Courtesy The Institute of Metals.*)

TABLE 14.1. TYPICAL MATERIALS AND TEMPERATURES USED TO MAKE REACTIVE ALLOY SEALS§

Ceramic material	Metal part	Shim material	Min. sealing temp. °C*	Max. sealing temp. °C†	Degassing temp. °C‡
Alumina, Forsterite	Cu	Ti	875	910	1000
Alumina, Forsterite	Cu	Zr	885	910	1000
Alumina, Forsterite	Ti	Ni	955	1050	1200
Alumina, Zircon	Zr	Ni	960	1050	1200
Alumina, Zircon	Zr	Fe	934	1015	1200

* Temperature for formation of eutectic alloy.
† Limited by vapor pressure of most volatile material.
‡ For the lowest melting material.
§ After J. E. Beggs.[33]

"Also listed is a temperature at which all of the parts can be degassed. It is limited by the lowest melting material. The other parts can usually be degassed at much higher temperatures if desired. In any event, it should be noted that all of the parts—metal, ceramic, and shim—can be degassed at temperatures above those used in sealing. Because of this, parts can be prepared so that no gases are evolved during the sealing procedure.

"There are many combinations of metals that can be used to form reactive alloys. One of the metal parts, either the shim or the part to be sealed must be an active metal such as titanium, zirconium, hafnium, tantalum, etc. The other must be one that will form an alloy. It makes no difference whether the active metal is supplied by the shim or by the part to be sealed. Nor does it make any difference whether or not the active metal is in contact with the ceramic. The sealing occurs as soon as the active metal is present in a liquid phase, when it can readily come in contact with and react with the ceramic material.

"The amount of alloy that is formed depends largely on the particular metals chosen and the thickness of the shim that is used. In addition, it depends on the sealing temperature and the ceramic composition. Usually, the thickness of the shim necessary to provide a reasonable amount of reactive alloy might be in the range from 0.0003 to 0.0005 inch. However, it may be as thin as 0.0001 inch when the sealing is done at a temperature considerably above the eutectic temperature, or when ceramic bodies are used that have constituents that contribute to the amount of liquid formed. In fact, vacuum-tight seals can be made directly between titanium and some ceramic materials by heating to a temperature high enough for one of the ceramic ingredients to form an alloy with the titanium.

"There are some metals, such as molybdenum and tungsten, which do not form alloys with the active metals except at extremely high temperatures. They can be sealed to ceramic parts by using shims of two metals, such as Ti and Ni, which will form a reactive alloy. In this case, it is usually desirable to use shim thicknesses that will give the eutectic proportions.

"These same techniques can be used to seal metal parts or ceramic parts. For instance, two pieces of titanium can be sealed by inserting a shim of nickel foil. Two ceramic pieces can be sealed by using metal shims that will form a eutectic alloy. In this latter case, the alloy can serve both as the bonding material and as an electrical connection.

"Powdered metals or metal hydrides can be used in lieu of foil shims. They can be painted on the ceramic surfaces in the manner well known to the art.[30, 31, 39, 41] The coated ceramics are placed in contact with the metal parts and, upon reaching an elevated temperature, a reactive alloy is formed and the seal is made as before.

"Metal powders can be used to form printed connections to internal electrodes or supports. The active metal powders can be bonded to a ceramic surface by heating to a temperature sufficiently high to form a reactive alloy; other metal powders can be bonded by adding enough active metal to form suitable amounts of a reactive alloy.

"Titanium parts can be sealed to ceramic pieces by first heating to a high temperature to obtain a clean titanium surface and then applying molten solder, such as tin, lead, aluminum, etc., to a region where the two surfaces are touching. The molten solder dissolves a small amount of the titanium, and surface tension pulls the alloy between the areas of contact. Zirconium parts can be sealed similarly by the addition of molten solder. Thus, a seal can be made between an active metal part and a ceramic part by adding solder at a temperature high enough for it to dissolve some of the active metal and react with the ceramic material.

"Satisfactory seals have been made to various alumina, forsterite, and zircon bodies. Usually, the strength of the seal is greater than 50 per cent of the strength of the ceramic part. For large parts or where considerable heat shock might be encountered, it is desirable to use strong insulators and parts made of metals having low tensile strengths such as copper or nickel, or materials having closely similar expansion-contraction characteristics, as is shown in Figure 14.7, for titanium and a special forsterite body.

"The seals are strongest when they are made in a vacuum of 10^{-4} mm Hg or better, or in a pure, dry, inert gas. Impurities such as oxygen, nitrogen, carbon monoxide, and water vapor are detrimental because they reduce the ductility of the alloy, impair its reaction with the ceramic, and in general weaken the bond.

"Prior to sealing, the parts must be flat to within a mil or less, if successful butt seals are to be made with a minimum amount of alloy. Enough

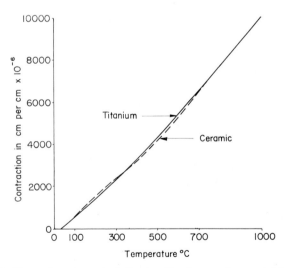

Figure 14.7. Expansion characteristics for titanium and a special forsterite body developed by the General Electric Company Research Laboratory. After Beggs.[33] (*Courtesy The Institute of Radio Engineers.*)

pressure must be applied during sealing to keep the parts intimately in contact. Formation of a minimum amount of sealing alloy is helpful in producing seals that are strong and is necessary when extremely small or thin insulators are being sealed. By stacking the parts one on the other, a large number of seals can be made at one time.

"The ability of an alloy to bond with a ceramic body depends on the active metal used and the stability of the ceramic ingredients. For instance, an alloy containing titanium is more reactive than one containing tantalum, so that it will make a stronger bond to a stable oxide like alumina. On the other hand, if the ceramic body contains a material which is readily dissociated by the reactive alloy, porous seals can result."

"Kovar" is frequently used as a metal in combination with high-alumina ceramics on account of its reasonably close match in expansion. Active-metal seals to "Kovar" receiving-tube envelopes have been made by interposing a sandwich washer of thin nickel and titanium between alumina header and "Kovar" bulb. Even better results are obtained when a molybdenum washer is added between the Ni-Ti washer and the bulb.[48]

"Kovar" becomes pervious to hydrogen at temperatures above 350°C, and must be suitably protected for high-temperature operation. Gold-plating has been used but fails due to peeling and cracking much above 350°C. Flame-sprayed ceramic coatings have been applied to "Kovar" bulbs with some measure of success, and coatings of glass offer great promise. Type 7052 glass powder is applied cataphoretically on oxidized "Kovar" bulbs and then air-fired to produce a continuous glass film. A final hydrogen firing treatment reduces the oxide on the inside of the bulb. (Reported by workers of the Sylvania Electric Products Inc. at Emporium.)

Brazing Operations and Processing Details

Many of the remarks made in Chapter 12 will necessarily apply to the brazing operations performed to produce ceramic-to-metal seals. A few observations may be in order, however, to emphasize some special precautions which are necessary for the production of successful seals. It is obvious that all components must be very clean and should be used within a reasonable time after their cleaning and outgassing treatment. Ceramics are usually fired in air at a temperature from 800–1000°C; suitable alkaline cleaning solutions are used at times, followed by immersion in dilute nitric acid for from two to five minutes and a subsequent rinsing in neutralizing solution, distilled water, and methyl alcohol. Mickey[49] remarks that trichloroethylene should be avoided as a cleaning agent for ceramics as it leaves a conductive coating.

Similarly, care should be taken that particles embedded in ceramics during grinding operations are removed. Some other comments on harmful effects of grinding have been made in Chapter 2.

In choosing a suitable filler metal or brazing alloy for a given ceramic-metal combination, several conditions must be satisfied which are not always easily met. The brazing operation must thus be considered during the design stage of the tube, and should enter into the planning of the entire processing sequence. The number of heat cycles to which the tube is subjected during processing and the maximum temperature of the joint during operation will have an important bearing on the selection of the most suitable brazing alloy.

Obviously, the flow-point of the alloy must be high enough on a first braze to permit subsequent brazes if step-brazing is to be employed. The vapor pressure of the metal or alloy must be low enough to allow operation at the specified temperature during the life of the tube and to prevent sublimation of metal during processing, which would result in the formation of conductive films on insulators and adversely affect interelectrode capacities. Copper-silver alloys are notorious offenders in this respect, and their widespread use in the past has led to many costly failures. Gold-nickel alloys have been substituted in many cases with good results; their flow-point is of course much higher and one has to worry about the simultaneous breakdown of oxide cathodes if they are part of the assembly to be brazed.

On a final braze (it may be the only one) it is entirely feasible to activate the cathode at the same time.[50] Repeated heat-cycling of active alloy seals may lead to failure in service owing to the exchange of oxygen and the different molar volumes of the resulting oxides when temperature levels of 700°C are encountered.[47] It is probably a good rule to keep the number of heat cycles during processing, and in operation, to a minimum when temperatures above 300°C are involved.

The amount of brazing alloy applied and its strategic location at or near the joint are also critical factors which frequently must be determined by experimentation on test samples. The furnace atmosphere has a critical influence on the seal quality. It is generally recognized that Mo/Mn seals require a slightly oxidizing atmosphere,[38] and a dew point of 25°C is often chosen for the hydrogen. When cracked ammonia is used as a source of hydrogen, there is some danger of stress corrosion cracking in the presence of remaining traces of ammonia, or ammonium compounds, and the combined influence of internal or external stresses in the copper. Particular attention must thus be given to the design of fixtures intended to hold the assembly components in alignment during the brazing operation, or retaining rings used to counteract the excessive expansion of copper members to which an internal ceramic seal is to be made. The purity of the copper will always have to be questioned first when difficulties are encountered, but when the copper has been proved satisfactory, the secondary effects just mentioned must be investigated. Copper has been used as an example in this discussion but other metals and alloys are subject to similar effects.[51]

One of the sources of stress in a metal-to-ceramic joint is the different rate of thermal expansion of the materials involved. Even if the materials are chosen to have closely similar expansion coefficients over a wide temperature range, as is the case in so-called matched seals, one has to consider the different heat capacities and the different rates at which the metal and ceramic parts reach equilibrium temperature before a proper evaluation of stresses can be made. It is practically impossible to obtain complete expansion and temperature match with available materials; for this reason, seals are often made flexible to a degree so that stresses are equalized by a slight movement of the metal members. Figure 14.8 gives some examples of such flexible joints.[52]

There is practically no limitation to the size in which such seals can be fabricated; ceramic cylinders 10 inches in diameter have been used, although the processing facilities required for the production of such large ceramic components and their sealing to metals become rather formidable.

The practical experience gained in the course of the years in regard to

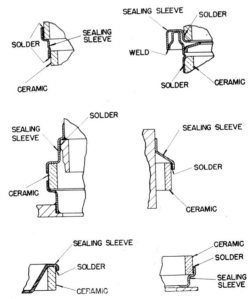

Figure 14.8. Flexible joints for ceramic-to-metal seals. After Manfredi and Nolte.[52] (*Courtesy* (*The American Ceramic Society.*)

the suitability of various metals and alloys for brazing high-alumina ceramics has recently been elucidated by Williams and Nielsen[52a] of the Bell Telephone Laboratories at Murray Hill who have systematically investigated the wetting properties of commonly used brazing metals and alloys on high-alumina ceramics which were either in their natural state or metallized and coated with a thin film of nickel. The degree of wetting between a liquid and solid is generally described by the contact angle of a sessile drop on a solid substrate as shown in Fig. 14.9. The configuration, which a liquid assumes when it contacts a solid and a surrounding gas, is determined by the condition that the interface energy be a minimum. The force required to extend a liquid surface per unit length is the surface tension and is numerically equal to the surface energy. Interfaces between two solids, or between a solid and a liquid, require work for their formation, and their presence in a system thus represents additional interface energy. For a multiphase system to be in equilibrium, the equation shown in Fig. 14.9 must be satisfied, and the solid surface thus remain flat. When the contact angle θ is greater than 90 degrees, the liquid is considered to be nonwetting, while values of θ less than 90 degrees are associated with a liquid which wets the surface. In the extreme case, a liquid which is completely nonwetting would, in the absence of gravity, assume the shape of a sphere so that the contact angle would be 180 degrees, while in the other extreme, for a completely wetting liquid the contact would approach a value of 0 degrees in the case where liquid spreads over the surface in the form of a thin film.

Williams and Nielsen observed the shape of a molten drop of brazing metal on a plaque of 100% pure aluminum oxide and other less pure alu-

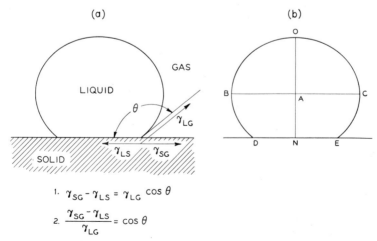

Figure 14.9. A sessile drop at equilibrium and the equation describing this condition. After Williams and Nielsen.[52a] (*Courtesy The American Ceramic Society.*)

mina plaques of commercial origin in a specially constructed furnace that permitted the observation of the shape of the drop by means of a split-beam telescope. An atmosphere of helium was supplied to the previously evacuated furnace at a pressure of 100 Torr. The contact angle was observed for a period of time after complete melting of the metal or alloy had been reached, and the observed values are quoted in graphs as shown in Figs. 14.10a,b,c,d,e.

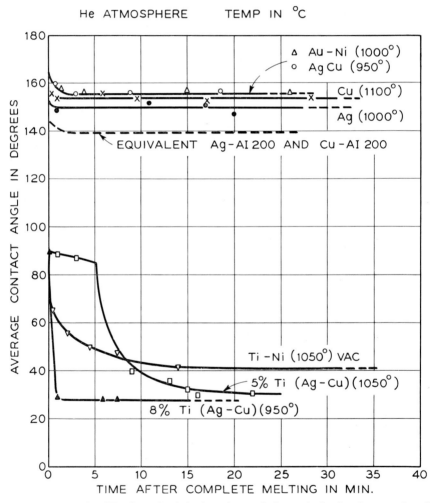

Figure 14.10(a). Wetting of original surfaces of sintered alumina by metal and eutectic alloy solders in He atmosphere. After Williams and Nielsen.[52a] (*Courtesy The American Ceramic Society.*)

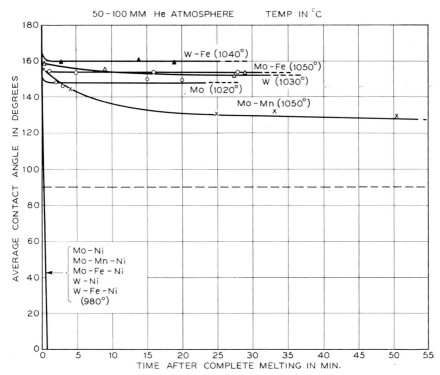

Figure 14.10(b). Wetting of metallized alumina ceramic surfaces by molten silver in He atmosphere at 50 to 100 Torr. After Williams and Nielsen.[52a] (*Courtesy The American Ceramic Society.*)

"Silver, copper, and the eutectic alloys of silver-copper and gold-nickel were nonwetting and did not adhere to the alumina. Silver and copper on the 96% alumina (Coors AI-200) were similarly nonwetting and without adherence. The lower contact-angle values of silver and copper on a 96% alumina suggest that the surface free energy between these metals and the 96% alumina was lower than for the same metals on the 100% alumina. In contrast, titanium-nickel was partly wetting and had a good bond, but there was a tendency to form a dish-shaped fracture in the ceramic beneath it.

"The delay in wetting by the 5% titanium core silver-copper eutectic alloy is reproducible and is believed to be due to the time required for the titanium to diffuse into the molten solder and become available for promoting wetting at the liquid-solid interface. The higher Ti content in the 8% material reached wetting equilibrium more quickly than the alloy of 5% Ti.

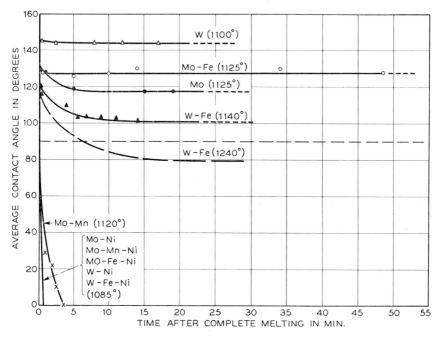

Figure 14.10(c). Wetting of metallized ceramic surfaces by molten copper in He atmosphere at 100 Torr. After Williams and Nielsen.[52a] (*Courtesy The American Ceramic Society.*)

"The 5 % titanium core solder also caused the ceramic to "dish." There was less tendency for such a failure in the case of the titanium content of 8 %. This is consistent with the knowledge that as the titanium content is increased from 5 to 8 % a better match of coefficients of thermal expansion between the alumina and metal phases is realized.

"The dishing effect predominated in systems using the 100 % alumina over systems using the 96 % alumina. This may be explained on the basis of the greater strength of the more dense 96 % alumina (AI-200). It is better able to resist stresses.

"Similar plots in Figs. 14.10b,c,d, and e illustrate the wetting behavior of molten solders on metallized alumina (AI-200) surfaces. The type of metallizing is indicated for each curve. In Fig. 14.10b is shown the wetting of metallized alumina surfaces by molten silver. Note the completeness and rapidity with which the specimens having the nickel coating were wetted. Otherwise, silver was nonwetting and nonadherent on the metallizings. Equilibrium was attained quickly in all cases except with molybdenum-20 %

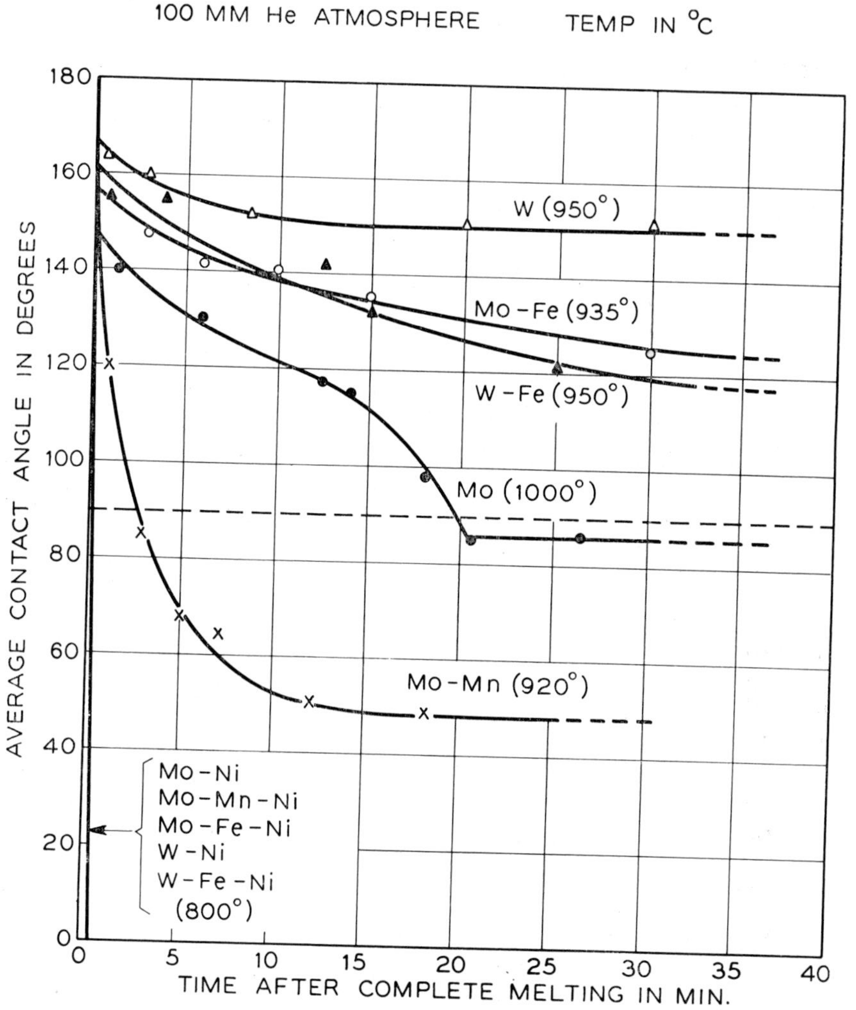

Figure 14.10(d). Wetting of metallized alumina ceramic surfaces by molten silver-copper eutectic alloy in He atmosphere at 100 Torr. After Williams and Nielsen.[52a] (*Courtesy The American Ceramic Society.*)

manganese. Inspection of this plaque after removal from the furnace revealed that the metallizing beneath the solder had alloyed with it to the extent that a complex and nonwetting alloy of silver, molybdenum, and manganese was resting on an unmetallized area. Contact angles above and below the dashed reference line at 90 degrees refer respectively to nonwetting and wetting conditions.

"The wetting by molten copper on similarly metallized plaques is shown

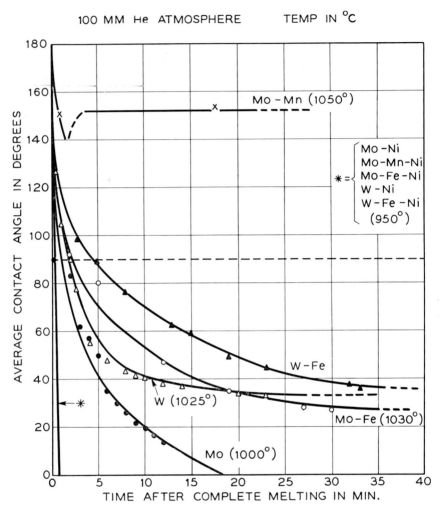

Figure 14.10(e). Wetting of metallized alumina ceramic surfaces by molten gold-nickel eutectic alloy in He atmosphere at 100 Torr. After Williams and Nielsen.[52a] (*Courtesy The American Ceramic Society.*)

in Fig. 14.10c. Complete and rapid wetting occurred on the molybdenum-manganese metallizing as well as on the nickel-coated specimens with good bonds for all. Although copper adhered to all the other metallizings, it was generally nonwetting in nature except for tungsten-iron, which tended to be more temperature dependent as shown.

"The wetting by silver-copper eutectic alloys is illustrated in Fig. 14.10d. Once again complete and rapid wetting of the nickel-coated specimens occurred. The bond appeared to be good. Molybdenum and molybdenum-manganese were wetted partly whereas the others were not wetted. In general, these systems were sluggish in reaching equilibrium. Adherence was good, except with molybdenum-manganese. Although wetting occurred, the metals in this system alloyed sufficiently to remove the metallizing layer beneath the drop and completely destroy any bond.

"The wetting of metallized alumina surfaces by molten gold-nickel eutectic alloy is shown in Fig. 14.10e. All the metallizings were wetted partly or completely except for molybdenum-manganese. The gold-nickel alloy wetted initially, but once again alloying occurred so rapidly and extensively that the metallizing was removed from the entire surface of the plaque. The resulting drop of the complex alloy of gold-nickel-molybdenum and manganese came to equilibrium at a contact angle of 152 degrees. It was characteristic of gold-nickel eutectic alloy to exhibit an excellent bond. Unfortunately, and in all cases, the metal layer became separated from the ceramic, taking an adherent layer of ceramic with it. This is indicative of a destructive mismatch between the thermal expansions of the ceramic and metal films. The rapid rate at which all speciemns were cooled in these experiments tended to exaggerate the effects of any thermal expansion mismatches."

Characteristics of commercial ceramic bodies for electronic applications are given in Table 14.2; Figure 14.11 gives thermal expansion characteristics for a number of ceramics and metals.

Ceramic-insulated terminals for high-temperature application and high-voltage insulation represent a group of components where ceramic-to-metal seals find commercial application. A few years ago, the present author was involved in a project where a special all-metal tube required some twenty such terminals in a row. Several different approaches could naturally be taken to achieve this objective; one could thus think of simple wire pin seals, but these are easily broken off on handling. The specimen application of the tube in question made it further necessary to economize on space. The maximum diameter that could be allotted to any one terminal was 0.25 inch, and any protrusions outside the tube wall were not desirable. A plug-in type terminal was thus developed as shown in Figure 14.12.[53]

The terminal consists of three parts, i.e., a thin-walled copper jack into which a plug can be inserted from the outside of the tube; a high-alumina ceramic sleeve which is metallized on its inner and outer surface by the Sintered Metal Powder Process; a copper ferrule which is brazed to the ceramic sleeve at its lower end and to the tube wall at its upper end. The copper parts were machined or formed from OFHC copper and brazed to the ceramic sleeve with "Nicoro,"* a nickel-copper-gold alloy (see Table

* Trade name, Western Gold and Platinum Company, Belmont, California.

TABLE 14.2. SELECTED CHARACTERISTICS OF SOME CERAMICS USED FOR CERAMIC-TO-METAL SEALS

Material	Type	Manufact.	Thermal Exp. Coeff. cm/cm/°C × 11^7	Safe Oper. Temp. °C	Thermal Conduct. cal/gm/cm/°C/sec (25°C)	Heat Shock Resistance (see Table 2.23)	Compres. Strength 10^3 psi	Dielectric Constant (25°C)	Loss Tangent × 10^4 (25°C)	Loss Factor (25°C)	Volume Resistivity ohm·cm	Dielectric Strength Volts/mil (25°C)
Alsimag 243	Forsterite ($2MgO \cdot SiO_2$)	A.L.C.[1]	100(25–300) 112(25–700)	1000	0.008	0.94	85	6.2 (1MC) 6.1 (100MC) 5.8 (10kMC)	4(1MC) 3(100MC) 10(10kMC)	0.002(1MC) 0.002(100MC) 0.0058(10kMC)	>10^{14}(R.T.) 5.0×10^{13}(100°C) 7.0×10^{11}(300°C) 1.2×10^9(500°C) 1.0×10^8(700°C)	240
Alsimag 475	Zircon $ZrO_2 \cdot SiO_2$	A.L.C.	44(25–300) 41(25–700)	1100	0.012		100	8.8 (1MC) 8.6 (100MC) 8.4 (10kMC)	10(1MC) 12(100MC) 27(10kMC)	0.009(1MC) 0.010(100MC) 0.023(10kMC)	>10^{14}(R.T.) 2.0×10^{13}(100°C) 5.5×10^{11}(300°C) 5.5×10^9(500°C) 1.4×10^9(700°C)	250
Alsimag 576	Alumina 85%	A.L.C.	65(25–300) 75(25–700)	1100	0.040		140	8.3 (1MC) 8.1 (100MC) 8.0 (10kMC)	7(1MC) 8(100MC) 15(10kMC)	0.006(1MC) 0.006(100MC) 0.012(10kMC)	>10^{14}(R.T.) 2.0×10^{13}(100°C) 5.0×10^{10}(300°C) 1.0×10^8(500°C) 3.0×10^6(700°C)	250
Alsimag 614	Alumina 96%	A.L.C.	65(25–300) 79(25–700)	1650	0.045	~4.8	400	9.3 (1MC) 9.1 (10kMC)	3(1MC) 14(10kMC)	0.0028(1MC) 0.013(10kMC)	>10^{14}(R.T.) 2.0×10^{13}(100°C) 7.3×10^7(500°C) 3.5×10^6(700°C)	230
Coors AD 96	Alumina 96%	C.P.C.[2]	67(25–200) 92(25–1000)	1700	0.048		>300	8.95(1MC) 8.95(100MC) 8.90(10kMC)	0.84(1MC) 2.4(100MC) 5.9(10kMC)	0.00075(1MC) 0.0021(100MC) 0.0053(10kMC)	>10^{14}(R.T.)	220–240
Coors AD 99	Alumina 99%	C.P.C.	67(25–200) 92(25–1000)	1725	0.070		>300	9.35(1MC) 9.31(100MC) 9.31(10kMC)	15(1MC) 0.6(100MC) 1.4(10kMC)	0.014(1MC) 0.00056(100MC) 0.0013(10kMC)	>10^{14}(R.T.)	220–240
Coors ZI-4	Zircon $ZrO_2 \cdot SiO_2$	C.P.C.	33.6(25–200) 57.8(25–1000)	1400(max)	0.010	1.6	70	6.3 (1MC) 6.29(100MC)	22(1MC) 23(100MC)	0.014(1MC) 0.0145(100MC)	>10^{14}(R.T.)	280–320
Ceramic 4462	Alumina 94%	F.P.C.[3]	73(25–700)	1450(max)	0.037(100°C)		300	8.95(1MC) 8.80(10kMC)	2(1MC) 4(100MC) 14(10kMC)	0.0018(1MC) 0.0036(100MC) 0.0123(10kMC)	>10^{14}(R.T.) 10^{13}(200°C) 10^{10}(400°C) 10^8(600°C)	210

[1] American Lava Corporation, Chattanooga 5, Tenn.
[2] Coors Porcelain Company, Golden, Colorado
[3] Frenchtown Porcelain Company, Trenton, N. J.

510

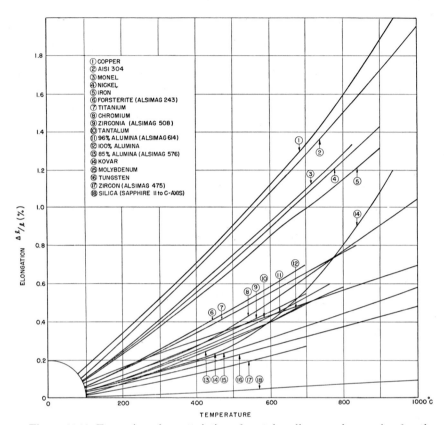

Figure 14.11. Expansion characteristics of metals, alloys, and ceramics for the evaluation of ceramic-to-metal seals.

12.1). After the individual terminal sub-assemblies had been leak-tested, all twenty of them were brazed to the copper housing in one operation using a silver-copper eutectic alloy. While all terminals were vacuum-tight on a first leak test of the strip, several leaks developed on subsequent heat cycling. Further refinements in technique were thus necessary before reliable results could be obtained. The purpose of the copper ferrule (Part 3) is, of course, to provide some degree of flexibility in order to avoid stresses that would result from the difference in expansion between copper and alumina.

When placing the small rings of filler metal as shown in Figure 14.12(b), in the upper row, a solid bridge was formed between the copper housing and the ceramic sleeve so that flexibility of the ferrule was lost. By placing the filler metal rings as shown at the bottom, this difficulty was avoided; the brazing alloy then flowed by virtue of the action of capillary forces into the

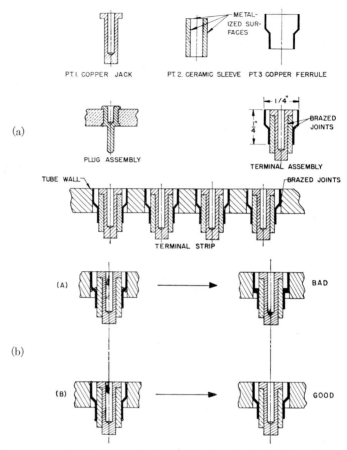

Figure 14.12. Flush-mounted, ceramic-insulated terminal for all-metal tubes. (a) shows the terminal components in the upper row and the assembled terminal in the middle row, at right. At left, the plug is shown which fits into the jack of the assembly at right. As 20 such terminals were built into the copper wall of a cyclotron resonance tube, as shown in the bottom row, in part, a connector strip with 20 plugs was used. (b) shows a detail in brazing technique. To avoid the formation of a solid bridge between copper housing and ceramic sleeve, the filler metal had to be fed from top and bottom in just the right amount to effect a braze without excess running onto the flexible part of the ferrule. After Kohl.[53] (*Courtesy Stanford University.*)

interspace between the ferrule and the copper housing without interfering with the desired flexibility of the ferrule at its expanded mid-plane. Good joints were thus obtained, and individual test seals were heat-cycled as much as ten times to 750°C, with rapid cooling, without developing any leaks. This particular difficulty was, of course, due to the very confined space within which the terminal had to be located.

Figure 14.13. Compound headers. (*Courtesy Varian Associates.*)

Whenever possible, an effort is made to arrange the metal part so that it surrounds the ceramic; thus the latter is in compression in the finished seal. When the ceramic surrounds the metal and the latter has a greater thermal expansion coefficient than the ceramic, the metal tends to shrink away from the ceramic, or put the interface into tension. Most ceramics will fail under these conditions, and closely matched expansion coefficients become a necessity. The production of pin seals for ceramic headers,* which was a stumbling block for quite some time in the production of ceramic-type receiving tubes, is an example of this configuration. Successful seals are now being made with high-alumina bodies using metals such a "Kovar," molybdenum, or tantalum, and employing either active-alloy seals or the Sintered Metal Powder Process. Figure 14.13 shows several double-ring headers.

Spacings between the pins and the holes in the ceramic header must be held to a very close tolerance and should preferably not be larger than 0.5 mil. The fillet at the end of the pin must also be held to the order of 1 mil, unless objectionable strains develop. Wheeler[54] has reported on the use of a nickel-titanium eutectic as filler metal in conjunction with tantalum pins.

---

* "Header" is a commonly used term for button stems containing a number of wires in a circular array.

Such pin seals were tested at 480°C for 1000 hours without failure and are likely to be useful for even higher temperatures. Molybdenum and tantalum deteriorate at high ambient temperatures and require protective coatings. Pins as large in diameter as 40 mils have been successfully used, but small-diameter, thin-walled tubing in the seal area is, of course, easier to handle because it will yield to the stresses; a solid pin must then be brazed to the tubing outside the ceramic body.

Ceramic wafers, or headers, for subminiature tubes, such as those recently developed at the RCA Electron Tube Division, offer special problems in manufacture. To braze eight .016 in.-dia. leads into a ceramic disk, about 0.320-in.-dia., by any of the conventional metallizing techniques so far described, proved to be impractical. Initial efforts were directed toward metallizing the walls of the small pinholes by the reaction of liquid reagents, such as lithium molybdate. A more recent technique, described by Stoeckert,[55] consists of pressing blended powders (35 % Ti + 65 % Ni) onto the lead wires in a separate operation, thus producing a 0.015 in.-thick washer on the wire which consists of molybdenum which is nickel-plated to a thickness of 0.2 mil and given an overflash of chromium (see Chapter 13, p. 426). These prepared leads with their washers are then placed into the wafer, the washers resting on the top surface. On heating to 1250°C in a vacuum bell jar, the pressed powder melts and flows into the interspace, thus effecting a vacuum-tight seal which has been tested at 500°C for 1000 hours.

The following processing details are quoted from Stoekert's paper as being of interest for active alloy seals in general:

"Titanium powder obtained from various sources may produce widely different effects. The best powder for this process was obtained from the United International Research Corp. under the trade name of "Unified" titanium. Each particle of this powder has a protective layer of oxide only a few Angstroms thick so that even the −325 fraction is non-pyroforic. The overall oxide content, however, is less than that of titanium obtained from other sources. The oxide content must be low so that the titanium is free to react with the ceramic and make a strong bond.

"It is important that the powders be annealed and outgassed by vacuum firing. Annealing produces powders which are more easily pressed into composite forms. Outgassing of the powders eliminates bubbles in the finished braze due to entrapped gas. The particle size of the powders should be about −200 + 325 mesh so that proper flow of the powder into the die cavity is assured."

Evaluation of Ceramic Seals

A variety of tests have been devised by different manufacturers in order to appraise the quality of a given seal in terms of vacuum tightness, shelf life, and tensile strength. These tests are generally of a destructive nature and must thus be carried out on specially prepared samples made in such a way that they suitably fit into a tensile-strength-testing machine. Heat shock, mechanical shock and vibration, deterioration in corrosive atmospheres, and damage by nuclear radiation are other parameters of the seal which are tested. The quality of the ceramic body itself can be separately investigated by the preparation of micro-sections.[43, 56-59]

Since it is difficult to pass judgement on the suitability of a ceramic body for sealing purposes on the basis of microscopic examination alone, many workers believe that the "tear test," consisting of tearing a finished seal apart and observing the adhesion of the ceramic to the metal, is the most reliable method of test.

A Task Force for a Standard Test Device for Metal-Ceramic Seals (C. P. Marsden, Chairman) has begun to operate in January, 1957, as part of Sub-Committee V on Metallic to Non-Metallic Seals (V. J. DeSantis, Chairman) of Committee F-1 on Materials for Electron Tubes and Semiconductor Devices, American Society for Testing Materials. This cooperative effort on the part of ceramic tube producers should in due course produce much valuable information.

REFERENCES

1. G. Gallet, "Ceramics in electron tubes" (in French), *Le Vide*, **11**, 420–430 (Sept./ Oct. 1956).
2. M. J. Cross, "New Vacuum Tube Techniques of the Telefunken Röhren-Werke, Berlin," Office of Military Government for Germany (U.S.) Field Information Agency, Technical Final Report No. 560 (1945).
3. H. Vatter, "Ceramic-to-Metal Brazes" (in German), *Glas-und Hochvakuum-Technik*, **1**, 79–85 (Aug. 1952).
4. D. E. P. Jenkins, "Ceramic-to-metal sealing, its development and use in the American radio valve industry," *Electronic Eng.*, **27**, 290–294 (June 1955).
5. H. Pulfrich, "Comments on the publication by D. E. P. Jenkins," Vacuum-tight ceramic-metal joints (in German), *Vakuum-Technik*, **4**, 113–115 (1955). This article contains three sectional drawings of the Telefunken tubes.
6. W. G. Shepherd, "A Study of Electron Tube Reliability," University of Minnesota, Contract W.8 onr 66211, Final Report, July 18–Dec. 31, 1951.
7. E. F. Rexer, "Report on Vacuum Tubes," Minneapolis-Honeywell Regulator Co., February 1952.
8. American Lava Corporation, Contract No. W 33-038-ac-15849, a contract assigned in 1946 by the U. S. Air Force to study the Telefunken Ceramic Tube.
9. Machlett Laboratories, Inc. Final Report, "Joining of metals to insulators for vacuum tube application," NObsr-39365, July 30, 1949; Supplement to Final Report, Dec. 10, 1949.
10. E. F. Rexer, J. N. Dempsey and G. W. Rusler, "A developmental ceramic vacuum tube," National Conference on Tube Techniques, New York (Oct. 1956).
11. Minneapolis-Honeywell Research Center, "Ceramic vacuum tube development," Final Report TR 4066-R1, Feb. 1957.

12. W. H. Kohl, "Electron tubes for critical environments," IRE Convention Record, Part III, pp. 141–149, 1957.

13. W. H. Kohl and P. J. Rice, "Electron tubes for critical environments," Final Report, TR 57-434, Wright Air Development Center, Electronic Components Laboratory, Task 41668; (AF 33(616)-3460), July 30, 1957. Stanford Research Institute, Menlo Park, California. Available from U. S. Department of Commerce, Office of Technical Services, under PB 131852 at a cost of $3.50. ASTIA No. AD 151158.

14. Final Report of the AGET Ad Hoc Committee on Ceramic Receiving Tubes, J. O. McNally, Chairman, Aug. 14, 1957, (Confidential). See also: J. O. McNally, "Status Report on the Ceramic Receiving Tube Development," Proceedings of the 1958 Electronic Components Conference, Los Angeles, April 22–24, 1958. Engineering Publishers, New York, N. Y., pp. 168–185.

15. Symposium on Ceramics and Ceramic-metal Seals: April 21, 1953, School of Ceramics, Rutgers Univ., New Brunswick, New Jersey. (Sponsored by the Subpanel on Tube Techniques, the Panel on Electronic Tubes, Research and Development Board, the Department of Defense.) (Papers presented at this Symposium were published in *Ceramic Age*, Feb.–Sept., 1954. An extensive bibliography prepared by the General Electric Company Research Laboratory is attached at the end of this Symposium Report and covers the literature up to 1951.)

16. L. Navias, "Advances in ceramics related to electronic tube development," *J. Am. Ceram. Soc.*, **37**, 329–350 (Aug. 1954).

17. H. Palmour, III, "Review of high-temperature metal-ceramic seals," *J. Electrochem. Soc.*, **102**, 160C–164C (July 1955).

18. D. G. Burnside, "Ceramic-metal seals of the tungsten-iron type," *RCA Rev.*, **15**, 46–61 (March 1954).

19. H. Bender, "New development in metal-ceramic seals," *Sylvania Technologist*, **8**, 22–25 (Jan. 1955).

19a. G. R. Van Houten, "A survey of ceramic-to-metal bonding," *Bull. Am. Ceram. Soc.* **38**, 301–307 (June 1959).

20. W. A. Wooster and G. L. MacDonald, "Smears of titanium metal," *Nature*, **160**, 260 (Aug. 23, 1947).

21. S. T. Bowden and D. Tabor, "The Friction and Lubrication of Solids," Oxford University Press, London, 1953.

22. R. B. Belser, "Frictional adhesion of metal-to-glass, quartz, and ceramic surfaces," *Rev. Sci. Instr.*, **25**, 862–864 (Sept. 1954).

23. A. Danzin and E. Destois, "Optically polished surfaces for vacuum tube seals" (in French), *Ann. radioélec.*, **3**, 281–289 (Oct. 1948).

24. J. Bleuze and P. Dussausoy, "Sealing techniques by optical polish" (in French), *Le Vide*, **7**, 1182–1190 (May 1952).

24a. M. P. Wilder, "A quasi-optical seal for vacuum tubes," Fourth National Conference on Tube Techniques, New York, Sept. 10–12, 1958. Proceedings published by New York University Press, New York, 1959.

24b. G. Lewin and R. Mark, "Theory of dissimilar tubular seals of glass, ceramics, and metals for critical applications," 1958 Vacuum Symposium Transactions, American Vacuum Society Transactions (1959).

24c. I. E. Martin and A. C. Tunis, "Development of the radial compression seal," *RCA Engr.*, **3**, No. 3, 9–11 (Dec. 1957–Jan. 1958).

25. R. Wellinger, "Soldering of Steatite to Metal and its Application to the Con-

struction of Electronic Tubes," Thesis, University of Zurich (in French), Leman & Co., Zurich, Switzerland, 1947.

26. S. Tank, "Methods of forming a vacuum-tight bond between ceramics and metals," U. S. Patent 2,564,738 (Aug. 21, 1951).
27. W. Espe and M. Knoll, "Werkstoffkunde der Hochvakuumtechnik," J. Springer Verlag, Berlin, 1936.
28. C. V. Litton, "Methods of making metal-to-ceramic seals," U. S. Patent 2,646,070 (July 28, 1953).
29. R. J. Bondley, "Metal-ceramic brazed seals," *Electronics*, **20**, 97–99 (July 1947).
30. H. Vatter, "On the history of ceramic-to-metal sealing techniques" (in German), *Vakuum-Technik*, **4**, 180 (Feb. 1956).
31. F. C. Kelley, "Metallizing and Bonding Non-metallic Bodies," U. S. Patent 2,570, 248 (Oct. 9, 1951).
32. C. S. Pearsall, "New brazing methods for joining non-metallic materials to metals," *Materials & Methods*, **30**, 61–62 (July 1949).
33. J. E. Beggs, "Sealing metal and ceramic parts by forming reactive alloys," *Trans. IRE*, Professional Group on Component Parts, **CP-4**, 28–31 (March 1957).
34. W. L. Knecht, "Application of pressed powder techniques for production of metal-to-ceramic seals," *Ceram. Age*, **63**, 12–13 (1954).
35. American Lava Corporation, Chattanooga, Tennessee; Final Report, Contract AF 33(600)-27329 (Dec. 1956): "Ceramic-to-Metal Seals by Pressed Powder Techniques," by H. C. Dunegan.
35a. M. D. Hare, R. F. Keller and H. A. Meneses, "Electro-formed ceramic-to-metal seal for vacuum tubes," Fourth National Conference on Tube Techniques, Sept. 10–12, 1958, New York; Proceedings published by New York University Press, New York 1959, pp. 25–28. Also: Tech. Rept. No. 453-3 (Nov. 17, 1958), Electron Devices Laboratory, Stanford Electronics Laboratories, Stanford University, Stanford, California.
36. H. A. Barr, L. E. Marchi, H. H. Rice and J. A. Stavrolakis, "Application of fundamental concepts of bonding metals and ceramics," Armour Research Foundation, Chicago, Ill. (Oct. 1953), Office of Tech. Serv., Washington, D. C. (PB-117936, AD-10554).
37. W. D. Kingery, "Metal-Ceramic Interactions: 1. Thermal factors effecting fabrication and properties of cermet bodies," *J. Am. Ceram. Soc.*, **36**, 362–365 (Nov. 1953); 2. "Metal oxides interfacial reactions at elevated temperatures," *ibid.*, **36**, 403–409 (Dec. 1953).
37a. W. D. Kingery, "Role of surface energies and wetting in metal-ceramic sealing," *Bull. Am. Ceram. Soc.*, **35**, 108–112 (March 1956).
38. A. G. Pincus, "Mechanism of ceramic-to-metal adherence," Symposium on Ceramics and Ceramic Metal Seals, Rutgers University, Apr. 21, 1953, published in *Ceram. Age*, **63**, 16–20, 30–32 (Mar. 1954).
39. H. Pulfrich, "Ceramic-to-metal seals," U. S. Patent 2,163,407 (June 20, 1939).
40. H. Pulfrich and R. Magner, "Ceramic-to-metal seal," U. S. Patent 2,163,410 (June 20, 1939).
41. H. J. Nolte and R. F. Spurck, "Metalizing and ceramic sealing with manganese," *Television Eng.*, **1**, 14–18, 39 (Nov. 1950). U. S. Patents 2,667,432 and 2,667,427 (Jan. 1954).
42. A. J. Chick and L. J. Speck, "Fabrication of metal-to-ceramic seals," U. S. Patent 2,708,787 (May 24, 1955).

43. H. Bender, "High-temperature metal-ceramic seals," *Ceram. Age* **63,** 15–24 (Apr. 1954).
44. L. H. LaForge, Jr., "Application of ceramic sections in high-power pulsed klystrons," *Am. Ceram. Soc. Bull.*, **35,** 117–127 (Mar. 1956).
45. A. MacDonald and E. J. Whitmore, "Method of Making Ceramic-to-Metal Seals," U. S. Patent 2,836,885 (June 3, 1958); Assigned to Ferranti Limited, Lancashire, England.
46. S. Goldberg, "Research Study on Hydrogen Thyratrons," Edgerton, Germeshausen & Grier, Inc., Final Report, Contract DA36-039sc-52589, T.D5-55, AD 90065 (July 1953–Oct. 1955). See also U. S. Patent 2,842,699 (July 8, 1958).
47. American Feldmuehle Corporation, New York, Technical Bulletin, 1956, "Metalizing of high-purity AFC alumina."
48. Sylvania Electric Products Inc., "Investigation of tube structures adapted to automatic production (NObsr 64542). Status Report No. 40 (Aug. 15, 1957) on the Military Reliable Tube Program; Advisory Group on Electron Tubes, New York.
49. D. D. Mickey, "The application of reactive metal seals to the design of a high performance metal-ceramic R.F. amplifier tube," Presentation before the Washington Conference of the IRE Professional Group on Electron Devices, Oct. 1956.
50. Eitel McCullough, Inc., 12th Interim Tech. Rept. (Mar. 8, 1955–Aug. 7, 1955); AF 33(600)-17125; AD 78497.
51. "Stress Corrosion Cracking and Embrittlement," W. D. Robertson, Ed. John Wiley & Sons, Inc., New York, 1957. (Collection of 14 papers presented at the Boston Symposium of the Electrochemical Society, 1954.)
52. R. E. Manfredi and H. J. Nolte, "Application of ceramics to vacuum tubes," *Bull. Am. Ceram. Soc.*, **35,** 105–107 (Mar. 1956).
52a. J. C. Williams and J. W. Nielsen, "Wetting of original and metallized high-alumina surfaces by molten brazing solders," *J. Am. Ceram. Soc.*, **42,** 229–235 (May 1959).
53. W. H. Kohl, "A flush-mounted terminal for all-metal tubes," presentation at the Second National Conference on Tube Techniques, Oct. 15, 1953, New York. See also *Ceram. Age*, **67,** 24–25 (Jan. 1956). Also "Construction of a sealed-off, all-metal cyclotron resonance tube," Stanford University Electronics Research Laboratory Technical Report No. 23 (Aug. 15, 1954).
54. W. R. Wheeler, "Ceramic stacked-mount receiving tubes," presentation at the second annual technical meeting of the Professional Group on Electron Devices, Washington, D. C., October 25–26, 1956.
55. A. J. Stoeckert, "A novel method of fabricating ceramic stems," Proceedings 1959 Electronic Components Conference, Philadelphia, Pa. (May 6–8), pp. 228–231.
56. A. G. Pincus, "Metalographic examinations of ceramic-metal seals," *J. Am. Ceram. Soc.*, **36,** 152–158 (May 1953).
57. E. W. Roberts, "Preparing polished surfaces for microscopic examination in reflected light," *Trans. Brit. Ceram. Soc.*, **54,** 120–136 (1955).
58. H. LaForge, Jr., "Ceramic tube structure quality," *Ceram. Age*, **63,** 13–21 (Feb. 1954).
59. L. J. Cronin, "Trends in design of ceramic-to-metal seals for magnetrons," *Bull. Am. Ceram. Soc.*, **35,** 113–116 (Mar. 1956).

CHAPTER 15

CATHODE MATERIALS AND STRUCTURES

Introduction

This chapter will present a brief description of the various types of cathodes available to the tube engineer, give their performance characteristics, and describe the materials from which they are made. In dealing with these subjects, the main emphasis will be on practical matters rather than on the mechanism of electron emission which has been amply described in the literature.[1-14]

While the cathode itself is the heart of any tube, and operation will be affected adversely by poor cathode performance, it must be realized that the proper choice of materials for all components of the tube, their careful processing before assembly, precautions taken during assembly, and the choice of an optimum exhaust schedule are of the utmost importance for achieving the best possible performance of the cathode during the life of the tube. It has been amply demonstrated by exhaustive tests in many laboratories that the observation of such care during all stages of processing pays great dividends. There is no shortcut, if consistent results are expected.

The inexperienced operator may wonder what all the fuss is about and be tempted to do things the quick and dirty way at times. This is a most dangerous approach because, on a short-term basis, it may occasionally not make any difference in the result and thus encourage such sloppy procedures until a general epidemic of low-emission, emission-slumping, or cathode peeling spreads over the production line and causes quite unnecessary losses. The continuous education of plant personnel, or of those engaged in tube construction in a laboratory, with the object of cultivating an appreciation of the need to observe process specifications rigorously and practice good housekeeping is thus just as important as the availability of a good technical staff who can design tubes according to best practice.

Cathodes are surfaces which emit electrons under the influence of an activating energy and generally in the presence of an electric field which permits the electrons thus released from the surface to travel in a desired direction. Depending on the form of the activating energy—be it heat, light, high-field energy, kinetic energy of incident particles—or the geometric shape of the cathode, many different classifications of cathodes are possible. There are cold cathodes and hot cathodes, photocathodes, field emitters, secondary emitters, filamentary cathodes, cylindrical cathodes, disk cathodes, and hollow cathodes, which take the form of an internally coated cavity, or of vane structures.[18-20, 29]

In cold cathodes, the activating energy may take the form of light quanta, or photons, which cause the emission of electrons from photocathodes. When the energy is provided by particles such as electrons or ions which impinge on the cold cathode from an external source, secondary electrons are emitted from the surface, and the secondary electron emitter is then frequently called a dynode. Very intense electrical fields will cause emission from sharp points which are present on a microscopic scale on apparently smooth surfaces and thus cause voltage breakdown. When a pointed wire is mounted in the center of a spherical tube which is coated with a conductive film, field emission will be obtained when a high positive voltage is applied to the coated bulb. The field emission microscope takes advantage of this effect.[15-17]

Hot cathodes are heated either by passing an electric current directly through the emitter (directly heated cathode), or by placing a separate heater in close proximity to the cathode surface (indirectly heated cathode); at times, recourse is also had to electron bombardment heating. The term "thermionic emitter" is erroneously used for such heated cathodes because they emit electrons and not ions; the terms "thermal electron emitter" and 'thermal electron emission" are much to be preferred and will be used in this text.

A description of the various types of cathodes in terms of their composition and structure, rather than shape, conveys in general terms an idea of the performance characteristics which may be expected from such cathodes. Emitters made from pure metals, film cathodes, composite cathodes, oxide cathodes, dispenser cathodes, matrix cathodes made from pressed and sintered powders—all these are main classifications which can be broken down into sub-groups depending on the particular material, or combination of materials, from which a specific cathode is made. Detailed descriptions of these various cathodes will be given in the following pages. The reader is also reminded of the fact that thermal emission constants of pure metals, which are treated in separate chapters of this book, are given in the respective tabulations of physical characteristics. Some of these metals, like copper, nickel, molybdenum, and others, have no practical importance as thermal emitters and will thus not be mentioned in this chapter.

Thermal electron emission from all types of cathodes is adequately described by the Richardson-Dushman equation:

$$I_s = A_0 T^2 \epsilon^{-\theta/kT} \tag{15.1}$$

where I_s = saturated thermal emission current in a/cm^2
    A_0 = Dushman's constant; the theoretical value is 120 a/cm^{2}deg^2
    T = temperature in degrees Kelvin
    ϵ = base of natural logarithms (2.71828)
    ϕ = true work function in electron volts (e.v.)
    k = Boltzmann's constant (1.3804 $\times$ 10^{-23} joule/°K; 8.6 $\times$ 10^{-5} e.v./°K)

Equation 15.1 should properly be multiplied by a factor $(1 - r)$, where r is the reflection coefficient for electrons whose energy is high enough to permit them to escape from the surface in the absence of an externally applied field. For most clean metals r is of the order of 0.05, and the multiplying term is thus of little practical importance. The value of the work function ϕ varies approximately linearly with temperature according to the relation

$$\phi = \phi_0 + \alpha T \tag{15.2}$$

where ϕ_0 = work function at $T = 0°$K
    $\alpha = d\phi/dT$, the temperature coefficient of the work function
For metals, the experimental values for α are of the order of 10^{-4} e.v./°K. By combining the two equations given above, one obtains

$$I_s = A_0 T^2 \epsilon^{-\alpha/k} \epsilon^{-\phi_0/kT} \tag{15.3}$$

If experimental values of ln I_s/T^2 are plotted against $1/T$, a straight line should be obtained; this is indeed the case for clean metals. The slope of this line is a measure of ϕ_0/k, and the intercept at $1/T = 0$ gives the value of $A_0 \epsilon^{-\alpha/k}$. A graph of this type is called a Richardson plot. Since the experimental value of α is of the same order as that of k, this intercept will be found near a value of 40 a/cm^{2}deg^2 for most metals.[4]

For most pure metals, the value obtained for A from a Richardson plot lies between 30 and 70 a/cm^{2}deg^2. For oxide cathodes and film cathodes, the emission constant assumes a value somewhere near 1, although it may be much less, or quite a bit more than 1. The important point is that the value of this constant for any particular emitter must be known before a valid prediction of the available emission can be made on the basis of the work function and the operating temperature. The saturated, temperature-limited, or pulsed emission that can be obtained from any given cathode thus depends on its physical size, the temperature at which it operates, the true work function of its surface, and the value of the Richardson constant A. Figure 15.1 gives a plot of I_s vs T for various values of ϕ, assuming $A_0 = 120$; corrections must thus be applied to satisfy specific emitters.

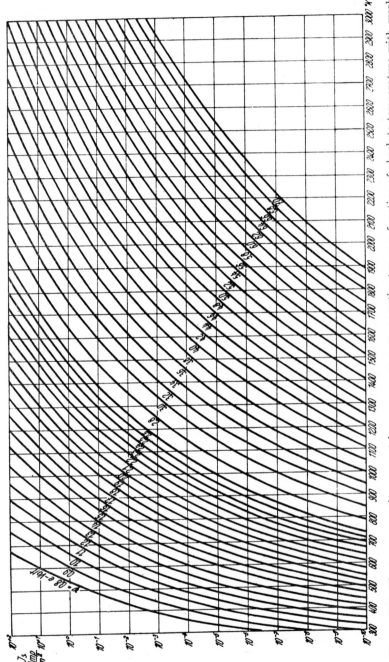

Figure 15.1. Electron saturation current in amperes per square centimeter as a function of absolute temperature with work function of the emitter as parameter. The values of I_s are calculated for $A = 120$ a/cm²deg². After Herrmann and Wagener.[9] (*Courtesy Verlag Johann Ambrosius Barth, Leipzig and Chapman & Hall, Ltd. London.*)

While cathode temperatures enter into the pertinent equations in terms of the Kelvin scale, many specifications and published texts refer to these temperatures in centigrade. This practice makes for some confusion at times, and very reputable authors have occasionally used the wrong scale by mistake. A simple guidepost is the fact that conventional oxide cathodes operate near 1000°K, and thoriated tungsten filaments near 2000°K.

Cathode Design Parameters

When faced with the problem of choosing a suitable thermal emitter for the fulfillment of a given design objective, a tube engineer must bear in mind a number of parameters which must influence his design. These parameters are listed in Table 15.1.

It is a basic requirement for most cathodes that the required emission density be obtained at a minimum cost. This objective can be realized only with cathodes that have a low work function and a low operating tempera-

TABLE 15.1 CATHODE DESIGN PARAMETERS

Emission density (Electron yield)	Y_s	$\dfrac{ma}{cm^2}$	
Heat factor (Emission efficiency)	H	$\dfrac{ma}{W}$	
Radiated power (Low thermal emissivity)	P_r	$\dfrac{W}{cw^2}$	$\left(P_r = \dfrac{Y_s}{H}\right)$
Richardson constant	A	$\dfrac{a}{cm^2 deg\ K^2}$	
Work function	ϕ	e.v.	
Operating temperature	T	°K	
Melting point	T_m	°K	
Vapor pressure temperature (for p = 10^{-5} Torr)	T_e	°K	
Evaporation rate	M	$\dfrac{g}{cm^2 sec}$	
Figure of merit	F	$\dfrac{e.v.}{°K}$	$\left(\dfrac{\phi_0}{T_e} \times 10^3\right)$
Life expectancy	L	hrs	
Ease of activation			
Resistance to poisoning			
Resistance to sparking			
Interface formation (choice of base metal for oxide cathodes)			
Mechanical strength (choice of base metal)			
Cost of fabrication and processing			
Compatibility with materials of adjacent electrodes			

ture, so that the electron yield and the heat factor* both assume high values. The power P_r radiated by the cathode should obviously be as low as possible so that the heater power which compensates for losses by radiation and conduction can be kept low. As a high vacuum of the order of 10^{-6} Torr, or better, must be maintained in a sealed-off high-vacuum tube, it is not possible to use some of the materials which have a very low work function because their vapor pressure is high.[26] Table 15.2 lists evaporation rates as a function of temperature for various metals used in vacuum tubes. To evaluate these parameters, Wright[4] has introduced the vapor pressure temperature, T_e, which represents the temperature of the cathode at which the vapor pressure is 10^{-5} Torr. By combining these two parameters, the same author has defined a figure of merit, F, which is equal to the ratio of the work function multiplied by 10^3 to the vapor pressure temperature T_e. As the value of T_e should be as high as possible, a low value of the figure of merit is desirable. Table 15.3 lists the figures of merit, and also the work functions, the emission constant, and the vapor pressure temperature T_e for a number of the elements.

When a new cathode design has been chosen, it is generally desirable that the cathode and its heater be first separately mounted, and characteristics taken of the cathode temperature as a function of heater voltage and power. Only on the basis of such data can a suitable activation schedule be worked out. A word of warning is also in order in regard to the measurement of cathode temperatures with an optical pyrometer.[27, 28] This instrument gives correct temperatures only when black-body conditions are simulated. If this is not the case, it is necessary to know the thermal emissivity of the surface under observation so that the proper corrections can be added to the reading obtained with the pyrometer. When pure metal emitters are observed in a bell jar, this correction may amount to several hundred degrees. On the other hand, back radiation from a surrounding anode can also have an appreciable effect on the temperature of an emitter, so that the conditions of measurement must always be taken into account. A plot of emissivities vs temperature for various materials is given in the Appendix as Figure A.2.

* It is unfortunate that the term emission efficiency is so firmly established in the literature; if it were really an efficiency, it should have no dimension, but, actually, the thermal yield of electrons in terms of the heater power input is expressed in milliamperes per watt. The term heat factor, H, has been used in Table 15.1 and derives from the German word 'Heizmass,' introduced by the late Professor H. Barkhausen. A true emission efficiency could be defined as the ratio of the number of electrons emitted and the number of atoms evaporated by the cathode surface, as used by Stout[75] in a recent review of dispenser cathodes.

TABLE 15.2. RATE OF EVAPORATION (IN G/CM^2 SEC) FOR VARIOUS METALS USED IN VACUUM TUBES

T °K	T °C	W*	Ta†	Mo‡	Pt‡	Fe‡	Ni‡	Cu‡	Ag§	Ba§§
700	427									1.7×10^{-8}
800	527				1.29×10^{-26}	1.25×10^{-20}	8.41×10^{-21}	1.16×10^{-18}	3.26×10^{-15}	9.1×10^{-7}
900	627				7.21×10^{-23}	3.17×10^{-17}	2.35×10^{-17}	1.64×10^{-15}	1.64×10^{-12}	2.0×10^{-5}
1000	727			1.37×10^{-24}	6.70×10^{-20}	1.38×10^{-14}	1.08×10^{-14}	3.64×10^{-13}	2.10×10^{-10}	2.5×10^{-4}
1100	827		1.33×10^{-28}	9.77×10^{-22}	1.81×10^{-17}	1.82×10^{-12}	1.42×10^{-12}	3.96×10^{-11}	9.97×10^{-9}	1.9×10^{-3}
1200	927	8.2×10^{-28}	1.27×10^{-25}	2.44×10^{-19}	2.06×10^{-15}	9.35×10^{-11}	7.48×10^{-11}	1.51×10^{-9}	2.29×10^{-7}	1.0×10^{-2}
1300	1027	3.16×10^{-25}	4.18×10^{-23}	2.53×10^{-17}	9.73×10^{-14}	2.43×10^{-9}	2.00×10^{-9}	3.11×10^{-8}	3.13×10^{-6}	4.3×10^{-2}
1400	1127	1.26×10^{-23}	6.04×10^{-21}	1.29×10^{-15}	2.92×10^{-12}	3.89×10^{-8}	3.19×10^{-8}	3.94×10^{-7}	1.6×10^{-4}	0.15
1500	1227	7.83×10^{-21}	4.50×10^{-19}	3.81×10^{-14}	5.23×10^{-11}	4.04×10^{-7}	3.38×10^{-7}	3.5×10^{-6}		0.43
1600	1327	4.36×10^{-19}	1.95×10^{-17}	7.60×10^{-13}	6.56×10^{-10}	3.04×10^{-6}	2.55×10^{-6}	1.0×10^{-4}	2.9×10^{-3}	1.1
1700	1427	1.51×10^{-17}	5.45×10^{-16}	1.05×10^{-11}	6.18×10^{-9}	1.74×10^{-5}	1.46×10^{-5}			2.5
1800	1527	3.52×10^{-16}	1.05×10^{-14}	1.06×10^{-10}	4.42×10^{-8}	8.11×10^{-5}	6.82×10^{-5}	1.4×10^{-3}	2.6×10^{-2}	5.2
1900	1627	5.92×10^{-15}	1.36×10^{-13}	7.52×10^{-10}	2.57×10^{-7}	3.08×10^{-4}	2.5×10^{-4}			10.0
2000	1727	7.48×10^{-14}	1.60×10^{-12}	5.34×10^{-9}	1.24×10^{-6}	2.9×10^{-3}	2.2×10^{-3}	1.1×10^{-2}	1.5×10^{-1}	18.0
2100	1827	7.43×10^{-13}	1.38×10^{-11}	2.82×10^{-8}						
2200	1927	6.00×10^{-12}	9.78×10^{-11}	1.30×10^{-7}	1.7×10^{-5}	2.6×10^{-2}	1.2×10^{-2}	5.9×10^{-2}	6.0×10^{-1}	
2300	2027	4.03×10^{-11}	5.88×10^{-10}	5.00×10^{-7}						
2400	2127	2.31×10^{-10}	3.04×10^{-9}	1.80×10^{-6}	1.5×10^{-4}	6.9×10^{-2}	5.0×10^{-2}	2.3×10^{-1}	1.9	
2500	2227	1.16×10^{-9}	1.37×10^{-8}	5.62×10^{-6}						
2600	2327	5.07×10^{-9}	5.54×10^{-8}	1.57×10^{-5}	8.5×10^{-4}	2.2×10^{-1}	1.6×10^{-1}	7.3×10^{-1}		
2700	2427	2.01×10^{-8}	2.00×10^{-7}	4.18×10^{-5}						
2800	2527	7.20×10^{-8}	6.61×10^{-7}	1.04×10^{-4}	4.0×10^{-3}					
2900	2627	2.36×10^{-7}	2.00×10^{-6}	2.35×10^{-4}						
3000	2727	7.15×10^{-7}	5.79×10^{-6}	5.00×10^{-4}						
3100	2827	2.01×10^{-6}	1.51×10^{-5}							
3200	2927	5.32×10^{-6}	3.82×10^{-5}							
3300	3027	1.27×10^{-5}								
3400	3127	3.13×10^{-5}								
3500	3227									
3600	3327									

* Ref. 21.   † Ref. 22.   ‡ Ref. 23.   § Ref. 24.   §§ Ref. 25.

525

TABLE 15.3 WORK FUNCTIONS OF THE ELEMENTS[4]

Group I—	Li	Na	K	Rb		Cs	Cs	Ag	Au
ϕ_0, eV..........	2.4	2.3	2.2	2.15		1.9	4.6	4.5	4.9
T_e, °K..........	750	440	360	340		320	1040	1010	1200
$\phi_0/T_e \times 10^3$.......	3.2	5.0	6.1	6.3		5.9	4.4	4.5	4.1
Group II—	Be	Mg	Ca	Sr		Ba	Zn	Cd	Hg
ϕ_0, eV..........	3.9	3.6	3.2	2.6		2.5	4.3	4.1	4.5
T_e, °K..........	1100	550	700	620		680	500	420	250
$\phi_0/T_e \times 10^3$.......	3.5	6.5	4.6	3.9		3.5	8.6	9.8	18
Group III—	Al		Ga			La	Ce	Pr	
ϕ_0, eV..........	4.2		3.8				3.3	2.8	2.7
T_e, °K..........	1170		—				—	—	—
$\phi_0/T_e \times 10^3$.......	3.6		—				—	—	—
Group IV—	Ti	Zr	Hf	Th	C	Si	Ge	Sn	Pb
ϕ_0, eV..........	3.9	3.57†	3.65†	3.4	4.4	3.6	4.8	4.4	4.0
$A_0\, \epsilon^{-\alpha}/k$..........	—	120†	31.9†	70	48	8	—	—	—
T_e, °K..........	1600	—	2350	1910	2400	—	—	1180	760
$\phi_0/T_e \times 10^3$.......	2.4	—	1.65†	1.8	1.8	—	—	3.7	5.2
Group V—	V	Cb	Ta	As	Sb	Bi			
ϕ_0, eV..........	4.1	4.0	4.1	5.2	4.0	4.6			
$A_0\, \epsilon^{-\alpha}/k$..........	—	37	37	—	—	—			
T_e, °K..........	—	—	2680	—	730	750			
$\phi_0/T_e \times 10^3$.......	—	—	1.5	—	5.5	6.1			
Group VI—	Cr	Mo	W	U					
ϕ_0, eV..........	4.6	4.2	4.5	3.3					
$A_0\, \epsilon^{-\alpha}/k$..........	48	55	70	—					
T_e, °K..........	1040	2230	2860	—					
$\phi_0/T_e \times 10^3$.......	4.4	1.9	1.6	—					
Group VII—........	Mn	Re							
ϕ_0, eV..........	4.0	4.7							
$A_0\, \epsilon^{-\alpha}/k$..........	—	700							
T_e, °K..........	1000	—							
$\phi_0/T_e \times 10^3$.......	4.0	—							
Group VIII—	Fe	Co	Ni	Rh	Pd	Os		Ir	Pt
ϕ_0, eV..........	4.5	4.4	4.6	4.80†	4.99†	4.7		5.40†	5.32†
$A_0\, \epsilon^{-\alpha}/k$..........	26	41	30	33	60	—		63	32
T_e, °k..........	1320	1420	1330	2640§	—	—		—	1860
$\phi_0/T_e \times 10^3$.......	3.4	3.1	3.5	1.83§	—	—		—	2.8

† These values are adjusted by the present author on the basis of more recent data.

§ These values were added by the present author.

Pure Metal Emitters

The choice of pure metals which are useful as thermal electron emitters is very limited; of the several metals plotted in Figure 15.2, only tungsten and tantalum have commercial importance at present; rhenium and hafnium have interesting properties which make them potentially useful in

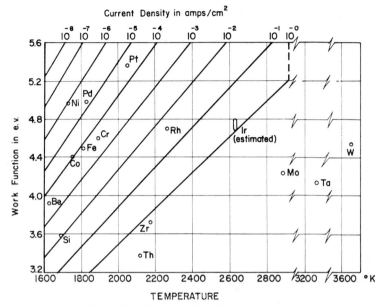

Figure 15.2. Plot of metallic elements according to their work function and melting point and also calculated curves of constant saturated current densities for A = 120 a/cm²deg². After Brunn.[29] (*By permission of Office of Naval Research and Air Research and Development Command, United States Air Force.*)

the future. Data for tungsten and tantalum have been given in Chapters 9 and 11, respectively; those for rhenium and hafnium will be given below.

Rhenium

An extensive survey of the literature on rhenium has been prepared by Sims and Wyler[30] of the Battelle Memorial Institute, where much of the recent research on rhenium has been carried out.[31-35] Its physical characteristics are listed in Table 15.4 and the chemical properties in Table 15.5. Pertinent references[37-49] are quoted for the various entries in the tables. Figure 15.3 gives the black-body vs brightness temperature for sintered rhenium bars after Sims. Figures 15.4 to 15.6 give the true stress-strain diagram, the ultimate tensile strength of annealed and cold-worked rhenium wire at elevated temperatures, and the effect of annealing treatments on the hardness and grain size of cold-worked rhenium, respectively, also after Sims and his co-workers.[34]

Rhenium is one of the precious metals which was considered to be quite rare until recently. Bars are produced by processes of powder metallurgy similar to those serving in the production of tungsten, molybdenum, and tantalum. Sheets, rods, and wire are then produced by cold-working. Ow-

TABLE 15.4. PHYSICAL CHARACTERISTICS OF RHENIUM

Atomic number[39]: 75
Atomic weight[39]: 186.31
Isotopes[39]: 182, 183, 184, *185*, 186, *187*, 188
Density (g/cc)[34]: 21.03
Melting point (°C)[34]: 3,180 ± 20
Boiling point (°C)[32]: 5,630
Heat of fusion, H_m(Kcal/mole)[32]: 7.9

Atomic valence[39]: 7, 4, −1
Valence orbitals[39]: $4f^{14}$, $5d^5$, $6s^2$
Lattice type: h.c.p. (A3)
Lattice constants[32]: a = 2.760 ± 0.001 A
c = 4.458 ± 0.001 A
c/a = 1.615
Atomic radius[39]: 1.375 A
Atomic volume (cc/gm atom)[40]: 9.3
Closest approach of atoms[40]: 2.734 A

Heat of vaporization, H_v(Kcal/mole)[32]: 152
Entropy of fusion, S_m(cal/mole/°K)[32]: 2.3
Entropy of vaporization, S_v(cal/mole/°K)[32]: 26.2
Entropy at 298.16°K, S(cal/mole/°K)[41]: 8.887 ± 0.023
Specific heat, (cal/gm/°C)[43]: 0.0332 (at 20°C)
Thermal conductivity (cal/cm/sec/°C)[43]: 0.111 (0–100°C)
Thermal expansion (cm/cm/°C)[34]: 67 × 10^{-7} (20–500°C)
(perpendicular to hexagonal axis) 68 × 10^{-7} (20–1000°C)

Vapor pressure[44] $\log_{10}$ P atm = 7.5237–40,865/$T_{°K}$ (2220–2725°C)
$\log_{10}$ P mm = 10.4038–40,865/$T_{°K}$ (2220–2725°C)

10^{-8}	10^{-7}	10^{-6}	10^{-5}	10^{-4}	10^{-3}	10^{-2}	10^{-1}	Torr
2200	2330	2480	2640	2830	3060	3330	3670	°K

Spectral emissivity (λ = 0.655μ)[32, 34, 45]: 0.42 (0–1600°C)
0.40 at 2400°C
0.366 at 2800 °C

Electrical resistivity (ohm·cm × 10^{-6}):

at 20°C:21.1[46]   temperature coefficient of resistivity decreases with
at 25°C:19.5[43]   temperature; hot-spot formation less likely but remains positive up to near the M.P.

100	500	1000	1500	2000	2400	°C
25.4	52.6	76.5	93.0	105.0	110.0	microhm-cm[32]

Magnetic suceptibility[43]: +0.37
Electron work function (e.v.)[35]: 4.80   (see also ref. 39–41 for other electronic properties)
Richardson constant A (a/cm²/deg²)[35]: 52.
Secondary electron emission coefficient[48]: δ = 1.25 (at 650 V)
δ_w = 1.36 (at 400 V) (for tungsten)

Mechanical Properties:
Proportional limit (10^3 psi)[34]: 26.3
Modulus of elasticity (10^6 psi)[35]: 67
Ultimate tensile strength (annealed) (10^3 psi): 164[34]; 150[43]
Elongation (annealed) (½ inch pct)[34]: 24
Reduction of area (pct)[34]: 21.7
Surface hardness (annealed) (V.H.N.): 250[35]: 200[43]
Recrystallization temperature (°C)[34]: 1300–1500
Annealing temperature (°C)[34]: 1250; 1700
Yield strength (0.1 pct offset) (10^3. psi)[34]: 42
Yield strength (0.2 pct offset) (10^3 psi)[34]: 46
True stress at unit strain, B, (10^3 psi)[34]: 367
Strain hardening exponent, n[34]: 0.353

TABLE 15.5 CHEMICAL PROPERTIES OF RHENIUM

Electrochemical equivalent: 0.27581 mg/coul
3.62568 coul/mg

A) *Reactions with gases and vapors:*
 dry air at 20°C: practically none[41]
 moist air at 20°C: gradual oxidation to $HReO_4$[41]
 dry air or oxygen at 350°C: oxidation to Re_2O_7[41]
 nitrogen: non, even at elevated temperatures[41]
 halogens (except iodine): rapid attack to form a red solid, $ReCl_3$, and $ReCl_5$[34]
 sulfur vapor (on Re powder): ReS_2 and Re_2S_7 are formed at elevated temperature;[41]
 ReS_2 is a soft black substance which acts as a lubricant[34]
 hydrocarbons: no formation of carbide;[36] carbon diffuses rapidly through Re.
 water vapor: Re shows substantially greater resistance to water-cycle effect than
 tungsten at all temperatures (tests at 1200 and 1750°C for 7,800 hrs.) Re-coated
 tungsten somewhat better in this respect than unalloyed Re, owing to higher
 purity of Re coating.[36]

B) *Reactions with liquids:*
 HCl: none[41]
 H_2SO_4 (cold): some attack[37]
 HNO_3: rapid oxidation to $HReO_4$[41]
 H_2SO_4 (hot): rapid oxidation to $HReO_4$[41]
 molten metals[32]: none with Sn, Zn, Ag, Cu slowly attacked by Al catastrophic attack by Ni, Fe

C) *Reactions with solids:*
 Al_2O_3: Thoriated Re (0.85 p.c. ThO_2 b.wt.) stable at 1750°C for 7000 hrs. (Tungsten
 not compatible with Al_2O_3 above 1400°C)[36]
 Boron: Boride formed which melts below 2250°C.

D) *Oxides of Rhenium:*
 Re_2O_3: sesquioxide, black; soluble in HNO_3
 ReO_2: dioxide, black; soluble in conc. HCl, H_2O_2
 ReO_3: trioxide, red; soluble in alkalis, HNO_3, H_2O_2
 Re_2O_7: heptoxide, brownish yellow; soluble in acids, alkalis, and alcohol M.P.
 297°C; B.P. 363°C[34] readily forms at grain boundaries when metal is worked hot
 in air[34]

ing to the high cost of its recovery from ores, and the extreme care required in processing, the price of rhenium ranges with that of platinum. The melting point of rhenium is second only to that of tungsten, and its vapor pressure is similar to that of tantalum. The electron work function of rhenium is a little higher than that of tungsten but it exhibits a remarkable resistance to the so-called "water cycle" which rapidly destroys tungsten filaments when they operate in the presence of traces of water vapor; it does not form a carbide and is thus not embrittled in the presence of hydrocarbon vapors. Rhenium has one of the highest values of Young's modulus among the metals and exhibits great strength at elevated temperatures; it also is not embrittled by recrystallization to the same extent as tungsten and retains some degree of ductility at high temperature.

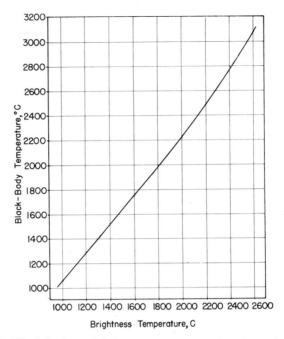

Figure 15.3. Black-body vs brightness temperature for sintered rhenium bars After Sims *et al.*[34] (*Courtesy American Society For Metals.*)

Rhenium work-hardens more rapidly than any other known metal and, for this reason, fabricated shapes can be produced only in steps with intermediate annealing in a protective atmosphere. Working properties can be improved materially by the addition of from 0.5 to 1.0 per cent thoria which causes only a slight reduction in strength, ductility, and high-melting properties.[34] For these reasons, rhenium offers advantages as a filament for electron tube applications and structural components; it also exhibits superior characteristics in comparison to other metals, particularly tungsten, when used as a contact material in magnetos and switches operating in corrosive atmospheres. Rhenium is available as "Mallory 750" from P. R. Mallory & Co., Inc. and from Chase Brass and Copper Co. in Waterbury, Conn. in wire form down to 0.003-in. dia.

Rhenium-molybdenum alloys have been investigated by Hughes and Geach,[50] Duke,[51] and Sims *et al.*[36] Alloys with about 35% molybdenum possess extraordinary ductility and are equivalent mechanically with unalloyed molybdenum for use as an electron tube construction material; tensile strength at elevated temperature, up to about 1000°C, is substantially higher than for molybdenum. This advantage in strength is still more pronounced when comparing recrystallized tungsten-rhenium alloy con-

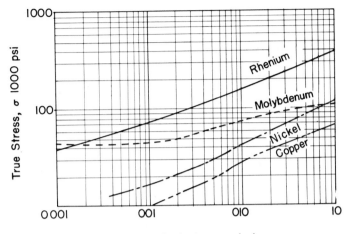

Figure 15.4. Average true stress-strain diagram for rhenium and other metals. After Sims *et al.*[34] (*Courtesy American Society For Metals.*)

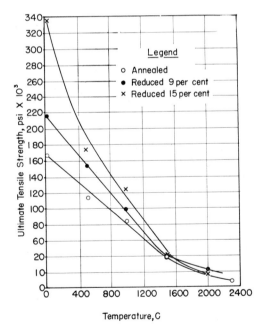

Figure 15.5. Ultimate tensile strength of annealed and cold-worked 0.050 to 0.065-in. dia. rhenium wire at elevated temperatures. After Sims *et al.*[34] (*Courtesy American Society For Metals.*)

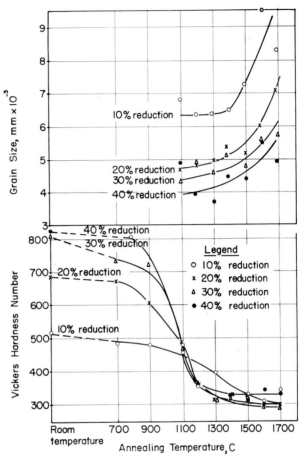

Figure 15.6. The effect of one-hour annealing treatments on the hardness and grain size of cold-worked rhenium. After Sims *et al.*[34] (*Courtesy American Society For Metals.*)

taining 30 % rhenium with plain tungsten; at 1000°C, the ultimate tensile strengths are 150,000 (W-30 Re) and 15,000 psi (W), respectively.[36] Tantalum-rhenium alloys are not as favorable in their characteristics; up to about 10 % rhenium, considerable solid-solution strengthening is observed but alloys become less and less workable as more rhenium is added.

Hafnium

This metal also is rare because it is very difficult to produce it in a pure state; its abundance in the earth's crust is actually greater than that of mercury, tantalum, niobium, and silver.[54] For the aforementioned reason,

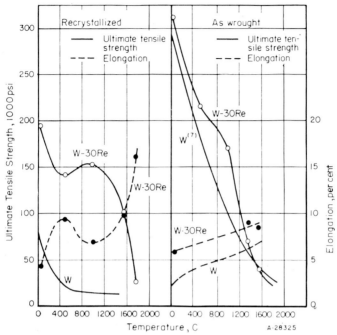

Figure 15.6(a). Properties of wrought and of crystallized molybdenum and Mo-35Re wire. After Sims *et al.*[36] (*Courtesy Air Force Cambridge Research Center, Air Research and Development Command, and Battelle Memorial Institute.*)

hafnium has not found, so far, any commercial application in the production of electron tubes, but, on an experimental scale, its potential usefulness has been investigated for filaments in incandescent lights, for cathodes in x-ray tubes, as an electrode material for high-pressure discharge tubes, where it has been used as an alloy with tungsten or molybdenum, and as a getter when alloyed with titanium.[41]

Table 15.6 presents the physical characteristics of hafnium, and the references to the literature from which the various data have been taken will serve as a guide to the more detailed study of the properties of hafnium.[54-59] Hafnium has many properties in common with zirconium, and it is very difficult to extract the last traces of zirconium from hafnium. Both metals have a great affinity for gases, in particular oxygen and nitrogen, and no deoxidizer is known which effectively removes oxygen from hafnium.

Like other high-melting metals, hafnium is produced by processes of powder metallurgy and can be rolled into sheet, swaged, hammered, or drawn into wire or rod; cold-worked hafnium can be annealed *in vacuo* or in an inert atmosphere; it recrystallizes between 700 and 800°C. Its ma-

TABLE 15.6. PHYSICAL PROPERTIES OF HAFNIUM

Atomic number: 72
Atomic weight: 178.6
Isotopes[40]: 174, 176, 177, 178, 179, *180*
Density (gm/cc)[55]:
  13.36 (calc.)
  13.09 (measured)

Melting point (°C)[54]: 1975
Boiling point (°C)[41]: 5,400
Specific heat (cal/gm/°C)[41]:
  0.0337 (1827°C)
  0.0352 (25–100°C)

Atomic valence: 4
Valence orbitals: $5d^2$, $6s^2$
Lattice type: h.c.p. (A3)
Lattice constants[54, 56]:
  a = 3.1883 A
  c = 5.0422 A
  c/a = 1.58
Atomic radius[41]: 1.442 A
Atomic volume (cc/gm atom)[54]: 13.37
Transformation temperature (h.c.p. →
  b.c.c.)[41]: 1950 ± 100°C

Thermal conductivity (cal/cm/sec/°C)[57]:

50	100	200	300	400	500°C
0.0533	0.0526	0.0514	0.0502	0.0495	0.0491

Thermal expansion (cm/cm/°C)[41]:

	20–204	20–427	20–649	20–871°C
cold worked:		59.18	58.98	57.41	56.89 × 10⁻⁷
annealed:		62.66			59.01 × 10⁻⁷

Vapor pressure[42]: $\log p = -30{,}200/T_{°K} + 9.46$

Evaporation rate (gm/cm²/sec)[47]: $\log W = 6.58 - 2.94 \times 10^4\, T_{°K}$

Spectral emissivity[58]: 0.445 ± 0.008 (1727°C); $\lambda = 0.651$ micron

Electrical resistivity (ohm.cm $\times 10^{-6}$)[57]:

0	50	100	150	200	250°C
34.1	40.6	47.1	53.6	60.1	66.6

Electron work function (e.v.): 3.60[59]; 3.65[58]

Richardson constant A (a/cm²deg²): 22.9[59]; 31.9[58]

Mechanical Properties
  Hardness[41, 54]: Vickers 152; Rockwell A43; Rockwell B78
  Malleability[54]: max. cold reduction 30 p.c.
  Recrystallization temperature (°C)[54]: 700–800
  Young's modulus (psi $\times 10^6$)[41]: 20.0 (annealed Hf)

chinability resembles that of stainless steel.[41] The presence of traces of zirconium in solid solutions with hafnium does not impair the cold-rolling properties of the latter; these are primarily affected adversely by dissolved gases. Once gas has been absorbed by hafnium, it is exceedingly difficult, if not impossible, to drive out such gases at temperatures as high as 1800°C.[59]

Thin Film Emitters

This type of emitter, as the name implies, is characterized by the presence of a thin film, of the order of one or more atomic layers thick, which exists on a pure base metal, or on one which contains admixtures from which the surface film is formed by diffusion of the additive to the surface. If the material deposited on the surface is of an electropositive nature and easily polarized, a dipole layer is formed which acts as though a sheet of positive charge were spread over the surface and so accelerates electrons near the surface inside the metal and facilitates their escape into the vacuum away from the metal. The effective work function of such a thin-film emitter is thus less than that of the base metal by itself and also less than that of the material from which the film is formed, if it were measured by itself in bulk form.

Cesium on oxygen on tungsten and thorium on tungsten are examples of such thin-film emitters; others are tabulated in Table 15.7 where the resulting work function and Richardson's constant are also given. Comparing some of these values with figures shown in Table 15.3, it is apparent that the work function of tungsten by itself is 4.5 e.v., that of thorium by itself is 3.4 e.v., and that of the combination tungsten-thorium is 2.7 e.v. The experimentally determined Richardson constant, on the other hand, which has a value of 70 for the pure metals just quoted, assumes a value of 4 for the thin-film emitter for reasons which have not as yet been clearly established. Some of the advantage gained by the action of the thin film in lowering the work function is thus lost in its also lowering the Richardson constant. The reader is referred to Chapter 9 for a more detailed discussion of thoriated tungsten emitters and their preparation.

TABLE 15.7. WORK FUNCTIONS FOR ADSORBED FILMS[4]

	ϕ_0	$A_0 e^{-\alpha/k}$
	eV	amp/cm²-deg²
Tungsten-cesium.	1.5	3
Tungsten-oxygen-cesium.	1.4	—
Tungsten-oxygen-barium.	1.3	—
Tungsten-barium.	1.6	1.5
Tungsten-thorium.	2.7	4
Tungsten-cerium.	2.7	8
Tungsten-lanthanum.	2.7	8
Tungsten-uranium.	2.8	3
Tungsten-yttrium.	2.7	8
Tungsten-zirconium.	3.1	5
Molybdenum-thorium.	2.6	1.5
Tantalum-thorium.	2.5	1.5

The practical usefulness of thin-film emitters is limited by a number of difficulties encountered in their operation. The greatest benefit is obtained when these films are of a monatomic nature; in the case of thorium on tungsten the optimum coverage is 0.67 monatomic layer, which is to say that the thorium atoms do not completely cover the tungsten surface. Such films are very tightly bound to the base metal by atomic forces so that their vapor pressure is much less than that of the film material in bulk; nevertheless they do evaporate, and they also are readily removed from the surface by sputtering when remaining gas ions impinge on the surface and transfer their momentum to the atoms of the thin film. An exceedingly good vacuum is thus a prerequisite for the successful operation of thin-film cathodes. Provisions must thus be made to lay down a film in the first place and maintain it, or replenish it if it has been depleted or removed entirely by one of the effects just mentioned.

A suitable film can be deposited on the base metal either from the outside by vapor deposition, or from the inside by diffusion. The practical choices available to achieve these ends are to fill the whole tube, say with cesium vapor, and maintain this vapor by operating the entire tube at elevated temperature, in this case at 150°C, or to draw on an internal reservoir embedded in the metal itself from which the surface film can be replenished. In most cases, the emitters do operate in a high vacuum, and for this reason the internal dispensing mechanism is preferred. We are thus led to the discussion of the broad category of dispenser cathodes on which a great amount of effort has been spent during the past several decades.

Dispenser Cathodes[60-75]

As suggested in the preceding paragraph, the term "dispenser cathode" may be interpreted in a very broad way in the sense that any mechanism leading to the deposition of a thin film at the cathode surface and its continuous replenishment would describe a dispenser cathode. It is thus suggested that all dispenser cathodes are essentially thin-film cathodes. The feature that distinguishes dispenser cathodes from film cathodes, such as thoriated-tungsten emitters, is the fact that a surface film is being continuously replenished at operating temperature by the "flow" of the active film-forming agent through a porous substrate. This basic idea has been pursued by many workers in different countries for a long time, but only in recent years has a cathode been developed which promises to satisfy most of the requirements imposed by modern tube technology. The workers at the Philips Laboratories, both in Holland and in the United States at Irvington-on-Hudson, have made very substantial contributions toward the realization of this goal. For this reason, the term "dispenser cathode" has often been associated specifically with the Philips cathodes of which

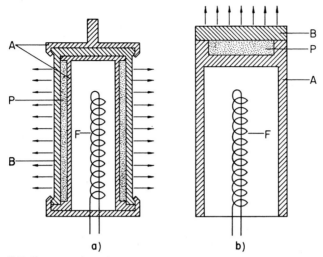

Figure 15.7. Cross-section of two basic forms of the L cathode; a) with cylindrical emitting surface; b) with flat, circular emitting surface. After Lemmens *et al.*[63] (*Courtesy Philips Gloelampenfabrieken, Eindhoven, Netherlands.*)

there are three types, i.e., the L Cathode, the Pressed Cathode, and the Impregnated Cathode.*[62]

The L Cathode, first described in 1950 by Lemmens, Jansen, and Loosjes[63] and now superseded by improved versions, is illustrated in Figure 15.7. Referring to the flat, circular emitter, shown at the right in the illustration, one sees a cylindrical housing, A, made from molybdenum which at its closed end is extended and welded to a porous tungsten disk, B, thus forming a cavity within which a pellet, P, of barium-strontium carbonate is located. A heater, F, furnishes the thermal energy. After the carbonates have been broken down to the oxides and some reduction of the oxides to free barium and strontium has taken place, the metal vapors pass through the pores of the tungsten plug by Knudsen flow and by migration of adatoms over internal surfaces to form a monatomic film at the surface which, in combination with adsorbed oxygen, effectively reduces the work function (ϕ (e.v.) $= 1.67 + 3.24 \times 10^{-4}\ T$). Needless to say, if too much free barium arrives at the surface, there is danger of excessive barium evaporation; also, if the porous tungsten plug is not well sealed to the molybdenum container, barium will escape at the periphery of the cathode surface.

* In the United States these cathodes may be purchased from the Philips Electronics, Inc., Hudson Division, Irvington-on-Hudson and from Semicon Associates, either at Lexington, Kentucky or at their West Coast branch at Watsonville, California. Licensing agreements can be arranged with North American Philips Co., Inc., New York.

Considerable trouble was encountered in the early L cathodes on both counts. The relatively high operating temperature of about 1300°K has also led to many burned-out heaters in the early models. An improved version of the L cathode has recently been developed by Venema and Van den Broek[64] of the Philips Laboratories in Eindhoven in which the Ba/Sr (CO₃) pellet of the older version is replaced by a pellet of tungsten and barium calcium aluminates of the same composition (20 % $BaO \cdot 2Al_2O_3 \cdot 3$ CaO + 80 %W) as that used in the Type B impregnated cathode described below. This new L cathode version permits rapid processing on the pump and is reported to have an extremely low barium evaporation rate; it is, however, more susceptible to poisoning than the impregnated cathode and, in view of the separate cavity for the pellet, structurally not as simple.

The "impregnated" cathode was described by Levi[65] in 1953 and an improved type was discussed in 1955.[66] As illustrated in Figure 15.8, the distinguishing feature of the impregnated cathode, as compared to the former L cathode, is the absence of a separate cavity for the alkaline-earth carbonates. The porous tungsten part is now directly impregnated with the active dispensing compound, which in the earlier model (Type A) consisted of a mixture of normal and basic barium aluminates and in the improved version (Type B) of barium-calcium aluminate. The addition of calcium oxide leads to an appreciable increase of the resulting electron emission, as shown in Figure 15.9, where the pulsed emission density measured in a/cm² is plotted for both types of the impregnated cathode when operated at a temperature of 1400°K (1130°C). Figure 15.10 gives the pulsed emission density measured in a close-spaced diode as a function of anode voltage for different operating temperatures.

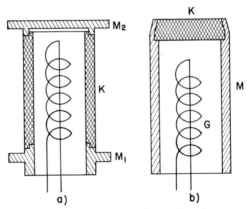

Figure 15.8. Cross-section of two basic forms of the "impregnated cathode," (a) with cylindrical emitting surfaces; (b) with flat, circular emitting surface. After Levi.[65,66] (*Courtesy American Institute of Physics.*)

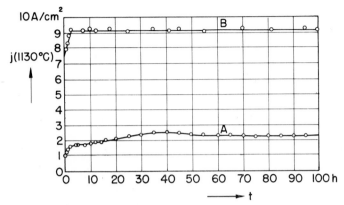

Figure 15.9. The improvement in the emission of an impregnated cathode on replacing the barium aluminate (curve A) by barium-calcium aluminate (curve B) as measured during activation after seal-off. After Levi.[66] (*Courtesy Philips Laboratories.*)

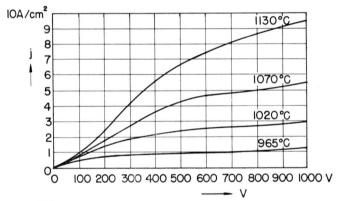

Figure 15.10. Pulsed emission density of an impregnated cathode (Type B) measured in a diode as a function of anode voltage at various cathode temperatures. After Levi.[66] (*Courtesy Philips Laboratories.*)

The pressed Philips cathode was first described by Coppola and Hughes[67] in 1956. This type of cathode is primarily intended for mass production applications, such as cathode ray tubes and picture tubes, and therefore made only as a flat-surface disk emitter, as shown in Fig. 15.11, where two of the cathodes are shown mounted in the usual ceramic support, and a cross-sectional view of the pressed cathode itself is also given. The molybdenum cylinder is made by rolling sheet molybdenum to form a lapped, unwelded seam. A pressed cathode button is made from a mixture of tungsten-molybdenum alloy, containing 75 per cent by weight molybdenum and 25 per cent by weight tungsten, and powdered barium-calcium alumi-

(a)

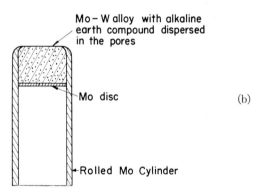

Mo – W alloy with alkaline
earth compound dispersed
in the pores

Mo disc   (b)

Rolled Mo Cylinder

Figure 15.11 (a) Photographs of pressed cathodes with flat emitting surface (3 mm dia.) mounted in ceramic spacers. (b) Sectional view of pressed cathode. After Coppola and Hughes.[67] (*Courtesy Philips Laboratories.*)

nate in the proportion of 5 moles BaO:2 moles Al₂O₃. This mixture is pressed in a hydraulic press at a pressure of 70 tons/sq.in. and sintered in vacuum, or hydrogen, at a temperature of 1750°C to form a hard, strong button which can then be inserted into the molybdenum sleeve, where it is positioned by the presence of a molybdenum disk which separates the cathode button from the space occupied by the heater. The end of the molybdenum cylinder is peened over the cathode end face by a pressing operation. The emission density obtained from pressed cathodes is essentially the same as that observed for improved dispenser cathodes when operated at the same temperature.

TABLE 15.8. THERMAL EMISSION DATA FOR PHILIPS CATHODES

Type of Cathode	L	Impregnated		Pressed Cathode	
		Type A	Type B		
Operating temperature T_0 (°K)	1400	1400	1400	1400	1290
Electron work function ϕ (e.v.)	1.67	1.53	1.67	1.7	
Emission density (pulsed), (a/cm²)	5	1.2	5	2.5	0.9
Richardson constant A (a/cm²deg²)	2.5	0.14	2.5	2.4	
Activation temperature (°K)	1520		1520	1470	
Time required for activation (minutes)			6	6	
Time required for ageing (minutes)		150	150		
Life (hrs)		8000	15,000	5000	
Rate of barium evaporation	high	low	low	med.	
Resistance to poisoning	good	good	v. good	good	
Resistance to ion bombardment	good	good	good	good	
Available shapes (f = flat or shaped disk c = cylindrical)	f or c	f or c	f or c		
Maximum sizes		¾ in. O.D. ¼ long			

The thermal emission constants of interest are tabulated in Table 15.8 for the various types of Philips cathodes. The impregnated cathodes follow a $t^{-1/2}$ law in their rate of barium evaporation, while the rate is substantially constant for the L cathode. As most of the barium in impregnated cathodes evaporates during the first few hours, it is possible to operate the cathodes for a suitable period of time in a separate envelope to get rid of the excess barium before installing them in the final tube.

Activated impregnated cathodes and pressed cathodes may be exposed to air, but must then be reactivated, whereupon they regain their original level of emission. Pulsed emission and d-c emission attain essentially the same values. The life of the cathode naturally depends on the operating temperature; while the value of 15,000 hours is given in Table 15.8 for a porous tungsten disk, 1 mm thick, operating at 1400°K, the life obtained when operating at 1350°K (1000°C) and a current density of 5 a/cm² (Type B) may extend to as much as 32,000 hours. It is estimated that an increase of the operating temperature by 50°C (brightness) will increase the emission density by a factor of 2.

While these test results are very impressive indeed, it must be remembered that they are obtained with close-spaced test diodes. Experience with full-scale tubes has not been as favorable, so far. Espersen[68] has, on the other hand, more recently published performance data of magnetrons equipped with impregnated Philips cathodes which indicate longer life than obtained with certain unspecified sintered nickel matrix cathodes. In Type

5780A x-band magnetron, a pulse primary emission of 100 ma/cm^2 was measured at 800°C and the total peak emission, largely produced by secondary emission, was 16 a/cm^2. For other types of magnetrons, 4J52 and 4J53, lower arcing rates during aging and greater current stability, when using longer pulses than ordinarily specified, were observed for L cathodes and impregnated cathodes.

Philips cathodes cannot be operated in the presence of mercury vapor and they are very sensitive to poisoning by platinum, palladium, titanium, or zirconium which migrate into the porous plug and kill the emission or increase the rate of barium evaporation.[68] It is thus not advisable to use platinum as a flux for spot welding the heater leads;[69] an 8-mil dia. tantalum wire can be inserted into the bare heater coil before spot welding and thus be used as a fluxing agent.* Owing to the relatively high operating temperature of the impregnated cathode, the materials for adjacent electrodes must also be carefully chosen for fear of depositing harmful metal films by sublimation from adjacent elements. Tantalum and molybdenum are best suited for close-spaced elements; titanium and zirconium are harmful; copper is harmless if kept sufficiently cool. Brodie and Jenkins[70] have used water-cooled copper anodes spaced as close as 1 mm to an impregnated cathode.

Magnetron Cathodes

One type of pressed cathode has been described in the preceding section as a member of the series of Philips cathodes. Many of the pressed cathodes to be described in the following paragraph rely for their emission on a combination of thin-film and dispenser mechanisms. A great amount of effort has been expended on the development of such pressed and sintered cathodes ever since World War II.[76-90] During the development of high-power magnetrons, it was found that conventional oxide-coated cathodes had a very limited life and disintegrated owing to excessive sparking induced, in part, by the high resistivity of the oxide coating; this caused hot spots and deformation, or arcs, when large current pulses were drawn from the surface.

In an attempt to increase the effective conductivity of the coating, a nickel wire mesh was spot-welded to the nickel face of the cathode and the oxide coating brushed or painted into the mesh interspaces, thus producing what became known as a *matrix cathode*. A next step in this development was to mix nickel powder with the alkaline-earth carbonates and apply the

---

* Brit. Pat. 792,046 (1958) reports on a dispenser cathode where at least part of the surface of a porous sintered body is made of a metal of the platinum family or an alloy thereof and adapted to form an alloy with an alkali metal or alkaline earth metal.

mixture to the mesh, thus arriving at a *"nickelized cathode."*[84] Instead of using a nickel wire mesh on the cathode base surface, it was then found advantageous to sinter nickel powder to the nickel base and brush or press a suspension of carbonates into the pores of the sintered powder matrix. These cathodes were known as *"mush cathodes."* If a nickel mesh is retained on the sintered nickel surface, one arrives at the *"mesh mush cathode."** These measures resulted in a considerable improvement of the arcing characteristics of magnetron cathodes and extended their useful life very much.[76]

The intrinsic emission density expected from a magnetron cathode at the temperature imparted by the heater is not very high because the temperature is further raised by back bombardment when electrons that have been emitted into the interaction space return to the cathode; secondary electrons are also emitted as a result of this action. The considerable reduction of the electron yield which results when nickel powder is mixed with the alkaline-earth carbonates to the extent of as much as 70 per cent has thus no harmful consequence for the operation of the tube.

Pressed and Sintered Cathodes

Endeavors in more recent years have been directed toward an improvement of the conventional oxide cathode in several respects. In many cases, it is desirable to be able to expose an activated cathode to the atmosphere when changes are made on a demountable system and then use the same cathode on a subsequent run with undiminished activity; for close-spaced triodes and for convergent-flow guns, it is desirable to have a machinable cathode surface; resistance to ion bombardment, poisoning, and sparking should be high. All these requirements are satisfied to varying degrees by a number of the recently developed matrix-type cathodes, and some of them are claimed to exceed the performance of impregnated Philips cathodes by a considerable margin.[85] These advantages are not obtained without paying a price. The activation of pressed cathodes takes about five times as long as that of conventional oxide-coated cathodes of similar dimensions.[75]

Several different approaches have been taken by various workers aiming at the production of a useful pressed sintered cathode. It would lead us too far afield to describe all these methods in detail, but, essentially, one can distinguish two types of fabrication. Nickel powders are mixed with the carbonates and a small amount of reducing agent, such as titanium, zirconium, tungsten, tantalum, or boron, is added to the mixture to accelerate the production of barium metal, bearing in mind that too liberal a rate

---

* The megawatt klystrons in use at the W. W. Hansen Laboratories of Physics at Stanford University utilize cathodes of this type even today; the geometrical shape of these cathodes is that of spherical cups which range in diameter up to 3 inches.[77]

of production of free barium will cause excessive barium evaporation. These mixtures are pressed into pellets at pressures of from 50 to 100 tons/sq.in., sintered at elevated temperature in a hydrogen atmosphere at about 600°C for 15 minutes, in one case, and then attached to a much thicker base layer of nickel powder which also has been enriched by an activator such as zirconium hydride.

Figure 15.12 shows the structure of such a molded nickel cathode recently described by Hadley, Rudy, and Stoeckert.[90] "The cathode sleeve is a nickel cylinder having an outer diameter of 0.125 in., a length of about 0.33 in., and a wall thickness of 0.004 in. The cathode pellet is composed of two layers; the lower layer, about 0.045 in. thick, contains nickel powder and an activator (ZrH_2) in the weight proportions of 99 to 1. The upper part of the pellet, which is 0.003 to 0.005 in. thick, contains nickel powder (69% by weight), alkaline earth carbonates (30%) and an activator (1%). The nickel powder is fired at 600°C for 15 minutes in a hydrogen atmosphere (-10°C dew point). All powders are thoroughly dried before use.

"The most useful emissive material is a triple carbonate, designated RCA-33C-311-B containing 57 per cent by weight barium carbonate, 39 per cent strontium carbonate, and 4 per cent calcium carbonate." Carbonyl nickel powders of various size ranges are generally used for molded nickel cathodes. The authors just quoted[90] found a size range from 1 to 3 microns giving the best results, but size ranges from 9 to 60 microns did not necessarily give different performance. Of the various reducing agents tested, zirconium hydride gave satisfactory results but others were also found useful; carbon produced excessive gassing and resulted in short lives.

The sintering operation is considered to be the most important step in

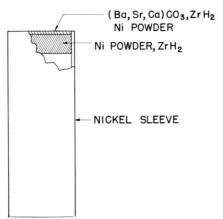

Figure 15.12. Structure of a molded nickel cathode. After Hadley, Rudy, and Stoeckert.[90] (*Courtesy The Electrochemical Society.*)

TABLE 15.9. TIME-TEMPERATURE SCHEDULE DURING SINTERING
OF MOLDED NICKEL CATHODES[90]

Temp, °C*	Atmosphere	Time (min)
Room to 600	H_2	8
600 to 1000	N_2	7
1000 to 600	N_2	7
600 to Room	H_2	8
Room	N_2	10

* Temperature is held constant during change of atmosphere from one gas to another, which may take as much as a minute.

the processing of molded nickel cathodes and brings about a remarkable improvement in life performance as compared with cathodes that have not been sintered. Table 15.9 gives the schedule used, and it should be noted that both nitrogen and hydrogen are passed in succession through the muffle furnace where the cathodes are held in a nickel boat within a "Vycor" tube. The gases are passed in series through a deoxidizer, an electro-drier, and a liquid-nitrogen trap; the hydrogen flows at a rate of 200 cc/sec. and the nitrogen at 50 cc/sec.

Activation on the pump is achieved by raising the heater voltage gradually in half-volt steps, making sure that the pressure in the tube does not exceed 10^{-4} Torr and holding the cathode temperature at a maximum of 1000°C brightness temperature until the pressure falls below 10^{-6} Torr. With a cathode-to-anode spacing of 0.015 in., the plate voltage is slowly increased to 50 volts and held at this value for about 15 minutes, at the end of which time the cathode current density is about 0.5 a/cm². The getter is then partially fired, the tube sealed off, and the getter completely fired. After seal-off, the cathode is aged for about 15 minutes at a temperature of 1000°C and a plate voltage of 50 volts.

"The mechanism of the sintering process is not completely understood. Presumably, it includes deoxidation of the nickel powder, decomposition of the zirconium hydride, and diffusion of a small amount of free zirconium into the nickel matrix. The zirconium which diffuses into the matrix later diffuses out and acts as a reducing agent throughout the life of the emitter. During sintering, at least part of the carbonate is broken down, as evidenced by the fact that sintered cathodes give off considerably less gas during exhaust than unsintered ones. A pulsed emission density of about 2–10 a/cm² is obtained under field-free conditions when operating the cathode at a temperature of 850°C brightness temperature. It is estimated that only about 70 per cent of the surface is emitting. This finding based on electrical measurements can be correlated with geometrical considerations and the proportions of carbonate and nickel used in the active pellet which suggests that less than 70 per cent of the active surface is composed of alkaline-earth oxide. It is believed that at least two sources of emission are required to explain this fact: (a) alkaline-earth-oxides are contained within the pores of the matrix; and (b) a monolayer of alkaline-earth-oxide (probably barium oxide), has migrated onto a small area of the nickel which surrounds each pore.

"The pulsed emission of the cathode is greater than the d-c emission, but by a factor much smaller than that usually reported for an alkaline-earth-oxide cathode. When used in a developmental projection kinescope with anode voltage of 40 kv and a beam current of 1 ma without an ion trap, the cathode was subjected to heavy ion bombardment and showed no deterioration after 1500 hours of operation while a conventional oxide cathode when used under such conditions lasts only about 600 hours." In another application, the authors report using the molded nickel cathode in a demountable vacuum system for the purpose of evaluating electron-optical structures; the beam current in this case was 150 μa, and the cathode performed satisfactorily and survived thirty openings of the vacuum system while an oxide cathode would only permit three exposures to the atmosphere.

Fane[89] has recently reported on a sintered nickel matrix cathode using boron as the reducing agent and demonstrated that lives of at least 8000 hours may be obtained at d-c current densities in excess of 0.5 a/cm². The general approach to the fabrication of this cathode follows that described by Hadley et al.,[90] but the use of boron is a distinct innovation. Boron powder (less than 300 mesh) was added to the carbonyl nickel powder (3–5 microns, 68% by weight), the barium/strontium/calcium carbonates, and barium stearate (1% by weight) which served as a binder and lubricant during pressing. The powders were ballmilled for 24–72 hours and then pressed in a hardened steel die at 50 tons/sq.in. and sintered in a hydrogen atmosphere at 1000°C for 15 minutes followed by 30 minutes at 1100°C. Sintered cathodes were spot-welded into a molybdenum or nickel retaining sleeve and then mounted in test diodes. Activation on the pump was carried out by raising the cathode temperature slowly to 1050–1075°C for about 5 minutes while maintaining the pressure in the tube below 5 × 10⁻⁴ Torr. Activation is then continued at 1000–1050°C at a pressure of 5 × 10⁻⁶ Torr.

After gettering and seal-off, ageing is continued for from 24 to 48 hours while gradually reducing the temperature to the required operating value. The total barium evaporation rate is given as 1.5 × 10⁻¹ μg/cm² hr. at 900°C, a temperature at which about 2.5 a/cm² is available. These figures are similar to those given by Brodie and Jenkins[70] for their impregnated cathodes. Photomicrographs suggest that the cathode surface consists of emitting oxide grains within a nickel matrix, the work function of the nickel being reduced by at least a partial barium coverage. Figure 15.13 gives Schottky curves of a typical cathode produced by Fane.

One such cathode, operating at 835°C drawing a space-charge limited emission of 1 a/cm² at an anode voltage of 1 kV, has shown a 25-percent decrease in emission in 10,000 hours compared with a 30-percent decrease in d-c emission and a 50-percent decrease in pulse emission over a period of 1000 hours reported by Hadley *et al.* for their molded cathodes operating under similar conditions. It is indicated that such cathodes will find useful application in travelling-wave tubes, backward-wave oscillators, and high-power pulse tubes where severe operating conditions seriously limit the capabilities of conventional oxide cathodes.

The second procedure used for the production of molded, sintered cathodes is more closely akin to the fabrication of impregnated cathodes described in the preceding section. In this case, a sintered nickel matrix of controlled porosity is impregnated with solutions which precipitate a mixed carbonate within the pores as described by Balas, Dempsey, and Rexer[82] and by Apelbaum.[84] The porosity of the nickel plug is of the order of 50 per cent, and sintering takes place at about 1000°C in a hydrogen atmosphere. Barium/strontium acetate or barium hydroxide have been

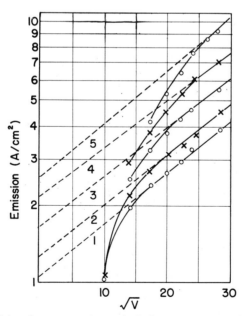

Figure 15.13. Schottky curves of a typical sintered-nickel matrix cathode. After Fane.[89] (*Courtesy The Institute of Physics, London.*)

used as the first impregnant, and ammonium carbonate as the precipitating agent. Activation at 850°C takes several hours and operation at 725°C results in relatively stable emission for several thousand hours. Saturated pulsed emission is given as 1 a/cm² at 775°C. The work function of the cathode ranges from 1.25–1.50 e.v. depending on the activation technique employed.

Nickel ribbons have been produced by powder metallurgical techniques and impregnated with alkaline-earth carbonates. Mesnard and Uzan[81] have investigated sandwich structures of such ribbons made from powdered tungsten mixed with alkaline earth carbonates and suitable additions of nickel.

Pressed refractory matrix cathodes for magnetrons have been described by Pondy, Becker, and Robinson.[85] Mixtures of molybdenum and tungsten are ball-milled with 10 % by weight of barium carbonate, 0.2 % zirconium hydride, and 1 % stearic acid, pressed at 40 tons/sq.in. onto a molybdenum sleeve to a tolerance of ±1 mil. A first firing in dry hydrogen takes place for one hour at 750°C and is followed by a second firing in nitrogen for about one hour at 1500°C. Pulse primary emission of 160 ma at 850°C was obtained in 4J52 magnetrons, a value which is about four times as much as needed for oscillation. Power output, pulling figure, missing pulse spectrum, all looked extremely promising.

Boride Cathodes

These cathodes have been described principally by Lafferty.[91] The alkaline-earth metals, the rare-earth metals, and thorium all form interstitial compounds of the same formula MB_6 and have the same crystal structure (Figure 15.14). The boron atoms form a three-dimensional framework which surrounds the large metal atoms in a cubic lattice such that a boron octahedron is found at each corner of a cube. The strong binding forces between the boron atoms lead to a series of compounds which are very refractory and have melting points above 2100°C. As the metal atoms are trapped in the boron cages and no free valence bonds exist between the metal atoms and the surrounding boron atoms, the valence electrons of the metal become free electrons and impart a metallic character to the compounds. When the hexaborides are heated to a sufficiently high temperature, the metal atoms evaporating from the surface are immediately replaced by diffusion of metal atoms from the lattice. The boron framework does not evaporate. The active metal is thus dispensed only when needed and evaporation losses are kept at a minimum, while an active cathode surface is maintained constantly.

A saturated emission density of about 2.5 a/cm² is obtained at 1500°C. The true work function of lanthanum boride is $\phi = 2.66 + 1.23 \times 10^{-4} T$;

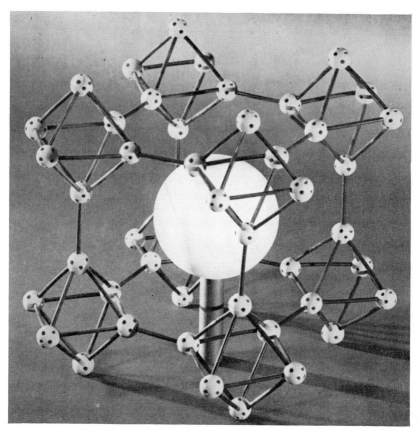

Figure 15.14. The hexaboride crystal structure. After Lafferty.[91] (*Courtesy American Institute of Physics.*)

the Richardson constant and work functions for various hexaborides are listed in Table 15.10. A monolayer coverage can be maintained at the surface of a lanthanum boride cathode at temperatures below about 2130°K, and one would expect an emission density of 70 a/cm² at this temperature. These cathodes stand up well under positive ion bombardment and are not affected by air or moisture, so that they are particularly well suited for use in experimental demountable systems.

They have, however, one disadvantage which has mitigated against their practical use in commercial tubes. The boron attacks the base metal to which the lanthanum boride coating is applied and forms interstitial boron alloys with the base. When this occurs, the boron framework around the alkaline-earth or rare-earth metals collapses and permits the latter to evaporate. With tantalum as the base metal, this effect is least pro-

TABLE 15.10. WORK FUNCTIONS FOR BORIDES[91]

Boride	ϕ_0	$A_0 \epsilon^{-\alpha/k}$
Calcium	2.86	2.6
Strontium	2.67	0.14
Barium	3.45	16.0
Lanthanum	2.66	29.0
Cerium	2.59	3.6
Thorium	2.92	0.5
Mischmetall*	2.64	14.0

* Mischmetall is an alloy of all the rare-earth metals. Mixed barium and cerium gives values between those of barium and cerium. Mixed thorium and cerium gives values between those of thorium and cerium.

Note.—At a temperature where evaporation rate is 10^{-8} g/cm²/sec
Molybdenum gives 0.01 amp/cm²
Thorium gives 0.08 amp/cm²
Columbium gives 0.4 amp/cm²
Tungsten gives 0.8 amp/cm²
Tantalum gives 1.2 amp/cm²
Lanthanum gives 10 amp/cm²

nounced. Borides do not react with graphite, and carburized tantalum has thus been used as a base metal. As borides do not adhere well to metal or ceramic surfaces, they cannot be applied in the conventional way but must be fastened in a coarse mesh according to the techniques described above for mesh cathodes, or be mechanically fastened to the surface. Boride cathodes have not been used in commercial tubes, so far.

Thoria Cathodes

Most extensive investigations have been carried out on thoria cathodes during the past 25 years at the Bartol Research Foundation of the Franklin Institute at Swarthmore, Pennsylvania, and the many reports that have been issued by the workers at this institution should be consulted for details.[92-97] In addition, much work on this subject has been done by industrial organizations and research laboratories in this country and abroad. These thoria cathodes are primarily intended for use in magnetrons to provide more stable emission and longer life under the critical conditions which prevail in these tubes. In the early stages of development, self-supporting, pure thoria sleeves were used which were indirectly heated; later work aimed at the production of directly heated thoria cathodes which were made conductive by the admixture of metal powders.[98] More recent work at Bartol is concerned with the perfection of thorium-impregnated tungsten or molybdenum matrix cathodes which have given promising results in test diodes.[97] Thorium is applied in the form of a slurry in heptane, and great care must be taken not to expose it to the atmosphere longer than absolutely necessary. When operating at a temperature of 1600°C, d-c emission of 3 a/cm² has been reported.

Thoria cathodes are essentially thin-film cathodes in which the thorium is furnished from the thoria by electrolytic action;[96] this mechanism leads to a rapid depletion of thorium and a limited life.

Thoria-coated tungsten or tantalum filaments are being used in some commercial tubes such as the RCA type 8D21[99] and a rectifier Type 552 made by United Electronics. The work function of such cathodes is 2.6 e.v. and an emission density of 5 a/cm² is available at 2000°K.[4] The coating is applied to an average weight of 20 mg/cm² by painting, spraying, or cataphoresis.[100] Activation takes place more rapidly when the filament is heated to temperatures of the order of 2200°K. The predominant role which electrolysis plays in the conduction mechanism results in depletion of thorium. The erosion loss of the coating is much faster than that by evaporation. Wright[4] has observed complete loss of a coating sprayed to 24 mg/cm² after 500 hours operation at 1900°K while drawing current at 0.5 a/cm².

Kyonghi Hong[100a] has recently described a new method for the preparation of thoria cathodes and emphasizes the advantage of using amyl acetate in the process, thus bringing about a carbonization of thoria on activation. A similar effect could be achieved by spraying a molybdenum sleeve with hydrocarbons (Krylon No. 32 was used) before applying a suspension of thoria powder by cataphoresis, according to Hanley.[100b] Stout and Gibbons[100c] found it beneficial to use an alloy sponge consisting of zirconium and tungsten on the base metal before applying the thoria coating which then filled the pores of the sponge (extended-interface cathodes). The authors report 4 a/cm² pulsed emission at 1500°C.

Cathodes of this type require no current processing for activation and withstand considerable ion bombardment. For (Ba/Sr)O coatings, alloy sponges consisting of 0–15 % Ti and 100-85 % Ni (by weight) were found to be most effective, giving pulsed emission of 0.7 a/cm² at 750°C.

Barium-Strontium-Calcium Oxide Cathodes

These emitters, to which reference has repeatedly been made in the preceding text as conventional oxide cathodes, are not only the oldest, historically, but also are most widely used at the present time in receiving tubes, cathode ray tubes, picture tubes, and similar devices. Needless to say, their mechanism of operation[1-14] and the techniques involved in their preparation[101-105] have been studied most extensively. Oxide cathodes are n-type semiconductors which rely in their operation on the presence of an adequate number of donors, the nature of which has not been established beyond all argument. The very much simplified picture of the mechanism of operation which is often presented in textbooks assumes that free barium is released within the bulk of the oxide coating during the activation process and then migrates to the surface to form a monatomic film of barium. If correct, this mechanism would make the oxide cathode essentially a dispenser type cathode, which it is not in its optimum state of operation; it may, however, revert to a thin-film dispenser-type cathode in various stages of deterioration.

The oxide coating is a discontinuous structure having a porosity of more than 50 per cent. Conduction through the coating takes place predominantly by the drift of electrons which at very low temperatures migrate through the solid structure of the crystalline semiconductor; at elevated temperatures, in the operating range, electrons will also traverse the pore cavities, and at very high temperatures, this free electron flight will be limited by space charge.[14]* It has been shown that a high electrical conductivity of the oxide coating parallels the high activity of the cathode. It is thus important to develop pores of an optimum size to give a higher conductivity than can be expected from a crystalline structure in the absence of pores. Creating the optimum number of donors, which are generally assumed to be oxygen deficiencies, and the proper amount of free barium, and maintaining these throughout life, is a very difficult problem, which requires careful attention to the proper choice of raw materials, both for the powder itself as well as the base metal to which the powder is applied, the activation schedule, the ageing procedure after seal-off, and many other details. It will not be possible to do justice to all these items in the summary to be presented in the following paragraphs, but an attempt will be made at least to emphasize the highlights and give the most pertinent references to the literature.

It is general practice throughout the industry to apply *the coating* in the form of either double or triple carbonates; single barium carbonate is not used, except for experimental study. The double carbonates are those of barium and strontium, and the triple carbonates contain, in addition to the generally equi-molar mixture of Ba/Sr carbonates, additions of $CaCO_3$ amounting to either 4, 6, or 13 per cent of the total weight. A typical triple carbonate supplied by the J. T. Baker Chemical Company in Philipsburg, New Jersey thus contains 13% $CaCO_3$ + 31% $SrCO_3$ + 56% $BaCO_3$.

The mixed carbonates are frequently obtained by co-precipitating the corresponding nitrates either with sodium carbonate, sodium bicarbonate, or

---

* In a private communication to the author, V. L. Stout of the General Electric Company Research Laboratory, Schenectady, points out that, according to his measurements, pore conduction in a really active oxide-coated cathode is not detectable. He concludes that conductivity through or over the oxide crystallites predominates over pore conduction even at high temperatures.

with ammonium carbonates; the shape of the crystallites so obtained, be they spherulites or needles, has a definite effect on the performance of the coating. The alkaline-earth carbonates may be obtained commercially in the form of dry powders, or as suspensions in organic binders such as butyl binder which consists of butyl alcohol, butyl acetate, and Pyroxylin cotton. Some coating mixtures contain certain organic accelerators which permit a more complete breakdown of the carbonates into oxides during the activation on the pump.

It is a fact worth noting that most commercial tube manufacturers produce their own coating compositions rather than relying on outside suppliers. In addition to the company noted above, coating mixtures can thus be obtained under established code numbers from Raytheon, RCA, Sylvania, General Electric Company, and probably others. The particle size of the coating ranges from 1–9 microns with a maximum particle size of 25 microns. The chemical composition prescribed for an ASTM diode is given as follows:[102]

    barium carbonate, 57.2 $\pm$ 2%
    strontium carbonate, 38.8 $\pm$ 2%
    calcium carbonate, 4.0 $\pm$ 0.5%
    water-soluble matter, 0.10% max.
    iron, 0.003% max.
    chloride, 0.003% max.
    heavy metals, 0.003% max.
    hydrochloric acid, insoluble 0.01%

It is recommended that the carbonate shall be dried for 12 hours at 110°C just before use and allowed to cool in a dry atmosphere.

The binder composition recommended for the ASTM diode is given as follows:

    nitrocellulose (25 sec.), 12.2%
    ethyl alcohol (dehydrated), 6.6%
    amyl acetate, 81.2%
    total solids, 12.2%

This binder composition applies to a product marketed by E. I. Dupont de Nemours and Company under the trade name Pyroxylin No. 5511. As mentioned above, other types of binder, such as butyl, are sometimes preferred as there is less danger of free carbon remaining dispersed throughout the coating on complete breakdown.

The coating mixture is prepared by diluting 60 ml of the stock binder solution just described with 400 ml amyl acetate and adding this diluted binder solution to 200 g of the carbonate powder. The mixture is then ground in a ball mill for about 20 hours with proper attention being given to the correct number and size of pebbles relative to the volume of the container. The viscosity of the binder by itself is given as 16 ± 5 centipoises and that of the milled carbonate mixture as 38 ± 1 centipoises at $25°C$.[102]

The coating mixture is generally applied to the cathode sleeve surface by spraying with a spray gun while a number of cathode sleeves are mounted in a spray frame, or rack, and provision is made for the sleeves to be exposed to the spray from all sides for a given amount of time; sometimes individual cathode sleeves are mounted on pins which rotate on a fixture. The type of nozzle used for the gun, the air pressure applied to the gun, the distance of the gun from the sleeves, and the relative humidity of the atmosphere in the spray chamber are all important parameters that determine the quality of the resulting coating. The apparent density of the coating is specified for the ASTM diode as $0.8 \pm 5\%$ and the coating weight as 8 mg/cm^2 $\pm$ 10%. The coating weight is determined either by weighing the cathode before and after spraying, or by measuring the coated diameter with a micrometer which permits reading to 0.0001 in. In practical cases, various manufacturers will digress from the prototypes just given; depending on requirements, the density may be as low as 0.7 or as high as 1.3; the coating weight may range from 2 to 8 mg/cm^2, or higher. Low densities are mostly used in amplifier tubes, while a dense, "wet" coating is often used for rectifiers. The thickness of the coating will rarely exceed 2 mils.

Instead of coating by spraying, the carbonates may also be applied by cataphoresis,[106, 107] by co-precipitation of the barium and strontium carbonates out of a solution of $(BaSr)$ $(HC_3O)_2$ when a current is passed through this solution while the cathode sleeve is mounted on a platinum electrode immersed in the bath.[108] In the laboratory, recourse is sometimes had to applying the coating by means of a brush;[77] this practice is not recommended, as the uniformity of the coating leaves much to be desired.

A unique and novel technique for the application of oxide coatings to the cathode base metal has recently been announced by Sylvania Electric Products, Inc. under the trade name "Sarong Cathodes."[109] The carbonate mixture is prepared as a separate film which is cut to size and wrapped around a cathode sleeve, or applied to a flat surface, as the case may be. Uniform thickness of the coating and sharp edges are thus readily achieved. Over one million tubes with "Sarong" coatings have been manufactured by Sylvania at this time of writing (April 1959), and a large fraction of the total production is scheduled to be converted to this type of coating in the near future. The greater control over thickness and density manifest themselves in more uniform temperature distribution over the coated sleeve, improved cut-off characteristics of the tubes, and a smaller number of rejects from grid-to-cathode shorts.

It may be proper at this point to emphasize to experimenters in university laboratories the importance of all the details so far enumerated. Costly failures can be avoided, if bottles containing coating solutions are properly labeled, indicating whether the content is a double carbonate or a triple carbonate, where it came from, when it was ordered and delivered; it should be known how long it was ballmilled, and to what thickness or weight the coating was applied to the cathode, and what the cathode base metal consists of. To leave all these items to happenstance is a dangerous procedure. Some degree of incoming inspection and material control should be exercised even in research laboratories.

Sometimes the complete assembly, including the getter, is dipped into boiling distilled water and then dried in air at about 100°C for approximately 20 minutes; this operation must be performed less than two hours before sealing if any benefit is to be derived from it. The essential feature of this treatment seems to be a steam cleaning of the internal glass wall by which poisoning agents such as chlorides are removed. There must thus be enough moisture left distributed throughout the bulb to effect this action, and excessive drying after dipping, or prolonged storage, would mitigate against the fulfillment of this condition.* There is no question that under certain circumstances, i.e., when bulbs or other parts are not clean, this washing has a very beneficial effect, but it is preferable that process operations be so well controlled that this operation is not necessary.

The *exhaust procedure* will vary considerably depending on whether one deals with the mass production of receiving tubes on sealex machines or with manifold exhaust of power tubes and microwave tubes where greater care in processing can be taken on account of economical factors. For this latter category, and for experimental tubes in the laboratory, the following remarks apply.

After all components of the tube have been carefully cleaned† prior to assembly, they should be vacuum-fired in a separate envelope on a separate pump station set aside for this purpose. It is obvious that the removal of gas and contaminants greatly enhances the degree of vacuum which can be obtained on the pump. The bulk of gas contained in nickel cathode sleeves is concentrated within a surface layer about 0.1 mil thick which

---

* Personal communication from G. D. O'Neill.

† The reader's attention is directed to a recent ASTM Symposium on "Cleaning of Electronic Device Components and Materials," held at Philadelphia, Pa. on October 13–14, 1958. The 21 papers presented at this Conference contain much valuable information. The Proceedings of the Symposium have been published by ASTM as Special Technical Publication No. 246 (1959). The "water break best" developed by workers at the Bell Telephone Laboratories has put cleaning methods on a rational basis for the first time so that quantitative measurements can be made and the merits of any particular cleaning procedure be evaluated.

can be removed by electropolishing and possibly by vacuum-firing.[104] Vacuum-firing is more effective than hydrogen-firing and less likely to prolong the pump cycle owing to the release of hydrogen from hydrogen-fired parts. On the other hand, hydrogen-firing removes contaminations and impurities more readily, especially when wet hydrogen is used. Sometimes a sequential firing in hydrogen, air, and hydrogen is used. Tube envelopes should be chemically cleaned by rinsing with a 10 percent solution of hydrofluoric acid to remove a surface skin on the glass which contains most of the absorbed water, then rinsed in a neutralizing solution such as ammonium bicarbonate followed by rinses in distilled water and acetone. Glass envelopes should then be prepumped and baked at as high a temperature as possible depending on the type of glass used. A baking treatment in dry air is equally effective.[110] Ceramic spacers should be fired in air at 1200°C to remove surface contamination and occluded gas, and mica spacers should be baked in air at about 350°C, or hydrogen-fired for 15 minutes at about 600°C. When these preoutgassed components have been assembled into the final tube, the latter is again exposed to a baking cycle at the maximum possible temperature for a prolonged period of time, or by applying a step baking cycle. Liquid nitrogen is filled into the trap in line with the manifold, provided that provisions have been made to keep the trap filled at all times at a given level and not permit this level to recede.[111] The electrodes within the tube are then again outgassed by induction heating, and they should be kept hot while the cathode is activated. This latter condition, however, can rarely be satisfied without cumbersome instrumentation.

The activation of the oxide cathode[112-116] involves three steps: (1) the removal of the nitrocellulose binder, unless this has already been removed by air baking as described above; (2) conversion of the carbonates into oxide; and (3) partial reduction of the oxides at the metal-coating interface to produce free barium throughout the coating by diffusion.

The organic binder remaining in the cathode coating must be removed by evaporation before conversion takes place. For this purpose, the cathode is heated to a black temperature of about 500°C and held there for a few minutes; the heater input is then increased to about 3 watts/cm², which still should not produce a visible color; the pressure should not rise above 10^{-5} Torr during this treatment. The color of the cathode changes during this procedure from a light gray to a patchy blackish gray and then to a patchy white followed by a pure white appearance; experience indicates that the cathode must be put into this state if a short and complete conversion is to be obtained thereafter.[3]

The conversion of the carbonates takes place at a brightness temperature between 850 and 900°C; onset of breakdown may be observed above 750°C. During the conversion process, the emissivity of the cathode decreases so that the heater wattage must be decreased correspondingly to maintain a constant temperature. Conversion should take place within a few minutes and be indicated by a fall of the system pressure from 10^{-3} to 10^{-6} Torr at the end of conversion. Experience has shown that cathodes which do not follow this pattern are generally poor emitters.[3]

After conversion of the carbonate into oxide has been completed, activation proper is achieved by raising the temperature of the cathode for a few minutes to a temperature that may range from 1000 to 1200°C depending on the type of coating used and the base metal employed. This increase in temperature may entail a pressure rise to about 3×10^{-6} Torr, but the pressure should then fall again in a short time. A d-c voltage may be applied to the electrode while keeping the pressure below 1×10^{-6} Torr until a cathode current of about 25 ma/cm², or more, is drawn for about one minute, whereupon the temperature is reduced to the operating range of 775–825°C for the purpose of stabilizing the emission. In general, ageing is done after seal-off. A well-activated cathode will permit drawing of continuous current of 500 ma/cm² for many thousands of hours, and peak emission values as high as 50 a/cm² are not uncommon. Owing to the many adverse effects that can limit the available emission and curtail its life, emission density in conventional receiving tubes is kept to a maximum level of about 60 ma/cm² and rarely exceeds 200 ma/cm² in special tubes where long life is not a primary consideration.*

Nickel-Base Alloys for Oxide Cathodes[117-123]

In almost all cases, nickel is used as the metal from which the cathode sleeve is made and on which the coating is applied. Very extensive studies have clearly established the fact that controlled amounts of reducing agents must be added to the nickel during the fabrication of the ingots in order to obtain optimum performance characteristics of the cathode during activation and life. This requirement presents a formidable metallurgical problem when it is considered that commercial melts are made in runs amounting to as much as 20,000 pounds.

Some of the reducing agents, the presence of which is required in the finished cathode sleeve, are also added to the melt for the purpose of deoxidizing it. It clearly depends on the amount of oxygen originally present in the melt, how much of a given reducing agent is combined with oxygen and removed from the melt as slag, and how much remains uncombined and available for future reducing action on the coating of the cathode. These uncertainties have made it necessary for the tube industry to approve a given melt by making trial runs of tubes and to determine their

---

* One manufacturer reports that Tube Type 2C39A operates at an average current of 250 ma/cm² in a microwave relay with a mean life of 8000 hours.

performance during manufacture and after life tests. The additional variation introduced by the different procedures used in various tube plants
for cleaning, coating, pumping, and activating, as well as those caused by
having the cathode operate in different environments within the tube, by
virtue of the fact that different materials are used for the anodes and other
parts, makes it very difficult to come to a clear-cut decision on the merit of
a melt for a given tube type. It is thus not surprising that certain cathode
lots made from one and the same melt are approved by some plants and
rejected by others. These difficulties are minimized when the size of the
melt is smaller but the production of such small lots becomes an uneconomi-
cal venture for the producer of cathode sleeves.

It has been demonstrated in recent years that the production of cathode
nickel by methods of powder metallurgy promises to circumvent these
difficulties, because small lots can be made from very pure nickel powder
to which the required reducing agents can be added in controlled amounts.
Furthermore, some alloys which cannot be produced by melting in the
conventional manner can be produced by powder metallurgical techniques.[100, 118, 124] Vacuum-melted nickel, deoxidized by carbon and rare
earths such as cerium and lanthanum, to which the desired cathode reducing agents are added at the end of the melting cycle, also promises to have
increasing importance for the production of cathode nickel.

Nickel, by itself, has a limited hot strength which makes for deformation
of cathode sleeves on exposure to vibration and shock. The improvement
of the mechanical strength of cathode sleeves is thus a further requirement,
which must be achieved by the addition of suitable alloying components
that must not have any adverse effect on the emission characteristics.
Tungsten-zirconium-nickel* is one of the new cathode alloys developed
under the sponsorship of the Bureau of Ships, Department of the Navy,
with the object of combining best hot strength and electrical performance.[101]
Reducing agents conventionally present in nickel cathode alloys are Mg,
Mn, Al, Si, Ti, W, and C. Other elements which have similar effects are
some of the rare earth metals and Be, Zr, Th, and U. Elements which are
present but believed to be inert in the presence of barium oxide are Ni,
Fe, Co, and Cu. Iron particles lodged on the surface of the nickel sleeve,
however, will cause nonemittive spots. Reducing agents are added to the
base nickel in amounts varying from 0.01 to 0.2 per cent; high-strength
nickel alloys may contain as much as 40 per cent tungsten.[122, 123]

Cathode alloys are classified into "passive alloys" and "active alloys,"
and sometimes the term "normal alloys" is used for compositions which
lie about half-way between the extremes in terms of the readiness with
which these cathodes activate. The different cathode alloys may be ob-

* Available under the code X-3012 from Superior Tube Company, Norristown, Pa.

tained from commercial suppliers.* The physical properties and chemical analyses of some of these cathode alloys are given in Table 15.11, and an evaluation of the performance characteristics according to Briggs[101] is given in Table 15.12 where a numerical rating system is used to indicate best performance under any one category by a rating "one" and lesser performance by higher numbers. The first cathode nickel that became commercially available many years ago was "220" nickel. "330" nickel is sometimes referred to as ' "A" nickel selected for electronic use'; the composition generally overlaps that of "220" but the sequence of additions of deoxidizers during melting is different; this creates significant variations in cathode performance. Active-grade nickel A-30 contains 0.05 per cent aluminum and has led to erratic behavior which is thought to be due to incomplete control of melting practices. The same remarks apply to active-grade A-32. Nickels type 399, 599, 699, and 225 are active-grade alloys which were very popular at one time but are now seldom used for new designs on account of their high content of silicon and/or magnesium. Magnesium shows an excessively high sublimation rate, and silicon has been the cause for an excessive interface formation, principally consisting of Ba_2SiO_4, by a reaction of the silicon with the barium oxide coating; this interface can build up high values of ohmic resistance which vary with temperature and may reach several hundred ohms. The effect on the operation of the tube is equivalent to that of a capacitor shunted by a resistor inserted in series with the cathode and offering a high impedance that leads to reduction of transconductance; aluminum, when used as an additive, gives similar results. Jackson and Jenkins[119] point out that the formation of a silicate interface may be an advantage in the case of mercury-filled rectifiers since it appears to protect the underlying nickel from attack by mercury while the tube is in storage. Some workers believe that a certain amount of interface of the right composition and thickness is useful as a "cement" which makes for good adhesion of the coating. An extensive investigation of interface impedance[125] has recently been conducted by Briggs Associates, Inc. under sponsorship of the U. S. Army Signal Research and Development Laboratory to which the reader is referred for details. The very excellent review by Noelcke[105] on deterioration mechanisms in electron tubes is also warmly recommended for study.

In order to avoid the formation of interface layers, the use of very pure

* Superior Tube Company, Norristown, Pa.
  International Nickel Company, 67 Wall Street, New York 5, N. Y.
  Driver-Harris Company, Harrison, New Jersey
  Radio Corporation of America, 151 Westside Avenue, Harrison, N. J.
  Wilbur B. Driver Company, Newark, N. J.
  General Electric Company, Springfield, N. J.
  Vacuum Metals Corporation, Syracuse 1, N. Y.

TABLE 15.11. CATHODE NICKELS

A) Chemical Requirements of Nickel Alloys as Cathode Sleeves 0.005 in. Wall Thickness or Less (ASTM Tentative Spec. F 239-57 T)

	Cu Max. %	Fe Max. %	Mn Max. %	C Max. %	Mg %	Si %	S Max. %	Ti Max. %	W %	Ni-Co Min. %
Active Alloy Types										
Grade........ 3	0.20	0.20	0.20	0.08	not specified	0.15–0.25	0.008	not specified	—	99.00
Grade........ 4	0.04	0.10	0.02–0.10	0.08	0.01 max.	0.15–0.25	0.005	0.02	—	99.25
Grade........ 6	0.04	0.05	0.02	0.08	0.01 max.	0.15–0.25	0.005	0.02	—	99.25
Grade........ 7	0.20	0.20	0.20	0.10	0.01–0.10	0.02–0.06	0.008	0.02	3.50–4.50	94.50
Grade........ 10	0.15	0.20	0.30	0.10	not specified	0.10 max.	0.008	not specified	—	99.00
Grade........ 11	0.20	0.20	0.20	0.08	0.01–0.10	0.01–0.05	0.008	not specified	—	99.10
Passive Alloy Types										
Grade........ 21	0.04	0.05	0.02	0.05	0.01 max.	0.01 max.	0.005	0.01	—	99.50
Grade........ 22	0.04	0.05	0.02	0.05	0.01 max.	0.02 max.	0.005	0.01	—	99.50

B) Typical Analyses of Commercial Cathode and Filament-Alloys

Material*		Cu Max. %	Fe Max. %	Mn Max. %	C Max. %	Mg %	Si %	S Max. %	Ti Max. %	Other Metals %	Ni+ Co Min. %	Use C-Cathode F-Filament
Active Alloy Types												
"202" Nickel (INCO)...........	7	0.20	0.20	0.20	0.10	0.01–0.10	0.02–0.06	0.008	0.02	W: 3.50–4.50	94.0	C
CATHALOY A-31 (STC)......	7	0.10	0.10	0.05	0.03–0.10	0.01–0.06	0.02–0.06	0.005	0.02	W: 3.75–4.50	94.50	C
N 30 (SEP, DH, WBD).........	7											
"220" Nickel (INCO)..........	11	0.10	0.10	0.20	0.08	0.01–0.08	0.01–0.05	0.008	0.01–0.05	—	99.0	C
200 (SEP, STC, WBD)..........	11											
N18 (RCA)												

Alloy (source)	No.									Other	Ni, %	
"225" Nickel (INCO)	3	0.10	0.10	0.20	0.08	0.01-0.08	0.15-0.25	0.008	0.01-0.05	—	99.00	C
225 Nickel (STC)	3	0.10	0.10	0.30	0.10	0.01-0.10	0.10 max.	0.008	0.005	—		C
N19, N34 (RCA)	3											
"330" Nickel (INCO)	10									—	99.00	C
330 Nickel (STC)	10											
N4 (SEP)	10	0.015	0.043	0.185	0.025	0.09	0.071	0.008	<0.005	Al: <0.005; Co: 0.110; Cr: 0.005		C
N109, N109TI (RCA)	10	0.15	0.10	0.15	0.15	0.03-0.10	0.01-0.05	0.009	0.005	Co: 1.0 max.		C
N132 (RCA); vac. melted		0.10	0.10	0.08	0.015-0.035	0.02-0.04	0.010-0.030	0.008	0.005	Co: 0.3–0.5		C
599 (DHC, STC)	6	0.04	0.05-0.10	0.02	0.08	0.01 max.	0.15-0.25	0.005	—	—	99.25	C
799 (DHC, STC)	4	0.04	0.05-0.10	0.05	0.08	0.01 max.	0.15-0.25	0.005	—	—	99.25	C
CATHALOY A-30 (STC)	2	0.05	0.10	0.05	0.03-0.10	0.01-0.06	0.02	0.005	0.01	Al: 0.03–0.08	99.25	C
CATHALOY A-32 (STC)		0.05	0.10	0.05	0.03-0.10	0.01-0.06	0.02	0.005	0.01	W: 2.00–2.50	96.25	C
"O" Nickel (British)		0.1	0.2	0.15	0.04	0.15	0.10	0.005	—	Al: 0.03–0.08	99.5	C
Ballast Nickel (WBD)			0.17	—							99.78	F
Sylvaloy (WBD); N91 (RCA)			5.0	0.25			3.0		2.0	Co: 0.08	97.0	F
Hilo (WBD); N97 (RCA)			0.5	0.25			1.0		0.3		93.0	F
Modified Hilo (WBD)											98.0	F
Cobanic (WBD)										Co: 18.0	100.0	F
Tensite (WBD); N1W (RCA)			7.50				3.0		2.25	Co: 20.0	98.0	F
Filnic-F (DHC)										Co: 45.0	92.25	F
Filnic-J (DHC)										Al: 2.0	97.0	F
Filnic-M (DHC)										Co: 17.0	100.0	F
Filnic-T (DHC)										Co: 45.0	98.0	F
W-4 (SCC)		0.01-0.03	0.01-0.04	0.06	0.04	0.21	0.04			Co: 0.9	98.0	F
210 (SCC); N9 (RCA)			0.09	0.10	0.34		0.08				98.0	F
C-43 (SCC)							3.52			Co: 0.62; Al: 0.10	99.1	F
213, 225 (SCC); N1W (RCA)										W: 1.0; Al: 1.90; U: 2.10	96.5	F
925-C (SCC)			2.50		0.25					Al: 1.90	95.0	F
531 (SCC)					0.20		1.50			Co: 19.0	98.1	F
213-M (SCC)										Al: 1.0; Mo: 2.0	96.0	F
N-93 (RCA)										Al: 1.0; W: 2.0	96.5	F
N-107 (RCA)										Co: 30	100.0	F, C

TABLE 15.11.—*Continued*

B) Typical Analyses of Commercial Cathode and Filament-Alloys

Passive Alloy Types

Material*	Cu Max. %	Fe Max. %	Mn Max. %	C Max. %	Mg %	Si %	S Max. %	Ti Max. %	Other Metals %	Ni + Co Min. %	Use: C-Cathode F-Filament
499 (DHC); N81 (RCA)..........22	0.04	0.05	0.02	0.05	0.01 max.	0.02 max.	0.005	0.01	—	99.50	C
499 (SEP); 999 (DHC)..........22	0.04	0.05	0.02	0.05	0.01 max.	0.02 max.	0.005	0.01	—	99.50	C
P50 (STC); N35 (SEP)..........22	0.04	0.05	0.02	0.05	0.01 max.	0.02 max.	0.005	0.01	W: 3.75–4.25	95.25	C
P51 (STC, SEP)..........22									W: 1.9; Al: 0.03/0.05; Co: 0.45; Cr: 0.9/1.0		C
N11 (SEP); vac. cast†	0.003–0.006	0.01	0.04	—	<0.01	0.02	—	<0.005			
HPM (INCO) nominal	0.01	0.04	0.01	0.02	0.005	0.01	0.005	—	Al: <0.005; Co: <0.005;	99.9	C
HPM (Wiggen)†	0.008	0.021	<0.005	<0.01	<0.005	<0.01	—	<0.005	Cr: <0.005		
Nivac-P (VMC)	0.005	.010	<0.002	0.007	<0.003	<0.010	0.005	<0.005	Co: 0.13; Al: 0.010	99.9	C

* Materials listed are covered by Trademarks of the following companies:

INCO—International Nickel Company, Inc., 67 Wall Street, New York, 5 N. Y.
STC—Superior Tube Company, 1968 Germantown Avenue, Norristown, Pa.
SEP—Sylvania Electric Products Inc., Chemical & Metallurgical Div., Towanda, Pa.
DH—Driver Harris Company, 201 Middlesex Street, Harrison, N. J.
WBD—Wilbur B. Driver Company, 1875 McCarter Highway, Newark 4, N. J.
RCA—Radio Corporation of America, RCA Victor Division, Harrison, N. J.
SCC—Sigmund Cohn Corporation, 121 S. Columbus Avenue, Mount Vernon, N. Y.
VMC—Vacuum Metals Corporation, Div. of Crucible Steel Company of America, Syracuse 1, N. Y

† Spectroscopic analysis of one specific melt, according to Wolk.[128a]

TABLE 15.12. SUMMARY OF CATHODE BASE METAL
PERFORMANCE CHARACTERISTICS[101]

Alloy	Rate of Activ.	Characteristic		Interface	Sublimation	Hot Strength
		Emission Level	Long Life			
P50	5	4	1	1	1	5
P51	4	4	1	1	1	2
220	3	3	4	2	3	3
330	2	3	3	3	5	3
A30	1	Highly	2	4	2	3
A31	3	Variable	1	2	3	2
A32	1	as a	1	5	3	2
W-Zr-Ni	1	Function	2	2	2	1
399	1	of	2	5	4	3
599	1	Tube	2	5	4	3
225	1	Life	2	5	4	3

Examples of numerical rating system: 1—best, 3—medium, 5—poorest
P50 = 541115, 220 = 334233, 220 melt variation = 224353, ideal alloy = 111111

base metals, such as platinum, has been recommended and practiced by
Metson[103, 126] and his associates at the thermionics group of the Post Office
Engineering Research Station, Dollis Hill, England; very satisfactory operation over long periods of time has been obtained with such platinum
cathodes used in submarine repeater tubes. While the formation of a harmful interface is thus effectively prevented, one must still provide, in the
light of modern experience, for the supply of reducing agents from other
tube parts, or rely on electrolytic action for the activation of the cathode.

The influence of the anode material on the activity of the cathode is an
important effect that may be beneficial as just indicated, or harmful when
the anode releases poisoning agents that may be produced by reduction of
surface films by the impinging electron beam.[127-130] Additional remarks on
the poisoning effect of various gases will be made in the following chapter,
but one cause of low emission in oxide cathodes, which has recently been
brought to the attention of tube producers is especially worthy of note. It
has been established by workers at the Bell Telephone Laboratories[131] in
cooperation with Corning Glass Works that Type 7052 "Kovar"-sealing
glass gives off a harmful fluorine compound during the sealing operation
which is absorbed by the cathode coating and reacts with it during activation to form a gray, amorphous, glassy, nonemissive material. Corning
"Kovar"-sealing glass Type 7040, and 7056, or the soft glasses 0120 and 0080
do not show any evidence of this harmful effect, and the maximum pulsed
emission levels obtained when using these latter glasses for envelopes were
1000 times greater than those obtainable when 7052 glass was used. Kimble
glass K-650 is also free from this particular effect.

Chlorine and sulfur are known to have a particularly deleterious effect on the emission capabilities of an oxide-coated cathode. It has been established that 0.02 per cent sulfur content in the base nickel is sufficient to reduce the emission below a useful value. Sulfur is a common impurity in metals and it has been found necessary to specify a maximum permissible sulfur content of 0.005% for cathode nickels (see Table 7.1).

"Although every care is taken by the alloy manufacturer to meet the specification for sulfur content, it is not generally realized by either the user or the manufacturer whose business it is to process the nickel, that sulfur contamination may occur at any stage where the hot metal can be brought into contact with sulfur-containing gases.

"Although the presence of magnesium and manganese may offer some protection and the attacked layer may be superficial, so that the mechanical properties of the nickel are not impaired, the presence of sulphur may have considerable effect upon thermionic emission of the cathode. Usually the effect, where emission is reduced, is sufficiently specific for the cause of the trouble to be known, but the damaging effect of sulfur may take another form when present at the internal surface of the cathode. The insulating properties of the alumina between the heater and cathode may be reduced, with resulting heater/cathode leakage, the insulation often being reduced by a factor of 100. The presence of sulfur contamination may be caused by the incomplete removal of sulfonated drawing oils before annealing, but it is more often caused by leakage of sulfur-containing gases from gas-fired annealing furnaces into the furnace chamber containing the charge. The use of an inner tube, separated from the furnace tube proper, is insufficient guarantee of freedom from sulfur attack, since this tube itself may be attacked and serve as a source of sulfur. The best safeguard against this trouble is the use of electric furnace heating with a cracked ammonia or hydrogen atmosphere to protect the charge. Where gas heating is necessary, every care to remove surface-attacked metal during manufacture and the regular checking of heat-treatment equipment for leakage is required."[119]

Filamentary emitters for battery tubes and the like present special problems because the power consumed for the purpose of heating must be kept at a minimum. The requirement results in the use of very fine wires of the order of 1 mil diameter, about 1 in. long, and weighing about 0.1 mg for filaments consuming 50 ma at 0.4 v. These wires are coated with the emissive material, a suspension of alkaline-earth carbonates, either by spraying, or more commonly by cataphoresis, and operate near 800°C. To take care of thermal expansion and to avoid microphony, i.e., filament vibration as a result of mechanical shock, the filament must be spring-loaded; thus it operates under conditions which are similar in many respects to the creep-to-rupture tests used for the examination of metals for high-temperature service. A tension of 0.5 gr applied to a wire of the dimensions just given amounts to an operating stress of 0.7 ton/sq. in., a figure which would not be considered onerous in high-temperature turbines, for example. As Jackson and Jenkins[119] point out, a major difference in these two high-temperature applications arises from the fact that normal engineering structures contain many grains in their cross-section, while in a cathode the grain size may be of the same order as the wire diameter, so that the wire may become effectively a series of single crystals placed end to end. Creep and failure for a system of this type may bear no simple relation to the results obtained on large polycrystalline specimens, although stress and temperature still have a profound effect upon the time-to-failure for the wire. The effect of surface conditions on wires of small diameter can also be very marked, and the nature of the interface between the coating and core can alter the time-to-failure very appreciably.

"Pure tungsten and alloys based on nickel have been used as core materials for filament cathodes. Tungsten has the advantage of remarkable strength at high temperatures, which removes any difficulty due to filament breakage. The emission results are not usually as satisfactory as in the case of nickel alloys, however, and its low resistivity and high thermal conductivity introduce difficulties in design, because of system lengths or because the wire diameter required is much smaller than that of a corresponding nickel alloy.

"For valve types with a higher rating than 50 ma, it is possible to make use of alloys which are essentially nickel with the addition of an activating agent. The percentage of the latter is usually greater than is used in indirectly heated cathodes, since the ratio of coating to core weight is higher. Typical alloys which have been used for the 100 ma cathodes include those containing respectively, 0.4 per cent aluminum and 0.25 per cent magnesium. Elements such as chromium and molybdenum, which have a pronounced strengthening effect on the nickel lattice, are unsuitable because of the formation of undesirable interface compounds. Titanium, silicon, magnesium, aluminum, or zirconium may only be added in small amounts, since larger quantities will either over-activate the coating, or form a heavy interface layer with damage to the emission. The metals which can be alloyed with nickel in substantial amounts are limited to tungsten and cobalt, both of which have an extensive solid solution range in nickel. Smaller quantities of activating agents can be added to improve the emission performance, or to increase the life performance, but these minor constituents must be carefully controlled for the reasons given." [119] This object can be realized more easily by using powder metallurgy methods for the production of the wire as described above.

In addition to the alloys listed in Table 7.8, a 5 Ni–95 Pt alloy should be mentioned; this was used as a base for oxide cathodes in long-life telephone communication tubes. According to Wise,[131a] this type of cathode is the only one among conventional oxide-coated cathodes which can be successfully reactivated after exposure to the atmosphere; for this reason it is being used in some commercial ionization gauges.

Cold Cathodes[132, 134]

Self-sustained electron emission from cold magnesium oxide films on nickel was discovered at the Signal Corps Research Development Laboratory at Fort Monmouth in 1956 by Dobischek and further developed at the Research and Development Laboratory of Tung-Sol Electric, Inc. under contract DA 36-039sc-73051. This work has been carried forward to a stage which warranted announcement. An audio output amplifier using this cold cathode develops 900 mw of power at 7% distortion or less, a dynamic transconductance up to 600 micromhos with sufficiently low noise to be comparable with thermionic tubes using conventional hot cathodes.

The thin layers of magnesium oxide applied to a nickel sleeve have a porous structure. Once emission has been started by a starter mechanism and a minimum of 300 volts is applied to the collector, a positive charge is developed at the surface of the MgO layer which produces a high electrical field on the order of 54,000 volts/cm inside the layer. Electrons liberated within the MgO coating are multiplied by an avalanche effect and gain sufficient energy to leave the surface. It is tentatively assumed that electrons initiating the avalanche are produced by a photoelectric effect within the coating. The emission current can be controlled by varying the voltage of the collector, and currents of several tens of milliamperes have been measured over a period of several thousand hours without any decrease in emission. The further development of this type of cathode should be of great interest to the tube industry.

REFERENCES

1. W. B. Nottingham, "Thermionic Emission," Technical Report No. 321 (Dec. 10, 1956), Research Laboratory of Electronics, Massachusetts Institute of Technology, Cambridge, Mass. This report has also been published in Vol. 21 of "Handbuch der Physik," S. Flügge, Ed., Julius Springer Verlag, Berlin, 1957.
2. L. P. Smith, "Thermionic Emission," Chapter 6 in "Handbook of Physics," E. U. Condon and H. Odishaw, Ed., McGraw-Hill Book Co., Inc., New York, 1958.
3. E. A. Coomes, "Thermionic Cathodes and Their Environment." A discussion series given at Eitel McCullough, Inc., (Sept. 1955). ASTIA No. 78498.
4. D. A. Wright, "A survey of present knowledge of thermionic emitters," *Proc. Inst. Elec. Engrs.*, **100**, Pt. 3, 125–142 (May 1953).

5. W. E. Danforth, "Elements of thermionics," *Proc. Inst. Radio Engrs.*, **39**, 485–499 (May 1951).

6. C. Herring and M. H. Nichols, "Thermionic emission," *Rev. Mod. Phys.* **21**, 185–270 (Apr. 1949).

7. A. L. Reimann, "Thermionic Emission," Chapman & Hall, Ltd., London 1934.

8. A. S. Eisenstein, "Oxide Coated Cathodes," in "Advances in Electronics," Vol. 1, Chapter 1, Academic Press, Inc., New York, 1948.

9. G. Herrmann and S. Wagener, "The Oxide-coated Cathode" (2 Vols.), Chapman & Hall, Ltd., London 1951.

10. R. H. Plumlee, "The Electron Donor Centers in the Oxide Cathode," RCA Industry Service Laboratory Report RB-59, July 12, 1956.

11. L. S. Nergaard, "The physics of the cathode," *RCA Rev.*, **18**, 486–511 (Dec. 1957).

12. E. S. Rittner, "A theoretical study of the chemistry of the oxide cathode," *Philips Research Repts.*, **8**, 184–238 (June 1953).

13. L. S. Nergaard, "Studies of the oxide cathode," *RCA Rev.*, **13**, 464–545 (Dec. 1952).

13a. L. S. Nergaard, "Thermionic emitters," *RCA Rev.*, **20**, 191–204 (June 1959).

14. R. Loosjes and H. J. Vink, "The conduction mechanism in oxide-coated cathodes," *Philips Research Repts.*, **4**, 449–475 (Dec. 1949).

15. T. J. Lewis, "High field electron emission from irregular cathode surfaces," *J. Appl. Phys.*, **26**, 1405–1410 (Dec. 1955).

16. W. P. Dyke, "Progress in electron emission at high fields," *Proc. Inst. Radio Engrs.*, **43**, 162–167 (Feb. 1955).

17. W. P. Dyke and W. W. Dolan, "Field Emission," in "Advances in Electronics and Electron Physics," L. Marton, Ed., Vol. 8, pp. 89–185, Academic Press, Inc., New York, 1956.

18. K. M. Poole, "Emission from hollow cathodes," *J. Appl. Phys.*, **26**, 1176–1179 (Sept. 1955).

19. P. O. Hawkins and J. S. Thorp, "Internally coated cathodes," *Nature (London)*, **178**, 380–381 (Aug. 18, 1956).

20. W. H. Kohl, "A hollow-cathode projection tube as a laboratory experiment in tube techniques," Report on 16th Annual Conference Physical Electronics, Massachusetts Institute of Technology, Mar. 22–24, 1956, pp. 111–115.

21. A. L. Reimann, "The evaporation of atoms, ions, and electrons from tungsten," *Phil. Mag.*, **25**, 834–838 (June 1938).

22. D. B. Langmuir and L. Malter, "The rate of evaporation of tantalum," *Phys. Rev.*, **55**, 743–747 (Apr. 15, 1939).

23. H. A. Jones, I. Langmuir, and G. M. J. Mackay, "The rates of evaporation and the vapor pressures of tungsten, molybdenum, platinum, nickel, iron, copper, and silver," *Phys. Rev.*, **30**, 201–214 (Aug. 1927).

24. R. W. Ditchburn and J. C. Gilmour, "The vapor pressures of monatomic vapors," *Rev. Mod. Phys.*, **13**, 310–327 (Oct. 1941).

25. J. A. M. Van Liempt, "The vapor pressure of barium" (in German), *Rec. Trav. Chim.*, **55**, 468–470 (1936).

26. R. E. Honig, "Vapor pressure data for the more common elements," *RCA Rev.*, **18**, 195–204 (June 1957).

27. T. R. Harrison, "Significance of emittance in radiation pyrometry"; "Industrial use of radiation pyrometers under non-black-body conditions," *J. Opt. Soc. Am.*, **35**, 706–723 (Nov. 1945).

28. "Temperature Measurement," Brit. Stand. Code 1041:1943; British Standards Institution, London, S.W.1.

29. K. R. Brunn, "An Investigation of the Hollow Spherical Cathode," Electrical Engineering Research Laboratory, Engineering Experiment Station, University of Illinois, Urbana, Ill. Scientific Report No. 10 (15 April 1957); Contract AF 19(604)-524; Technical Report No. 3, Contract Nonr-1834(08) Project No. 373-162.

30. C. T. Sims, E. N. Wyler, *et al.*, "Survey of the Literature on Rhenium," Report for June 1952–Jan. 1956 on "Solid State Research for Advancement of Electronic Materials." Battelle Memorial Institute Report No. WADC-TR-56-319, 224 pp. (June 1956) (Contract AF 33(616)232).

31. C. T. Sims and R. I. Jaffee, "Further studies of the properties of rhenium metal and the platinum/rhenium thermocouple," *J. Metals, Trans. AIME*, **8**, 913–917 (Aug. 1956).

32. C. T. Sims, *et al.*, "Investigations of Rhenium," Battelle Memorial Institute for Wright Air Development Center, Aeronautical Research Laboratory, Air Research and Development Command, United States Air Force. WADC Tech. Report 54-371 (June 1954); Supplement 1 (Sept. 1956); AD 97301. Contract AF 33 (616)-232.

33. C. T. Sims *et al.*, "Investigations of Rhenium for Electron Tube Applications," Battelle Memorial Institute for Air Force Cambridge Research Center, Air Research and Development Command, United States Air Force, AFRC-TN-57-158 (Jan. 1, 1957). AD 110292 (2nd Quarterly Progress Report, Period Oct. 1, 1956–Dec. 31, 1956).

34. C. T. Sims, C. M. Craighead and R. I. Jaffee, "Physical and mechanical properties of rhenium," *J. Metals, Trans. AIME*, **7**, 168–179 (Jan. 1955).

35. C. T. Sims, "Rhenium metal," *Materials & Methods*, **41**, 109–111 (Mar. 1955).

36. C. T. Sims, G. B. Gaines, J. B. Baker, N. Sandler, W. Nexsen, C. S. Peet and R. I. Jaffee, "Investigations of Rhenium for Electron Tube Applications," Battelle Memorial Institute, Fifth Scientific Rept. (June 1, 1958), for Air Force Cambridge Research Center; Contract No. AF19(604)-1741; Task No. 46310; AFCRC-TN-58-176. ASTIA No. AD 152419.

37. L. W. Kates, "Rhenium metal—its properties and future," *Materials & Methods*, **39**, 88–91 (Mar. 1954).

38. J. G. F. Druce, "Rhenium," Cambridge University Press, 1948.

39. "American Institute of Physics Handbook," D. E. Gray, Coord. Ed., McGraw-Hill Book Co., Inc., New York, 1957.

40. C. L. Mantell, Ed., "Engineering Materials Handbook," McGraw-Hill Book Co., Inc., New York, 1958.

41. A. D. Melaven, "Rhenium," Chapter 17, in "Rare Metals Handbook," C. A. Hampel, Ed., Reinhold Publishing Corp., New York, 1954.

42. Encyclopaedia Britannica," Vol. 19, W. Benton, Publisher, 1957.

43. M. Davis and J. F. Duke, "An investigation into the possibility of fabricating rhenium metal," *Services Electronic Research Lab. Tech. J.*, **6**, No. 2, 65–79 (Aug. 1956).

44. E. M. Sherwood, D. M. Rosenbaum, J. M. Blocher, Jr. and I. E. Campbell, "The vapor pressure of rhenium," *J. Electrochem. Soc.*, **102**, 650–654 (Nov. 1955).

45. D. T. F. Marple, "The spectral emissivity of rhenium," *J. Opt. Soc. Amer.*, **46**, 490–494 (July 1956).

46. C. E. Ludington and C. T. Sims, "Rhenium—a high-temperature metal,"

A.G.E.T. News Bull., **2**, 7–13 (Jan. 1, 1958) (Advisory Group on Electron Tubes, Office of the Assistant Secretary of Defense, Research and Engineering).

47. R. Levi and G. A. Esperson, "Preparation of rhenium emitters and measurement of their thermionic properties," *Phys. Rev.*, **78**, 231 (May 1950).
48. F. C. Todd, E. N. Wyler and D. N. Gideon, "Properties of rhenium of interest for electronic applications," Report on 14th Annual Conference on Physical Electronics, (Mar. 25–27, 1954). Massachusetts Institute of Technology, pp. 131–136.
49. G. Barnes, "Field emission of rhenium," *Phys. Rev.*, **97**, 1579–1583 (Mar. 15, 1955).
50. J. Hughes and G. Geach, "The alloys of rhenium with molybdenum or tungsten having good high-temperature properties," Proceedings of the Plansee Seminar (1955).
51. J. F. Duke, "A ductile rhenium-molybdenum alloy with useful high-temperature properties," *Services Electronics Research Lab. Tech. J.*, **6**, No. 2, 80–84 (Aug. 1956).
52. R. Jaffee and C. Sims, "Effect of rhenium on fabrication and ductility of molybdenum," AIME Annual Meeting 1958, New York City, and Plansee Seminar 1958.
53. J. Dickinson and L. Richardson, "The constitution of rhenium-molybdenum alloys," ASM Preprint No. 72 (1958).
54. F. B. Litton, "Preparation and some properties of hafnium metal," *J. Electrochem. Soc.*, **98**, 488–494 (Dec. 1951).
55. "Hafnium—An Atomic Age Metal," Advanced Materials Technology, Vol. 1, No. 4 (Sept. 1958), Published by Carborundum Company.
56. D. S. Eppelsheimer and D. S. Gould, "The cold-rolled texture of hafnium," *J. Inst. Metals*, **85**, 158–160 (Dec. 1956).
57. H. W. Deem, "Thermal Conductivity and Electrical Resistivity of Hafnium," Battelle Memorial Institute Report BMI-853 (July 14, 1953).
58. M. D. Gibbons, "Evaluation of polycrystalline hafnium as a thermionic emitter," *Bull. Am. Phys. Soc.*, **2**, 269 (June 20, 1957).
59. H. D. Hagstrum, "Thermionic constants and sorption properties of hafnium," *J. Appl. Phys.*, **28**, 323–328 (Mar. 1957).
60. A. W. Hull, "The dispenser cathode, a new type of thermionic cathode," *Phys. Rev.*, **56**, 86–93 (July 1, 1939).
61. H. Katz, "Metal capillary cathodes," *J. Appl Phys.*, **24**, 597–603 (May 1953).
62. A. Venema, R. C. Hughes, P. P. Coppola and R. Levi, "Dispenser cathodes," *Philips Tech. Rev.*, **19**, No. 6, 177–190 (1957/58).
63. H. J. Lemmens, M. J. Jansen and R. Loosjes, "A new thermionic cathode for heavy loads," *Philips Tech. Rev.*, **11**, No. 12, 341–350 (June 1950).
64. C. A. M. Van den Broek and A. Venema, "New Developments in the L Cathode," Electrochemical Society, Washington Spring Meeting, May 12–16, 1957.
65. R. Levi, "New dispenser type thermionic cathode," *J. Appl. Phys.*, **24**, 233 (Feb. 1952).
66. R. Levi, "Improved 'Impregnated Cathode'," *J. Appl. Phys.*, **26**, 639 (May 1955).
67. P. P. Coppola and R. C. Hughes, "A new pressed dispenser cathode," *Proc. IRE*, **44**, 351–359 (Mar. 1956).
68. G. A. Espersen, "Dispenser cathode magnetrons," *IRE Trans.*, **ED-6**, 115–118 (Jan. 1959).

69. "Behavior of Philips impregnated cathodes in high-voltage cathodes," Navy Material Laboratory Project 5032-K-10.9, AGET Status Report No. 34 (15 Aug. 1956), pp. 12–13.

70. I. Brodie and R. O. Jenkins, "Impregnated dispenser cathodes containing strontium or calcium oxide," *J. Appl. Phys.*, **27**, 417–418 (Apr. 1956).

71. T. Hashimoto, "Cavity-type barium-tungsten cathode," Repts. Elec. Comm. Lab. Nippon Telegraph and Telephone Public Corporation (Japan), Vol. 5, pp. 1–8 (Oct. 1957).

72. E. S. Rittner, R. H. Ahlert and W. L. Rutledge, "Studies on the mechanism of operation of the L cathode." I. *J. Appl. Phys.*, **28**, 156–166 (Feb. 1957); II. *ibid.*, 167–173.

73. E. S. Rittner, W. C. Rutledge and R. H. Ahlert, "On the mechanism of operation of the barium aluminate impregnated cathode," *J. Appl Phys.*, **28**, 1468–1473 (Dec. 1957).

74. "New forms of thermionic cathode," *Nature (London)*, **174**, 1176–1177 (Dec. 25, 1954). Report on a colloquium on this subject, held on Oct. 21, 1954 at Wembley and sponsored by the Institute of Physics and the Physical Society.

74a. *Radiotekhnika i elektronika* (in Russian), **2**, No. 12, 1471–1478 (1957) contains several papers on dispenser-type cathodes by the following authors: N. D. Morgulis, Yu. G. Ptushinskii and B. A. Chuikov, Ya. P. Zingesman and V. Ya. Soltyk, Yu. S. Vedula and V. M. Gavrilyuk, I. M. Dykman, V. A. Morozovskii, P. M. Marchuk, E. A. Lozovaya.

75. V. L. Stout, "A survey of dispenser cathodes," Fourth National Conference on Tube Techniques, Sept. 10–12, 1958, New York, N. Y. (Proceedings published by New York University Press, New York, 1959.)

76. J. B. Fisk, H. D. Hagstrum and P. L. Hartman, "The magnetron as a generator of centimeter waves," *Bell System Tech. Jour.*, **25**, 167–348 (Apr. 1946).

77. M. Chodorow, E. L. Ginzton, I. R. Neilsen and S. Sonkin, "Design and performance of a high-power pulsed klystron," *Proc. IRE*, **41**, 1584–1602 (Nov. 1953).

77a. M. Chodorow, E. L. Ginzton, J. J. Jasberg, J. V. Lebacqz and H. J. Shaw, "Development of high-power pulsed klystrons for practical applications," *Proc. IRE*, **47**, 20–29 (Jan. 1959).

78. D. MacNair, R. T. Lynch and N. B. Hannay, "Molded thermionic cathodes," *J. Appl. Phys.*, **24**, 1335–1336 (Oct. 1953).

79. A. H. Beck, A. D. Brisbane, A. B. Cutting and G. King, "A new type of diffusion cathode," *Le Vide*, **9**, 302–309 (Nov. 1954).

80. G. Mesnard and R. Uzan, "Molded thermionic cathodes made from nickel and alkaline earth oxides" (in French), *Le Vide*, **9**, 1492–1507 (Mar. 1954). See also *Compt. rend. acad. sci.*, **239**, 484–486 (Aug. 1954).

81. G. Mesnard and R. Uzan, "Thermionic emission of sintered mixtures of powders of tungsten and alkaline earth carbonates" (in French), *Le Vide*, **10**, 105–118 (July/Sept. 1955).

82. W. Balas, J. Dempsey and E. F. Rexer, "Oxide-impregnated nickel matrix cathode," *J. Appl. Phys.*, **26**, 1163–1165 (Sept. 1955).

83. A. P. LaRocque, "A columbium-nickel matrix cathode," *Bull. Am. Phys. Soc.* Ser. 2, **1**, No. 4, 167 (Apr. 26, 1956).

84. J. Apelbaum, "A long-life cathode for use at high emission densities," Proc. Third National Conference on Tube Techniques, Sept. 12–14, 1956, New York, pp. 56–59. Published by New York University Press, New York, (1958).

85. P. R. Pondy, E. J. Becker and H. J. Robinson, "A pressed refractory matrix cathode system," Presented at Third National Conference on Tube Techniques, Sept. 12–14, 1956, New York.

86. H. J. Robinson, "Recent developments of the refractory matrix cathode," Presented at Fourth National Conference on Tube Techniques, Sept. 10–12, 1958, New York.

87. G. A. Haas and J. T. Jensen, Jr., "Molded Cathodes," Naval Research Laboratory Report No. 4856 (Nov. 9, 1956).

88. J. F. Richardson, "The effect of oxygen and sulphur on the thermionic emission from matrix cathodes," *Brit. J. Appl. Phys.*, **8**, 361–362 (Sept. 1957).

89. R. W. Fane, "A sintered nickel matrix cathode," *Brit. J. Appl. Phys.*, **9**, 149–153 (Apr. 1958).

90. C. P. Hadley, W. G. Rudy and A. J. Stoeckert, "A study of the molded nickel cathode," *J. Electrochem. Soc.*, **105**, 395–398 (July 1958).

91. J. M. Lafferty, "Boride cathodes," *J. Appl. Phys.*, **22**, 299–309 (Mar. 1951).

92. M. A. Pomerantz, "Thorium Oxide Cathodes," National Defense Research Committee, Div. 14, Rept. 517 (Oct. 31, 1945). Bartol Research Foundation.

93. W. E. Danforth, "Abstract of Summary of Bartol Cathode Work," *J. Franklin Inst.*, **248**, 449 (Nov. 1949).

94. Bartol Foundation Cathode Research Group, Technical Progress Report, Feb. 1, 1951.

95. Bartol Research Foundation, Final Report, Feb. 1957. Contr. NObsr 72536, Navy Department, Bureau of Ships.

96. D. L. Goldwater and W. E. Danforth, "Electrolytic decomposition of thorium oxide," Proc. Third National Conference on Tube Techniques, Sept. 12–14, 1956, New York, pp. 66–69.

97. D. L. Goldwater and W. E. Danforth, "Thorium-impregnated matrix cathodes," *ibid*, pp. 64–65. Also Proc. Fourth National Conference on Tube Techniques Sept. 10–12, 1958, pp. 190-193.

98. H. Y. Fan, "Thermionic emission from sintered cathode of thoria and tungsten mixture," *J. Appl. Phys.*, **20**, 682–690 (July 1949).

99. L. P. Garner, U. S. Patent No. 2,339,392 (Jan. 18, 1944) (RCA). See also Machlett Cathode Press, Spring Issue, 1950, pp. 26–27.

100. G. Mesnard and R. Uzan, "Preparation of thoria cathodes by cataphoresis" (in French), *Le Vide*, **26**, 769–776 (Mar. 1950).

100a. Kyonghi Hong, "Carbonization of thoria cathodes," *J. Appl. Phys.*, **30**, 945–946 (June 1959).

100b. T. E. Hanley, "Spectral emissivity and electron emission constants of thoria cathodes," *J. Appl. Phys.*, **19**, 583–589 (June 1948).

100c. V. L. Stout and M. D. Gibbons, "Extended Interface Cathodes," Report on Seventeenth Annual Conf. Physical Electronics, MIT Cambridge, Mass., March 21–23, 1957, p. 40.

101. T. H. Briggs, "Some Parameters Influencing Oxide Cathode Emission and Methods for Testing." Report to Electron Tube Branch, Wright Air Development Center, Wright-Patterson Air Force Base (1958).

102. "Relative Thermionic Emissive Properties of Materials Used in Electron Tubes," Tentative Method for Test, ASTM F270-52T (1952). Copies available for 25¢ from American Society For Testing Materials, 1916 Race St., Philadelphia 3, Pa.

103. G. H. Metson, "On the Electrical Life of an Oxide-Cathode Receiving Tube,"

Advances in Electronics and Electron Physics, L. Marton, Ed. Vol. 8, pp. 404–446, Academic Press, Inc., New York, 1956.

104. T. H. Briggs, "A study of Cathode Emission and Measurements," Report to Superior Tube Company (Jan. 16, 1957).

105. C. L. Noelcke, "Deterioration Mechanisms in Electron Tubes," Arinc Research Monograph No. 6 (Nov. 7, 1958), Arinc Research Corporation, Washington 6, D. C.

106. M. Benjamin and A. B. Osborn, "The deposition of oxide coatings by cataphoresis," *Trans. Faraday Soc.*, **36**, 287–295 (Jan. 1940).

107. B. Wolk, "Observations of the relation between cataphoresis, conductivity, and particle size of single alkaline-earth carbonates," *J. Phys. & Colloid Chem.*, **54**, 472–482 (Apr. 1950).

108. J. R. Nall and C. P. Marsden, "Electroprecipitated coatings of barium and strontium carbonates," Rept. of 15th Annual Conference Physical Electronics, March 24–26, 1955. Massachusetts Institute of Technology, Cambridge, Mass, pp. 36–39.

109. "Sarong Cathodes," Sylvania Electric Products Inc.; Patents pending. For descriptive data see *Electronic Industr.*, **18**, No. 4. 53–55 (Apr. 1959).

110. B. J. Todd, "Outgassing of glass," *J. Appl. Phys.*, **26**, 1238–1243 (Oct. 1955).

111. G. F. Wells, "Precision liquid nitrogen trap level controller," *Rev. Sci. Instr.*, **29**, 893–895 (Oct. 1958).

111a. B. Richelmann, "Liquid nitrogen level control," *Rev. Sci. Instr.*, **30**, 598–599 (July 1959).

112. G. H. Metson, "Activation of high-vacuum, oxide-cathode valves," *Vacuum* (W. Edwards and Company, Ltd., London, England), **1**, No. 4, 283–293 (Oct. 1951).

113. H. J. Curnow, "Effects observed during the activation of oxide-coated cathodes," *Services Electronics Research Lab. Tech. J.*, **6**, 15–16 (Apr. 1956).

114. B. Wolk, "The breakdown of cathode coatings," *Sylvania Technologist*, **10**, No. 4, 106–110 (Oct. 1957).

115. B. Wolk, "The relationship between thermal decomposition in vacuum and the microstructure of alkaline earth carbonates," *J. Electrochem. Soc.*, **105**, 89–93 (Feb. 1958).

116. S. J. Stoll, "Origin and analysis of gas in electron tubes," *Brit. J. Appl. Phys.*, **7**, 94–96 (Mar. 1956).

116a. G. A. Haas and J. T. Jensen, Jr., "Preconversion of oxide cathodes," *Rev. Sci. Instr.* **30**, 562–565 (July 1959).

117. M. Benjamin, "The influence of impurities in the core metal on thermionic emission from oxide-coated nickel," *Phil. Mag. (London)*, **20**, 1–24 (July 1935).

118. F. Violet and J. Riethmuller, "Contribution to the study of oxide cathodes" (in French), *Ann. radioél. compagn. franc. assoc. T.S.F.*, **4**, 184–215 (July 1949).

119. K. Jackson and R. O. Jenkins, "Nickel in electronics," *Metallurgia*, **47**, 277–282 (June 1953).

119a. B. Wolk, "Hot strength properties of filamentary nickel alloys," *IRE Trans.*, **ED-5**, 58–65 (Apr. 1958).

120. R. W. Peterson, D. E. Anderson and W. G. Shepherd, "Influence of the cathode base on the chemical activation of oxide cathodes," *J. Appl. Phys.*, **28**, 22–33 (Jan. 1957).

121. H. A. Poehler, "The influence of the core material on the thermionic emission of oxide cathodes," *Proc. Inst. Radio Engrs.*, **40**, 190–196 (Feb. 1952).

122. M. Davis and C. E. Densem, "Nickel-tungsten alloys for oxide-coated cathodes," *Services Electronics Research Lab. Tech. J.*, **4**, No. 3, 85–90 (Sept. 1954).

123. M. Davis, C. E. Densem and J. H. Rendall, "The manufacture and properties of high-strength nickel-tungsten alloys," *J. Inst. Metals*, **84**, Pt. 6, 160–164, (Feb. 1956).

124. J. A. Lund, "Roll-compacting produces pure nickel strip," *J. Metals*, **10**, 731–734 (Nov. 1958).

125. Briggs Associates, Inc., Norristown, Pa., "Study of Cathode Interface Impedance," Final Report, 1 May 1956–31 Oct. 1958 (2 Vols.); Contr. No. DA36-039-sc-72336, U. S. Army Signal Research and Development Laboratory, Fort Monmouth, N. J.

126. G. H. Metson, "Platinum-cored thermionic valves in the transatlantic telephone cable," *Platinum Metals Rev.*, **2**, 2–6 (Jan. 1958). Johnson, Matthey & Co., Limited, Hatton Garden, London, E.C.1.

126a. B. Wolk, "Studies of the effect of anode materials on oxide cathode performance," *Sylvania Technologist*, **12**, 41–45 (Apr. 1959).

126b. H. B. Frost, "Titanium as an Anode Material," Report on 19th Annual Conference Physical Electronics, Massachusetts Institute of Technology, Cambridge, March 26–28, 1959, pp. 124–130.

126c. J. Morrison, "Titanium in Vacuum Tubes," Report on 19th Annual Conference Physical Electronics, Massachusetts Institute of Technology, Cambridge, March 26–28, 1959, pp. 118–123.

127. H. Jacobs, "Dissociation of surface films of various oxides as determined by emission measurements of oxide-coated cathodes," *J. Appl. Phys.*, **17**, 596–603 (July 1946).

128. K. M. Poole, "Electrode contamination in electron optical systems," *Proc. Phys. Soc.*, **66B**, 542–547 (July 1953).

129. T. Imai and N. Shibata, "Effect of the base metal on the electron dissociation of deposited barium oxide films," *J. Phys. Soc. Japan*, **9**, 1034–1035 (Nov./Dec. 1954).

130. P. Wargo and W. G. Shepherd, "Electron-bombardment induced dissociation of alkaline earth oxides," *Phys. Rev.*, **106**, 694–703 (May 15, 1957).

131. H. E. Kern, E. T. Graney and D. O. Feder, "Glass envelope composition as a factor in oxide cathode poisoning," 1958 Electron Devices Conference, Washington, D. C.

131a. E. M. Wise, "Nickel in the radio industry," *Proc. IRE*, **25**, 714–751 (June 1937).

132. "New self-sustained emission tube," *Electronics*, **36**, No. 6, 66–67 (Feb. 6, 1959).

132a. D. Dobischek, J. A. Schweitzer and P. T. Ward, "Method of Making an Electron Emitter," U. S. Patent 2,873,218 (Feb. 10, 1959).

133. "Utilization of self-sustained electron emission investigation," Tung-Sol Electric, Inc. Advisory Group on Electron Tubes, Military Reliable Tube Program, Status Report No. 49 (15 Feb. 1959).

134. A. M. Skellett, B. G. Firth and D. W. Mayer, "The magnesium oxide cold cathode and its application in vacuum tubes," *Proc. IRE*, **47**, 1704–1712, (Oct. 1959).

CHAPTER 16

GETTER MATERIALS AND THEIR USE

Introduction

In this last chapter, we are concerned with measures taken to produce, or preserve an adequate vacuum after the pumps have done their part in reducing the pressure within the envelope to as low a value as is economically feasible in mass production, or possible with available pumps. This task is performed by getters which have the property of sorbing gases remaining after seal-off from the pump, or released into the vacuum by the walls of the envelope, or structural components. In both cases, the getter acts as an auxiliary pump, but, in the first case of high-speed machine exhaust of small tubes, a major part of the evacuation is assigned to the getter which lowers the pressure from about 10^{-4} Torr to $< 10^{-6}$ Torr and keeps on pumping throughout the life of the tube if gases are released; in the second case, when the seal-off pressure is very low ($< 10^{-6}$ Torr), in the case of individual exhaust, the getter is only a second line of defense to make sure that a low pressure is preserved in operation. It goes without saying that the getter itself must be well outgassed before it can function effectively.

When the processing of all tube parts has been done with extreme care so that their surfaces are essentially free of contaminants and adsorbed gases, all these surfaces will be eager to take up gases, and there is thus no need to put a getter into the tube; the surfaces of the clean components act as getters. This practice is followed in many power tubes and microwave tubes where special processing and prolonged pumping are economically feasible. It should also be realized that surfaces which have a porous texture, in particular oxide cathodes, have a great propensity to absorb gases when they are relatively colder than other parts from which gases are released; this may lead to poisoning effects, a result which can be circumvented in laboratory operations by attaching a small appendix to the manifold and filling it with $Ba/Sr(CO_3)$ in powder form. The very much greater volume of this gas sink will result in preferred absorption of harmful gases given off during processing on the pump and substantially raise the activity of the cathode in cases where it was difficult to obtain adequate emission.

The usefulness of a particular getter may be appraised on the basis of the following requirements:

(a) Ability to sorb a large part of the different gases encountered during

574

the operation of the tube. This condition implies that the getter should have a high sorption capacity for several gases and not just for one.

(b) High gettering rate, which may be measured by the decrease in pressure per unit of time when the getter is exposed to a given gas. Gettering rate can also be expressed in terms of the volume of gas sorbed per second (cc/sec).

(c) High getter capacity (a) and high sorption rate (b) over a wide range of temperature.

(d) Low desorption rate (release of gettered gases) at the highest temperature encountered in operation.

(e) Chemical stability in the presence of electron bombardment and at elevated ambient temperature.

(f) Low vapor pressure before activation.

(g) Ease of outgassing before activation.

(h) Ready activation at a convenient temperature.

(i) Low vapor pressure after activation.

(j) Absence of loose particles during or after activation.

(k) Ease of fabrication and storage.

(l) Ready availability and low cost.

In addition, the electrical operation of the tube must not be adversely affected by the presence of the getter. It is essential to prevent the deposition of getter films on insulating components of the tube, or on such areas of the bulb where the interelectrode capacity of the electrodes would be affected. This condition is usually satisfied by providing getter shields and by suitable shaping of the getter dispenser.[1]

Reimann[2] and Metson[3] have shown that a getter film deposited on a glass wall may assume different electrical potentials depending on many factors, such as geometry, secondary emission yield, sequence in which potentials are applied to cathode and anode, and external illumination. It is not recommended to operate getter films at a positive potential because bombardment by electrons may cause release of sorbed gases.[2, 4]

The literature on getters, up to early 1950, has been listed by Espe, Knoll, and Wilder[5] in their review article which is recommended to the reader as an introduction to the subject.* The very recent book by Knoll and Kazan[6] reproduces this same list of references essentially without additions beyond 1950. The bibliography at the end of this present chapter thus takes over about 1950 and carries on to the present (June 1959).

Reimann[2] discusses in great detail the properties of getters and especially the practical aspects of their use. The well-known book by Dushman[7] pre-

---

* A most up-to-date review of the practical aspects of gettering and the history of gettering technique has been published by Della Porta.[1a]

sents the theoretical background on sorption and desorption phenomena. Alpert [8] describes the use of getters in the production of ultra-high vacuum in a very recent and comprehensive review article on this subject. It may be said that quantitative, and therefore meaningful, investigations of getter action were not undertaken until 1950.

In dealing with getters, one is principally concerned with the physics and chemistry of surfaces, mechanisms of adsorption and absorption, diffusion, oxide film formation, desorption, and other effects. In many cases, a full understanding of these phenomena has not been established.[7-15]

It is probably in order at this point to emphasize the importance of surface effects to electron device technology in general. Thin films play a very important role, not only as unavoidable by-products even in the best possible vacuum, but also as desirable end-products by themselves, as exemplified by thin-film cathodes, secondary electron emission surfaces, photocathodes, and microwave attenuators; the magnetic properties of thin films applied to storage elements are another example of many important applications.[16]

Types of Getters

A distinction is generally made between flash getters and coating getters both of which consist of prepared surface deposits which are of a metallic nature. In addition, bulk getters may be used in the form of wires or structural elements made from tantalum, niobium, zirconium, or titanium. These metals absorb gases at elevated temperatures and must therefore be run hot to perform most effectively.

The temperature for maximum sorption of one gas may not coincide with that for greatest sorption of another so that a compromise is necessary unless two separate getters are run at different temperatures by either heating them by an external power supply, or attaching them to internal parts which operate at different temperatures.

Flash Getters

Barium getters have for some time occupied a preferred position in the electronics industry and are used today almost exclusively in tube production; these getters are available in many different weights, shapes, and alloy compositions,[1a, 2, 5, 6, 17, 18] but present-day use favors the aluminum-stabilized barium (50:50 b.wt.) which affords protection from oxidation in humid atmospheres during handling, or "mount washing," i.e., dipping in water or alcohol before seal-in (see p. 555). The Ba/Al alloy is filled into steel tubing 0.020 to 0.030 in. dia. which is cut to suitable short lengths and sealed off at the ends. One side of the tubular wall is flattened and thinned to about 3 mils so that on heating to about 850°C barium diffuses through the thin section and is dispersed to the wall of the tube. The thin section may actually melt and form a gap through which the barium vapor escapes.[1a] Getters are shipped in sealed containers and should be stored in a desiccator after the can has been opened; preoutgassing in an evacuated bulb, which can be sealed off, is still better practice. Table 16.1 gives the characteristics of various types of getters from different sources in the literature.[16, 19, 20]*

Barium satisfies many of the requirements listed above; it has a relatively high sorptive capacity for the gases encountered in larger quantities in vacuum tubes: i.e., O_2, CO, CO_2, N_2, H_2, H_2O, C_nH_m, in decreasing order.[21-23]†

The speed of pumping of a barium getter film varies with time and temperature.[25, 26] Typical plots of speed vs time obtained by Bloomer[26] are shown in Figure 16.1 for a getter film area of 8cm^2 at room temperature, 40°C, and 70°C. The question whether the pumping speed of such a getter is affected by an ionizing electron beam or an incandescent filament in the vicinity of the getter was also investigated by Bloomer. Many earlier workers had reported such effects.[2] It was found that the speed of pumping oxygen was unaltered during the period when it is steady, or rising (Fig. 16.1), no matter whether a nearby ionizing electron beam, or an incandescent filament, was switched on or off; in the right-hand, falling-speed range, a nearby filament had to be kept hot for the getter to have any speed. An ionizing electron beam was not necessary.

"A tungsten filament became effective when its temperature was raised above about 1800°K. An increase of temperature to 2100°K did not further increase the speed of pumping. A hot filament caused a film to pump even when it was several centimeters away, around a bend or two, in 25mm bore glass tubing. The amount of gas taken up by the getter (the capacity) was found to increase with temperature. At room temperature the capacity was the same for films of different thicknesses but the same area. At higher temperatures the capacity increased with the thickness of the film, as shown in Table 16.3. Getter films which had ceased to pump oxygen at room temperature did so again when heated to 200°C."[26]

---

* Such compilations are always fraught with the danger of being misleading because the experimental conditions and the methods of measurement are rarely the same for two sources. Multiple entries and the reference to the origin of the figures used are thus given in many cases.

† According to Wagener,[24] CO is preponderantly released from nickel, iron, and molybdenum, while tantalum gives off CO and H_2 as major gas constituents, and titanium $H_2O + H_2$. Ba getters release mainly H_2, H_2O, and CO during outgassing prior to flashing. (Zn/Cd)S luminescent screens deposited on glass show a preponderance of CO and CO_2 when bombarded by an electron beam (100 μa/cm^2 at 1500 v) (Table 16.2). Gases released by mica are given in Table 3.3 (p. 133).

TABLE 16.1. PERFORMANCE CHARACTERISTICS OF GETTER MATERIALS[19]

Material	M.P. °C	T_{p1} ($p_1=10^{-5}$) °C	T_{p2} ($p_2=10^{-2}$) °C	Getter Type F = Film B = Bulk	AT AT = Activation OT = Operation Temperature °C	OT °C	Gas Sorbed	Initial Sorption Rate a) b)* at 20°C	Sorptive Capacity 1μ/mg(T°C)†	Sorptive Capacity 1μ/cm² at 20°C	References
Aluminum	660	900	1220	F		500	O_2	0	7.5–38.5 (20)	1^{20}	19, 20, 69, 70
							H_2	0	0		69
							N_2		0		69
							CO_2	<0.005 (a)	0		37, 69
							CO	<0.005 (a)			37
Barium	717	417	687	F	900^{20}		air		56 (400)		18, 31
						>40	O_2	0.3 (a)	57 (300)	1^{20}	4, 18, 20, 25, 26, 31, 37, 69, 71
						200	H_2	0.05 (a)	100 (400)	0^{20}	18, 20, 30, 31, 37, 69
							H_2O		72 (300)		18, 31
						>100	N_2	0.003 (a)	3–25 (<100)	0^{20}	20, 25, 37, 69
									43–51 (>100)		18, 30, 31, 72
							CO_2	5.0 (a)	66 (400)	0.2^{20}	18, 20, 25, 31, 37, 69
						>80	CO	3.5 (a)	100 (400)	0.2^{20}	18, 25, 31, 40, 73
							CH_4			0^{20}	20
Ba/Al alloy (50: 50 b.wt.) (sintered ring getter)				F	1100^{20}		air			2.6	1a
							O_2		50 (20)	13	1a, 20
							H_2				1a
							H_2O		61 (20)	2.25	1a
							N_2			1.8	1a
							CO_2				1a
							CO			3.7	1a

Table of gases in metals (rotated 90°):

Metal				F/B	Temp	Temp	Gas	(a)	20–200 (20)	0[20]	References
Magnesium	651	287	437		650[20]		O_2	0			69
							H_2	0			2, 69
							N_2	<0.005 (a)			69
							CO_2	<0.005 (a)			37, 69
							CO				4, 20, 37
Molybdenum	2622	1987	2627	F			O_2			0.5[20]	
							H_2			0.05[20]	
							N_2	2.7 (a)	1.0 (30)	0.05[20]	73
							CO	3.5 (a)	3.0 (30–200)	0.15[20]	73
							CH_4			0[20]	
Tantalum	2996	2400	3075	F			O_2			1	20
							H_2	>2.5 (a)		0.5	20
							N_2			0.1	20, 73
							CO_2			0	20
							CO			0.08[20]	20, 73–75
							CO	>2.5 (a)		0	20
Sheet (0.1 mm thick)				B	1200					0.01 (600°C)	20
										9.0 (900°C)	20
Thorium	1827	1637		F		450	O_2		7.5–33.1 (20)		69
						650	H_2		19.5–53.7 (20)		69
							CO_2				
				B	900		O_2	0.40 (675°C)		0.2 (75°C)	20
										6.5 (675°C)	20
							H_2	0.020 (a) (675°C)		0.04 (75°C)	20
										0.25 (225°C)	20
										0.55 (350°C)	20
										0.50 (475°C)	20
										0.08 (675°C)	20

TABLE 16.1.—Continued

Material	M.P. °C	T_{p1} (p = 10^{-5}) °C	T_{p2} (p = 10^{-2}) °C	Getter Type F = Film B = Bulk	AT (AT = Activation OT = Operation) °C	OT °C	Gas	Initial Sorption Rate a) b)* at 20°C	Sorptive Capacity		References
									1μ mg(T°C)†	1μ/cm² at 20°C	
Thorium (continued)							N_2	0.010(a) (675°C)			20
							CO_2	0.75(a) (675°C)			20
							CO	0.6(a) (675°C)			20
Misch metal (Ce/La)	785			F	1000^{20}		O_2		21.7-51(20)		60
							H_2		46.1-64(20)		69
							N_2		3.2-16(20)		69
							CO_2		2.2-45(20)		69
Titanium	1660	1327	1727	F	2000^{20}		O_2			1.0	20
							H_2			2.0	20
							N_2	3.0(a)	1.9-2.5 (30-300)	0.05^{20}	20, 63, 64, 73
							CO_2	4.3(a)	4.3 (20)	0.13^{20}	20, 63, 64, 73
							CO	12.0(a)	3.4-4.2 (30-200)	0.15^{20}	20, 63
							CH_4				20
				B	1000^{20}	>650	O_2	2.01(b) (800°C)	90 (800)	0	20, 58
						20-400	H_2				58
						300-400	H_2O				58

580

Material						Gas				Ref
Titanium (continued)					>700	N_2	0.08(b) (1000°C)	160 (1000)		58
					>700	CO_2	0.81(b) (1100°C)	50 (1100)		58
						CO			0.003	20
									0.020 (325°C)	20
									0.10 (450°C)	20
									1.4 (600°C)	20
									7.0 (700°C)	20
Tungsten	3370	2547	3297	F		N_2	>2.5 (a)			73
						CO	>2.5 (a)			73
Uranium	1132	1462	1750	F	240	O_2		10.6–9.3 (20)		69
						H_2		8.9–21.5 (20)		69
Zirconium	1857	1857		B	1300	O_2			1.5 (25°C)	20
									8.0 (400°C)	20
						H_2			0.35 (25°C)	20
									53 (350°C)	20
						N_2			3.4 (500°C)	20
									5.8 (800°C)	20
						CO_2			2.3 (500°C)	20
									12.2 (800°C)	20
						CO			0 (25°C)	20
									1.7 (500°C)	20
									14.6 (800°C)	20

* (a) $l/sec/cm^2$ (b) $l\mu/sec/cm^2$.

† Where two values are quoted, the second figure is for a diffuse or black deposit.

TABLE 16.2. PERCENTAGE COMPOSITION OF GAS EVOLVING
FROM DIFFERENT MATERIALS*

Type of material	Approx. out-gassing tem-perature °C	mm	CO_2	H_2O	CH_4	CO	N	H_2
Ni	1000	1.9×10^{-6}	2	4		92		2
Fe	1000	4.6×10^{-6}		3		95	2	
Mo	1800	3.8×10^{-6}	4	5		80	10	1
Ta	2200	2.3×10^{-6}		3		50	6	40
Ti	1100	1.6×10^{-7}		45	5			50
Ba getter 1.5 mg	900	7.8×10^{-7}	5	40	5	15	5	30
Ba TV getter 20 mg	900	6×10^{-7}		30		20	5	45
Luminescent screen	—	—	25	5		50		20

* After Wagener and Marth.[24]

This increase of sorption capacity with temperature applies not only to oxygen, but also to other gases and vapors normally sorbed by barium and extends far beyond 200°C.* Della Porta[31] has more recently shown that the sorptive capacity of fresh, bright barium films increases substantially up to 450°C, and that the sorption of saturated Ba getter films can be restored, at least in part, by heating the getter film to about 300°C for a certain period, about one hour. Table 16.4 gives the total absorption capacity† as measured by Della Porta at various temperatures.

* The maximum operating temperature for Ba getters was given in 1950[5] as being 200°C. This now obsolete statement has unfortunately been repeated in quite recent publications.[17, 27, 28] The present author, being responsible for one of these,[28] offers his apologies. Wagener[20] has recently mentioned 300°C as the maximum permissible temperature before volatility of Ba becomes a serious factor. At 420°C, the vapor pressure is 10^{-5} Torr.[30]

† The experimental technique employed for the measurement of the gettering rate G has been established by Wagener[32] and adopted by most investigators. It provides for connecting a getter bulb to the pump manifold by a capillary of conductance F and measuring the pressure p_g in the getter bulb by means of an ionization gauge directly connected to it while keeping the manifold pressure p_m constant. G is then expressed by the volume of gas sorbed per second, or as the product of conductance F times the pressure ratio p_m/p_g according to the following equations:

$$G p_g = F(p_m - p_g)$$

$$G = \frac{F(p_m - p_g)}{p_g}$$

When $p_m \gg p_g$

$$G = F \frac{p_m}{p_g}$$

Carbon monoxide is not only released by a number of metals, as pointed out previously, but also is a major constituent of gases present in tubes containing oxide cathodes. Carbon dioxide formed during breakdown of the earth alkali carbonates is adsorbed on the anode and other electrodes where it is likely to combine with barium, similarly deposited from the cathode, according to the reaction

$$Ba + CO_2 \rightarrow BaO + CO\uparrow$$

when these surfaces are being bombarded by electrons. Stoll[22] has more

---

It can also be shown[21] that

$$V \frac{dp}{dt} = E(t) - p_g G(t)$$

Where V = volume of the getter bulb
P = residual pressure
$E(t)$ = amount of gas instantaneously evolved from the various parts of the tube under study
$G(t)$ = instantaneous speed of absorption of gas by the getter

By integration and choice of suitable limits, one obtains the following expression for the residual pressure:

$$p = \frac{E(t)}{G(t)}$$

As long as $E(t)$ is constant, the final pressure is thus dependent only on $G(t)$.

By measuring the actual quantities absorbed by the getter, Della Porta[18] established that $G(t)$ is dependent on p_g and that more generally applicable data on getter action can be obtained by keeping p_g constant; the merits of such an approach were appreciated by Wagener[33] in 1953 but not reduced to practice. Bills and Carleton,[34] in their study of adsorption of activated gases, more recently state that "maintaining constant pressure in the adsorption vessel allows a more straightforward theoretical analysis and avoids uncertainties due to evolution of adsorbed gas when the pressure decreases." The instantaneous quantity of gas $Q_{inst} = F(p_m - p_g)$ entering the getter chamber is called instantaneous absorption capacity by Della Porta and corresponds to the evolution rate (measured in cm³/sec adjusted to 1 micron pressure). The total absorption capacity per unit surface (expressed in liter × micron, as $Q = V \times p$) represents the total quantity of gas which a getter can absorb; the figures entered in Table 16.4 are determined in this manner. Figure 16.2 illustrates the difference in the curves obtained when measuring (a) at p_m = const. and (b) at p_g = const. In the latter case the results become practically independent of the size of the capillary used in the experiment. In a more recent presentation, Wagener[20] has shown that the two alternative methods give the same results (personal communication). The experts thus do not agree on this point. The present author was unfortunately unsuccessful in his efforts to procure an advance copy of Wagener's recent paper which was not yet in print at the time of going to press with this chapter.

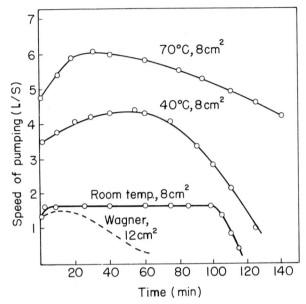

Figure 16.1. The variation with time and temperature of the speed of pumping of oxygen by barium (manifold pressure $p_m = 2 \times 10^{-5}$ Torr). After Bloomer.[41] (*Courtesy The Institute of Physics, London.*)

TABLE 16.3. CAPACITIES FOR DIFFERENT TEMPERATURES AND FILM
THICKNESSES OF BARIUM GETTERS*

Time for which 10 A firing current passed (min)	Temperature of getter film	Area of getter film (cm²)	Quantity of oxygen taken up (l.μ.)	Number of monolayers
1	room	4	2.7	23
2	room	5	3.0	20
5	room	4	2.2	19
6	room	5	2.8	19
2	205°C	4	4.5	38
2	220°C	4	10	85
7	200°C	4	23.5	200

* After Bloomer[41]

recently studied this effect in some detail and shown that the amount of CO present in the tube after cathode conversion can be reduced to low levels by keeping the anode hot (650°C) during conversion and thus preventing adsorption of CO_2 and Ba.*

* Curnow[35] has pointed out that condensation of CO_2 in a liquid nitrogen trap will cause a residual pressure of 6×10^{-6} Torr at -183°C. To attain lower pressures

TABLE 16.4. TOTAL ABSORPTION CAPACITY OF BRIGHT BARIUM MIRRORS*

Gases	Quantity absorbed at				
	20°C	100°C ($l\mu$/cm.²)	200°C ($l\mu$/cm.²)	300°C	400°C
Oxygen.......	50 $l\mu$/mg			57 $l\mu$/mg.	
Moisture......	35 $l\mu$/mg			72 $l\mu$/mg.	
Hydrogen.....	4.48 $l\mu$/cm²	5	5.5	9 $l\mu$/cm² (90 $l\mu$/mg)	10 $l\mu$/cm² (100 $l\mu$/mg)
Carbon di-oxide......	0.60 $l\mu$/cm²	2	3.3	5.8 $l\mu$/cm² (58 $l\mu$/mg)	6.6 $l\mu$/cm² (66 $l\mu$/mg)
Carbon mon-oxide	0.72 $l\mu$/cm²	4	4.4	9 $l\mu$/cm² (90 $l\mu$/mg)	10 $l\mu$/cm² (100 $l\mu$/mg)
Nitrogen......	0.33 $l\mu$/cm²	0.48	3.4	5 $l\mu$/cm² (50 $l\mu$/mg)	5.1 $l\mu$/cm² (51 $l\mu$/mg)
Dry air.......	0.64 $l\mu$/cm²	1.60	4.6	5.6 $l\mu$/cm² (56 $l\mu$/mg)	5.6 $l\mu$/cm² (56 $l\mu$/mg)

* After Della Porta[31]

The absorption of CO by Ba getters has been studied by Wagener,[21, 36, 37] Arizumi and Kotani,[38a-e] Morrison and Zetterstrom,[39] Della Porta,[18, 31] and Bloomer.[40] Figures 16.2 to 16.4 illustrate the results obtained by Bloomer who studied the absorption effects in a pressure range of 10^{-6} to 10^{-7} Torr and found that the mechanism of absorption is similar to that for oxygen and can be explained with the aid of Mott's theory.[41, 42]

"Carbon monoxide is dissociated at the surface of the barium film, and an oxide layer containing free carbon is formed. Below 80°C, the layer of reaction products is protective once it has grown to a thickness of about 50Å. Above 80°C, the whole of the barium is used up in the reaction.

"The condensation coefficient at room temperature is 0.012. Thus, about 1 in 80 of the carbon monoxide molecules striking the getter surface in any period is taken up by a barium film at room temperature (1 in 40 at 170°C). The condensation coefficient is limited to these low values by the superficial density of interstitial barium ions in the free surface of the oxide layer. A nearby ionizing discharge has very little influence upon the frac-

would thus require that the trap be filled only after conversion of the cathode, a practice followed in a few laboratories. By far the more general procedure provides for filling of the trap at the end of the bake-out cycle, if not when the peak temperature of the oven has been reached, but certainly before cathode conversion. The effect of this difference in processing has not been evaluated on a large scale, but it makes good sense to favor the practice recommended by Curnow.

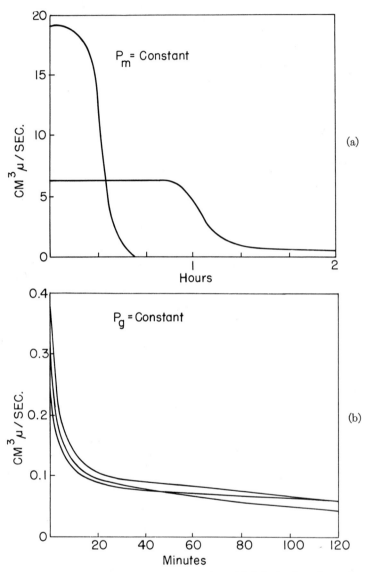

Figure 16.2. (a) Instantaneous getter capacity of bright barium for carbon monoxide determined at $p_m = 5.7 \times 10^{-4}$ Torr = constant, using two different capillaries: 1) F = 34 cm³/sec. 2) F = 11 cm³/sec. (b) Instantaneous getter capacity of bright barium for dry air determined at $p_g = 3 \times 10^{-4}$ Torr = constant, using three different capillaries: 1) F = 2.75 cm³/sec. 2) F = 5.5 cm³/sec. 3) F = 14.4 cm³/sec. After Della Porta.[31] (*Courtesy Edwards High Vacuum Ltd., England.*)

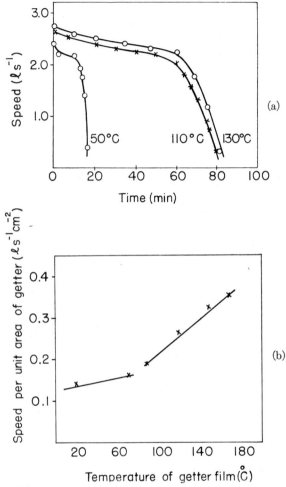

Figure 16.3. (a) The variation with time and temperature of the speed of pumping of carbon monoxide by barium (manifold pressure $p_m = 4 \times 10^{-5}$ Torr). (b) The variation with temperature of the speed of pumping of unit (apparent) area of getter film (measured a few minutes after the start of each run). After Bloomer.[40] (*Courtesy The Institute of Physics, London.*)

tion of incident molecules which is condensed upon and taken up by a barium film."

Coating Getters

The enhancement of the sorptive power, which can be achieved by heating a barium film to a few hundred degrees, has been referred to on preced-

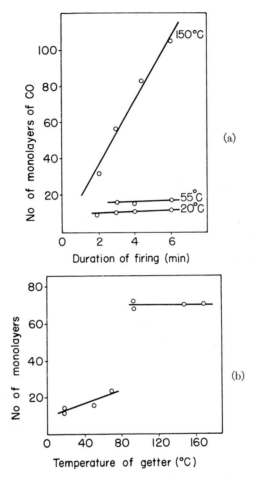

Figure 16.4. (a) The variation of capacity of barium getter for carbon monoxide with thickness of deposit at different temperatures. (b) The influence of temperature upon the capacity for carbon monoxide for barium films of equal thickness. After Bloomer.[40] (*Courtesy The Institute of Physics, London.*)

ing pages; Della Porta[31] gives 400°C as an upper limit because considerable evolution of gas was observed at 500°C. The trend toward operating electron tubes at ever-increasing ambient temperatures thus establishes a need for getters which can effectively operate in such critical environments. Research in this area is being currently sponsored by the Armed Forces.

The sorptive properties of tantalum, zirconium, and thorium were mentioned above. These metals can be applied to less refractory base metals used for electrodes by sintering a powder film onto them; they require a fairly high operating temperature to be effective.

The Telefunken Laboratories in Germany developed the "Ceto" getter during World War II which contains the metals cerium and thorium; it is prepared from a mixture of thorium powder and a cerium-aluminum alloy powder, with thorium comprising at least 80 per cent of the mixture. Espe[43] has given a detailed description of its preparation as practiced in Germany for the production of microwave tubes. After being degassed at 800°C, such powder coatings exhibit marked getter action already near 100°C and have an absorption maximum at several hundred degrees centigrade.

During the past few years, extensive development of Ceto-type getters has been carried out by Wyman and Kuhnapfel[44] at the Reliable Tube Section of Bendix Aviation Corporation and by Briggs Associates[27] under sponsorship of New Process Metals, Inc.,* from which company Ceto-type getters are commercially available under the tradename "CerAlloy 400."

The early approach, following that practiced by Telefunken, was to sinter the powder onto metal flags which were attached to electrodes of the tube structure in such positions that the getter was raised to a suitable temperature in operation. Direct coating of electrodes, such as anodes, was also practiced. The sintered powder is black and thus has a high thermal emissivity; it can be applied to iron, steel, "Kovar," nickel, nickel-plated steel, molybdenum, Monel, and copper.

More recently, work at Bendix[45] has culminated in the production of pressed pellets contained in nickel cups which are strategically located within the tube. The over-all effectiveness of the getter is thereby increased and no doubt also the ease of handling.

The process of manufacture is described as follows:[45]

(1) Pure thorium powder is produced by reducing ThO_2 with calcium in an iron crucible (50 pts ThO_2 + 30 pts Ca (b.wt.)). The mixture is heated to 400°C in a vacuum of $< 10^{-4}$ Torr and then fired at 950°C in a dry argon atmosphere at a pressure of 20 Torr, or more. After cooling, the resultant compound is washed in water and acetic acid until pure thorium remains; after washing in methanol, the thorium powder is vacuum dried.

(2) An alloy of cerium and aluminum is made by mixing fine shavings of cerium, which have been degreased in acetone, with aluminum granules in a weight ratio of 72 Ce:28 Al and heating in a BeO crucible at 800°C in vacuo at 10^{-4} Torr. An exothermic reaction occurs, and much gas is released so that pumps with adequate speed ($\sim$ 100 l/sec in the micron range) must be used. The resulting alloy is shiny and brittle; it is ground to a fineness of 240 mesh and stored in an argon atmosphere.

(3) The Ce-Al alloy powder and thorium powder are mixed in a weight ratio 1:4, and 50 gm of the mixed powder is compacted at high pressure into 1-in.-long rods and sintered at 1000°C in a vacuum furnace at a pres-

* 45–65 Manufacturers Place, Newark 5, N.J.

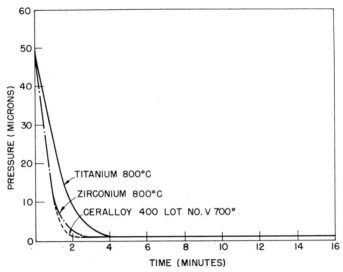

Figure 16.5. Sorption rate of various getters for carbon dioxide. After Wyman and Kuhnapfel.[44] (*Courtesy Bendix Aviation Corporation.*)

sure of 5×10^{-5} Torr, or less, for 1 hr. Melting must be avoided, as the getter properties of the sintered alloy are by far superior to those of the cast material and also because the cast material is ductile and cannot easily be pulverized.[43]

(4) The sintered compacts are ground to granules and screened to 340 mesh size under acetone. Small nickel cups are filled with the granules and pressed into pellet form, ready for mounting in the tube.

Extreme precautions are necessary in all the processing steps because thorium and the alloy powders are not only pyrophoric but also emit α-radiation. Any attempt to duplicate these procedures should be undertaken only after reading the much more detailed original references[43, 45] and consultation with those already experienced in handling these materials.*

The results reported on the merits of Ceto-type getters evidently warrant the considerable effort involved in their production. Wargo and Shepherd[46] made brief reference to these getters and report that a mixture of 80 % Th + 5 % Al + 15 % Mischmetal sintered onto a molybdenum ribbon and outgassed at 1100°C at 10^{-7} Torr did thereafter getter all gases except helium when operated in the range from 350 to 500°C. Wyman and Kuhnapfel[44] and Briggs[27] have given more detailed accounts of results obtained. Figure 16.5 shows the pressure drop *vs.* time observed in a 2-liter volume

* New Process Metals, Inc. has issued several bulletins on CerAlloy 400.

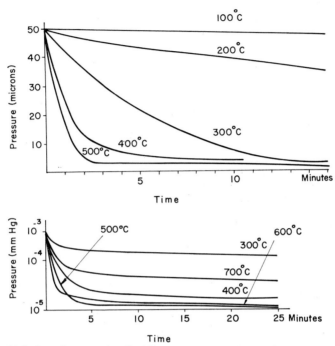

Figure 16.6. Sorption rate for CerAlloy 400 getters in carbon dioxide at different temperatures. After Wyman and Kuhnapfel.[44] (*Courtesy Bendix Aviation Corporation.*)

after CO_2 was admitted at $p = 5 \times 10^{-2}$ Torr and the different getters were heated to the temperatures indicated on the curves. Figure 16.6 gives the sorption rate for CO_2 at various getter temperatures, as read by a Pirani gauge. The CerAlloy 400 getter was heated by induction and temperatures read by a thermocouple. Briggs[27] has reported improved emission levels, greater uniformity of emission, low values of heater-cathode leakage, low grid leakage, and low contact potential on controlled tests with Standard Diodes and receiving tubes. Bendix reports that no desorption of gas was noticeable after baking some of their tubes on life test at 400°C for 96 hrs, a condition under which all conventional getters had caused failure owing to excessive gas currents.

Tantalum, zirconium, and thorium have been used as coating getters in power tubes for many years. Powders of these metals are usually sintered onto the anode surfaces to which they can be applied by spraying a suspension of the powder in a binder solution, or by cataphoresis.

Tantalum is capable of absorbing several hundred times its own volume of gas ($740 \times$ for H_2) when it has been properly outgassed near 2000°C (see

p. 347) and is then operated at a red heat, anywhere between 700 and 1200°C. The relatively high cost of Ta mitigates against its use as a bulk anode material, except in special-purpose tubes, so that coating with powders offers an economic advantage provided the processing cost is not excessive.

Tantalum is also a very effective flash getter when placed in the form of a wire loop in a separate bulb connected with the tube under study. Becker[47] was able to produce and maintain ultra-high vacua of the order of 10^{-14} Torr in a field emission microscope by repeatedly laying down a film of Ta.*

Zirconium[48-54] is an effective getter for O_2, N_2, CO, CO_2, and H_2O; it does not react with mercury and can thus be used in mercury vapor rectifiers. According to Fast,[52] 40 atomic per cent of oxygen and 20 atomic per cent of nitrogen are taken up by zirconium without compound formation, the gases dissolving in the metal and being retained up to 1650°C. Both gases are rapidly sorbed at 800°C, and so are CO and CO_2.[53] Hydrogen is sorbed most copiously at 300°C, desorbed at higher temperatures but taken up in a narrow temperature range near 870°C. As suggested above, several Zr getters may thus be operated at different temperatures in one tube.

The form of the Zr getter may be a coating on an electrode, a tab attached to the heater leg, a separate wire wound on a higher-melting support wire which can be externally heated, or a component made from Zr in bulk. Zirconium hydride, rather than pure Zr powder, may be used as a coating material which decomposes on heating during processing of the tube. These materials are highly flammable in finely dispersed form and will ignite on exposure to shock or abrasion. Extreme precautions must be taken in handling them.

Thorium falls into the same category. It is not only useful as a constituent of Ceto-type getters, as described above, but may also be used as a coating or flash getter by itself.[32, 33] Wagener[33] found that thorium powder electrolytically deposited on cathode nickel sleeves exhibited a higher sorption rate for oxygen than it did for hydrogen. The rate of sorption for O_2 is also higher than it is for H_2, and the decay of the sorption rate is smaller for O_2. The sorption rate for H_2 increases with temperature to a maximum at 750°K.

By heating the Th powder to 1150°K for about 5 minutes, sorbed hydrogen is completely released. Oxygen is released by heating to this temperature only when the sorbed quantity has been small. It is suggested on

---

* It is of passing interest to note that the endpoint of life for a Ta filament was found to be reached after a 6-percent reduction of the wire diameter; this agrees with the most recent findings for tungsten filaments (see p. 273).

the basis of these observations that oxygen is sorbed by chemisorption in which a stable oxide, probably ThO_2, is formed; the activation energy for this process is 0.75 Kcal/mole. Hydrogen, on the other hand, reaches an equilibrium of solution in Th and can be injected or removed at will; the heat of solution of H_2 in Th is 13 Kcal/mole.

As thorium is a constituent of Ceto-type getters, desorption of hydrogen and of oxygen in part must be expected above 850°C, as stated above.

Titanium has a very high reactivity with gases, especially at elevated temperatures, as shown by Gulbransen and Andrew,[55-57] and other investigators. Stout and Gibbons have studied the sorption properties of Ti for various gases and vapors and found that O_2, N_2, and CO_2 are gettered above 700°C while H_2 is absorbed in the temperature range of 25 to 400°C. The sorption rates for the various gases are markedly different at any given temperature, oxygen being sorbed at a much greater rate than nitrogen or carbon dioxide throughout the temperature range from 700 to 1100°C. Rare gases and mercury do not interfere with the gettering action of Ti.

Carbon, oxygen, and nitrogen form stable compounds with Ti and are not released when the metal is heated to elevated temperatures. The presence of a surface film of oxide will prevent sorption of hydrogen at room temperature.[58, 59]

Champion concluded from his studies on the suitability of Ti as a grid material for the suppression of primary and secondary emission that Ti should not be operated above 900°C when in the proximity of an oxide-coated cathode (see Chapter 8, p. 251). Recent investigations in several laboratories suggest that the outgassing temperature of Ti should be held in the range of 1030 to 1050°C.

The gettering properties of titanium-zirconium alloys have been described by Stout and Gibbons.[57] An alloy containing 87 atomic per cent Zr was found most suited for gettering, as it will dissolve its surface oxide film below 200°C and thus be active in sorbing hydrogen in addition to oxygen, nitrogen, and carbon dioxide.

Getter-ion Pumps

The degree of vacuum that is attainable by commercially available pumps has been steadily advanced in recent years; the term "ultra-high vacuum" has thus been introduced for pressures below 10^{-8} Torr.[60] Pressures as low as 10^{-13} Torr have been reached in special systems in the laboratory. Initial advances were principally due to the utilization of ion gauge pumping coupled with the use of all-metal valves, according to Alpert,[8] which permitted separation of the tube under exhaust from the oil diffusion pump after it had done its duty by reducing the pressure to the level of 10^{-7} Torr.

TABLE 16.5. PHYSICAL CHARACTERISTICS OF TITANIUM, ZIRCONIUM, THORIUM

Property	Unit	Ti	Zr	Th
Atomic number		22	40	90
Atomic weight		47.90	91.22	232.05
Isotopes		46, 47, 48, 49, 50, (51)	(89), 90, 91, 92, 94, (95), 96, (97)	224, 225, 226, 227
Atomic valence		3, 4	4	4
Valence orbitals		$3d^2 4s^2$	$4d^2 5s^2$	$6d^2 7s^2$
Lattice type		$\alpha(<882°C)\beta$ cph bcc	$\alpha(<863°C)\beta$ cph bcc	f.c.c. (Al)
Lattice constants	A	a = 2.904 a = 3.3065 c = 4.683 (900°C)	a = 3.2321 a = 3.16 c = 5.1474 (867°C)	a = 5.0871 (26.2°C)
Atomic radius	A			1.745
Atomic volume	cc/gm atom	10.6	14	20.2
Closest approach of atoms	A	2.91	3.16	3.59
Density	gm/cc	4.51	6.4	11.2
Melting point	°C	1660 ± 10	1852 ± 2	1690 ± 10
Boiling point	°C	3,535	>2,900	>3,000
Specific heat (0–100°C)	cal/gm/°C	0.126	0.066	0.034
Thermal conductivity	cal/cm/cm²/°C/sec	0.0407 (20°C) 0.0383 (100°C) 0.0354 (300°C) 0.0364 (500°C)	0.051	0.090 (100°C) 0.108 (650°C)
Thermal expansion coeff	10^{-7}/°C	89 (0–100) 91 (30–200) 94 (30–400) 97 (30–600) 99 (30–800) 98 (20–400) 102 (400–600) 106 (600–800)	61.5 (c-axis) 25°C 56.9 (a-axis)	113 (20–100) 121 (20–300) 137 (20–600)

	Units	10^{-8}	10^{-7}	10^{-6}	10^{-5}	10^{-4}	10^{-3}	10^{-2}	10^{-1}	1	Torr
Vapor pressure Ti	°K	1330	1415	1500	1600	1715	1850	2000	2200	2450	
Vapor pressure Zr	°K	1745	1850	1975	2110	2275	2460	2670	2920	3250	
Thermal emissivity	e_λ %					48 (α) (λ = 0.652μ)		43 (β)			
Electrical resistivity	μ ohm·cm		55.4 (20°C) 70.1 (100°C) 137 (516°C)				40 (0°C) 58 (100°C) 100 (400°C)			18 (20°C)	
Electron work function	e.v.			3.9			4.12; 3.57			3.4	
Richardson constant	a/cm²/°K²						330; 120			70	
Secondary emission yield	δ max						1.1 (300v)				
Magnetic susceptibility	10^{-6} c.g.s.			3.15 ± 0.02			−0.45			0.13	
*Mechanical Properties**					high-purity iodide refined						
Hardness	Vickers No.			80–100			100–250			40–80	
Tensile strength	10^3 psi			30–40			26–38			22–30	
Yield strength	10^3 psi			16–24			~17			~25	
Elongation	%			40–60			25–40			~60	
Reduction of area	%			70–90						73–95	
Elastic modulus	10^6 psi			15.5			13.8			~10	
Poisson's ratio							0.32–0.35			0.25–0.27	

* Greatly dependent on method of preparation, impurity content, and cold working. See commercial literature for alloys.

595

TABLE 16.6. SUMMARY OF PUMPING SPEEDS AND HALF-VALUE
CAPACITIES FOR THE GASES TESTED*

Gas	External ionization gauge alone		External and internal ionization gauges	
	Initial speed L/sec	Half-value capacity mm L	Initial speed L/sec	Half-value capacity mm L
Air	0.9–1.5	30	6–9	—
Argon	0.01	—	0.2	—
Pure carbon dioxide	50	—	70–120	—
Tank hydrogen	30–50	350	—	—
Pure hydrogen	140	—	140	500
Tank nitrogen	10	25	17	45
Tank oxygen	2–5	—	—	—
Pure oxygen	50–60	650	120–220	—

* After Cloud, Beckman, and Trump.[30]

The mechanism by which gas is removed from the volume of an ion gauge of the Bayard-Alpert type, or, more generally, in the presence of an electron beam, is very complicated indeed and not fully understood. Alpert has given a detailed review of the recent literature on this subject.[8]

Pumping by continuous, or repetitive, deposition of getter films on the walls of the vacuum envelope has been practiced by Cloud, Beckman, and Trump[30] for the evacuation of fairly large systems. Bulk barium in quantities ranging from 10 to 1000 gm is placed in a separate container (Type 304 stainless steel) attached to the tube under exhaust and heated to near 800°C by an external heater. A barium film of 4-mil minimum thickness is thus deposited on the walls of the container and reduces the pressure from 10^{-2} Torr to a final vacuum of 10^{-7} Torr. To facilitate the sorption of rare gases and that of large organic molecules, a Penning-type ion gauge is operated in a side tube and, at times, also within the barium container. Table 16.6 gives the pumping speeds for various gases and also the half-value capacity which is defined as the amount of gas sorbed (measured in mm $\times$ liter) at the time the pumping speed is reduced to one-half of its initial value. Speeds on the order of 100 l/sec for CO_2 and 200 l/sec for O_2 were obtained when both ion gauges were operated.

The evapor-ion pump developed by Herb et al.[63, 64] in 1953 is based on similar principles but utilizes evaporated titanium as the sorbing agent which is deposited on the wall of a 12-in. dia. container, 24 in. high. The pumping speeds obtained for O_2, H_2, N_2 are on the order of several thousand liters per second in the range of 10^{-5} to 10^{-6} Torr; the ultimate pressure attainable is 10^{-7} Torr.* As potentials of the order of 1000 v are in-

* Evapor-Ion Pump Type E1, available from Consolidated Electrodynamics, Rochester Division.

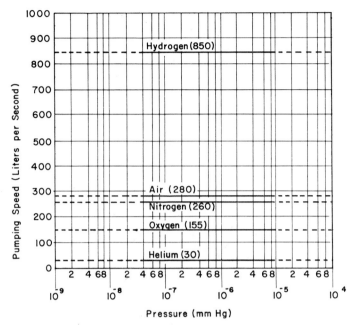

Figure 16.7. Pumping speed vs pressure for Varian Vac-Ion high-vacuum pump Model VA-1408 (250 1/sec). (*Courtesy Varian Associates.*)

volved in the operation of the pump, it is necessary to rough out the pump and the system to be evacuated to a low pressure of about 10^{-5} Torr.

A noteworthy advance in the design of getter-ion pumps has been made by Hall[65] who combined the four phenomena involved in the gas clean up in such pumps, i.e., ionization, excitation, sputtering, and gettering to achieve greater pumping speed, lower ultimate pressure, and longer life. A cold-cathode discharge between electrodes made of reactive metals, such as Ti, creates positively charged particles (ions), atoms (dissociated molecules), and metastable atoms and molecules. The anode is of an open, cellular structure, where most of the gettering likely takes place. With the aid of a magnetic field (several thousand gauss) and suitably high voltages (several thousand volts), high-density ion beams bombard the cathodes where they cause sputtering of the cathode metal. The sputtered atoms are deposited on the walls of the anode cells and, to some extent, on the opposite cathode. Atoms and metastable particles which strike the sputtered deposits will be bound by physisorption or chemisorption and are thus permanently removed from the volume of the pump. By carefully optimizing the geometry of the pump elements, "Vac-Ion" Pumps* have been perfected

* Registered Trademark, Varian Associates, Palo Alto, California.

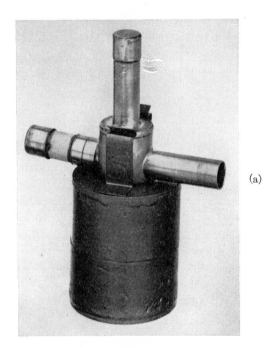

(a)

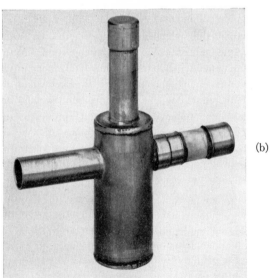

(b)

Figure 16.8 (a). ULTEK UlteVac 110A high-vacuum pump and magnet with two exhaust tubulations and high-voltage terminal at left. Magnet diameter 2 in. Weight 2 lb. Pumping speed 0.5 l/sec. The same unit is shown at (b) with magnet removed. (*Courtesy ULTEK Corp.*)

which achieve an ultimate pressure of less than 10^{-10} Torr. Several models are commercially available which have pumping speeds ranging from 1 1/sec to 250 1/sec for air, as illustrated in Figure 16.7. It is to be noted that the speed of these pumps is essentially independent of pressure below 10^{-5} Torr.

Vac-Ion pumps require a forevacuum of 10^{-2} Torr to initiate pumping; for continuous operation, no forepump is required. The pumps may be baked out at 450°C for 5-hr periods if the magnet is temporarily removed. Life is stated to be of the order of 20,000 hrs. There are no moving parts, or pump fluids, and no hot filaments in the pump; power failure will thus not damage the pump or spoil the vacuum. The pumps also serve as pressure gauges.

The use of these pumps for the processing of microwave tubes has made it possible to materially reduce pumping time and at the same time improve the quality of tubes. It is also feasible to permanently attach a small getter-ion pump to large power tubes. The pressure inside the tube can thus be monitored, as the pump also acts as a gauge, and the vacuum be improved by additional pumping, whenever necessary. Figure 16.8 shows such a pump developed by L. D. Hall.*

Huber and Warnecke[66] have described a titanium pump intended for similar applications. Several models are being marketed by CSF,† and illustrations have been published in technical journals. Titanium is continuously evaporated in these pumps by bombarding a Ti-coated grid, maintained at a positive potential, with electrons emitted from a hot tungsten filament. The grid temperature is thus raised to 1000°C and the evaporated Ti deposited on the water-cooled wall of the pump. Starting pressure is 10^{-4} Torr, and ultimate pressure is 10^{-9} Torr. Life of the pump is given as 2000 hrs. Pumping speeds range from 1 to 12 1/sec.

Diels[67] and Holland[19] have recently reviewed the design and performance of getter-ion pumps. There is no question that these pumps will assume increasing importance in modern vacuum technology, but, in cases where a high gas throughput is to be maintained, conventional diffusion pumps are likely to hold their place of usefulness.

REFERENCES

1. M. Berthand and J. Bailleul-Langlais, "Directionality of getters" (in French), *Le Vide*, **78**, 293–295 (Nov.–Dec. 1958).
1a. P. Della Porta, "The gettering process in modern receiving valve manufacture," Vacuum, 6, 41–58 (Oct. 1956); published Apr. 1959 in combined volumes 6–8 (1956–58).

---

* Ultek Corp., Palo Alto, California.
† Compagnie général de télégraphie Sans Fil., Paris, France.

2. A. L. Reimann, "Vacuum Technique," Chapman & Hall Ltd., London, 1952.

3. G. H. Metson, "On the electrical life of an oxide-cathode receiving tube," in "Advances in Electronics and Electron Physics," Vol. 8, p. 403–446 (see p. 445). L. Marton, Ed., Academic Press, Inc., New York, 1956.

4. S. Wagener, "Influence of electronic impact on the rate of sorption of gases on to getter materials," *Nature*, **173**, 684–685 (Apr. 10, 1954).

5. W. Espe, M. Knoll and M. P. Wilder, "Getter materials for electron tubes," *Electronics*, **23**, 80–86 (Oct. 1950).

6. M. Knoll and B. Kazan, "Materials and Processes of Electron Devices," Springer-Verlag, Berlin (1959).

7. S. Dushman, "Scientific Foundations of Vacuum Technique," John Wiley & Sons, Inc., New York, 1949.

8. D. Alpert, "Production and Measurement of Ultrahigh Vacuum" (in English, sic.), "Handbuch der Physik," S. Flügge, Ed., Vol. 12, pp. 609–663, Springer-Verlag, Berlin, 1958.

9. A. R. Miller, "The Adsorption of Gases on Solids," Cambridge University Press, 1949.

10. J. A. Becker, "The Structure and Properties of Solid Surfaces," University of Chicago Press, 1952.

11. P. Kisluik, "The sticking probabilities of gases chemisorbed on the surfaces of solids," in "The Physics and Chemistry of Solids," Vol. 3 (Apr. 1957), pp. 95–101 (Pt. 1); Vol. 5 (No. 1/2 1958), pp. 78–84 (Pt. 2). See also Bell Telephone System Monograph 3067.

12. D. G. Bills and N. P. Carleton, "Adsorption of activated gases," *J. Appl. Phys.*, **29**, 692–697 (Apr. 1958).

13. S. Brunauer, "The Adsorption of Gases and Vapors," Vol. 1. "Physical Adsorption," Princeton University Press, Princeton, 1943.

14. G. Strotzer, "On the electric sorption of gases in the pressure range of high vacuum" (in German), *Z. angew. Physik*, **10**, 207–216 (May 1958).

15. B. M. W. Trapnell: (a) "The activities of evaporated metal films in gas chemisorption," *Proc. Royal Soc.* (A), **218**, 566–577 (1953), (b) "The surface areas of evaporated films," *Trans. Faraday Soc.*, **51**, 368–370 (1955).

16. L. W. Wolf, H. W. Katz and A. E. Brain, "The fabrication and properties of memory elements using electrodeposited thin magnetic films of 82–18 nickel iron," Proc. 1959 Electronic Components Conference (May 6–8, 1959), Philadelphia, Pa., pp. 15–20.

17. K. Diels and R. Jaeckel, "Leybold Vakuum Taschenbuch," Springer-Verlag, Berlin/Göttingen/Heidelberg, 1958.

18. P. Della Porta, "Performance characteristics of barium getters with particular reference to their application in thermionic valves," *Vacuum*, **4**, 284–302 (July 1954—published Feb. 1957).

19. L. Holland, "Theory and design of getter-ion pumps," *J. Sci. Instr.*, **36**, 105–116 (Mar. 1959).

20. S. Wagener, "Properties of getters in electron tubes," Proc. Fourth Nat'l Conf. Tube Techniques, New York, Sept. 10–12, 1958. Proceedings by New York University Press, New York, 1959, pp. 1–19.

21. S. Wagener, "The production of very high vacua by the use of getters," *Proc. Inst. Elec. Engrs.*, **99**, Pt. 3, 135–147 (May 1952). See also *Z. angew. Phys.*, **6**, 433–442 (Oct. 1954).

22. S. J. Stoll, "Origin and analysis of gas in electron tubes," *Brit. J. Appl. Phys.*, **7**, 94–96 (Mar. 1956).

23. P. Della Porta, "The kinetics of the adsorption of nitrogen on barium getters," Transact. Fifth National Vacuum Symposium (American Vacuum Society), San Francisco, Calif., Oct. 22–24, 1958, pp. 25–29.

23a. J. J. B. Fransen and H. J. R. Perdijk, "Barium getter films," Philips Tech. Rev., 19, 290–300 (Apr. 1938).

24. J. S. Wagener* and P. T. Marth, "Analysis of gases at very low pressures by using the omegatron spectrometer," J. Appl. Phys., 28, 1027–1030 (Sept. 1957). See also Report, Seventh Annual Conf. Physical Electronics, MIT, Cambridge, Mar. 21–23, 1957, pp. 164–169.

25. S. Wagener, "Efficiency and mechanism of barium getters at low pressures," Brit. J. Appl. Phys., 2, 132–138 (May 1951).

26. R. N. Bloomer, "Barium getters and oxygen," Brit. J. Appl. Phys., 8, 40–43 (Jan. 1957); S. J. Gregg and W. P. Jepson, "A note on the paper by Bloomer," ibid, 9, 417–419 (Oct. 1958).

27. T. H. Briggs, "Continuous Getters for Electron Tubes," Proc. Third National Conference on Tube Techniques, Sept. 12–14, 1956, pp. 117–123.

28. W. H. Kohl and P. Rice, "Electron Tubes for Critical Environments," (see Introductory Review, Ref. 4).

29. R. Jaeckel, "Kleinste Drucke," Springer-Verlag, Berlin, 1950.

30. R. W. Cloud, L. Beckman and J. G. Trump, "Barium absorption pumps for high-vacuum systems," Rev. Sci. Instr., 28, 889–892 (Nov. 1957).

31. P. Della Porta, "Performance characteristics of barium getters at elevated working temperatures of the valves," Vacuum, 4, 464–475 (Oct. 1954–published June 1957).

32. S. Wagener, "A method for measuring the efficiency of getters at low pressures," Brit. J. Appl. Phys., 1, 225–231 (Sept. 1950).

33. S. Wagener, "Sorption of gases at very low pressures by thorium powder," Proc. Phys. Soc. (London), 66(B), 400–413 (May 1953).

34. D. G. Bills and N. P. Carleton, "Adsorption of activated gases," J. Appl. Phys., 29, 692–697 (Apr. 1958).

35. H. J. Curnow, "Effects observed during the activation of oxide-coated cathodes," Services Electronics Research Lab. Tech. J., 6, 15–16 (Apr. 1956).

36. S. Wagener, "The use of getters for the production of very high vacua," Vacuum, 3, 11–23 (Jan. 1953) (Publ. Aug. 1954).

37. S. Wagener, "Adsorption measurements at very low pressures," J. Phys. Chem., 60, 567–573 (May 1956).

38a. T. Arizumi and S. Kotani, "Absorption of Carbon Mono-Oxide by the Barium Getter. I. Experiments at low temperatures," J. Phys. Soc. Japan, 7, 152–158 (Mar.–Apr. 1952).

  b. T. Arizumi and S. Kotani, "Absorption of Carbon Mono-Oxide by the Barium Getter. II. Theory of physical adsorption," J. Phys. Soc. Japan, 7, 158–163 (Mar.–Apr. 1952).

  c. T. Arizumi and S. Kotani, "Absorption of Carbon Mono-Oxide by the Barium Getter. III. Lattice imperfections," J. Phys. Soc. Japan, 7, 163–166 (Mar.–Apr. 1952).

  d. T. Arizumi and S. Kotani, "Absorption of Carbon Mono-Oxide by the Barium

* J. S. Wagener has added a second initial to his name and thus is identical with S. Wagener; to avoid confusion, all his papers published as single author are listed in this book under S. Wagener.

Getter. IV. Absorption experiments in the temperature range between 0°C and 250°C," *J. Phys. Soc. Japan*, **7**, 415–421 (July–Aug. 1952).

e. T. Arizumi and S. Kotani, "Absorption of Carbon Mono-Oxide by the Barium Getter. V. Theory of absorption," *J. Phys. Soc. Japan*, **7**, 422–426 (July–Aug. 1952).

39. J. Morrison and R. B. Zetterstrom, "Barium getters in carbon monoxide," *J. Appl. Phys.*, **26**, 437–442 (Apr. 1955).

40. R. N. Bloomer, "Barium getters and carbon monoxide," *Brit. J. Appl. Phys.*, **8**, 352–355 (Sept. 1957).

41. R. N. Bloomer, "The oxidation of evaporated barium films (getters)," *Brit. J. Appl. Phys.*, **8**, 321–329 (Aug. 1957).

42. T. Arizumi and S. Kotani, "Gettering process of Barium-sorption properties of Oxygen to Barium," *J. Phys. Soc. Japan*, **7**, 300–307 (May–June 1952).

43. W. Espe, "New getter materials for the high-vacuum technique," *Powder Met. Bull. (Yonkers, N. Y.)*, **3**, 100–111 (Oct. 1948).

44. J. H. Wyman and R. H. Kuhnapfel, "Vacuum tubes for 500°C envelope bulb temperature and high-vibration environment," Presented at the IRE National Conference on Aeronautical Electronics, Dayton, Ohio, May 13, 1957.

45. J. E. Idot, R. H. Kuhnapfel and J. H. Wyman, Bendix Aviation Corporation, Red Bank Division, Eatontown, N. J. Final Report, Jan. 31, 1958. "Production Refinement Contract For Ceramic Metal Tubes." Contract No. AF33(600)-26860. (AD 204 375).

46. P. Wargo and W. G. Shepherd, "Electron-bombardment induced dissociation of alkaline earth oxides," *Phys. Rev.*, **106**, 694–703 (May 15, 1957) (See p. 695).

47. J. A. Becker, "Use of getters for ultra-high vacua," Rept. Eleventh Annual Conference on Physical Electronics, Cambridge, Mar. 29–31, 1951, pp. 94–95.

48. W. B. Blumenthal, "The Chemical Behavior of Zircnoium," D. Van Nostrand & Co., Princeton, N. J. 1958.

49. B. Lustman and F. Kerze, Jr., "The Metallurgy of Zirconium," McGraw-Hill Book Co., Inc., New York, 1955. National Nuclear Energy Series, Vol. 74, pp. 26–29.

50. A. N. Rogers, "Use of zirconium in the vacuum tube." *Trans. Electrochem. Soc.*, **88**, 205–210 (Oct. 1945).

51. G. A. Espersen, "Zirconium for electron tubes," *Foote Prints*, **18**, No. 1, 3–7 (1946).

52. J. D. Fast, "Zirconium as a getter," *Foote Prints*, **13**, No. 1, 22–30 (June 1940).

53. W. G. Guldner and L. A. Wooten, "Reactions of zirconium with gases at low pressures," *Trans. Electrochem. Soc.*, **93**, 223–235 (June 1948).

54. W. Espe, "Zirconium—its production, properties and applications in vacuum technique" (in German), Winter'sche Verlagsbuchhandlung, Fuessen, Bavaria, Germany, 1953. 174 pp.

55. E. A. Gulbransen and K. F. Andrew, "Kinetics of the reactions of titanium with O_2, N_2, and H_2," *Trans. Am. Inst. Mining Met. Engrs.*, **185**, 741–748 (1949).

56. E. A Gulbransen, "Reactions of zirconium, titanium, columbium, and tantalum with the gases oxygen, nitrogen, and hydrogen at elevated temperatures," *J. Electrochem. Soc.*, **96**, 364–376 (June 1949).

57. V. L. Stout and M. D. Gibbons, "Gettering Properties of Titanium-Zirconium Alloys," Paper presented at the 115th Meeting of the Electrochemical Society in Philadelphia, Electronics-Thermionics Section, May 6, 1959.

58. V. L. Stout and M. D. Gibbons, "Gettering of gas by titanium," *J. Appl. Phys.*, **26**, 1488–1492 (Dec. 1955).

59. J. E. Beggs, "Use of titanium metal in vacuum devices," Transact. IRE, Professional Group on Electron Devices, Vol. ED-3, pp. 93–96 (Apr. 1956).

59a. J. Morrison, "Titanium in Vacuum Tubes," Report on 19th Annual Conference Physical Electronics, Massachusetts Institute of Technology, Cambridge, March 26–28, 1959, pp. 118–123.

60. "Glossary of Terms used in Vacuum Technology," Committee on Standards, American Vacuum Society, Inc. Pergamon Press, Inc., New York, 1958.

61. P. A. Redhead, "A Penning gauge for extremely low pressures," Report, Seventeenth Annual Conf. Physical Electronics, MIT, Cambridge, March 21–23, 1957, pp. 170–176.

62. J. P. Hobson and P. A. Redhead, "Experiments at pressures below 10^{-10} mm Hg using liquid helium," Report, Seventeenth Annual Conf. Physical Electronics, MIT, Cambridge, March 21–23, 1957, pp. 177–183.

63. R. G. Herb, R. H. Davis, A. S. Divatia and D. Saxon, "Evapor-ion pump," (Abstract only); *Phys. Rev.*, **89**, 897 (Feb. 15, 1953).

64. R. H. Davis and A. S. Divatia, "Design and operation of evapor-ion pumps," *Rev. Sci. Instr.*, **25**, 1193–1197 (Dec. 1954).

65. L. D. Hall, "Ionic vacuum pumps," *Science*, **128**, 279–285 (Aug. 8, 1958).

66. H. Huber and R. Warnecke, "The titanium pump: a device for the maintenance of vacuum in electronic tubes," *Le Vide*, **74**, 84–90 (Mar./Apr. 1958).

67. K. Diels, "Results of recent studies on oil diffusion pumps and ion-getter pumps" (in French), *Le Vide*, **75**, 143–152 (May/June 1958).

68. W. C. Michels and S. Wilford, "The physical properties of titanium. I. Emissivity and resistivity of the commercial metal," *J. Appl. Phys.*, **20**, 1223–1226 (Dec. 1949).

69. L. F. Ehrke and C. M. Slack, "Gettering powers of various metals for the gases: H_2, O_2, N_2, CO_2, air," *J. Appl. Phys.*, **11**, 129–137 (Feb. 1940).

70. E. Brown and J. H. Leck, "Desorption of gas in the cold cathode ionization gauge," *Brit. J. Appl. Phys.*, **6**, 161–164 (May 1955).

71. S. J. Gregg and W. B. Jepson, "A note on the paper (The oxidation of evaporated barium films [getters])" *Brit. J. Appl. Phys.*, **9**, 417–418 (Oct. 1958).

72. Y. Sasaki, "Study on the state of nitrogen adsorbed on evaporated barium film," *J. Chem. Phys.*, **27**, 281–285 (July 1957).

73. S. Wagener, "Adsorption measurements at very low pressures. II." *J. Phys. Chem.* **61**, 267–271 (Mar. 1957).

74. A. Dravnieks, "The oxidation of several metals in activated oxygen at high temperatures," *J. Amer. Chem. Soc.*, **72²**, 3761–3767 (Aug. 1950).

75. A. Dravnieks, "Action of hot ionized gases upon zirconium and copper," *J. Phys. Chem.*, **55**, 540–549 (Apr. 1951).

APPENDIX

TABLE A1. CORRELATION OF CURRENT FOUR-DIGIT CORNING GLASS
CODES WITH OBSOLETE LABORATORY CODE NUMBERS

Current	Obsolete	Current	Obsolete
0010	G-1	7210	G-720-Pn
0014	G-14	7230	G-707-GS-1
0041	G-4-D	7240	G-715-AO
0050	G-5	7250	G-720-OI
0080	G-8	7251	G-720-WH
0081	G-124-HD	7252	G-726-XP
0100	G-164-EC	7290	G-167-GL
0110	G-164-HC	7330	G-733-A
0120	G-12	7331	G-108-PN
0240	G-125-BB	7340	G-733-B
0250	G-125-AJ	7500	G-750-AH
0280	G-128-G	7510	G-750-AI
0281	G-128-AQ	7520	G-750-AJ
1710	G-172-RM	7530	G-805-F
1720	G-172-AJ	7550	G-805-G
1723	G-889-AEW	7560	G-750-AL
1990	G-189-IY	7570	G-750-GL
1991	G-184-IY	7720	G-702-P
2473	G-240-PY	7730	G-1752-A
2475	G-240-HP	7740	G-726-MX
3320	G-371-BN	7741	G-726-YM
3530	G-353-GE	7742	G-726-ABE
3540	G-350-Z	7750	G-705-R
4320	G-431-AM	7760	G-720-GO
4407	G-40-D	7780	GT-70
5380	G-534-A	7900	G-790-H
5420	G-542-P	7910	G-790-J
5810	G-570-G	7911	G-798-BE
5830	G-570-AT	7912	G-790-N
5890	G-586-CK	7981	G-707-HN
5911	G-586-EW	7991	G-704-EO
6611	G-61-I	8110	G-813-BJ
6992	G-63-AK	8160	G-814-KW
7030	G-704-BA	8800	G-80
7040	G-705-BA	8830	G-866-LC
7050	G-705-AJ	8870	G-858-V
7051	G-705-FD	8871	G-189-IA
7052	G-705-FN	9010	G-856-DO
7055	G-710-HY	9012	G-174-PA
7056	G-840-MF	9700	G-970-G
7060	G-705-AO	9720	G-970-L
7070	G-707-DG	9730	G-972-A
7120	G-712-O	9740	G-970-HW
7200	G-707-GU-1	9741	G-970-OF
		9820	G-981-TJ

TABLE A2. PHYSICAL CHARACTERISTICS OF KIMBLE INDUSTRIAL GLASSES

Glass	Working Point °C	Softening Point °C	Annealing Point °C	Strain Point °C	Expansion Coefficient 0-300°C × 10⁷/°C	Contraction Coefficient Ann. Pt.-25°C × 10⁷/°C	Density gm/cc	Volume Resistivity (ρ) ohm-cm (Expressed as logarithm of ρ)				Dielectric Properties 25°C						Refractive Index nD	Stress Optical Coefficient mu/cm/kg/cm²
								50°C	150°C	250°C	350°C	60 Cycles K	60 Cycles Δ%	60 Cycles Loss Factor %	1 Megacycle K	1 Megacycle Δ%	1 Megacycle Loss Factor %		
KG-12	980	630	433	400	89	101	3.05	18.*	13.0	9.9	7.8	6.8	.2	1.4	6.7	.15	1.0	1.56	2.9
K-30	1030	660	442	410	90	103	2.67	17.*	12.3	9.3	7.3	6.4	.3	1.9	6.2	.15	.9	1.52	2.7
K-52	1018	655	447	415	89	105	2.64	17.*	11.9	9.0	7.0	6.6	.35	2.3	6.4	.2	1.3	1.52	2.6
K-51	999	682	485	454	93	111	2.54	14.7*	10.5	8.0	6.2	7.0	.75	5.2	6.7	.3	2.0	1.52	2.5
K-650	1015	705	502	472	51	61	2.25	13.5	9.9	7.7	6.2	5.5	1.7	9.4	5.1	.55	2.8	1.48	3.7
K-704	1065	713	481	449	49	59	2.24	16.*	11.7	9.2	7.4	5.2	.55	2.9	5.0	.3	1.5	1.48	3.8
K-705	1011	709	496	466	47	56	2.25	15.*	11.1	8.6	6.9	5.1	.65	3.3	4.8	.35	1.7	1.48	3.8
K-772	1120	755	518	486	36	50	2.35	16.*	11.8	9.1	7.4	4.7	.45	2.1	4.6	.2	.9	1.48	3.6
N-10	1090	754	557	528	59	75	2.54	11.9	8.7	6.8	5.5	7.5	5.5	41.2	6.4	1.1	7.0	1.52	3.1
N-51A	1175	795	574	542	49	63	2.36	12.1	8.9	6.9	5.6	6.5	4.8	31.2	5.6	1.0	5.6	1.49	3.2
R-5** }R-6	984	702	522	493	93	111	2.53	11.9	8.6	6.6	5.2	8.0	4.8	38.4	7.2	.85	6.1	1.52	2.4
Insulator	1020	715	523	493	89	106	2.49	11.5	8.4	6.5	5.2	8.2	4.6	37.7	7.1	.8	5.7	1.52	2.5

* Extrapolated value
** R-5 when melted in pots; R-6 when melted in tanks.
(*Courtesy Owens Illinois Glass Company*)

TABLE A3. PHYSICAL CHARACTERISTICS OF

1	2	3	4	5	6	7 UPPER WORKING TEMPERATURES (Mechanical Considerations Only)				8 Thermal Shock Res. Plates 6"x6"		
						Annealed		Tempered		Annealed		
Glass Code	Type	Color	Principal Use	Forms Usually Available	Thermal Expansion Coeff.—/°C.	Normal Service °C.	Extreme Limit °C.	Normal Service °C.	Extreme Limit °C.	$\frac{1}{8}$" Thk. °C.	$\frac{1}{4}$" Thk. °C.	$\frac{1}{2}$" Thk. °C.
0010	Potash Soda Lead......	Clear	Lamp Tubing	T	91×10^{-7}	110	380	—	—	65	50	35
0041	Potash Soda Lead......	Clear	Thermometers	T	85×10^{-7}	110	400	—	—	70	60	40
0080	Soda Lime	Clear	Lamp Bulbs	B M T	92×10^{-7}	110	460	220	250	65	50	35
0120	Potash Soda Lead......	Clear	Lamp Tubing	T M	89×10^{-7}	110	380	—	—	65	50	35
0281	Soda Lime	Clear	General Purpose	—	87×10^{-7}	110	475	240	270	70	60	40
1720	Aluminosilicate	Clear	Ignition Tube	—	42×10^{-7}	200	650	400	450	135	115	75
1990	Low Loss Iron Sealing...	Clear	Sealing	—	127×10^{-7}	100	310	—	—	45	35	25
2405	Hard Red.............	Red	General	B P U	43×10^{-7}	200	480	—	—	135	115	75
2475	Soft Red.............	Red	Neon Signs	T	93×10^{-7}	110	440	—	—	65	50	35
3320	Hard Sealing..........	Canary	Tungsten Sealing	—	40×10^{-7}	200	480	—	—	145	110	80
6720	Opal	White	General	P	80×10^{-7}	110	480	220	275	70	60	40
6750	Alabaster	White	Lighting Ware	B P R	87×10^{-7}	110	420	220	220	65	50	35
6810	Opal	White	Lighting Ware	B P R	69×10^{-7}	120	470	240	270	85	70	45
7050	Borosilicate	Clear	Series Sealing	T	46×10^{-7}	200	440	235	235	125	100	70
7052	Borosilicate	Clear	Kovar Sealing	B M P T	46×10^{-7}	200	420	210	210	125	100	70
7070	Borosilicate	Clear	Low Loss Electrical	B M P T	32×10^{-7}	230	430	230	230	180	150	100
7250	Borosilicate	Clear	Baking Ware	P	36×10^{-7}	230	460	260	260	160	130	90
7340	Borosilicate	Clear	Gauge Glass	T	67×10^{-7}	120	510	240	310	85	70	45
7570	Soldering Glass........	Clear	Sealing	—	84×10^{-7}	100	330	—	—	—	—	—
7720	Borosilicate	Clear	Tungsten Sealing	B P T	36×10^{-7}	230	460	260	260	160	130	90
7740	Borosilicate	Clear	General	B P S T U	32.5×10^{-7}	230	490	260	290	180	150	100
7760	Borosilicate	Clear	Electrical	B P	34×10^{-7}	230	450	250	250	160	130	90
7900	96% Silica	Clear	High Temp.	B P T U M	8×10^{-7}	800	1090	—	—	1250	1000	750
7910	96% Silica	Clear	u v Transmission	B T U	8×10^{-7}	800	1090	—	—	1250	1000	750
7911	96% Silica	Clear	u v Transmission	T	8×10^{-7}	800	1090	—	—	1250	1000	750
7940	Fused Silica..........	Clear	Ultrasonic	—	5.6×10^{-7}	900	1100	—	—	1250	1000	750
8160	Radiotron Tube	Clear	Electrical	—	91×10^{-7}	110	380	—	—	65	50	35
8800	Borosilicate	Clear	Thermometers	—	60×10^{-7}	200	510	—	—	100	80	60
8870	High Lead	Clear	Sealing or Electrical	M T U	91×10^{-7}	110	380	180	180	65	50	35
8871	Capacitor	Clear	Electrical	—	103×10^{-7}	125	360	—	—	55	45	35
9700	....	Clear	u v Transmission	T U	37×10^{-7}	220	500	—	—	150	120	80
9741	....	Clear	u v Transmission	B U T	39×10^{-7}	200	390	—	—	150	120	80

COLUMN 5
B—Blown Ware   S—Plate Glass
M—Multiform Ware   P—Pressed Ware   T—Tubing and Rod
   R—Rolled Sheet   U—Panels

COLUMN 7
These data approximate only. Freedom from excessive thermal shock is assumed. See Column 8.
At extreme limits annealed glass will be very vulnerable to thermal shock. Recommendations in this range are based on mechanical considerations only. Tests should be made before adopting final designs.

COLUMN 6
From 0° to 300°C. in/in/°C. or cm/cm/°C.

COLUMN 8
These data approximate only. See Text Page 5.
Based on plunging sample into cold water after oven heating. Resistance of 100°C. means no breakage if heated to 110°C. and plunged into water at 10°C. Tempered samples have over twice the resistance of annealed glass. Glasses 7900, 7910, 7911 cannot be tempered.

All data subject to normal manufacturing variations.

[*Courtesy Corning Glass Works*, Corning, N. Y. Bulletin B-83 (1957)]

Corning Industrial Glasses

9	10				11	12	13	14			15			16
Thermal Stress Resistance °C.	Viscosity Data				Impact Abrasion Resistance	Density (Sp. Gr.)	Modulus of Elasticity lb./sq. in.	Log₁₀ of Volume Resistivity			Dielectric Properties at 1 Mc and 20°C.			Refractive Index Sod. D Line (.5893 Microns)
	Strain Point °C.	Annealing Point °C.	Softening Point °C.	Working Point °C.				25°C.	250°C.	350°C.	Power Factor	Dielectric Const.	Loss Factor	
19	395	430	626	970	—	2.85	9.0×10^6	17.+	8.9	7.0	.16%	6.7	1.%	1.539
19	425	465	648	990	—	2.89		—	7.5	5.9	—	—	—	1.545
17	470	510	696	1000	1.2	2.47	9.8×10^6	12.4	6.4	5.1	.9	7.2	6.5	1.512
17	395	435	630	975	—	3.05	8.2×10^6	17.+	10.1	8.0	.12	6.7	.8	1.560
18	490	530	707	1015	—	2.48		—	6.5	5.2	—	—	—	
29	670	715	915	1200	—	2.53	12.7×10^6	—	11.4	9.5	.38	7.2	2.7	1.530
13	330	360	496	755	—	3.47	8.4×10^6	—	10.1	7.7	.04	8.3	.33	—
36	505	540	770	1085	—	2.50		—	—	—	—	—	—	1.507
17	460	505	690	1040	—	2.59		—	7.8	6.2	—	—	—	1.511
40	495	540	780	1155	—	2.29		—	8.6	7.1	.30	4.9	1.5	1.481
19	495	535	775	1015	—	2.58		—	—	—	—	—	—	1.507
18	440	475	672	1040	—	2.63		—	—	—	—	—	—	1.513
23	490	530	768	1010	—	2.65		—	—	—	—	—	—	1.508
34	460	500	703	1025	—	2.25		16.	8.8	7.2	.33	4.9	1.6	1.479
34	435	480	708	1115	—	2.28		17.	9.2	7.4	.26	5.1	1.3	1.484
70	455	495	—	1100	4.1	2.13	7.3×10^6	17.+	11.2	9.1	.06	4.0	.24	1.469
43	485	530	780	1190	3.2	2.24		15.	8.2	6.7	.27	4.7	1.3	1.475
20	535	580	785	1140	—	2.43	11.5×10^6	16.	8.5	6.9	—	—	—	1.506
—	345	365	440	560	—	5.42	8.1×10^6	—	10.6	8.7	.22	15.	3.3	—
45	485	525	755	1110	3.2	2.35	9.5×10^6	16.	8.8	7.2	.27	4.7	1.3	1.487
48	520	565	820	1220	3.1	2.23	9.3×10^6	15.	8.1	6.6	.46	4.6	2.1	1.474
51	480	525	780	1210	—	2.23	9.1×10^6	17.	9.4	7.7	.18	4.5	.79	1.473
200	820	910	1500	—	3.5	2.18	9.6×10^6	17.	9.7	8.1	.05	3.8	.19	1.458
200	820	910	1500	—	3.5	2.18	9.6×10^6	17.+	11.2	9.2	.024	3.8	.091	1.458
200	820	910	1500	—	3.5	2.18	9.7×10^6	17.+	11.7	9.6	.019	3.8	.072	1.458
290	1050—approx.		1500+	—	—	2.20	10.5×10^6	—	—	—	.001	3.8	.038	1.459
18	395	435	627	975	—	2.98		—	10.6	8.4	.09	7.0	.63	1.553
27	530	570	755	—	—	2.39		—	—	—	—	—	—	1.502
22	390	430	580	805	.6	4.28	7.6×10^6	17.+	11.8	9.7	.08	9.5	.86	1.693
15	350	385	527	770	—	3.84	8.3×10^6	—	11.1	8.8	.05	8.4	.42	—
42	520	565	804	1195	—	2.26		15.	8.0	6.5	—	—	—	1.478
40	410	450	705	—	—	2.16		17.+	9.4	7.6	—	—	—	1.468

COLUMN 9
Resistance in °C. is the temperature differential between the two surfaces of a tube or a constrained plate that will cause a tensile stress of 1000 p.s.i. on the cooler surface. See Text Page 5.

COLUMN 10
See Page 13. These data subject to normal manufacturing variations.

COLUMN 11
Data show relative resistance to sandblasting.

COLUMN 12
Units are grams/c.c.

COLUMN 14
Data at 25° extrapolated from high temp. readings and are approximate only.

GLASSES 7910 AND 7911
Electrical properties measured on lamp worked specimens.

TABLE A4—CONVERSION FACTORS FOR PRESSURE AND STRESS UNITS*

Microbar (Barye) Dyne cm²	Micron μ (10⁻³ mm Hg)	Newton per m² (10⁵ dynes/m²)	Kilogram per m²	Millibar	Torr (mm Hg)	Poundal per in.²	Inches of Mercury	Pounds per in.² (psi)	Newton per cm²	Kilogram per cm²	Bar (10⁶ dynes cm²)	Atmosphere (normal) (760 mm Hg)	Kilogram per mm²	Long Tons per in.² (British)	Kilobar
1.0	7.5006×10^{-1}	1.0×10^{-1}	1.0197×10^{-2}	1.0×10^{-3}	7.5006×10^{-4}	4.6665×10^{-4}	2.9530×10^{-5}	1.4504×10^{-5}	1.0×10^{-5}	1.0197×10^{-6}	1.0×10^{-6}	9.8692×10^{-7}	1.0197×10^{-8}	6.4728×10^{-9}	1.0×10^{-9}
1.3332	1.0	1.3332×10^{-1}	1.3595×10^{-2}	1.3332×10^{-3}	1.0×10^{-3}	6.2215×10^{-4}	3.9370×10^{-5}	1.9337×10^{-5}	1.3332×10^{-5}	1.3595×10^{-6}	1.3332×10^{-6}	1.3158×10^{-6}	1.3595×10^{-8}	8.6334×10^{-9}	1.3332×10^{-9}
1.0×10	7.5006	1.0	1.0197×10^{-1}	1.0×10^{-2}	7.5006×10^{-3}	4.6665×10^{-3}	2.9530×10^{-4}	1.4504×10^{-4}	1.0×10^{-4}	1.0197×10^{-5}	1.0×10^{-5}	9.8692×10^{-6}	1.0197×10^{-7}	6.4728×10^{-8}	1.0×10^{-8}
9.8067×10	7.3556×10	9.8067	1.0	9.8067×10^{-2}	7.3556×10^{-2}	4.5763×10^{-2}	2.8959×10^{-3}	1.4223×10^{-3}	9.8067×10^{-4}	1.0×10^{-4}	9.8067×10^{-5}	9.6784×10^{-5}	1.0×10^{-6}	6.3477×10^{-7}	9.8067×10^{-8}
1.0×10^3	7.5006×10^2	1.0×10^2	1.0197×10	1.0	7.5006×10^{-1}	4.6665×10^{-1}	2.9530×10^{-2}	1.4504×10^{-2}	1.0×10^{-2}	1.0197×10^{-3}	1.0×10^{-3}	9.8692×10^{-4}	1.0197×10^{-5}	6.4728×10^{-6}	1.0×10^{-6}
1.3332×10^3	1.0×10^3	1.3332×10^2	1.3595×10	1.3332	1.0	6.2215×10^{-1}	3.9370×10^{-2}	1.9337×10^{-2}	1.3332×10^{-2}	1.3595×10^{-3}	1.3332×10^{-3}	1.3158×10^{-3}	1.3595×10^{-5}	8.6334×10^{-6}	1.3332×10^{-6}
2.1430×10^3	1.6074×10^3	2.1430×10^2	2.1859×10	2.1430	1.6074	1.0	6.3283×10^{-2}	3.1081×10^{-2}	2.1430×10^{-2}	2.1859×10^{-3}	2.1430×10^{-3}	2.1150×10^{-3}	2.1859×10^{-5}	1.3874×10^{-5}	2.1430×10^{-6}
3.3865×10^4	2.5401×10^4	3.3865×10^3	3.4532×10^2	3.3865×10	2.5401×10	1.5803×10	1.0	4.9116×10^{-1}	3.3865×10^{-1}	3.4532×10^{-2}	3.3865×10^{-2}	3.3421×10^{-2}	3.4532×10^{-4}	2.1927×10^{-4}	3.3865×10^{-5}
6.8947×10^4	5.1715×10^4	6.8947×10^3	7.0307×10^2	6.8947×10	5.1715×10	3.2174×10	2.0360	1.0	6.8947×10^{-1}	7.0307×10^{-2}	6.8947×10^{-2}	6.8046×10^{-2}	7.0307×10^{-4}	4.4643×10^{-4}	6.8947×10^{-5}
1.0×10^5	7.5006×10^4	1.0×10^4	1.0197×10^3	1.0×10^2	7.5006×10	4.6665×10	2.9530	1.4504	1.0	1.0197×10^{-1}	1.0×10^{-1}	9.8692×10^{-2}	1.0197×10^{-3}	6.4728×10^{-4}	1.0×10^{-4}
9.8067×10^5	7.3556×10^5	9.8067×10^4	1.0×10^4	9.8067×10^2	7.3556×10^2	4.5763×10^2	2.8959×10	1.4223×10	9.8067	1.0	9.8067×10^{-1}	9.6784×10^{-1}	1.0×10^{-2}	6.3477×10^{-3}	9.8067×10^{-4}
1.0×10^6	7.5006×10^5	1.0×10^5	1.0197×10^4	1.0×10^3	7.5006×10^2	4.6665×10^2	2.9530×10	1.4504×10	1.0×10	1.0197	1.0	9.8692×10^{-1}	1.0197×10^{-2}	6.4728×10^{-3}	1.0×10^{-3}
1.0133×10^6	7.600×10^5	1.0133×10^5	1.0332×10^4	1.0133×10^3	7.600×10^2	4.7277×10^2	2.9921×10	1.4696×10	1.0133×10	1.0332	1.0133	1.0	1.0332×10^{-2}	6.5607×10^{-3}	1.0133×10^{-3}
9.8067×10^7	7.3556×10^7	9.8067×10^6	1.0×10^6	9.8067×10^4	7.3556×10^4	4.5763×10^4	2.8959×10^3	1.4223×10^3	9.8067×10^2	1.0×10^2	9.8067×10	9.6784×10	1.0	6.3477×10^{-1}	9.8067×10^{-2}
1.5445×10^8	1.1589×10^8	1.5445×10^7	1.5749×10^6	1.5445×10^5	1.1589×10^5	7.2061×10^4	4.5626×10^3	2.240×10^3	1.5445×10^3	1.5749×10^2	1.5448×10^2	1.5242×10^2	1.5749	1.0	1.5445×10^{-1}
1.0×10^9	7.5006×10^8	1.0×10^8	1.0197×10^7	1.0×10^6	7.5006×10^5	4.6665×10^5	2.9530×10^4	1.4504×10^4	1.0×10^4	1.0197×10^3	1.0×10^3	9.8692×10^2	1.0197×10	6.4728	1.0

*From MATERIALS AND TECHNIQUES FOR ELECTRON TUBES by WALTER H. KOHL. Copyright 1959 by REINHOLD PUBLISHING CORP., NEW YORK.

Nominal composition: Ni:29; Co:17; Fe:Bal.
Minor constituents: Mn:0.5; Si:0.20; C:0.06; Al:0.10; Mg:0.10; Zr:0.10; Ti:0.10;
(Max. wt. percent) (Al + Mg + Zr + Ti):0.20
Melting point (°C): 1450 (approx.)
Density (g/cc): 8.36 8.20 (Nilo K)
(lb/cu in.): 0.302 0.296 (Nilo K)

Electrical resistivity:

25	100	200	400	600	°C
49	62.7	80.4	107.3	116.6	microhm·cm

Thermal conductivity (cal/cm²/cm/sec/°C): 0.0395 (30°C)
  0.0485 (300°C)
Specific heat (cal/gm/°C): 0.105 (0°C)
  0.155 (430°C)
Heat of fusion (cal/gm): 64
Vapor pressure (Torr): 10^{-5} (1000°C)
Phase transformation ($\gamma \rightarrow \alpha$): < −80°C (see Fig. 13.33; p. 452)
Thermal expansion coefficient (cm/cm/°C) $\times 10^{-7}$: 45.4 to 50.8 (30–400°C)
(hydrogen-annealed 1 hr at 900°C or 15 min. at 50.3 to 53.7 (30–450°C)
1100°C); see Figs. 13.30–13.32 (pp. 450, 451) and
Fig. 13.34 (p.452)

30–200	30–300	30–400	30–500	30–600	30–700	30–800	30–900	°C
50.4	48.6	47.4	61.9	78.9	93.1	103.9	114.7	[92]

Magnetic Properties:
Flux density (gauss): 500 2000 7000 12000 17000
Permeability (B/H): 1000 2000 3700 2280 213
Curie Point (°C): 435 (approx. inflection point)

Mechanical Properties: (strain rate 800%/hr)[92] (see Fig. 13.29, p. 449)

Temperature of test (°C)	Yield strength 0.5% (psi)	Ultimate strength (psi)	Breaking strength (psi)	Uniform elongation (%)	Total elongation (%)	Reduction of area (%)
21	59,500	77,500	44,000	16.78	35.4	69.0
213	39,000	58,500	37,500	18.59	32.08	73.2
308	32,500	54,500	37,500	22.12	34.79	65.2
400	30,000	50,000	31,000	20.90	36.33	74.0
500	26,500	42,000	29,000	21.69	33.96	71.0
600	23,500	36,000	32,500	19.45	28.40	35.0
738	21,500	25,000	22,000	6.87	18.23	25.0
790	17,100	19,000	15,000	5.21	14.65	21.6

Annealed temper (Rockwell hardness): B 82 max.
Cold-worked temper (Rockwell hardness): B 100 max.

Tradenames and Suppliers:
"Kovar"*—The Carborundum Company, Refractories Division, Latrobe, Pa.
"Therlo"—Driver Harris Company, Harrison, N. J.
"Rodar"—Wilbur B. Driver Company, Newark, N. J.
"Sealvac-A"—Vacuum Metals Corporation, Cambridge, Mass.
"Nilo K"—Henry Wiggin & Company Limited, Birmingham, England
"Dilver P"—Aciéries d'Imphy, Imphy (Nièvre), France
"Vacon"—Vakuumschmelze AG, Hanau/Main, Germany

* Kovar is a registered trademark of Westinghouse Electric Corporation; the alloy
is fabricated and distributed under this tradename by The Carborundum Company,
Refractories Division. Most of the data given above are taken from their Bulletin
"Kovar Alloy" (1958), but an error in the values for thermal conductivity has been
corrected.

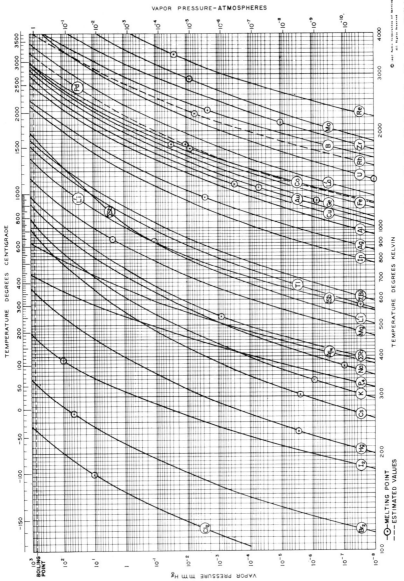

Figure A1(a). Vapor pressure curves for the more common elements. After Honig (Ref. 5:14). *(Courtesy RCA Laboratories.)*

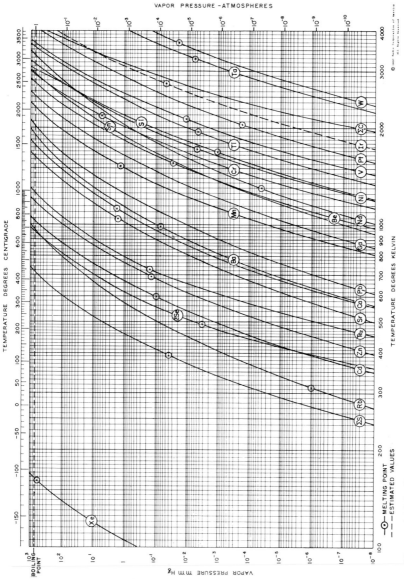

Figure A1(b). Vapor pressure curves for the more common elements (cont.). After Honig (Ref. 5:14). (*Courtesy RCA Laboratories.*)

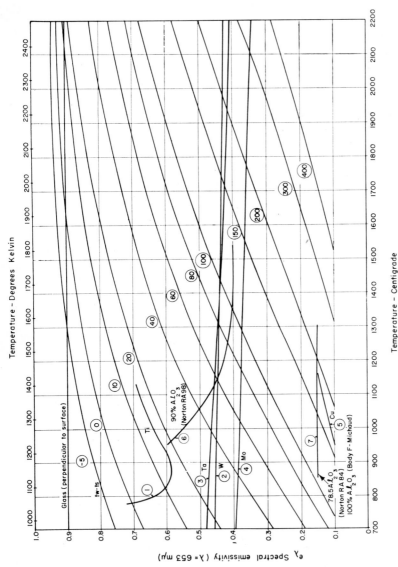

Figure A2. Corrections to be applied to Centigrade temperatures measured with an optical pyrometer at an effective wavelength $\lambda = 0.653$ micron (C_2 1.438). Adapted from corrections published in "High-temperature Technology," I. E. Campell, Editor; John Wiley & Sons, Inc., New York, 1956 (p. 341). Curves for emissivities of various materials are based on published data, as follows:
(1) Titanium: W. C. Michels and S. Wilford (1949); Ref. 16:68.   (2) Tungsten: R. D. Larrabee (1959); Ref. 9:16.   (3) Tantalum: L. Malter and D. B. Langmuir (1939); Ref. 11:7.   (4) Molybdenum: E. A. Coomes (1955); Ref. 10:30.   (5) Copper: A. Butts (1954); Ref. 6:4.   (6) and (7) Alumina: M. Michaud (1954); Ref. 2:63.

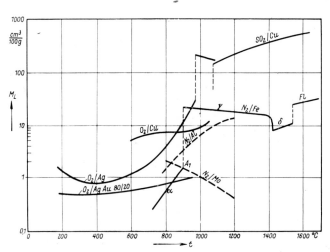

Figure A3. Solubility of oxygen, nitrogen, and sulfur dioxide in various metals, as a function of temperature. After Waldschmidt (Ref. 7:35). (*Courtesy Metall-Verlag GMBH, Berlin.*)

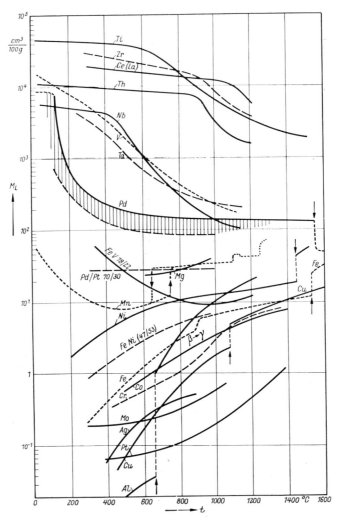

Figure A4. Solubility of hydrogen in various metals, as a function of temperature. After Waldschmidt (Ref. 7:35). (*Courtesy Metall-Verlag GMBH, Berlin.*)

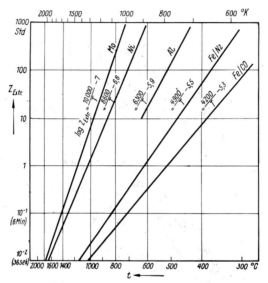

Figure A5. Time required to outgas various sheet metals, 3 mm thick, to about 5 per cent of their original gas content, as a function of temperature. After Waldschmidt (Ref. 7:35) and Jaeckel (Ref. 16:29). (*Courtesy Springer-Verlag, Berlin.*)

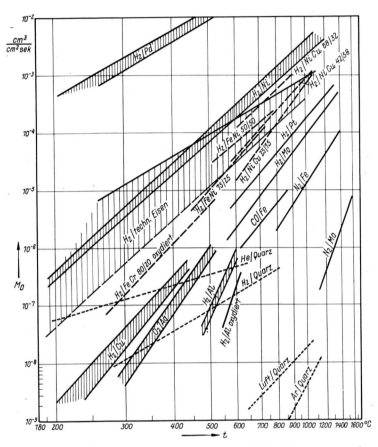

Figure A6. Permeation of gases through various metals at temperatures from 200 to 1600°C. Compilation of literature data after Waldschmidt (Ref. 7:35). (*Courtesy Metall-Verlag GMBH, Berlin.*)

AUTHOR INDEX

The numbers after the name indicate the pages on which the names appear either in full or by reference number. At the end of each chapter, all references are listed in the sequence in which they appear in the text. These reference numbers, together with the chapter in which they appear, are listed below after the letter R. Example: Abbot, H. W., 148, 163; R 4:8, 4:53, i.e., in Chapter 4, Mr. Abbot appears as reference 8 and 53 on pages 148 and 163. RIR refers to references appearing in the Introductory Review.

SUBJECT INDEX